INSTRUCTOR'S SOLUTIONS MANUAL FOR

Glover and Sarma's

Power System
ANALYSIS AND DESIGN

THIRD EDITION

Mulukutla S. Sarma

J. Duncan Glover

Tom Overbye, *PowerWord Problems*

THOMSON
BROOKS/COLE

Australia • Canada • Mexico • Singapore • Spain • United Kingdom • United States

Printed in the United States of America
1 2 3 4 5 6 7 05 04 03 02 01

Printer: Victor Graphics, Inc.

ISBN: 0-534-95368-9

For more information about our products,
contact us at:
Thomson Learning Academic Resource Center
1-800-423-0563

For permission to use material from this text, contact us by:
Phone: 1-800-730-2214
Fax: 1-800-731-2215
Web: http://www.thomsonrights.com

Asia
Thomson Learning
5 Shenton Way #01-01
UIC Building
Singapore 068808

Australia
Nelson Thomson Learning
102 Dodds Street
South Street
South Melbourne, Victoria 3205
Australia

Canada
Nelson Thomson Learning
1120 Birchmount Road
Toronto, Ontario M1K 5G4
Canada

Europe/Middle East/South Africa
Thomson Learning
High Holborn House
50/51 Bedford Row
London WC1R 4LR
United Kingdom

Latin America
Thomson Learning
Seneca, 53
Colonia Polanco
11560 Mexico D.F.
Mexico

Spain
Paraninfo Thomson Learning
Calle/Magallanes, 25
28015 Madrid, Spain

CONTENTS

CHAPTER 2

2.1

(a) $\bar{A}_1 = 5\angle 60^\circ = 5\left[\cos 60^\circ + j\sin 60^\circ\right] = 2.5 + j\,4.33$

(b) $\bar{A}_2 = -3 - j4 = \sqrt{9+16}\;\angle \tan^{-1}\frac{-4}{-3} = 5\angle 233.13^\circ = 5\,e^{j233.13^\circ}$

(c) $\bar{A}_3 = \bar{A}_1 + \bar{A}_2 = (2.5 + j4.33) + (-3 - j4) = -0.5 + j0.33 = 0.599\angle 146.6^\circ$

(d) $\bar{A}_4 = \bar{A}_1\bar{A}_2 = (5\angle 60^\circ)(5\angle 233.13^\circ) = 25\angle 293.13^\circ = 9.821 - j22.99$

(e) $\bar{A}_5 = \bar{A}_1/\bar{A}_2 = 5\angle 60^\circ / 5\angle 233.13^\circ = 1\angle 293.13^\circ = 1\,e^{j293.13^\circ}$

2.2

(a) $\bar{I} = 400\angle -30^\circ = 346.4 - j200$

(b) $i(t) = 5\sin(\omega t + 15^\circ) = 5\cos(\omega t + 15^\circ - 90^\circ) = 5\cos(\omega t - 75^\circ)$

$\bar{I} = (5/\sqrt{2})\angle -75^\circ = 3.536\angle -75^\circ = 0.9151 - j3.415$

(c) $\bar{I} = (4/\sqrt{2})\angle -30^\circ + 5\angle -75^\circ = (2.449 - j1.414) + (1.294 - j4.83)$

$= 3.743 - j6.244 = 7.28\angle -59.06^\circ$

2.3

(a) $V_{max} = 678.8\text{ V}$; $I_{max} = 200\text{ A}$

(b) $V = 678.8/\sqrt{2} = 480\text{ V}$; $I = 200/\sqrt{2} = 141.4\text{ A}$

(c) $\bar{V} = 480\angle -105^\circ\text{ V}$; $\bar{I} = 141.4\angle -5^\circ\text{ A}$

2.4

(a) $\bar{I}_1 = 10\angle 0^\circ \dfrac{-j6}{8 + j6 - j6} = 10\dfrac{6\angle -90^\circ}{8} = 7.5\angle -90^\circ\text{ A}$

$\bar{I}_2 = \bar{I} - \bar{I}_1 = 10\angle 0^\circ - 7.5\angle -90^\circ = 10 + j7.5 = 12.5\angle 36.87^\circ\text{ A}$

$\bar{V} = \bar{I}_2(-j6) = (12.5\angle 36.87^\circ)(6\angle -90^\circ) = 75\angle -53.13^\circ\text{ V}$

2.4 contd.

(b)

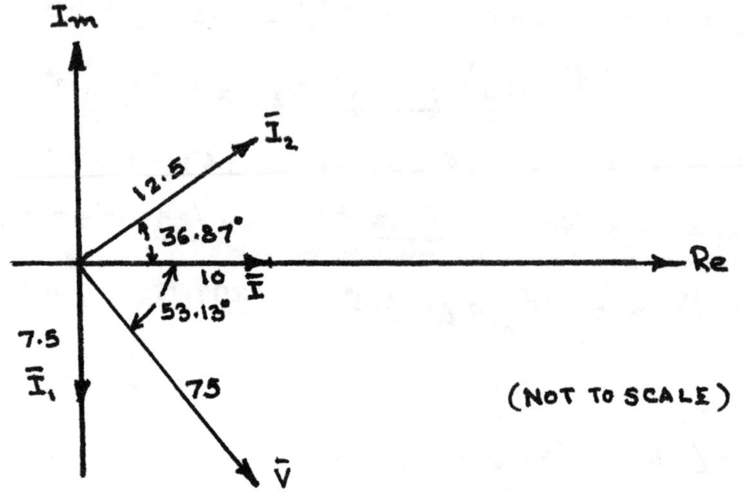

2.5

(a) $v(t) = 277\sqrt{2}\cos(\omega t + 30°) = 391.7\cos(\omega t + 30°)$ V

(b) $\bar{I} = \bar{V}/20 = 13.85\angle 30°$ A

$i(t) = 19.58\cos(\omega t + 30°)$ A

(c) $\bar{Z} = j\omega L = j(2\pi\, 60)(10\times 10^{-3}) = 3.771\angle 90°\ \Omega$

$\bar{I} = \bar{V}/\bar{Z} = (277\angle 30°)/(3.771\angle 90°) = 73.46\angle -60°$ A

$i(t) = 73.46\sqrt{2}\cos(\omega t - 60°) = 103.9\cos(\omega t - 60°)$ A

(d) $\bar{Z} = -j25\ \Omega$

$\bar{I} = \bar{V}/\bar{Z} = (277\angle 30°)/(25\angle -90°) = 11.08\angle 120°$ A

$i(t) = 11.08\sqrt{2}\cos(\omega t + 120°) = 15.67\cos(\omega t + 120°)$ A

2.6

(a) $\bar{V} = (100/\sqrt{2})\angle -30° = 70.7\angle -30°$; ω DOES NOT APPEAR IN THE ANSWER.

(b) $v(t) = 100\sqrt{2}\cos(\omega t + 20°)$; WITH $\omega = 377$,

$v(t) = 141.4\cos(377t + 20°)$

2.6 CONTD.

(c) $\bar{A} = A\angle\alpha$; $\bar{B} = B\angle\beta$; $\bar{C} = \bar{A} + \bar{B}$

$c(t) = a(t) + b(t) = \sqrt{2}\,\mathrm{Re}\left[\bar{C}\,e^{j\omega t}\right]$

THE RESULTANT HAS THE SAME FREQUENCY ω.

2.7

(a) THE CIRCUIT DIAGRAM IS SHOWN BELOW:

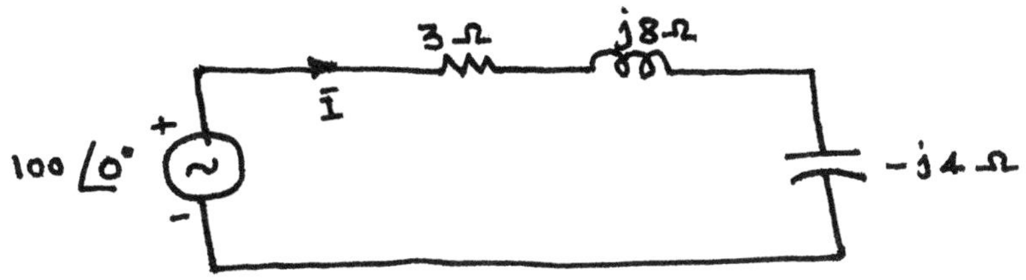

(b) $\bar{Z} = 3 + j8 - j4 = 3 + j4 = 5\angle 53.1^\circ\ \Omega$

(c) $\bar{I} = (100\angle 0^\circ)/(5\angle 53.1^\circ) = 20\angle -53.1^\circ$ A

THE CURRENT LAGS THE SOURCE VOLTAGE BY 53.1°

POWER FACTOR $= \cos 53.1^\circ = 0.6$ LAGGING

2.8

(a) $p(t) = v(t)\,i(t) = [678.8\cos(\omega t - 105^\circ)][200\cos(\omega t - 5^\circ)]$

$= \frac{1}{2}(678.8)(200)\,[\cos 100^\circ + \cos(2\omega t - 110^\circ)]$

$= -1.179\times 10^4 + 6.788\times 10^4 \cos(2\omega t - 110^\circ)$ W

(b) $P = VI\cos(\delta - \beta) = 480 \times 141.4 \cos(-105^\circ + 5^\circ)$

$= -1.179\times 10^4$ W ABSORBED $= +11.79$ kW DELIVERED

(c) $Q = VI\sin(\delta - \beta) = 480 \times 141.4 \sin(-100^\circ)$

$= -6.685\times 10^4$ VAR ABSORBED $= +66.85$ kVAR DELIVERED

(d) THE PHASOR CURRENT $(-\bar{I}) = 141.4\angle -5^\circ - 180^\circ = 141.4\angle -185^\circ$ A

LEAVES THE POSITIVE TERMINAL OF THIS GENERATOR. THE GENERATOR

POWER FACTOR IS THEN $\cos(-105^\circ + 185^\circ) = 0.1736$ LAGGING

2.9

(a) $p(t) = v(t)\,i(t) = 391.7 \times 19.58 \cos^2(\omega t + 30°)$

$= 0.7669 \times 10^4 \left(\tfrac{1}{2}\right)[1 + \cos(2\omega t + 60°)]$

$= 3.834 \times 10^3 + 3.834 \times 10^3 \cos(2\omega t + 60°)$ W

$P = VI \cos(\delta - \beta) = 277 \times 13.85 \cos 0° = 3.836$ kW

$Q = VI \sin(\delta - \beta) = 0$ VAR

SOURCE POWER FACTOR $= \cos(\delta - \beta) = \cos(30° - 30°) = 1.0$

(b) $p(t) = v(t)\,i(t) = 391.7 \times 103.9 \cos(\omega t + 30°)\cos(\omega t - 60°)$

$= 4.07 \times 10^4 \left(\tfrac{1}{2}\right)[\cos 90° + \cos(2\omega t - 30°)]$

$= 2.035 \times 10^4 \cos(2\omega t - 30°)$ W

$P = VI \cos(\delta - \beta) = 277 \times 73.46 \cos(30° + 60°) = 0$ W

$Q = VI \sin(\delta - \beta) = 277 \times 73.46 \sin 90° = 20.35$ kVAR

$pf = \cos(\delta - \beta) = 0$ LAGGING

(c) $p(t) = v(t)\,i(t) = 391.7 \times 15.67 \cos(\omega t + 30°)\cos(\omega t + 120°)$

$= 6.138 \times 10^3 \left(\tfrac{1}{2}\right)[\cos(-90°) + \cos(2\omega t + 150°)]$

$= 3.069 \times 10^3 \cos(2\omega t + 150°)$ W

$P = VI \cos(\delta - \beta) = 277 \times 11.08 \cos(30° - 120°) = 0$ W

$Q = VI \sin(\delta - \beta) = 277 \times 11.08 \sin(-90°)$

$= -3.069$ kVAR ABSORBED $= +3.069$ kVAR DELIVERED

$pf = \cos(\delta - \beta) = \cos(-90°) = 0$ LEADING

2.10

(a) $p_R(t) = 678.8 \times 67.88 \cos^2(\omega t + 45°)$

$= 4.608 \times 10^4 \left(\tfrac{1}{2}\right)[1 + \cos(2\omega t + 90°)]$

$= 2.304 \times 10^4 + 2.304 \times 10^4 \cos(2\omega t + 90°)$ W

2.10 CONTD

(b) $p_X(t) = [678.8 \cos(\omega t + 45°)]\,[27.15 \cos(\omega t + 45° + 90°)]$

$= 1.843 \times 10^4 \cos(\omega t + 45°) \cos(\omega t + 135°)$

$= 1.843 \times 10^4 \left(\tfrac{1}{2}\right) [\cos(-90°) + \cos(2\omega t + 180°)]$

$= 9.215 \times 10^3 \cos(2\omega t + 180°)$

$= -9.215 \times 10^3 \sin 2\omega t \quad W$

(c) $P = V^2/R = (678.8/\sqrt{2})^2/10 = 2.304 \times 10^4$ W ABSORBED

(d) $Q = V^2/X = (678.8/\sqrt{2})^2/25 = 9.215 \times 10^3$ VAR DELIVERED

(e) $(\beta - \delta) = \tan^{-1}(Q/P) = \tan^{-1}\left(\dfrac{9.215 \times 10^3}{2.304 \times 10^4}\right) = 21.8°$

$pf = \cos(\delta - \beta) = \cos(-21.8°) = 0.9285$ LEADING

2.11

(a) $\bar{Z} = R - jX_c = 10 - j25 = 26.93 \angle -68.2° \ \Omega$

$i(t) = (678.8/26.93) \cos(\omega t + 45° + 68.2°)$

$= 25.21 \cos(\omega t + 113.2°)$ A

$p_R(t) = [25.21 \cos(\omega t + 113.2°)]\,[252.1 \cos(\omega t + 113.2°)]$

$= 6.355 \times 10^3 \cos^2(\omega t + 113.2°)$

$= 3.178 \times 10^3 + 3.178 \times 10^3 \cos(2\omega t + 226.4°)$ W

(b) $p_X(t) = [25.21 \cos(\omega t + 113.2°)]\,[630.2 \cos(\omega t + 113.2° - 90°)]$

$= 7.944 \times 10^3 \sin[2(\omega t + 113.2°)]$ W

(c) $P = I^2 R = (25.21/\sqrt{2})^2 (10) = 3.178$ kW ABSORBED

(d) $Q = I^2 X = (25.21/\sqrt{2})^2 (25) = 7.944$ kVAR DELIVERED

(e) $pf = \cos[\tan^{-1}(Q/P)] = \cos[\tan^{-1}(7.944/3.178)]$

$= 0.3714$ LEADING

2.12

(a) $\bar{I} = 4\angle 0°$ kA

$\bar{V} = \bar{Z}\bar{I} = (2\angle -45°)(4\angle 0°) = 8\angle -45°$ kV

$v(t) = 8\sqrt{2}\cos(\omega t - 45°)$ kV

$p(t) = v(t)\,i(t) = [8\sqrt{2}\cos(\omega t - 45°)][4\sqrt{2}\cos\omega t]$

$= 64\left(\frac{1}{2}\right)[\cos(-45°) + \cos(2\omega t - 45°)]$

$= 22.63 + 32\cos(2\omega t - 45°)$ MW

(b) $P = VI\cos(\delta - \beta) = 8 \times 4\cos(-45° - 0°) = 22.63$ MW DELIVERED

(c) $Q = VI\sin(\delta - \beta) = 8 \times 4\sin(-45° - 0°) =$

$= -22.63$ MVAR DELIVERED $= +22.63$ MVAR ABSORBED

(d) $pf = \cos(\delta - \beta) = \cos(-45° - 0°) = 0.707$ LEADING

2.13

(a) $\bar{I} = [(4/\sqrt{2})\angle 60°]/(2\angle 30°) = \sqrt{2}\angle 30°$ A

$i(t) = 2\cos(\omega t + 30°)$ A WITH $\omega = 377$ rad/s.

$p(t) = v(t)\,i(t) = 4[\cos 30° + \cos(2\omega t + 90°)]$

$= 3.46 + 4\cos(2\omega t + 90°)$ W

(b) $v(t)$, $i(t)$, and $p(t)$ are plotted below: (see next page)

(c) The instantaneous power has an average value of 3.46 W, and the frequency is <u>twice</u> that of the voltage or current.

2.13 CONTD.

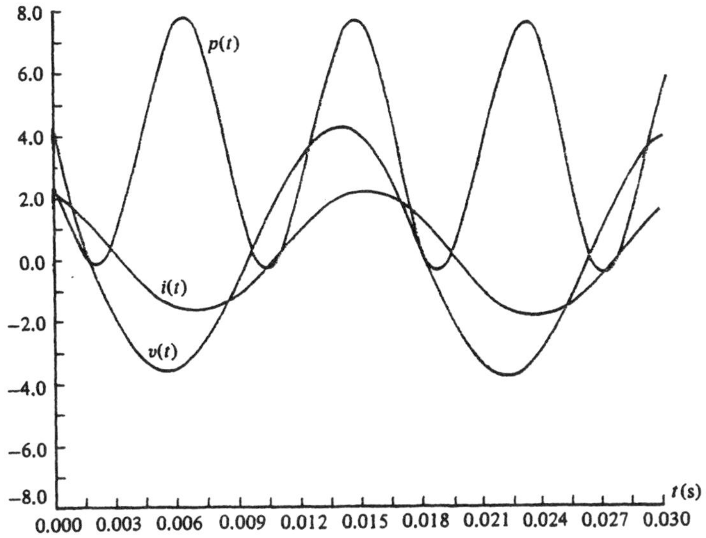

2.14

(a) $\bar{Z} = 10 + j\,120\pi \times 0.04 = 10 + j\,15.1 = 18.1\angle 56.4^\circ\ \Omega$

$pf = \cos 56.4^\circ = 0.553$ LAGGING

(b) $\bar{V} = 120\angle 0^\circ$ V

THE CURRENT SUPPLIED BY THE SOURCE IS

$\bar{I} = (120\angle 0^\circ)/(18.1\angle 56.4^\circ) = 6.63\angle -56.4^\circ$ A

THE REAL POWER ABSORBED BY THE LOAD IS GIVEN BY

$P = 120 \times 6.63 \times \cos 56.4^\circ = 440$ W

WHICH CAN BE CHECKED BY $I^2R = (6.63)^2\,10 = 440$ W

THE REACTIVE POWER ABSORBED BY THE LOAD IS

$Q = 120 \times 6.63 \times \sin 56.4^\circ = 663$ VAR

(c) PEAK MAGNETIC ENERGY $= W = LI^2 = 0.04\,(6.63)^2 = 1.76$ J

$Q = \omega W = 377 \times 1.76 = 663$ VAR IS SATISFIED.

2.15

(a) $\bar{S} = \bar{V}\,\bar{I}^* = (150\angle -10^\circ)(5\angle -50^\circ)^* = 750\angle 60^\circ$

$= 375 + j\,649.5$

$P = \mathrm{Re}(\bar{S}) = 375$ W ABSORBED; $Q = \mathrm{Im}(\bar{S}) = 649.5$ VAR ABSORBED

THE POWER TRIANGLE IS GIVEN BELOW:

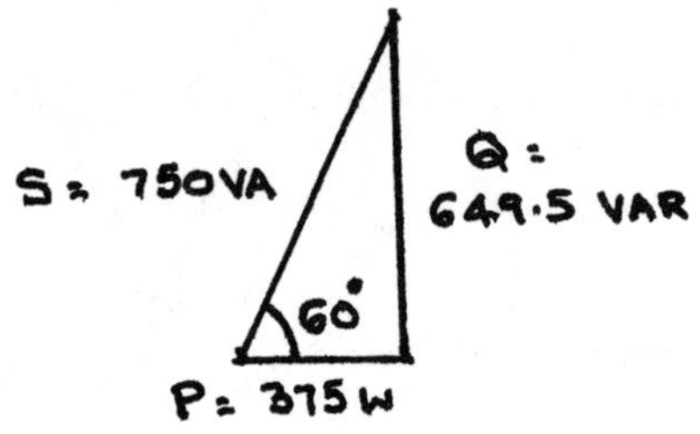

(b) $pf = \cos 60^\circ = 0.5$ LAGGING

(c) $Q_S = P \tan\theta_S = 375 \tan(\cos^{-1} 0.9) = 181.62$ VAR

$Q_C = Q_L - Q_S = 649.5 - 181.62 = 467.88$ VAR

2.16

$\bar{Y}_1 = \dfrac{1}{\bar{Z}_1} = \dfrac{1}{20\angle 30^\circ} = 0.05\angle -30^\circ = 0.0433 - j0.025 = G_1 - jB_1$

$\bar{Y}_2 = \dfrac{1}{\bar{Z}_2} = \dfrac{1}{14.14\angle -45^\circ} = 0.0707\angle 45^\circ = 0.05 + j0.05 = G_2 + jB_2$

$P_1 = V^2 G_1 = (100)^2\, 0.0433 = 433$ W ABSORBED

$Q_1 = V^2 B_1 = (100)^2\, 0.025 = 250$ VAR ABSORBED

$P_2 = V^2 G_2 = (100)^2\, 0.05 = 500$ W ABSORBED

$Q_2 = V^2 B_2 = (100)^2\, 0.05 = 500$ VAR DELIVERED

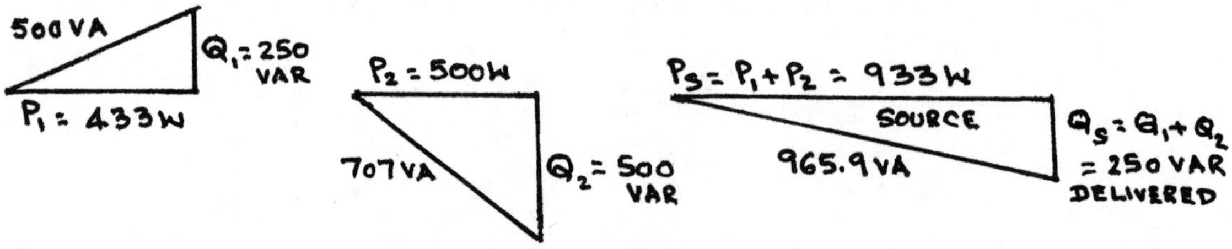

2.17

(a)

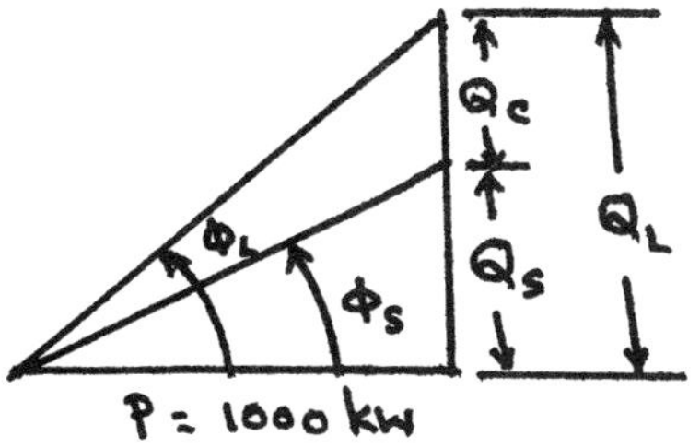

$\phi_L = \cos^{-1} 0.7 = 45.57°$

$Q_L = P \tan \phi_L = 1000 \tan(45.57°)$

$= 1020.2$ kVAR

$\phi_S = \cos^{-1} 0.9 = 25.84°$

$Q_S = P \tan \phi_S = 1000 \tan(25.84°) = 484.3$ kVAR

$Q_C = Q_L - Q_S = 1020.2 - 484.3 = 535.9$ kVAR

$S_C = Q_C = 535.9$ kVA

(b) SYNCHRONOUS MOTOR ABSORBS $P_m = \dfrac{1000 \times 0.746}{0.9} = 828.9$ kW

and $Q_m = 0$ kVAR

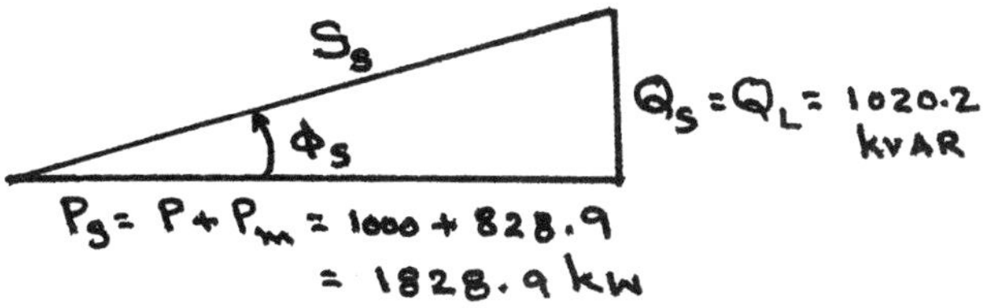

SOURCE pf $= \cos\left[\tan^{-1} \dfrac{1020.2}{1828.9}\right]$

$= 0.873$ LAGGING

2.18

(a) $\bar{Y}_1 = \dfrac{1}{\bar{Z}_1} = \dfrac{1}{3+j5} = \dfrac{1}{5.831\angle 59.04°} = 0.1715\angle -59.04°$

$= 0.08824 - j\,0.1471$ S

$\bar{Y}_2 = \dfrac{1}{\bar{Z}_2} = \dfrac{1}{10} = 0.1$ S

$P = V^2(G_1 + G_2)$; $V = \sqrt{\dfrac{P}{(G_1+G_2)}} = \sqrt{\dfrac{2000}{(0.08824+0.1)}}$

$= 103.08$ V

$P_1 = V^2 G_1 = (103.08)^2 (0.08824) = 937.6$ W

$P_2 = V^2 G_2 = (103.08)^2 (0.1) = 1062.6$ W

(b) $\bar{Y}_{eq} = \bar{Y}_1 + \bar{Y}_2 = 0.1882 - j\,0.1471 = 0.2389\angle -38.01°$

$I_S = V\,Y_{eq} = (103.08)(0.2389) = 24.63$ A

2.19

$$\bar{S} = \bar{V}\,\bar{I}^* = (120\angle 0^\circ)(25\angle -30^\circ) = 3000\angle -30^\circ$$

$$= 2598.1 - j\,1500$$

$P = \text{Re}(\bar{S}) = 2598.1$ W DELIVERED

$Q = \text{Im}(\bar{S}) = -1500$ VAR DELIVERED $= +1500$ VAR ABSORBED

2.20

$$\bar{S}_1 = P_1 + jQ_1 = 10 + j0 \quad ; \quad \bar{S}_2 = 10\angle \cos^{-1} 0.9 = 9 + j4.359$$

$$\bar{S}_3 = \frac{10 \times 0.746}{0.85 \times 0.95} \angle -\cos^{-1} 0.95 = 9.238\angle -18.19^\circ = 8.776 - j\,2.885$$

$$\bar{S}_S = \bar{S}_1 + \bar{S}_2 + \bar{S}_3 = 27.78 + j1.474 = 27.82\angle 3.04^\circ$$

$$P_S = \text{Re}(\bar{S}_S) = 27.78 \text{ kW}$$

$$Q_S = \text{Im}(\bar{S}_S) = 1.474 \text{ kVAR}$$

$$S_S = |\bar{S}_S| = 27.82 \text{ kVA}$$

2.21

$$\bar{S}_R = \bar{V}_R\,\bar{I}^* = R\,\bar{I}\,\bar{I}^* = I^2 R = (20)^2\,3 = 1200 + j0$$

$$\bar{S}_L = \bar{V}_L\,\bar{I}^* = (jX_L\bar{I})\,\bar{I}^* = jX_L I^2 = j\,8\,(20)^2 = 0 + j\,3200$$

$$\bar{S}_C = \bar{V}_C\,\bar{I}^* = (-j\,\bar{I}X_C)\,\bar{I}^* = -jX_C I^2 = -j\,4\,(20)^2 = 0 - j\,1600$$

COMPLEX POWER ABSORBED BY THE TOTAL LOAD $\bar{S}_{LOAD} = \bar{S}_R + \bar{S}_L + \bar{S}_C = 2000\angle 53.1^\circ$

POWER TRIANGLE:

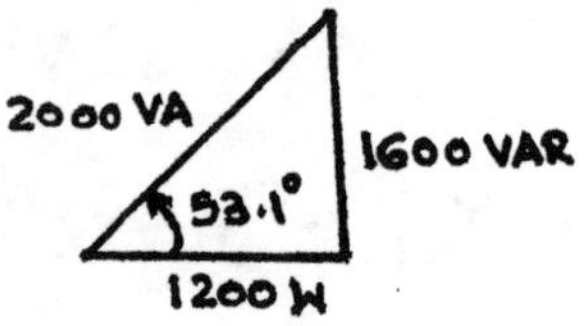

COMPLEX POWER DELIVERED BY THE SOURCE IS

$$\bar{S}_{SOURCE} = \bar{V}\,\bar{I}^* = (100\angle 0^\circ)(20\angle -53.1^\circ)^* = 2000\angle 53.1^\circ$$

THE COMPLEX POWER DELIVERED BY THE SOURCE IS EQUAL TO THE TOTAL COMPLEX POWER ABSORBED BY THE LOAD.

2.22

(a) THE PROBLEM IS MODELED AS SHOWN IN FIGURE BELOW:

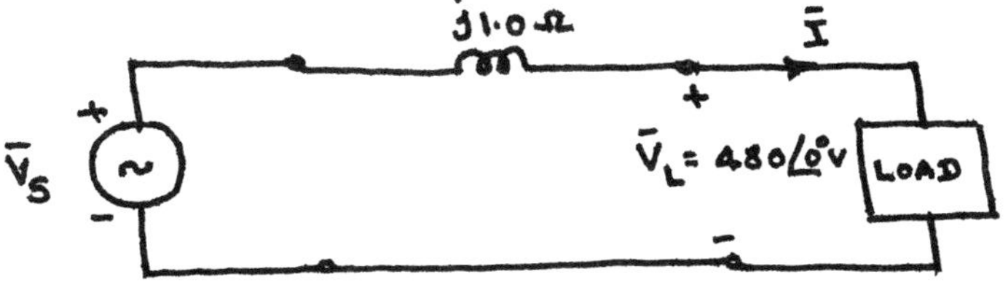

$P_L = 120$ kW

$pf_L = 0.85$ LAGGING

$\theta_L = \cos^{-1} 0.85 = 31.79°$

POWER TRIANGLE FOR THE LOAD:

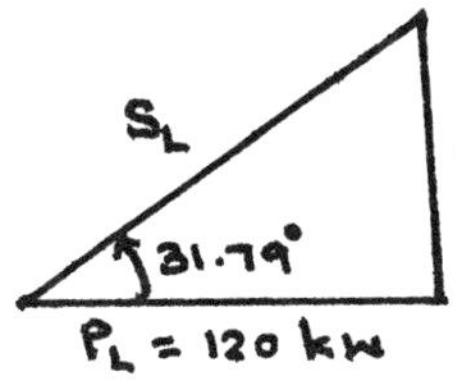

$Q_L = P_L \tan(31.79°)$
$= 74.364$ kVAR

$\bar{S}_L = P_L + jQ_L = 141.18 \angle 31.79°$ kVA

$I = S_L / V = 141{,}180 / 480 = 294.13$ A

REAL POWER LOSS IN THE LINE IS ZERO.

REACTIVE POWER LOSS IN THE LINE IS $Q_{LINE} = I^2 X_{LINE} = (294.13)^2\, 1$
$= 86.512$ kVAR

$\therefore\ \bar{S}_S = P_S + jQ_S = 120 + j(74.364 + 86.512) = 200.7 \angle 53.28°$ kVA

THE INPUT VOLTAGE IS GIVEN BY $V_S = S_S / I = 682.4$ V (rms)

THE POWER FACTOR AT THE INPUT IS $\cos 53.28° = 0.6$ LAGGING

(b) APPLYING KVL, $\bar{V}_S = 480\angle 0° + j1.0\,(294.13 \angle -31.79°)$

$= 635 + j250 = 682.4 \angle 21.5°$ V (rms)

$(pf)_S = \cos(21.5° + 31.79°) = 0.6$ LAGGING

2.23

THE CIRCUIT DIAGRAM IS SHOWN BELOW:

$P_{old} = 50$ kW; $\cos^{-1} 0.8 = 36.87°$; $\theta_{OLD} = 36.87°$; $Q_{old} = P_{old} \tan(\theta_{old})$
$= 37.5$ kVAR

2.23 CONTD.

$$\therefore \ \bar{S}_{old} = 50{,}000 + j\,37{,}500$$

$$\theta_{new} = \cos^{-1} 0.95 = 18.19° \ ; \quad \bar{S}_{new} = 50{,}000 + j\,50{,}000 \tan(18.19°)$$

$$= 50{,}000 + j\,16{,}430$$

HENCE $\bar{S}_{cap} = \bar{S}_{new} - \bar{S}_{old} = -j\,21{,}070 \text{ VA}$

$$\therefore \ C = \frac{21{,}070}{(377)(220)^2} = 1155 \ \mu F$$

Problem 2.24
Qcap=6MVR minimizes the real power line losses (0.36 MW)

If Qcap has a value of 6.5 or 7 MVR the MVA power flow is minimized with a value of 12.36 MVA.

Problem 2.25

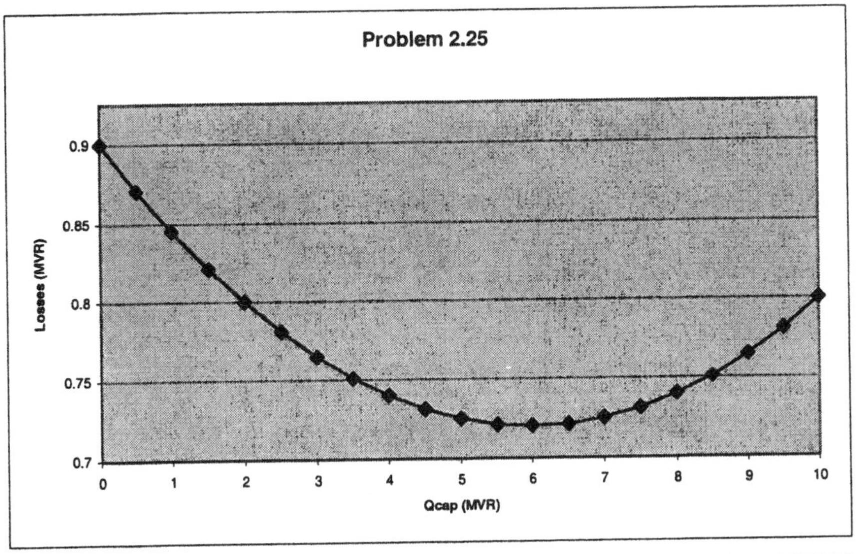

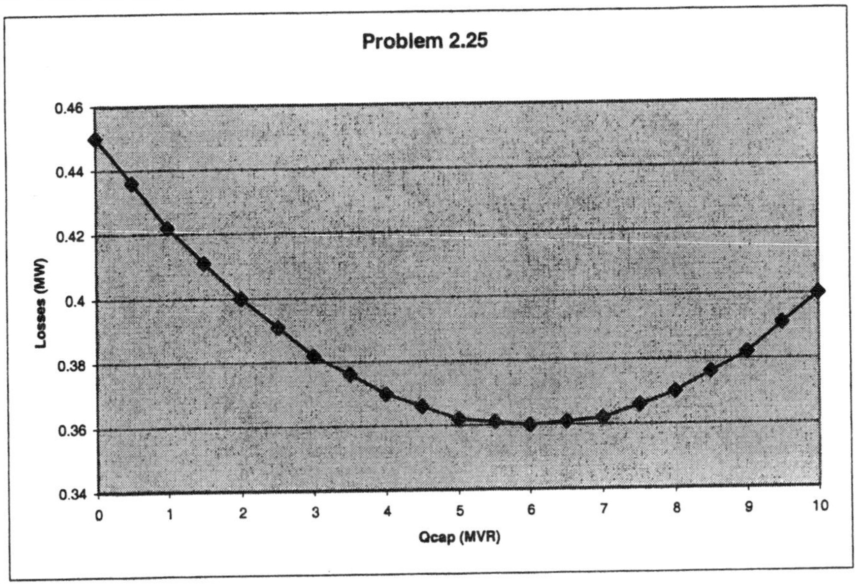

Problem 2.26
Qcap=8MVR

2.27

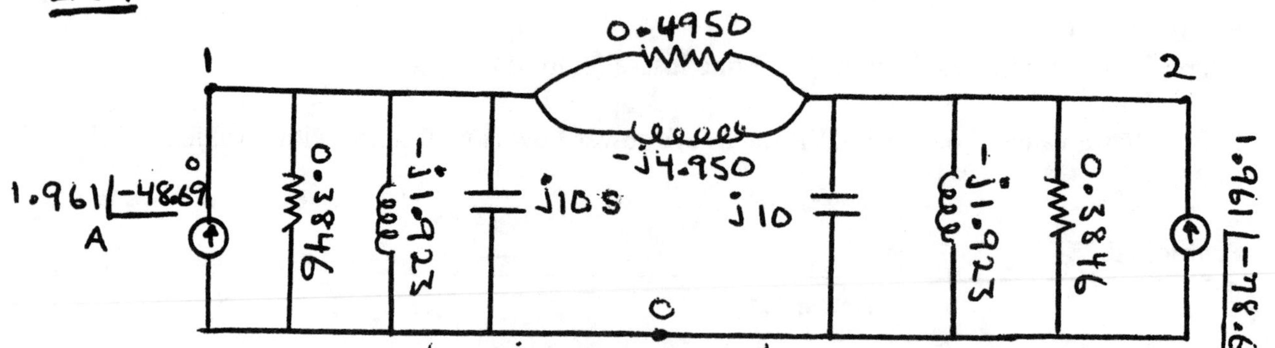

(Admittance values are shown)

$$\begin{bmatrix} (.3846+.4950)+j(10-1.923-4.950) & -(.4950-j4.950) \\ -(.4950-j4.950) & (.3846+.4950)+j(10-1.923-4.95) \end{bmatrix} \begin{bmatrix} \bar{V}_{10} \\ \bar{V}_{20} \end{bmatrix} = \begin{bmatrix} 1.961\angle -48.69^\circ \\ 1.961\angle -78.69^\circ \end{bmatrix}$$

$$\begin{bmatrix} 0.8796+j3.127 & -0.4950+j4.950 \\ -0.4950+j4.950 & 0.8796+j3.127 \end{bmatrix} \begin{bmatrix} \bar{V}_{10} \\ \bar{V}_{20} \end{bmatrix} = \begin{bmatrix} 1.961\angle -48.69^\circ \\ 1.961\angle -78.69^\circ \end{bmatrix}$$

2.28

NOTE THAT THERE ARE TWO BUSES PLUS THE REFERENCE BUS AND ONE LINE FOR THIS PROBLEM. AFTER CONVERTING THE VOLTAGE SOURCES IN FIG. 2.23 TO CURRENT SOURCES, THE EQUIVALENT SOURCE IMPEDANCES ARE:

$$\bar{Z}_{S1} = \bar{Z}_{S2} = (0.1+j0.5)\,//\,(-j0.1) = \frac{(0.1+j0.5)(-j0.1)}{0.1+j0.5-j0.1}$$

$$= \frac{(0.5099\angle 78.69^\circ)(0.1\angle -90^\circ)}{0.4123\angle 75.96^\circ} = 0.1237\angle -87.27^\circ$$

$$= 0.005882 - j0.1235\ \Omega$$

THE REST IS LEFT AS AN EXERCISE TO THE STUDENT.

2.29

After converting impedance values in Figure 2.24 to admittance values, the bus admittance matrix is:

$$\bar{Y}_{bus} = \begin{bmatrix} 1 & -1 & 0 & 0 \\ -1 & (1+\frac{1}{2}+\frac{1}{3}+\frac{1}{4}-j1) & -(\frac{1}{3}-j1) & -(\frac{1}{4}) \\ 0 & -(\frac{1}{3}-j1) & (\frac{1}{3}-j1+j\frac{1}{4}+j\frac{1}{2}) & -(j\frac{1}{4}) \\ 0 & -(\frac{1}{4}) & -(j\frac{1}{4}) & (\frac{1}{4}+j\frac{1}{4}-j\frac{1}{3}) \end{bmatrix}$$

Writing nodal equations by inspection:

$$\begin{bmatrix} 1 & -1 & 0 & 0 \\ -1 & (2.083-j1) & (-0.3333+j1) & -0.25 \\ 0 & (-0.3333+j1) & (0.3333-j0.25) & -j0.25 \\ 0 & -0.25 & -j0.25 & (0.25-j0.08333) \end{bmatrix} \begin{bmatrix} \bar{V}_{10} \\ \bar{V}_{20} \\ \bar{V}_{30} \\ \bar{V}_{40} \end{bmatrix} = \begin{bmatrix} 1\angle 0^\circ \\ 0 \\ 0 \\ 2\angle 30^\circ \end{bmatrix}$$

2.30

THE ADMITTANCE DIAGRAM FOR THE SYSTEM IS SHOWN BELOW:

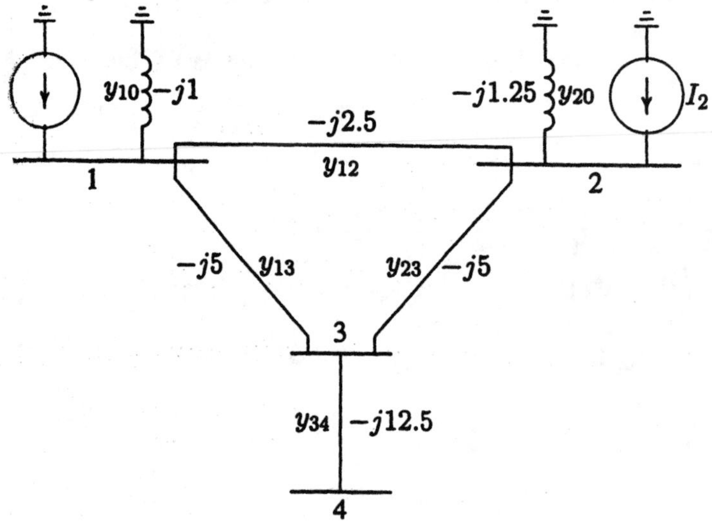

$$\bar{Y}_{BUS} = \begin{bmatrix} \bar{Y}_{11} & \bar{Y}_{12} & \bar{Y}_{13} & \bar{Y}_{14} \\ \bar{Y}_{21} & \bar{Y}_{22} & \bar{Y}_{23} & \bar{Y}_{24} \\ Y_{31} & Y_{32} & Y_{33} & Y_{34} \\ \bar{Y}_{41} & \bar{Y}_{42} & \bar{Y}_{43} & \bar{Y}_{44} \end{bmatrix} = j \begin{bmatrix} -8.5 & 2.5 & 5.0 & 0 \\ 2.5 & -8.75 & 5.0 & 0 \\ 5.0 & 5.0 & -22.5 & 12.5 \\ 0 & 0 & 12.5 & -12.5 \end{bmatrix} \text{ S}$$

WHERE $\bar{Y}_{11} = \bar{y}_{10} + \bar{y}_{12} + \bar{y}_{13}$; $\bar{Y}_{22} = \bar{y}_{20} + \bar{y}_{12} + \bar{y}_{23}$; $\bar{Y}_{23} = \bar{y}_{13} + \bar{y}_{23} + \bar{y}_{34}$

$\bar{Y}_{44} = \bar{y}_{34}$; $\bar{Y}_{12} = \bar{Y}_{21} = -\bar{y}_{12}$; $\bar{Y}_{13} = \bar{Y}_{31} = -\bar{y}_{13}$; $\bar{Y}_{23} = \bar{Y}_{32} = -\bar{y}_{23}$

AND $\bar{Y}_{34} = \bar{Y}_{43} = -\bar{y}_{34}$

2.31

(a)

$$\begin{bmatrix} \bar{Y}_c + \bar{Y}_d + \bar{Y}_f & -\bar{Y}_d & -\bar{Y}_c & -\bar{Y}_f \\ -\bar{Y}_d & \bar{Y}_b + \bar{Y}_d + \bar{Y}_e & -\bar{Y}_b & -\bar{Y}_e \\ -\bar{Y}_c & -\bar{Y}_b & \bar{Y}_a + \bar{Y}_b + \bar{Y}_c & 0 \\ -\bar{Y}_f & -\bar{Y}_e & 0 & \bar{Y}_e + \bar{Y}_f + \bar{Y}_g \end{bmatrix} \begin{bmatrix} \bar{V}_1 \\ \bar{V}_2 \\ \bar{V}_3 \\ \bar{V}_4 \end{bmatrix} = \begin{bmatrix} \bar{I}_1 = 0 \\ \bar{I}_2 = 0 \\ \bar{I}_3 \\ \bar{I}_4 \end{bmatrix}$$

2.31 CONTD.

(b)

$$j\begin{bmatrix} -14.5 & 8 & 4 & 2.5 \\ 8 & -17 & 4 & 5 \\ 4 & 4 & -8.8 & 0 \\ 2.5 & 5 & 0 & -8.3 \end{bmatrix}\begin{bmatrix} \bar{V}_1 \\ \bar{V}_2 \\ \bar{V}_3 \\ \bar{V}_4 \end{bmatrix} = \begin{bmatrix} 0 \\ 0 \\ 1\angle -90^\circ \\ 0.62\angle -135^\circ \end{bmatrix}$$

$\bar{Y}_{BUS}\bar{V} = \bar{I}$; $\bar{Y}_{BUS}^{-1}\ \bar{Y}_{BUS}\ \bar{V} = \bar{Y}_{BUS}^{-1}\ \bar{I}$

WHERE $\bar{Y}_{BUS}^{-1} = \bar{Z}_{BUS} = j\begin{bmatrix} 0.7187 & 0.6688 & 0.6307 & 0.6194 \\ 0.6688 & 0.7045 & 0.6242 & 0.6258 \\ 0.6307 & 0.7045 & 0.6840 & 0.5660 \\ 0.6194 & 0.6258 & 0.5660 & 0.6840 \end{bmatrix}\Omega$

$$\bar{V} = \bar{Y}_{BUS}^{-1}\ \bar{I}$$

WHERE $\bar{V} = \begin{bmatrix} \bar{V}_1 \\ \bar{V}_2 \\ \bar{V}_3 \\ \bar{V}_4 \end{bmatrix}$ AND $\bar{I} = \begin{bmatrix} 0 \\ 0 \\ 1\angle -90^\circ \\ 0.62\angle -135^\circ \end{bmatrix}$

THEN SOLVE FOR $\bar{V}_1$, $\bar{V}_2$, $\bar{V}_3$, AND $\bar{V}_4$.

2.32

(a) $\bar{V}_{AN} = \frac{208}{\sqrt{3}}\angle 0^\circ = 120.1\angle 0^\circ$ V (ASSUMED AS REFERENCE)

$\bar{V}_{AB} = 208\angle 30^\circ$ V; $\bar{V}_{BC} = 208\angle -90^\circ$ V; $\bar{I}_A = 10\angle -90^\circ$ A

$$\bar{Z}_Y = \frac{\bar{V}_{AN}}{\bar{I}_A} = \frac{120.1\angle 0^\circ}{10\angle -90^\circ} = 12.01\angle 90^\circ = (0 + j\,12.01)\ \Omega$$

(b) $\bar{I}_{AB} = \frac{\bar{I}_A}{\sqrt{3}}\angle 30^\circ = \frac{10}{\sqrt{3}}\angle -90^\circ + 30^\circ = 5.774\angle -60^\circ$ A

$$\bar{Z}_\Delta = \frac{\bar{V}_{AB}}{\bar{I}_{AB}} = \frac{208\angle 30^\circ}{5.774\angle -60^\circ} = 36.02\angle 90^\circ = (0 + j\,36.02)\ \Omega$$

NOTE: $\bar{Z}_Y = \bar{Z}_\Delta / 3$

2.33

$$\bar{S}_{3\phi} = \sqrt{3}\, V_{LL} I_L \angle \cos^{-1}(pf) = \sqrt{3}\; 208 \times 20 \angle \cos^{-1} 0.8$$

$$= 7.205 \times 10^3 \angle 36.87^\circ = 5.764 \times 10^3 + j\,4.323 \times 10^3$$

$P_{3\phi} = Re(\bar{S}_{3\phi}) = 5.764$ kW DELIVERED ; $Q_{3\phi} = Im(\bar{S}_{3\phi}) = 4.323$ kVAR DELIVERED

POWER TRIANGLE:

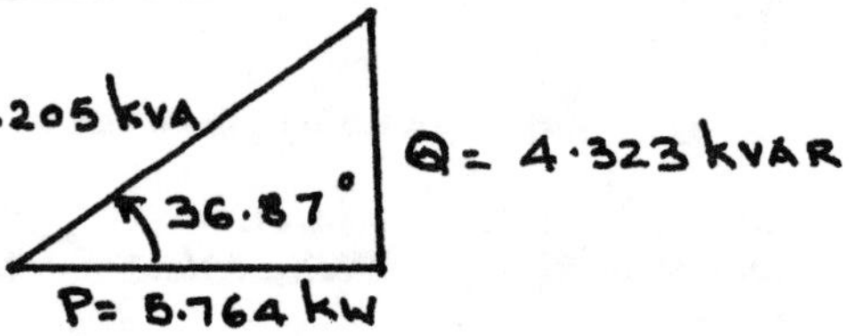

2.34

(a) WITH $\bar{V}_{ab}$ AS REFERENCE

$$\bar{V}_{an} = \frac{208}{\sqrt{3}} \angle -30^\circ$$

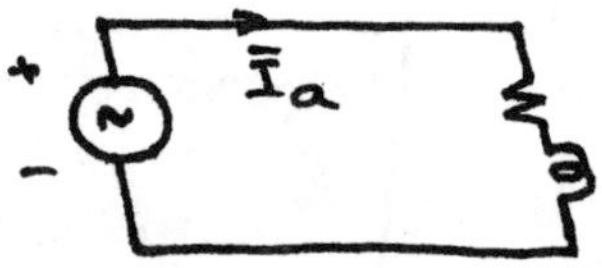

$$\frac{\bar{Z}_\Delta}{3} = 4 + j3 = 5 \angle 36.87^\circ\ \Omega$$

$$\bar{I}_a = \frac{\bar{V}_{an}}{(\bar{Z}_\Delta / 3)} = \frac{120.1 \angle -30^\circ}{5 \angle 36.87^\circ} = 24.02 \angle -66.87^\circ \text{ A}$$

$$\bar{S}_{3\phi} = 3\, \bar{V}_{an} \bar{I}_a^{*} = 3(120.1 \angle -30^\circ)(24.02 \angle +66.87^\circ)$$

$$= 8654 \angle 36.87^\circ = 6923 + j\,5192$$

$P_{3\phi} = 6923$ W ; $Q_{3\phi} = 5192$ VAR ; BOTH ABSORBED BY THE LOAD

$pf = \cos(36.87^\circ) = 0.8$ LAGGING; $S_{3\phi} = |\bar{S}_{3\phi}| = 8654$ VA

(b)

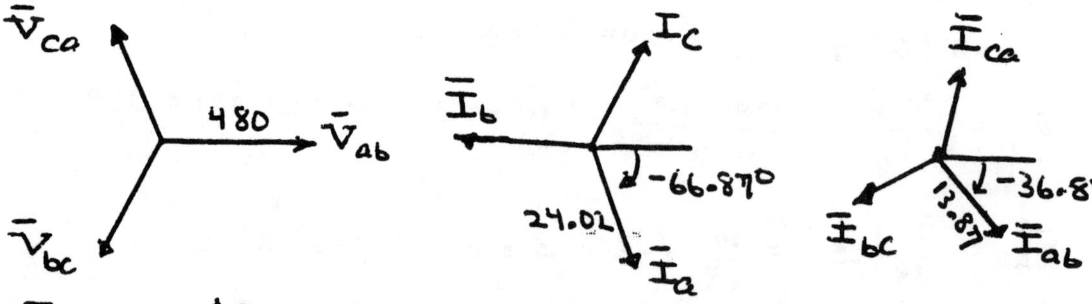

$\bar{V}_{ab} = 208 \angle 0^\circ$ V $\qquad \bar{I}_a = 24.02 \angle -66.87^\circ$ A $\qquad 13.87 \angle -36.87^\circ$ A

2.35

(a) TRANSFORMING THE Δ- CONNECTED LOAD INTO AN EQUIVALENT Y,

THE IMPEDANCE PER PHASE OF THE EQUIVALENT Y IS

$$\bar{Z}_2 = \frac{60 - j45}{3} = (20 - j15)\ \Omega$$

WITH THE PHASE VOLTAGE $V_1 = \dfrac{120\sqrt{3}}{\sqrt{3}} = 120\text{V}$ TAKEN AS A REFERENCE,

THE PER-PHASE EQUIVALENT CIRCUIT IS SHOWN BELOW:

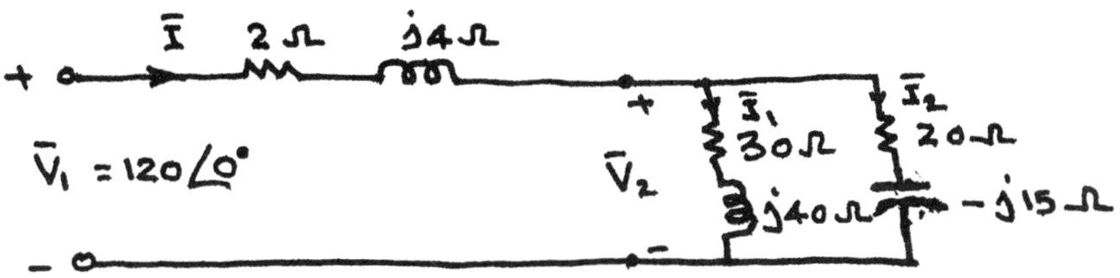

TOTAL IMPEDANCE VIEWED FROM THE INPUT TERMINALS IS

$$\bar{Z} = 2 + j4 + \frac{(30 + j40)(20 - j15)}{(30 + j40) + (20 - j15)} = 2 + j4 + 22 - j4 = 24\ \Omega$$

$$\bar{I} = \frac{\bar{V}_1}{\bar{Z}} = \frac{120\angle 0^\circ}{24} = 5\angle 0^\circ \text{ A}$$

THE THREE-PHASE COMPLEX POWER SUPPLIED $= \bar{S} = 3\bar{V}_1\bar{I}^* = 1800\text{ W}$

$P = 1800$ W and $Q = 0$ VAR DELIVERED BY THE SENDING-END SOURCE

(b) PHASE VOLTAGE AT LOAD TERMINALS $\bar{V}_2 = 120\angle 0^\circ - (2 + j4)(5\angle 0^\circ)$

$$= 110 - j20 = 111.8\angle -10.3^\circ \text{ V}$$

THE LINE VOLTAGE MAGNITUDE AT THE LOAD TERMINAL IS

$$(V_{LOAD})_{L-L} = \sqrt{3}\ 111.8 = 193.64 \text{ V}$$

(c) THE CURRENT PER PHASE IN THE Y-CONNECTED LOAD AND IN THE EQUIV. Y OF THE Δ-LOAD:

$$\bar{I}_1 = \frac{\bar{V}_2}{\bar{Z}_1} = 1 - j2 = 2.236\angle -63.4^\circ \text{ A}$$

$$\bar{I}_2 = \frac{\bar{V}_2}{\bar{Z}_2} = 4 + j2 = 4.472\angle 26.56^\circ \text{A}$$

THE PHASE CURRENT MAGNITUDE IN THE ORIGINAL Δ-CONNECTED LOAD

$$(I_{ph})_\Delta = \frac{I_2}{\sqrt{3}} = \frac{4.472}{\sqrt{3}} = 2.582 \text{ A}$$

2.35 CONTD.

(d) THE THREE-PHASE COMPLEX POWER ABSORBED BY EACH LOAD IS

$$\bar{S}_1 = 3\bar{V}_2 \bar{I}_1^* = 450\,W + j\,600\ VAR$$

$$\bar{S}_2 = 3\bar{V}_2 \bar{I}_2^* = 1200\,W - j\,900\ VAR$$

THE THREE-PHASE COMPLEX POWER ABSORBED BY THE LINE IS

$$\bar{S}_L = 3(R_L + jX_L) I^2 = 3(2+j4)(5)^2 = 150\,W + j300\ VAR$$

THE SUM OF LOAD POWERS AND LINE LOSSES IS EQUAL TO THE POWER DELIVERED FROM THE SUPPLY:

$$\bar{S}_1 + \bar{S}_2 + \bar{S}_L = (450 + j600) + (1200 - j900) + (150 + j300)$$

$$= 1800\,W + j0\ VAR$$

2.36

(a) THE PER-PHASE EQUIVALENT CIRCUIT FOR THE PROBLEM IS SHOWN BELOW:

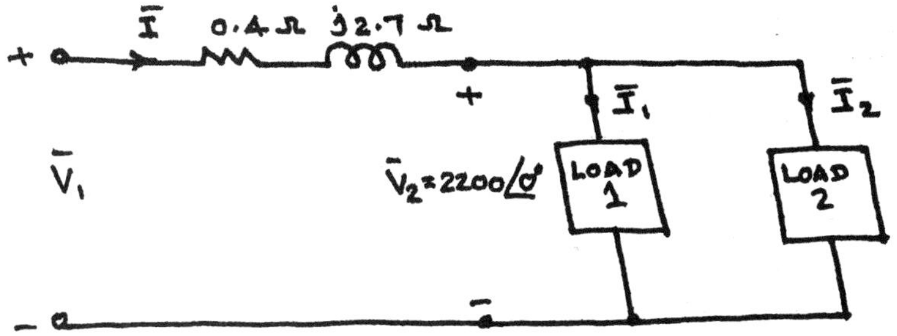

PHASE VOLTAGE AT THE LOAD TERMINALS IS $V_2 = \dfrac{2200\sqrt{3}}{\sqrt{3}} = 2200$ V TAKEN AS REF.

TOTAL COMPLEX POWER AT THE LOAD END OR RECEIVING END IS

$$\bar{S}_{R(3\phi)} = 560.1(0.707 + j0.707) + 132 = 528 + j396 = 660\angle 36.87° \text{ kVA}$$

WITH PHASE VOLTAGE $\bar{V}_2$ AS REFERENCE,

$$\bar{I} = \frac{\bar{S}^*_{R(3\phi)}}{3\bar{V}_2^*} = \frac{660{,}000\angle -36.87°}{3(2200\angle 0°)} = 100\angle -36.87° \text{ A}$$

PHASE VOLTAGE AT SENDING END IS GIVEN BY

$$\bar{V}_1 = 2200\angle 0° + (0.4 + j2.7)(100\angle -36.87°) = 2401.7\angle 4.58° \text{ V}$$

THE MAGNITUDE OF THE LINE TO LINE VOLTAGE AT THE SENDING END OF THE LINE IS

$$(V_1)_{L-L} = \sqrt{3}\, V_1 = \sqrt{3}(2401.7) = 4160 \text{ V}$$

(b) THE THREE-PHASE COMPLEX-POWER LOSS IN THE LINE IS GIVEN BY

$$\bar{S}_{L(3\phi)} = 3RI^2 + j3XI^2 = 3(0.4)(100)^2 + j3(2.7)(100)^2$$
$$= 12 \text{ kW} + j81 \text{ kVAR}$$

(c) THE THREE-PHASE SENDING POWER IS

$$\bar{S}_{S(3\phi)} = 3\bar{V}_1\bar{I}^* = 3(2401.7\angle 4.58°)(100\angle 36.87°)$$
$$= 540 \text{ kW} + j477 \text{ kVAR}$$

NOTE THAT $\bar{S}_{S(3\phi)} = \bar{S}_{R(3\phi)} + \bar{S}_{L(3\phi)}$

2.37

(a)

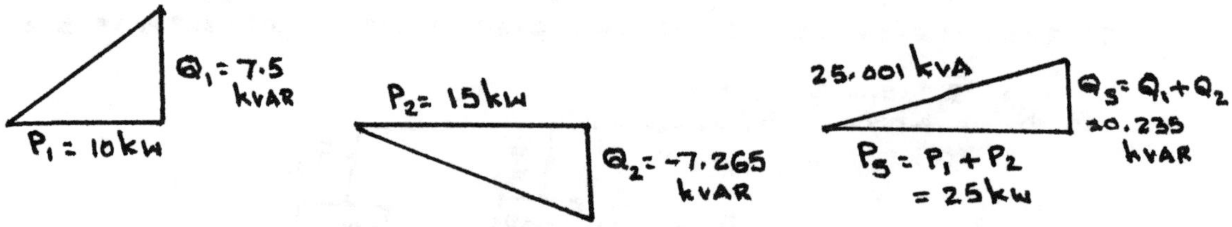

$$I_S = \frac{S_S}{\sqrt{3}\,V_{LL}} = \frac{25.001 \times 10^3}{\sqrt{3}\,(480)} = 30.07\text{ A}$$

(b) THE AMMETER READS ZERO, BECAUSE IN A BALANCED THREE-PHASE SYSTEM, THERE IS NO NEUTRAL CURRENT.

2.38

(a) $\bar{V}_{an} = \frac{208}{\sqrt{3}} \angle 0°$

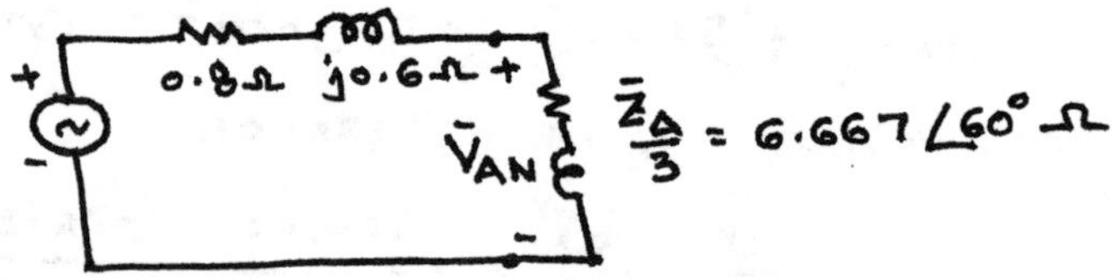

USING VOLTAGE DIVISION: $\bar{V}_{AN} = \bar{V}_{an}\dfrac{\bar{Z}_\Delta/3}{(\bar{Z}_\Delta/3) + \bar{Z}_{LINE}}$

$$\bar{V}_{AN} = \frac{208}{\sqrt{3}} \cdot \frac{6.667\angle 60°}{6.667\angle 60° + (0.8 + j0.6)} = 105.4\angle 2.96°\text{ V}$$

LOAD VOLTAGE $V_{AB} = \sqrt{3}\,105.4 = 182.6\text{ V (L-L)}$

(b)

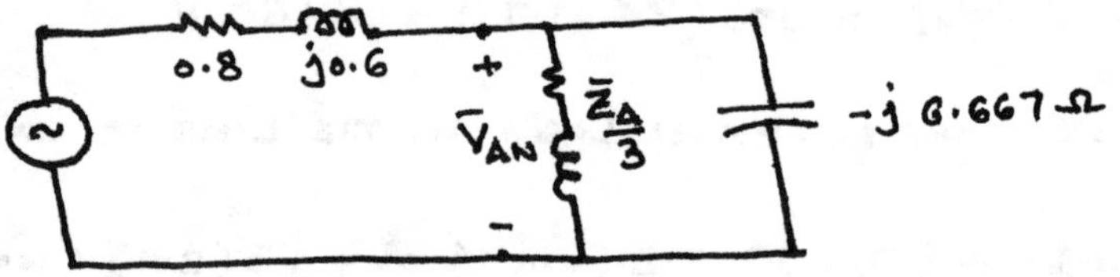

$\bar{V}_{AN} = \bar{V}_{an}\dfrac{\bar{Z}_{eq}}{\bar{Z}_{eq} + \bar{Z}_{LINE}}$; $\bar{Z}_{eq} = (6.667\angle 60°)\,\|\,(-j6.667)$

$= 12.88\angle -15°\ \Omega$

$$\bar{V}_{AN} = \left(\frac{208}{\sqrt{3}}\angle 0°\right)\left[\frac{12.88\angle -15°}{(12.88\angle -15°) + 0.8 + j0.6}\right] = 114.4\angle -3.33°\text{ V}$$

THE LOAD LINE TO LINE VOLTAGE IS $V_{AB} = \sqrt{3}\,114.4 = 198.1\text{ V}$

2.39

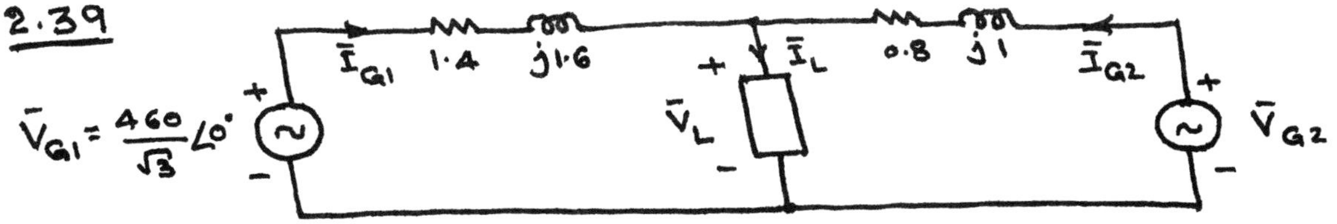

(a) $\bar{I}_{G1} = \dfrac{15\times 10^3}{\sqrt{3}(460)(0.8)} \angle -\cos^{-1}0.8 = 23.53 \angle -36.87°$ A

$\bar{V}_L = \bar{V}_{G1} - \bar{Z}_{LINE\,1}\,\bar{I}_{G1} = \dfrac{460}{\sqrt{3}}\angle 0° - (1.4 + j1.6)(23.53\angle -36.87°)$

$= 216.9 \angle -2.73°$ V LINE TO NEUTRAL

LOAD VOLTAGE $V_L = \sqrt{3}\ 216.9 = 375.7$ V LINE TO LINE

(b) $\bar{I}_L = \dfrac{30\times 10^3}{\sqrt{3}(375.7)(0.8)} \angle -2.73° - \cos^{-1}0.8 = 57.63 \angle -39.6°$ A

$\bar{I}_{G2} = \bar{I}_L - \bar{I}_{G1} = 57.63\angle -39.6° - 23.53 \angle -36.87°$

$= 34.14 \angle -41.49°$ A

$\bar{V}_{G2} = \bar{V}_L + \bar{Z}_{LINE\,2}\ \bar{I}_{G2} = 216.9 \angle -2.73° + (0.8 + j1)(34.14 \angle -41.49°)$

$= 259.7 \angle -0.63°$ V

GENERATOR 2 LINE-TO-LINE VOLTAGE $V_{G2} = \sqrt{3}\,(259.7)$

$= 449.8$ V

(c) $\bar{S}_{G2} = 3\,\bar{V}_{G2}\,\bar{I}^*_{G2} = 3\,(259.7\angle -0.63°)(34.14\angle 41.49°)$

$= 20.12\times 10^3 + j\,17.4\times 10^3$

$P_{G2} = 20.12$ kW ; $Q_{G2} = 17.4$ kVAR ; BOTH DELIVERED

2.40

(a)

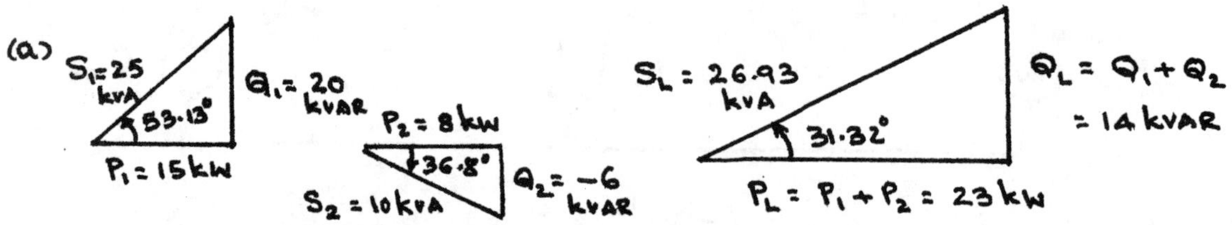

(b) $pf = \cos 31.32° = 0.854$ LAGGING

(c) $$I_L = \frac{S_L}{\sqrt{3}\, V_{LL}} = \frac{26.93 \times 10^3}{\sqrt{3}\,(480)} = 32.39\ \text{A}$$

(d) $$Q_C = Q_L = 14 \times 10^3 \ \text{VAR} = 3\,(V_{LL})^2 / X_\Delta$$

$$X_\Delta = \frac{3\,(480)^2}{14 \times 10^3} = 49.37\ \Omega$$

(e) $$I_C = V_{LL} / X_\Delta = 480 / 49.37 = 9.72\ \text{A}$$

$$I_{LINE} = \frac{P_L}{\sqrt{3}\, V_{LL}} = \frac{23 \times 10^3}{\sqrt{3}\ 480} = 27.66\ \text{A}$$

2.41

(a) LET $\bar{Z}_Y = \bar{Z}_A = \bar{Z}_B = \bar{Z}_C$ FOR A BALANCED Y-LOAD

$\bar{Z}_\Delta = \bar{Z}_{AB} = \bar{Z}_{BC} = \bar{Z}_{CA}$ FOR A BALANCED Δ-LOAD

USING EQUATIONS IN FIG. 2.27

$$\bar{Z}_\Delta = \frac{\bar{Z}_Y^2 + \bar{Z}_Y^2 + \bar{Z}_Y^2}{\bar{Z}_Y} = 3\bar{Z}_Y$$

AND $$\bar{Z}_Y = \frac{\bar{Z}_\Delta^2}{\bar{Z}_\Delta + \bar{Z}_\Delta + \bar{Z}_\Delta} = \frac{\bar{Z}_\Delta}{3}$$

(b)

$$\bar{Z}_A = \frac{(j10)(-j25)}{j10 + j20 - j25} = -j50\ \Omega$$

$$\bar{Z}_B = \frac{(j10)(j20)}{j5} = j40\ \Omega \ ; \quad \bar{Z}_C = \frac{(j20)(-j25)}{j5} = -j100\ \Omega$$

CHAPTER 3

3.1

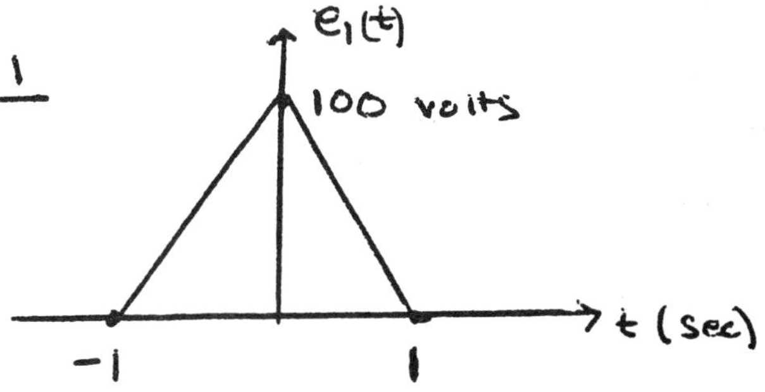

$e_2(t) = \frac{N_2}{N_1} e_1(t) = \frac{1}{6} e_1(t)$

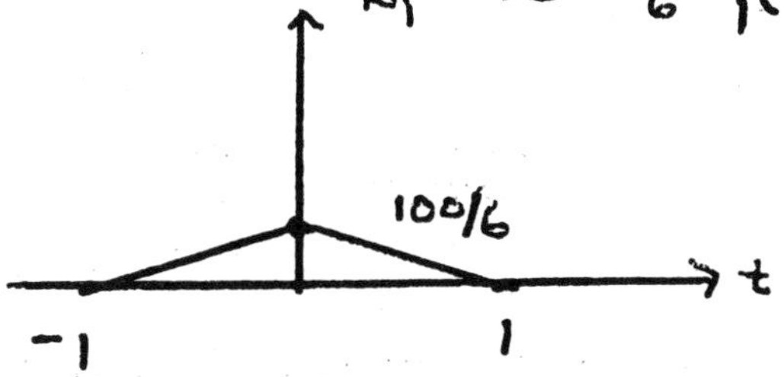

$i_1(t) = \frac{N_2}{N_1} i_2(t) = \frac{1}{6} i_2(t)$

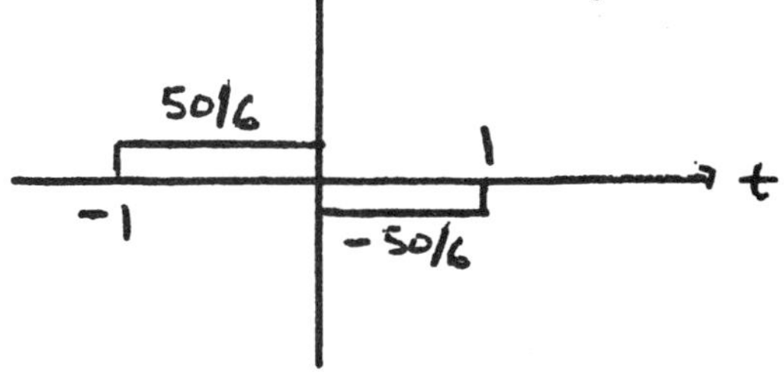

$i_2(t) = C\frac{de_2}{dt} = 3\frac{de_2}{dt}$

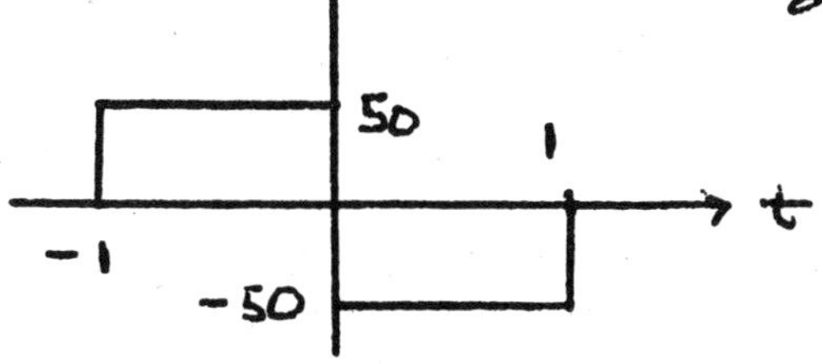

3.2

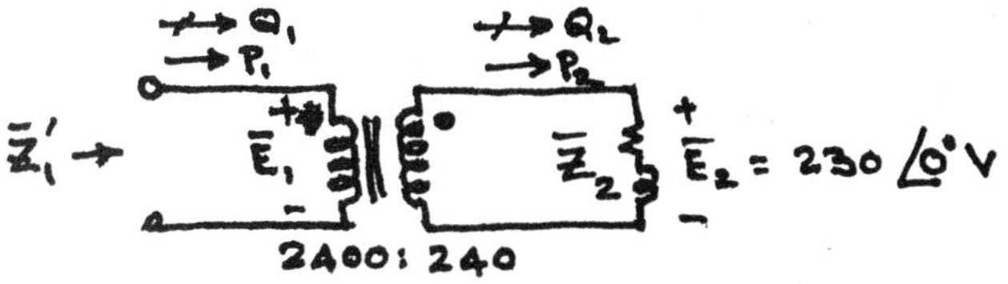

(a) $E_1 = \frac{N_1}{N_2} E_2 = \frac{2400}{240}(230) = 2300 \text{ V}$

(b) $\bar{S}_2 = \bar{E}_2 \bar{I}_2^* \;;\; \bar{I}_2 = \left(\frac{\bar{S}_2}{\bar{E}_2}\right)^* = \left[\frac{80\times10^3 \angle \cos^{-1}0.8}{230\angle 0^\circ}\right]^* = 347.8\angle -36.87^\circ$

$\bar{Z}_2 = \frac{\bar{E}_2}{\bar{I}_2} = \frac{230\angle 0^\circ}{347.8\angle -36.87^\circ} = 0.6613\angle 36.87^\circ \;\Omega$

$= 0.529 + j0.397 \;\Omega$

(c) $\bar{Z}_1' = \left(\frac{N_1}{N_2}\right)^2 \bar{Z}_2 = 100\,\bar{Z}_2 = 66.13\angle 36.87^\circ \;\Omega$

(d) $P_1 = P_2 = 80(0.8) = 64 \text{ kW}$

$Q_1 = Q_2 = 64 \tan(36.87^\circ) = 48 \text{ kVAR}$

3.3

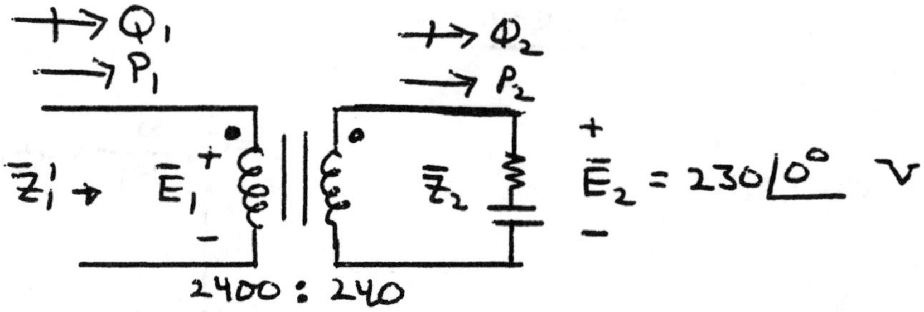

(a) $E_1 = \frac{N_1}{N_2} E_2 = \left(\frac{2400}{240}\right)(230) = \underline{\underline{2300.\ V}}$

(b) $\bar{I}_2 = \left(\frac{\bar{S}_2}{\bar{E}_2}\right)^* = \left[\frac{110\times10^3 \angle -\cos^{-1}0.85}{230\angle 0^\circ}\right]^* = 478.26\angle +31.79^\circ$ A

$\bar{Z}_2 = \frac{\bar{E}_2}{\bar{I}_2} = \frac{230\angle 0^\circ}{478.26\angle 31.79^\circ} = 0.4809\angle -31.79^\circ\ \Omega$

$\bar{Z}_2 = \underline{\underline{0.4088 - j0.2533\ \Omega}}$

(c) $\bar{Z}_1' = \left(\frac{N_1}{N_2}\right)^2 \bar{Z}_2 = 100 \bar{Z}_2 = \underline{\underline{48.09\angle -31.79^\circ}}\ \Omega$

(d) $P_1 = P_2 = (110)(0.85) = \underline{\underline{93.5}}$ kW

$Q_1 = Q_2 = 110 \tan(-31.79^\circ) = \underline{\underline{-68.17}}$ kvars supplied to primary winding

3.4

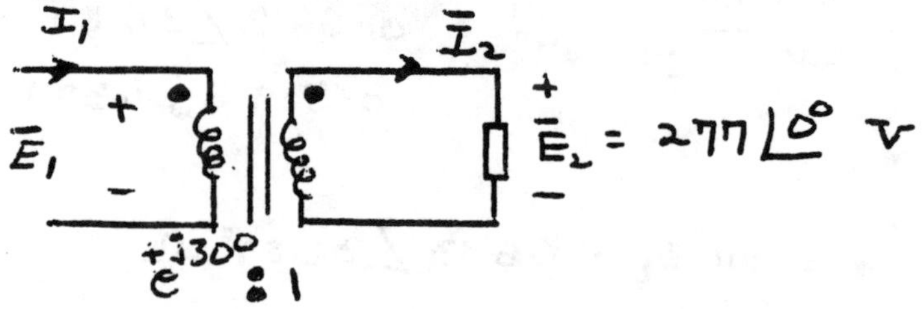

(a) $\bar{E}_2 = 277\angle 0^\circ$ V $\qquad \bar{E}_1 = e^{j30^\circ}\bar{E}_2 = \underline{\underline{277\angle 30^\circ}}$ V

(b) $\bar{I}_2 = \frac{S_2}{E_2}\angle +\cos^{-1}(\text{P.F.}) = \frac{50\times10^3}{277}\angle \cos^{-1}(0.9) = 180.5\angle +25.84^\circ$ A

3.4 CONTD.

$$\bar{I}_1 = \frac{\bar{I}_2}{(e^{j30°})^*} = \bar{I}_2 e^{j30°} = \underline{\underline{180.5 \angle 55.84°}} \text{ A}$$

(c) $$\bar{Z}_2 = \frac{\bar{E}_2}{\bar{I}_2} = \frac{277 \angle 0°}{180.5 \angle 25.84°} = 1.5346 \angle -25.84° \ \Omega$$

$$\bar{Z}_2' = \bar{Z}_2 = \underline{\underline{1.5346 \angle -25.84°}} \ \Omega$$

(d) $$\bar{S}_1 = \bar{S}_2 = 50 \angle -\cos^{-1}(0.9) = \underline{\underline{50 \angle -25.84°}} \text{ kVA}$$

$\bar{S}_1 = 45$ kW $- j\,21.79$ kvars delivered to primary

3.5

(a)

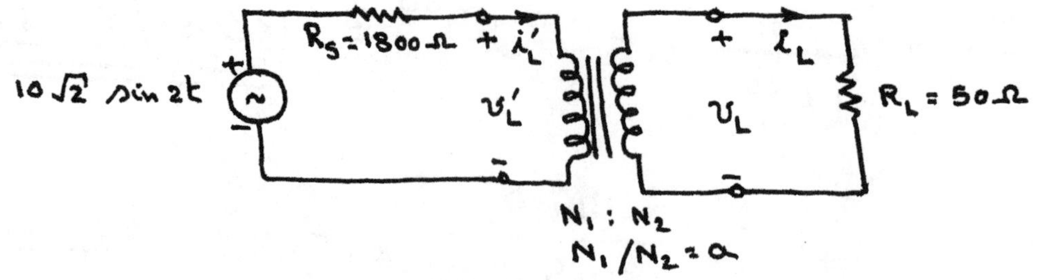

FOR MAXIMUM POWER TRANSFER TO THE LOAD, $R_L' = a^2 R_L = R_S$

OR $50a^2 = 1800$ OR $a = 6 = N_1/N_2$

(b) BY VOLTAGE DIVISION,

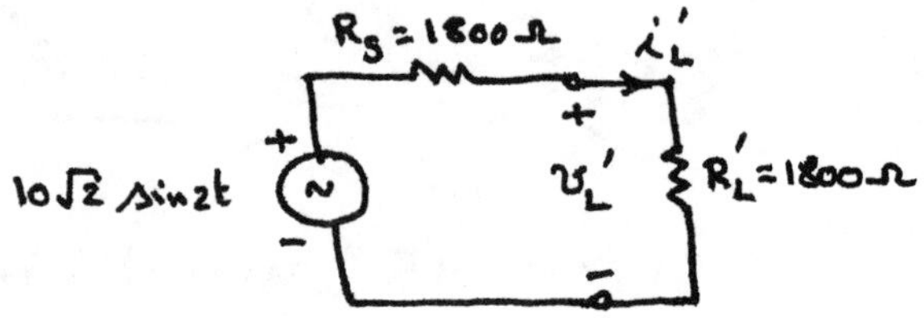

$v_L' = 5\sqrt{2}\sin 2t$ V

$(V_L')_{RMS} = 5$ V

$$P_{av} = \frac{[(V_L')_{RMS}]^2}{1800} = \frac{25}{1800}\text{ W} \simeq 13.9\text{ mW}$$

3.6

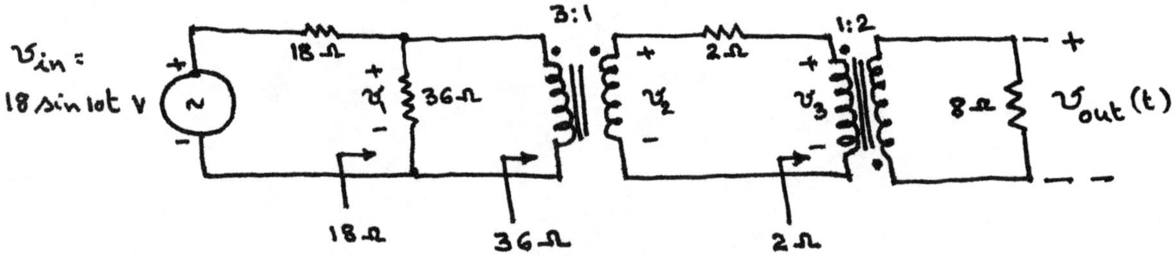

$v_1 = (18\sin 10t)/2 = 9\sin 10t$ V

$v_2 = \frac{1}{3}v_1 = 3\sin 10t$ V

$v_3 = \frac{1}{2}v_2 = 1.5\sin 10t$ V

$v_{out}(t) = -2v_3 = -3\sin 10t$ V

3.7

(a)

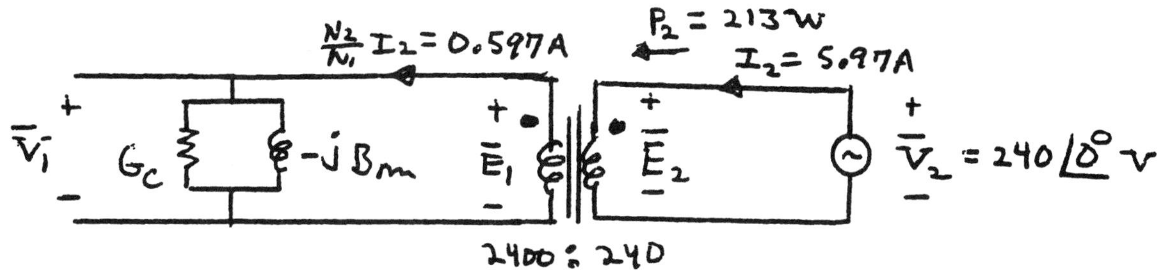

Neglecting the series impedance:

$$\bar{E}_1 = \frac{N_1}{N_2}\bar{E}_2 = \frac{N_1}{N_2}\bar{V}_2 = \left(\frac{2400}{240}\right)240\angle 0^\circ = 2400\angle 0^\circ \text{ V}$$

$$\frac{N_2}{N_1} I_2 = \left(\frac{240}{2400}\right)(5.97) = 0.597 \text{ A}$$

$$G_c = P_2 / E_1^2 = 213/(2400^2) = 3.698 \times 10^{-5} \text{ S}$$

$$Y_c = \left(\frac{N_2}{N_1} I_2\right) / E_1 = 0.597/2400 = 2.4875 \times 10^{-4} \text{ S}$$

$$B_m = \sqrt{Y_c^2 - G_c^2} = \sqrt{(2.4875 \times 10^{-4})^2 - (3.698 \times 10^{-5})^2}$$

$$B_m = 2.460 \times 10^{-4} \text{ S}$$

$$\bar{Y}_c = G_c - jB_m = \underline{\underline{3.698 \times 10^{-5} - j2.460 \times 10^{-4}}} = \underline{\underline{2.4875 \times 10^{-4}\angle -81.45^\circ}} \text{ S}$$

3.7 CONTD.

(b)

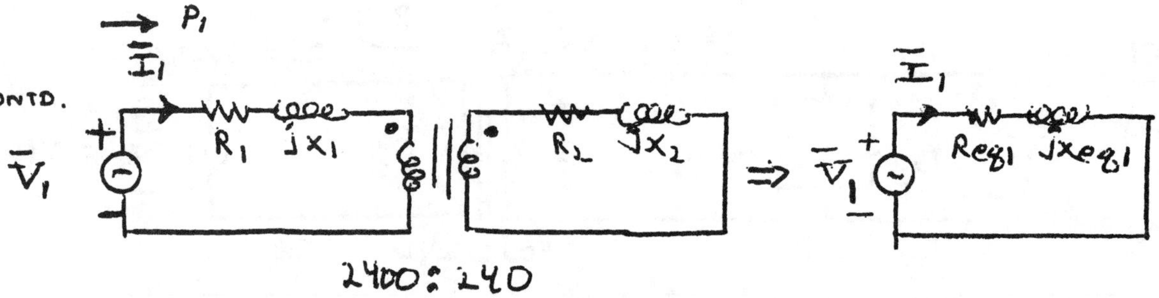

$$R_{eq1} = P_1 / (I_1^2) = 750/(20.8^2) = 1.734\ \Omega$$

$$Z_{eq1} = V_1 / I_1 = 60/(20.8) = 2.885\ \Omega$$

$$X_{eq1} = \sqrt{Z_{eq1}^2 - R_{eq1}^2} = \sqrt{(2.885)^2 - (1.734)^2} = 2.306\ \Omega$$

$$\bar{Z}_{eq1} = R_{eq1} + jX_{eq1} = 1.734 + j2.306 = 2.885\,\underline{/53.06^\circ}\ \Omega$$

(c)

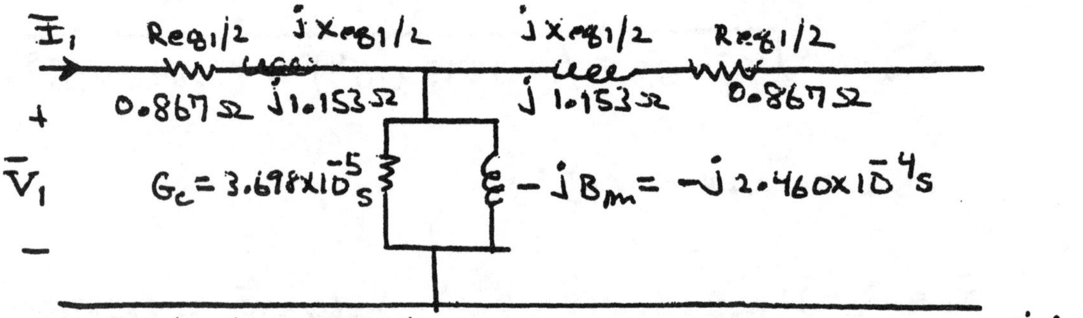

Equivalent T circuit referred to High Voltage Side

3.8.

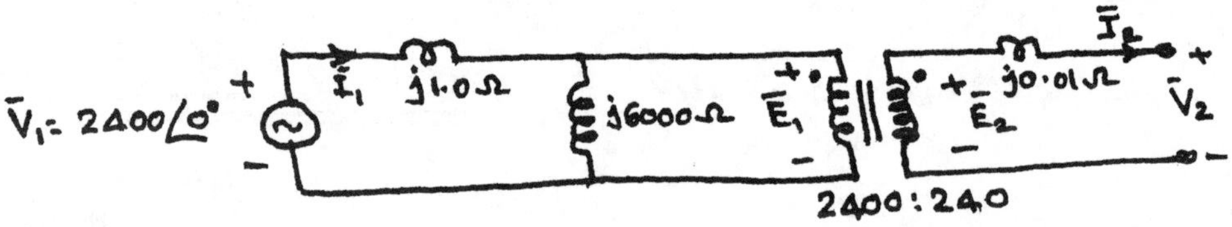

USING VOLTAGE DIVISION:

$$\bar{E}_1 = (2400\angle 0^\circ)\frac{j6000}{j(6000+1)} = 2399.6\angle 0^\circ\ \text{V}$$

$$\bar{V}_2 = \bar{E}_2 = \left(\frac{N_1}{N_2}\right)\bar{E}_1 = 239.96\angle 0^\circ\ \text{V}$$

3.9

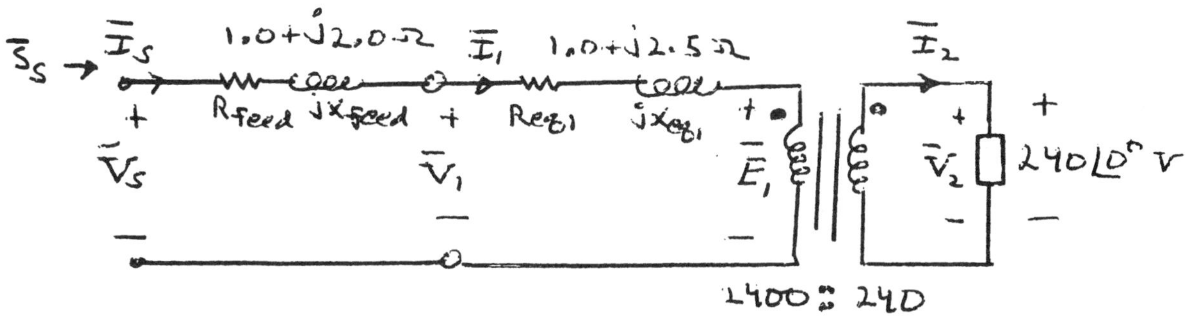

(a) $$\bar{I}_2 = \frac{S_{rated}}{V_2} \angle -\cos^{-1}(P.F.) = \frac{50\times10^3}{240} \angle -\cos^{-1}(0.8) = 208.3\angle -36.87^\circ \text{ A}$$

$$\bar{I}_1 = \frac{N_2}{N_1}\bar{I}_2 = \frac{1}{10}(208.3\angle -36.87^\circ) = 20.83\angle -36.87^\circ \text{ A}$$

$$\bar{E}_1 = \frac{N_1}{N_2}\bar{V}_2 = 10(240\angle 0^\circ) = 2400\angle 0^\circ \text{ V}$$

$$\bar{V}_1 = \bar{E}_1 + (R_{eq1} + jX_{eq1})\bar{I}_1$$

$$\bar{V}_1 = 2400\angle 0^\circ + (1 + j2.5)(20.83\angle -36.87^\circ)$$

$$= 2400 + 56.095\angle 31.329^\circ$$

$$= 2447.9 + j29.166 = \underline{\underline{2448.\angle 0.683^\circ}} \text{ V}$$

(b) $$\bar{V}_S = \bar{E}_1 + (R_{feed} + jX_{feed} + R_{eq1} + jX_{eq1})\bar{I}_1$$

$$= 2400\angle 0^\circ + (2.0 + j4.5)(20.83\angle -36.87^\circ)$$

$$= 2400 + 102.59\angle 29.168^\circ$$

$$= 2489.6 + j50.00 = \underline{\underline{2490.\angle 1.1505^\circ}} \text{ V}$$

(c) $$\bar{S}_S = \bar{V}_S \bar{I}_S^* = (2490\angle 1.1505^\circ)(20.83\angle 36.87^\circ)$$

$$= 51875.\angle 38.02^\circ = 40.87\times10^3 + j31.95\times10^3$$

$P_S = \text{Re}(\bar{S}_S) = 40.87$ kW
$Q_S = \text{Im}(\bar{S}_S) = 31.95$ kvars

} delivered to the sending end of feeder.

3.10

(a) $\bar{I}_1 = 20.83 \angle 0^\circ$

$\bar{V}_1 = 2400\angle 0^\circ + (1 + j2.5)(20.83\angle 0^\circ)$

$= 2400 + 56.095\angle 68.199^\circ = 2420.8 + j52.08$

$= 2421.\angle 1.232^\circ$ V

$\bar{V}_S = 2400\angle 0^\circ + (2.0 + j4.5)(20.83\angle 0^\circ)$

$= 2400 + 102.59\angle 66.04^\circ = 2441.7 + j93.74$

$= 2443.\angle 2.199^\circ$ V

$\bar{S}_S = \bar{V}_S \bar{I}_S^* = (2443\angle 2.199^\circ)(20.83\angle 0^\circ) = 50896.\angle 2.199^\circ$

$= 50{,}859. + j1953.$

$P_S = 50.87$ kW
$Q_S = 1.953$ kvars } delivered

(b) $\bar{I}_1 = 20.83 \angle 36.87^\circ$ A

$\bar{V}_1 = 2400\angle 0^\circ + (1 + j2.5)(20.83\angle 36.87^\circ)$

$= 2400 + 56.095\angle 105.07^\circ = 2385.4 + j54.17$

$= 2386 \angle 1.301^\circ$ V

$\bar{V}_S = 2400\angle 0^\circ + (2.0 + j4.5)(20.83\angle 36.87^\circ)$

$= 2400 + 102.59\angle 102.91^\circ = 2377.1 + j100.0$

$= 2379.\angle 2.409^\circ$ V

$\bar{S}_S = \bar{V}_S \bar{I}_S^* = (2379.\angle 2.409^\circ)(20.83\angle -36.87^\circ)$

$= 49{,}566.\angle -34.46^\circ = 40868. - j28047.$

$P_S = 40.87$ kW delivered

$Q_S = -28.05$ kvars delivered by source to feeder $= +28.04$ kvars absorbed by source

Note: Real and reactive losses, 0.87 kW and 1.95 kvars, absorbed by the feeder and transformer, are the same in all cases. Highest efficiency occurs for unity P.F (EFF = $P_{out}/P_S \times 100 = (50/50.87) \times 100 = 98.29\%$

3.11

(a)

$$a = 2400/240 = 10$$

$$R_2' = a^2 R_2 = \left(\frac{2400}{240}\right)^2 0.0075 = 0.75\ \Omega$$

$$X_2' = a^2 X_2 = (10)^2\ 0.01 = 1.0\ \Omega$$

REFERRED TO THE HV-SIDE, THE EXCITING BRANCH CONDUCTANCE AND SUSCEPTANCE ARE GIVEN BY

$$(1/a^2)\ 0.003 = (1/100)\ 0.003 = 0.03 \times 10^{-3}\ \text{S}$$

AND $$(1/a^2)\ 0.02 = (1/100)\ 0.02 = 0.2 \times 10^{-3}\ \text{S}$$

THE EQUIVALENT CIRCUIT REFERRED TO THE HIGH-VOLTAGE SIDE IS SHOWN BELOW:

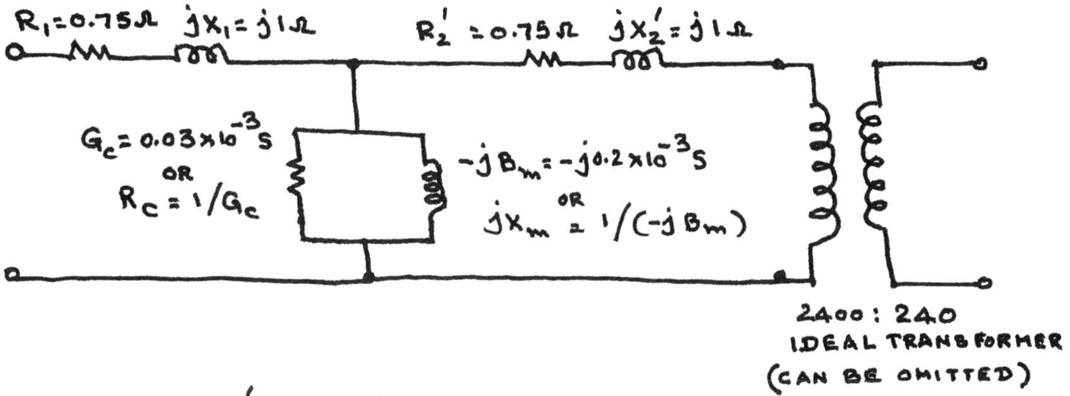

(b)

$$R_1' = R_1/a^2 = 0.0075\ \Omega$$

$$X_1' = X_1/a^2 = 0.01\ \Omega$$

THE EQUIVALENT CIRCUIT REFERRED TO THE LOW-VOLTAGE SIDE IS SHOWN BELOW:

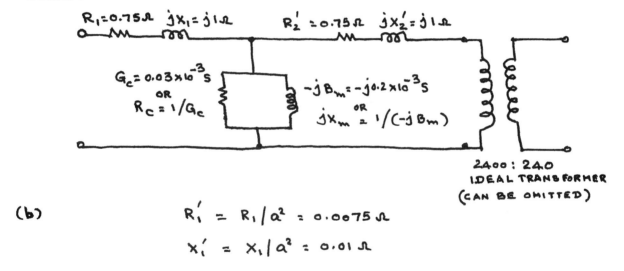

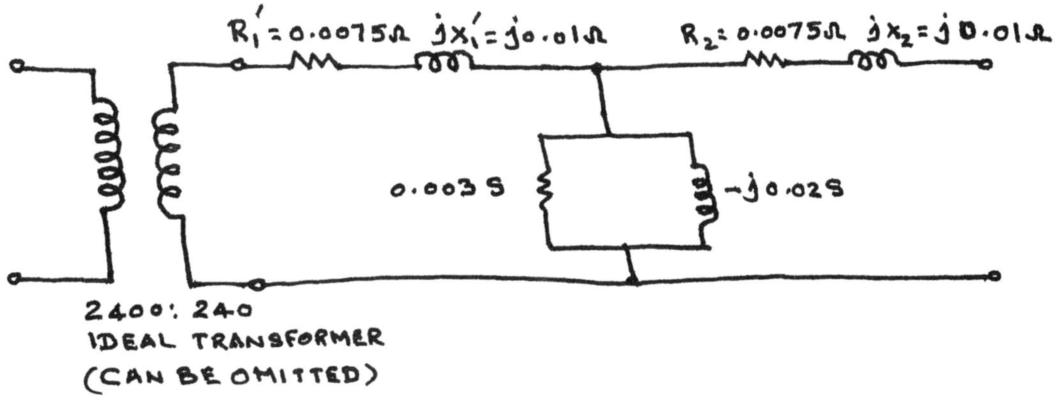

3.12

(a) NEGLECTING THE EXCITING CURRENT OF THE TRANSFORMER, THE EQUIVALENT CIRCUIT OF THE TRANSFORMER, REFERRED TO THE HIGH-VOLTAGE (PRIMARY) SIDE IS SHOWN BELOW:

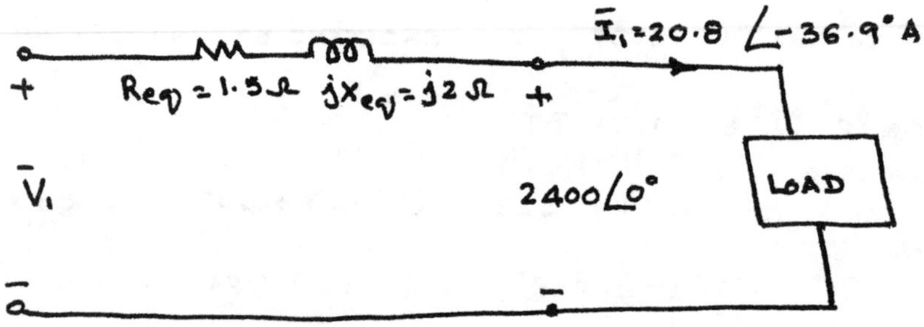

THE RATED (FULL) LOAD CURRENT, REF. TO HV-SIDE, IS GIVEN BY

$$(50 \times 10^3) / 2400 = 20.8 A$$

WITH A LAGGING POWER FACTOR OF 0.8, $\bar{I}_1 = 20.8 \angle -\cos^{-1} 0.8 = 20.8 \angle -36.9° A$

USING KVL, $\bar{V}_1 = 2400 \angle 0° + (20.8 \angle -36.9°)(1.5 + j2) = 2450 \angle 0.34° V$

(b) THE CORRESPONDING PHASOR DIAGRAM IS SHOWN BELOW:

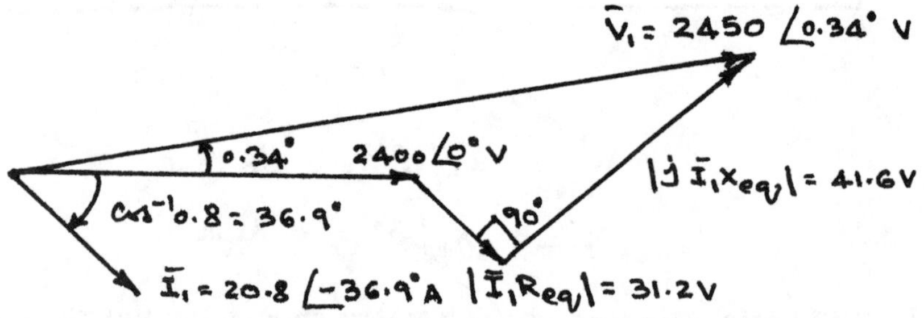

(c)

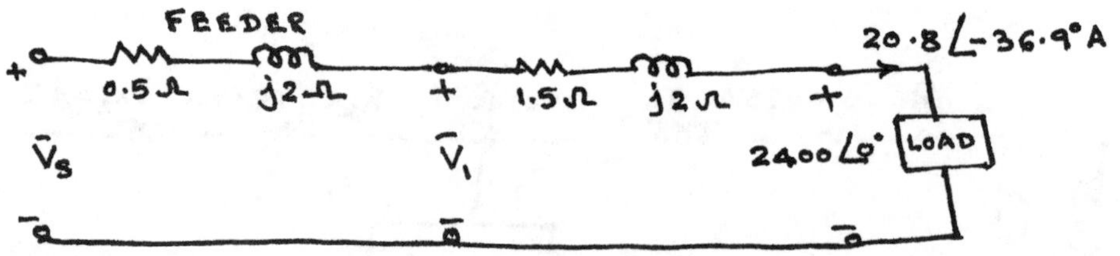

USING KVL, $\bar{V}_S = 2400 \angle 0° + (20.8 \angle -36.9°)(2 + j4) = 2483.5 \angle 0.96° V$

pf AT THE SENDING END IS $\cos(36.9° + 0.96°) = 0.79$ LAGGING

3.13

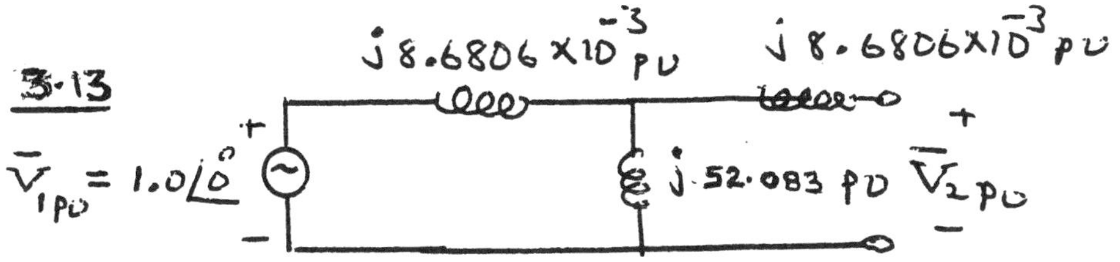

$S_{Base1} = 50\,kVA$

$V_{Base1} = 2400\,V$

$Z_{Base1} = (2400)^2/50\times10^3 = 115.2\,\Omega$

$S_{Base2} = 50\,kVA$

$V_{Base2} = 240\,V$

$Z_{Base2} = (240)^2/50\times10^3 = 1.152\,\Omega$

Using voltage division:

$$\bar{V}_{2pu} = (1.0\angle 0^\circ)\frac{j\,52.083}{j(52.083+8.6806\times10^{-3})} = 0.9998\angle 0^\circ\ pu$$

$$\bar{V}_2 = \bar{V}_{2pu}V_{Base2} = (0.9998\angle 0^\circ)(240) = \underline{\underline{239.95\angle 0^\circ\ V}}$$

3.14

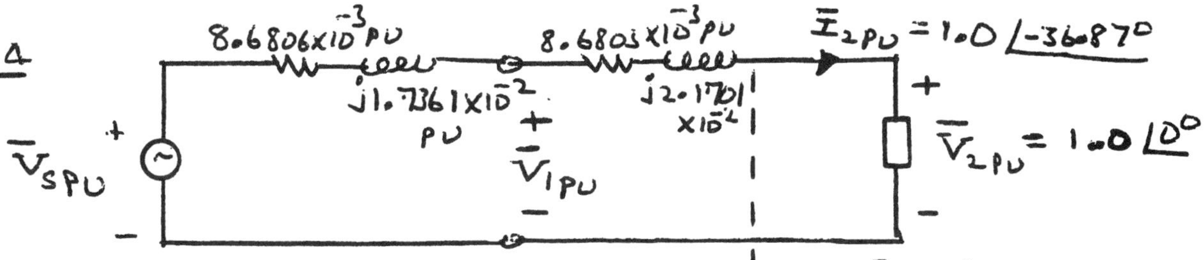

$S_{base} = 50\,kVA$

$V_{base1} = 2400\,V$

$Z_{base1} = (2400)^2/50\times10^3 = 115.2\,\Omega$

$V_{Base2} = 240\,V$

(a) $\bar{V}_{1pu} = 1.0\angle 0^\circ + (8.6803\times10^{-3} + j\,2.1701\times10^{-2})(1.0\angle -36.87^\circ)$

$= 1.0 + 0.023373\angle 31.33^\circ = 1.01997 + j\,0.012157$

$= 1.020\angle 0.683^\circ\ pu$

$$\bar{V}_1 = \bar{V}_{1pu}V_{base} = (1.020\angle 0.683^\circ)(2400) = \underline{\underline{2448.\angle 0.683^\circ\ V}}$$

3.14 CONTD.

(b) $\bar{V}_{Spu} = 1.0\angle 0^\circ + (1.7361 \times 10^{-2} + j\,3.9063 \times 10^{-2})(1.0\angle -36.87^\circ)$

$= 1.0 + 0.042747 \angle 29.168^\circ$

$= 1.03733 + j\,0.020833 = 1.0375 \angle 1.1505^\circ$ pu

$\bar{V}_S = \bar{V}_{Spu} V_{base1} = (1.0375 \angle 1.1505^\circ)(2400) = \underline{\underline{2490. \angle 1.1505^\circ}}$ V

(c) $P_{Spu} + jQ_{Spu} = \bar{V}_{Spu} \bar{I}^*_{Spu} = (1.0375 \angle 1.1505^\circ)(1.0 \angle 36.87^\circ)$

$= 1.0375 \angle 38.02^\circ = 0.8173 + j\,0.6390$ per unit

$P_S = (0.8173)(50) = 40.87$ kW
$Q_S = (0.6390)(50) = 31.95$ kvars } delivered

3.15

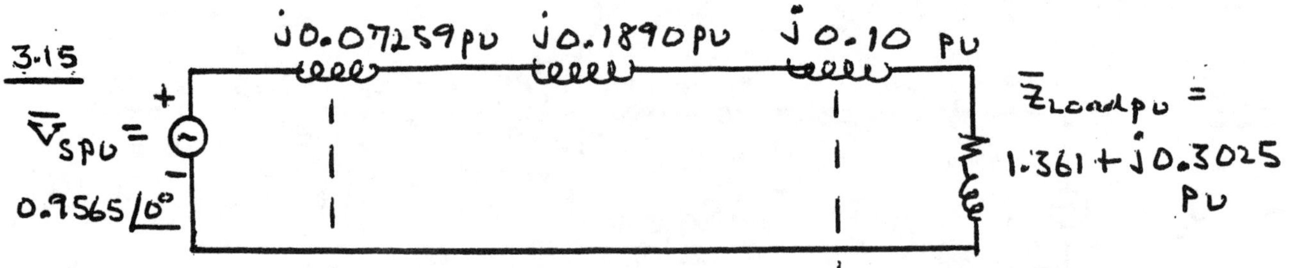

Zone 1

$V_{base1} = \left(\frac{240}{480}\right) 460 = 230$ V

Zone 2

$V_{base2} = \left(\frac{460}{115}\right) 115 = 460$ V

$Z_{base2} = \frac{(460)^2}{20{,}000} = 10.58\ \Omega$

Zone 3

$V_{base3} = 115$ V

$Z_{base3} = \frac{(115)^2}{20{,}000} = 0.6613\ \Omega$

$I_{base3} = \frac{20{,}000}{115} = 173.9$ A

$\bar{Z}_{Loadpu} = \frac{0.9 + j0.2}{0.6613} = 1.361 + j\,0.3025$

$X_{T2pu} = 0.10$ pu

$X_{Line\,pu} = \frac{2}{10.58} = 0.1890$ pu

$X_{T1pu} = (0.10)\left(\frac{480}{460}\right)^2 \left(\frac{20}{30}\right) = 0.07259$ pu

3.15 CONTD. $V_{SPU} = \dfrac{220}{230} = 0.9565$ pu

$$\bar{I}_{Load\,pu} = \frac{\bar{V}_{SPU}}{j(X_{T1pu} + X_{T2pu} + X_{Line}) + \bar{Z}_{Load\,pu}}$$

$$= \frac{0.9565\angle 0^\circ}{j(.07259 + .1890 + .10) + (1.361 + j.3025)}$$

$$= \frac{0.9565\angle 0^\circ}{1.361 + j\,0.6641} = \frac{0.9565\angle 0^\circ}{1.514\angle 26.01^\circ}$$

$$= 0.6316\angle -26.01^\circ \text{ pu}$$

$$\bar{I}_{Load} = \bar{I}_{Load\,pu}\, I_{base3} = (0.6316\angle -26.01^\circ)(173.9)$$

$$= \underline{\underline{109.8\angle -26.01^\circ \text{ A}}}$$

3.16

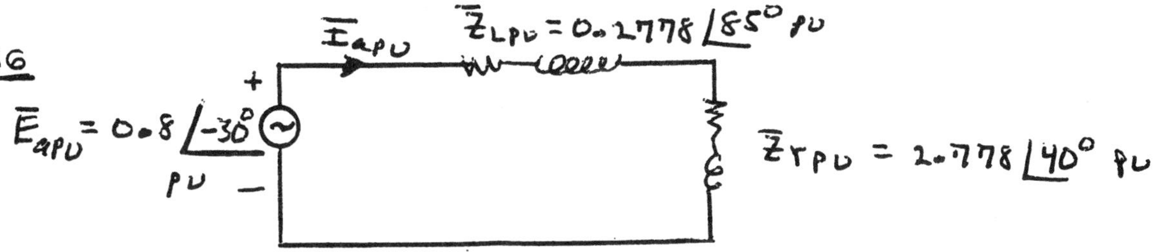

$$Z_{base} = \frac{(600)^2}{100\times10^3} = 3.6\,\Omega \qquad I_{base} = \frac{100\times10^3}{\sqrt{3}\,(600)} = 96.23\text{ A}$$

$$\bar{Z}_{Lpu} = \frac{1\angle 85^\circ}{3.6} = 0.2778\angle 85^\circ \text{ pu}$$

$$\bar{Z}_{Ypu} = \frac{10\angle 40^\circ}{3.6} = 2.778\angle 40^\circ \text{ pu}$$

$$\bar{E}_{apu} = \frac{480/\sqrt{3}}{600/\sqrt{3}}\angle -30^\circ = 0.8\angle -30^\circ \text{ pu}$$

3.16 CONTD.

$$\bar{I}_{apu} = \frac{\bar{E}_{apu}}{\bar{Z}_{Lpu} + \bar{Z}_{Ypu}} = \frac{0.8\angle{-30^\circ}}{0.2778\angle{85^\circ} + 2.778\angle{40^\circ}}$$

$$\bar{I}_{apu} = \frac{0.8\angle{-30^\circ}}{2.1521 + j2.0622} = \frac{0.8\angle{-30^\circ}}{2.9807\angle{43.78^\circ}}$$

$$\bar{I}_{apu} = \underline{\underline{0.2684\angle{-73.78^\circ}}} \text{ pu}$$

$$\bar{I}_a = \bar{I}_{apu} I_{base} = (0.2684\angle{-73.78^\circ})(96.23)$$

$$\bar{I}_a = \underline{\underline{25.83\angle{-73.78^\circ}}} \text{ A}$$

3.17

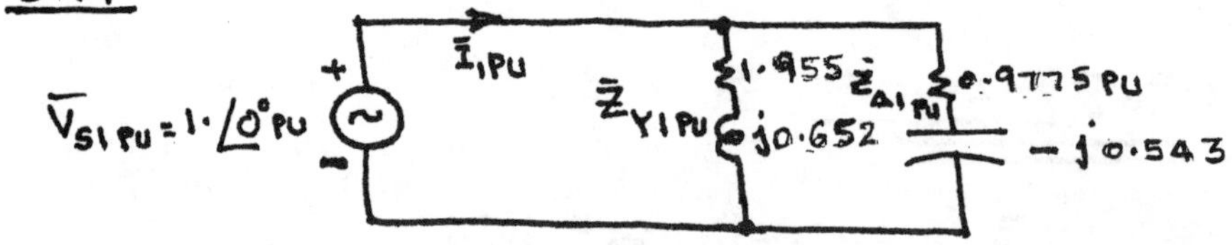

$$Z_{base} = \frac{277^2}{5\times10^3} = 15.346\ \Omega \quad ; \quad I_{base} = \frac{5\times10^3}{277} = 18.05\text{A}$$

$$\bar{Z}_{Y1\,pu} = \frac{30+j10}{15.346} = 1.955 + j0.652 = 2.061\angle{18.43^\circ} \text{ PU}$$

$$\bar{Z}_{\Delta1\,pu} = \frac{45-j25}{3\times15.346} = 0.9775 - j0.543 = 1.118\angle{-29.05^\circ} \text{ PU}$$

$$\bar{I}_{1\,pu} = \frac{\bar{V}_{S1\,pu}}{\bar{Z}_{Y1pu} \parallel \bar{Z}_{\Delta1\,pu}} = \frac{1\angle{0^\circ}}{\left[\dfrac{(2.061\angle{18.43^\circ})(1.118\angle{-29.05^\circ})}{(1.955+j0.652)+(0.9775-j0.543)}\right]}$$

$$= 1.274\angle{12.74^\circ} \text{ PU}$$

$$\bar{I}_1 = \bar{I}_{1pu} I_{base} = (1.274\angle{12.74^\circ})(18.05) = 22.99\angle{12.74^\circ} \text{ A}$$

3.18

SELECT A COMMON BASE OF 100 MVA AND 22 kV (NOT 33 kV PRINTED WRONGLY IN THE TEXT) ON THE GENERATOR SIDE;

BASE VOLTAGE AT BUS 1 IS 22 kV; THIS FIXES THE VOLTAGE BASES FOR THE REMAINING BUSES IN ACCORDANCE WITH THE TRANSFORMER TURNS RATIOS.

USING EQ. 3.3.11, PER-UNIT REACTANCES ON THE SELECTED BASE ARE GIVEN BY

G: $X = 0.18\left(\frac{100}{90}\right) = 0.2$; T_1: $X = 0.1\left(\frac{100}{50}\right) = 0.2$

T_2: $X = 0.06\left(\frac{100}{40}\right) = 0.15$; T_2: $X = 0.06\left(\frac{100}{40}\right) = 0.15$

T_3: $X = 0.064\left(\frac{100}{40}\right) = 0.16$; T_4: $X = 0.08\left(\frac{100}{40}\right) = 0.2$

M: $X = 0.185\left(\frac{100}{66.5}\right)\left(\frac{10.45}{11}\right)^2 = 0.25$

FOR LINE 1, $Z_{BASE} = \frac{(220)^2}{100} = 484\,\Omega$ AND $X = \frac{48.4}{484} = 0.1$

FOR LINE 2, $Z_{BASE} = \frac{(110)^2}{100} = 121\,\Omega$ AND $X = \frac{65.43}{121} = 0.54$

THE LOAD COMPLEX POWER AT 0.6 LAGGING PF IS $\bar{S}_{L(3\phi)} = 57\angle 53.13^\circ$ MVA

$\therefore$ THE LOAD IMPEDANCE IN OHMS IS $\bar{Z}_L = \frac{(10.45)^2}{57\angle 53.13^\circ} = \frac{V_{LL}^2}{\bar{S}^*_{L(3\phi)}}$

$= 1.1495 + j\,1.53267\ \Omega$

THE BASE IMPEDANCE FOR THE LOAD IS $(11)^2/100 = 1.21\,\Omega$

$\therefore$ LOAD IMPEDANCE IN PU $= \frac{1.1495 + j\,1.53267}{1.21} = 0.95 + j\,1.2667$

THE PER-UNIT EQUIVALENT CIRCUIT IS SHOWN BELOW:

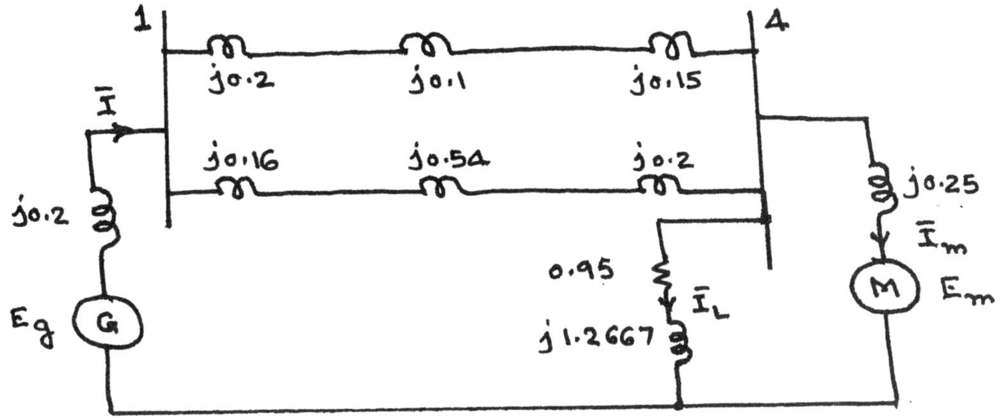

PER-UNIT IMPEDANCE DIAGRAM

3.19

(a) THE PER-UNIT VOLTAGE AT BUS 4, TAKEN AS REFERENCE, IS

$$\bar{V}_4 = \frac{10.45}{11} \angle 0° = 0.95 \angle 0°$$

AT 0.8 LEADING PF, THE MOTOR APPARENT POWER $\bar{S}_m = \frac{66.5}{100} \angle -36.87°$

∴ CURRENT DRAWN BY THE MOTOR IS $\bar{I}_m = \frac{\bar{S}_m^*}{\bar{V}_A^*} = \frac{0.665 \angle 36.87°}{0.95 \angle 0°}$

$$= 0.56 + j0.42$$

CURRENT DRAWN BY THE LOAD IS $\bar{I}_L = \frac{\bar{V}_4}{\bar{Z}_L} = \frac{0.95 \angle 0°}{0.95 + j1.2667} = 0.36 - j0.48$

TOTAL CURRENT DRAWN FROM BUS 4 IS $\bar{I} = \bar{I}_m + \bar{I}_L = 0.92 - j0.06$

EQUIVALENT REACTANCE OF THE TWO LINES IN PARALLEL IS

$$X_{eq} = \frac{0.45 \times 0.9}{0.45 + 0.9} = 0.3$$

GENERATOR TERMINAL VOLTAGE IS THEN $\bar{V}_1 = 0.95 \angle 0° + j0.3(0.92 - j0.06)$

$$\bar{V}_1 = 0.968 + j0.276 = 1.0 \angle 15.91° \text{ PU} = 22 \angle 15.91° \text{ kV}$$

(b) THE GENERATOR INTERNAL EMF IS GIVEN BY

$$\bar{E}_g = \bar{V}_1 + \bar{Z}_g \bar{I} = 0.968 + j0.276 + j0.2(0.92 - j0.06)$$

$$= 1.0826 \angle 25.14° \text{ PU} = 23.82 \angle 25.14° \text{ kV}$$

THE MOTOR TERMINAL EMF IS GIVEN BY

$$\bar{E}_m = \bar{V}_4 - \bar{Z}_m \bar{I}_m = 0.95 + j0 - j0.25(0.56 + j0.42)$$

$$= 1.064 \angle -7.56° \text{ PU} = 11.71 \angle -7.56° \text{ kV}$$

3.20

(a)

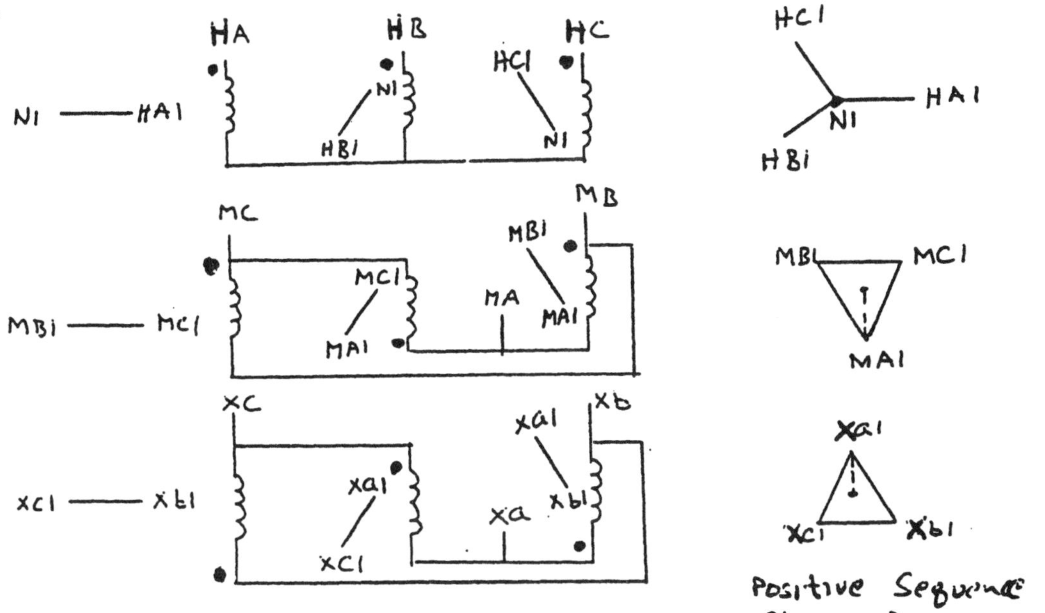

Positive Sequence Phasor Diagram

For positive sequence, $\bar{V}_{H1}$ leads $\bar{V}_{M1}$ by 90°, and $\bar{V}_{H1}$ lags $\bar{V}_{X1}$ by 90°.

For negative sequence, $\bar{V}_{H2}$ lags $\bar{V}_{M2}$ by 90°, and $\bar{V}_{H2}$ leads $\bar{V}_{X2}$ by 90°.

3-20 CONTD.

(b)

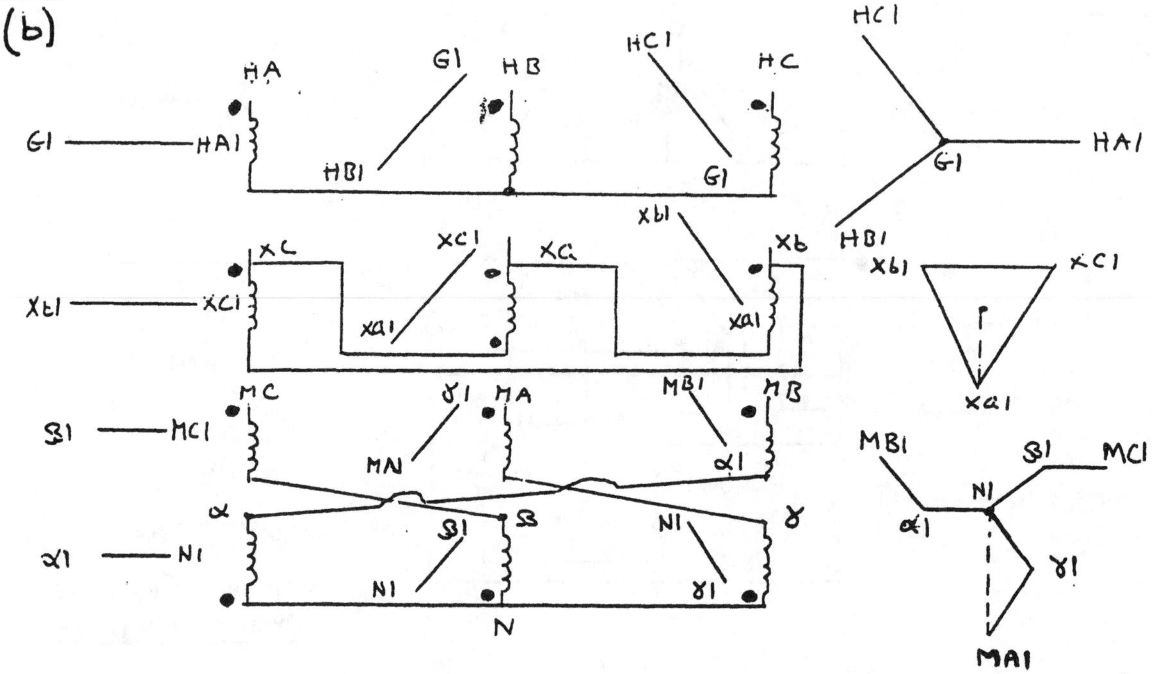

For positive sequence $\bar{V}_{H1}$ leads $\bar{V}_{X1}$ by 90° and $\bar{V}_{X1}$ is in phase with $\bar{V}_{M1}$. For negative sequence $\bar{V}_{H2}$ lags $\bar{V}_{X2}$ by 90° and $\bar{V}_{X2}$ is in phase with $\bar{V}_{m2}$. Note that a Δ-zig/zag transformer can be used to obtain the advantages of a Δ-Y transformer without phase shift.

(c)

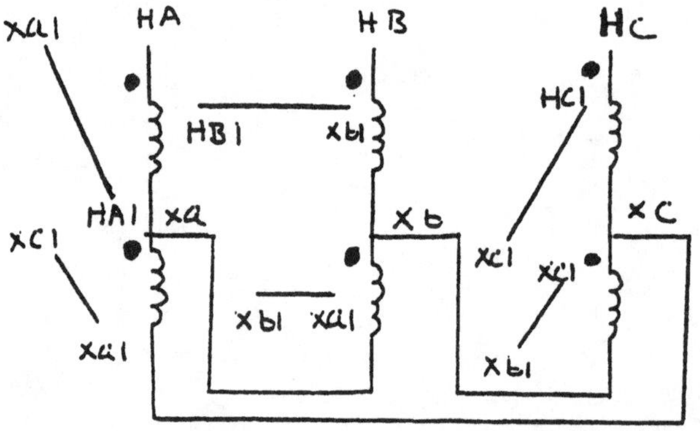

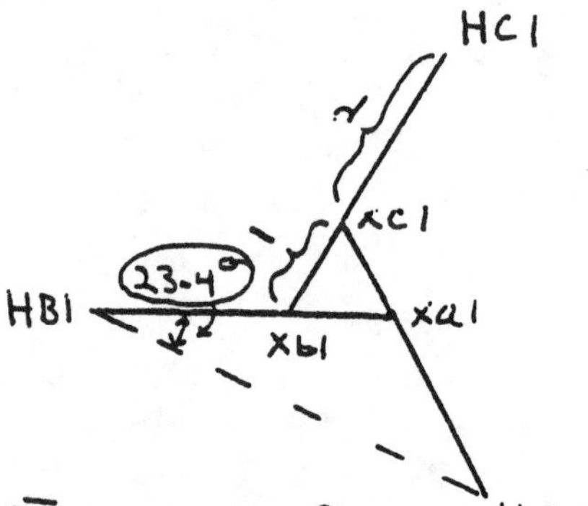

For positive sequence, $\bar{V}_{H1}$ lags $\bar{V}_{X1}$ by 23.4°.
For negative sequence, $\bar{V}_{H2}$ leads $\bar{V}_{X2}$ by 23.4°.

3.21

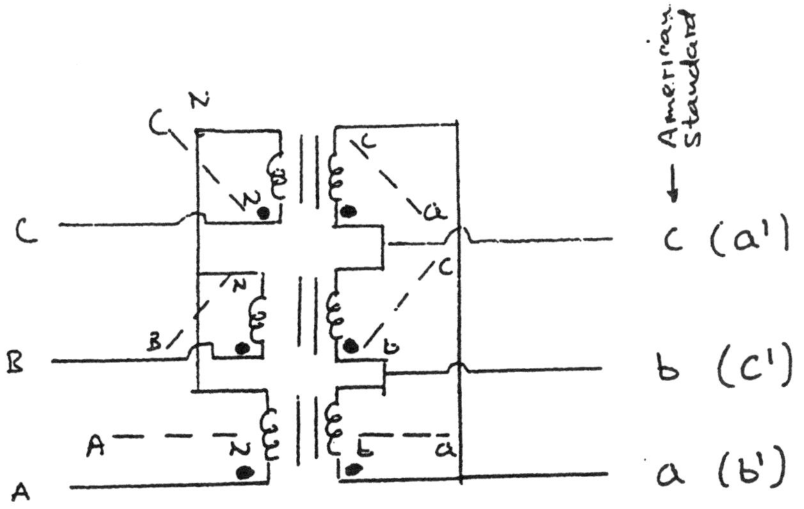

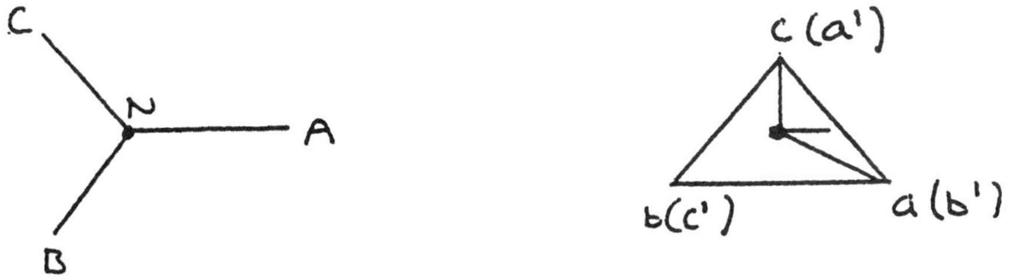

3.22

(a)

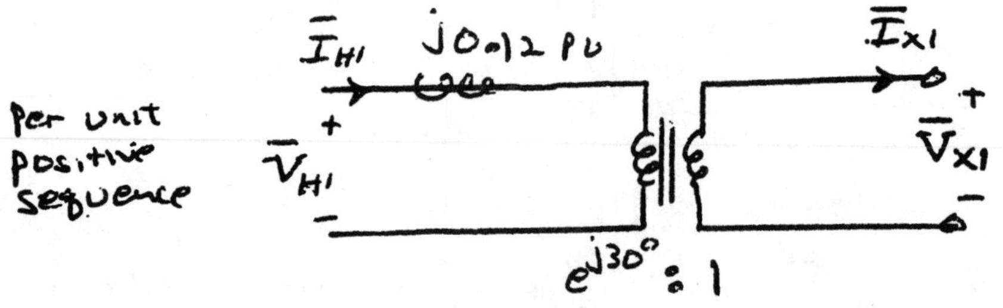
Per unit positive sequence
$\bar{I}_{H1}$
j0.12 pu
$\bar{I}_{X1}$
+
$\bar{V}_{H1}$
−
+
$\bar{V}_{X1}$
−
$e^{j30°} : 1$

(b)

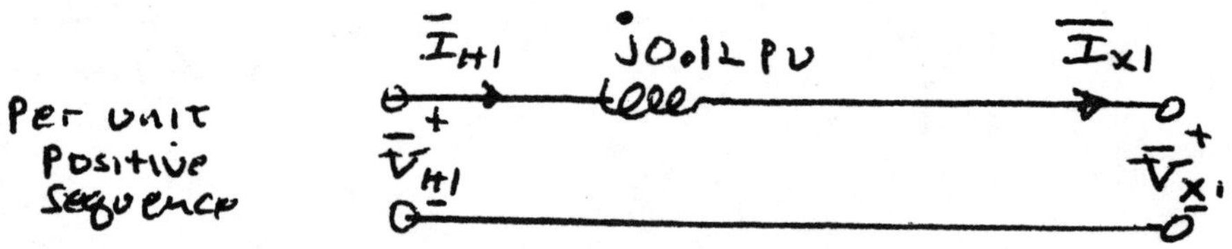
Per unit positive sequence
$\bar{I}_{H1}$
j0.12 pu
$\bar{I}_{X1}$
+
$\bar{V}_{H1}$
−
+
$\bar{V}_{X1}$
−

3.23

(a) Three-phase rating: 2.1 MVA 13.8 kV Y / 2.3 kV Δ

Single-phase rating: $\frac{2.1}{3} = 0.7$ MVA $\frac{13.8}{\sqrt{3}} \Big| 2.3 = 7.97/2.3$ kV

(b) Three-phase rating: 2.1 MVA 13.8 kV Δ / 2.3 kV Y

Single-phase rating: 0.7 MVA $13.8 \Big/ \frac{2.3}{\sqrt{3}} = 13.8/1.33$ kV

(c) Three-phase rating: 2.1 MVA 13.8 kV Y / 2.3 kV Y

Single-phase rating: 0.7 MVA 7.97 / 1.33 kV

(d) Three-phase rating: 2.1 MVA 13.8 kV Δ / 2.3 kV Δ

Single-phase rating: 0.7 MVA 13.8 / 2.3 kV

3.24

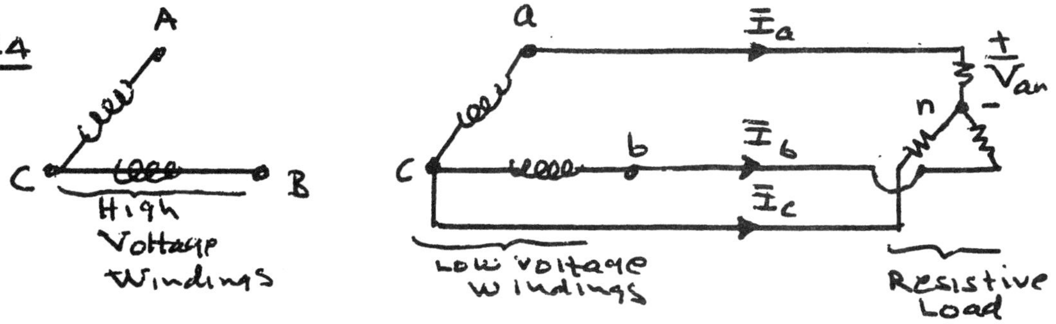

OPEN Δ TRANSFORMER

(a) $\bar{V}_{bc}$ and $\bar{V}_{ca}$ remain the same after one, single-phase transformer is removed. Therefore, $\bar{V}_{ab} = -(\bar{V}_{bc} + \bar{V}_{ca})$ remains the same. The load voltages are then balanced, positive-sequence. Selecting $\bar{V}_{an}$ as reference:

$$\bar{V}_{an} = \frac{13.8}{\sqrt{3}}\angle 0^\circ = 7.967\angle 0^\circ \text{ kV} \qquad \bar{V}_{bn} = 7.967\angle -120^\circ \text{ kV}$$

3-24 CONTD.

$\bar{V}_{cn} = 7.967 \angle +120^\circ$ kV

(b) $\bar{I}_a = \dfrac{S_{3\phi}}{\sqrt{3}\, V_{LL}} \angle 0^\circ = \dfrac{43.3 \times 10^6}{\sqrt{3}\,(13.8 \times 10^3)} = 1.812 \angle 0^\circ$ kA

$\bar{I}_b = 1.812 \angle -120^\circ$ kA $\qquad \bar{I}_c = 1.812 \angle +120^\circ$ kA

(c) $\bar{V}_{bc} = 13.8 \angle -120^\circ + 30^\circ = 13.8 \angle -90^\circ$ kV

Transformer bc delivers $\bar{S}_{bc} = \bar{V}_{bc} \bar{I}_b^*$

$\bar{S}_{bc} = (13.8 \angle -90^\circ)(1.812 \angle +120^\circ) = \underline{\underline{25. \angle 30^\circ}}$ MVA

$\bar{S}_{bc} = (21.65 + j12.5) \times 10^6$

Transformer ac delivers $\bar{S}_{ac} = \bar{V}_{ac} \bar{I}_a^*$

where $\bar{V}_{ac} = -\bar{V}_{ca} = -13.8 \angle 120^\circ + 30^\circ = 13.8 \angle -30^\circ$ kV

$\bar{S}_{ac} = (13.8 \angle -30^\circ)(1.812 \angle 0^\circ) = 25. \angle -30^\circ$ MVA

$\bar{S}_{ac} = (21.65 - j12.5) \times 10^6$

The open-Δ transformer is not overloaded. Note that transformer bc delivers 12.5 Mvars and transformer ac absorbs 12.5 Mvars. The total reactive power delivered by the open-Δ transformer to the resistive load is therefore zero.

3.25

NOTING THAT $\sqrt{3}\,(38.1) = 66$, THE RATING OF THE 3-PHASE TRANSFORMER BANK IS 75 MVA, 66Y / 3.81Δ kV.

BASE IMPEDANCE FOR THE LOW-VOLTAGE SIDE IS $\dfrac{(3.81)^2}{75} = 0.1935\ \Omega$

ON THE LOW-VOLTAGE SIDE, $R_L = \dfrac{0.6}{0.1935} = 3.1$ PU

BASE IMPEDANCE ON HIGH-VOLTAGE SIDE IS $\dfrac{(66)^2}{75} = 58.1\ \Omega$

THE RESISTANCE REF. TO HV-SIDE IS $0.6\left(\dfrac{66}{3.81}\right)^2 = 180\ \Omega$

OR $R_L = \dfrac{180}{58.1} = 3.1$ PU

3.26

(a) THE SINGLE-LINE DIAGRAM AND THE PER-PHASE EQUIVALENT CIRCUIT, WITH ALL PARAMETERS IN PER UNIT, ARE GIVEN BELOW:

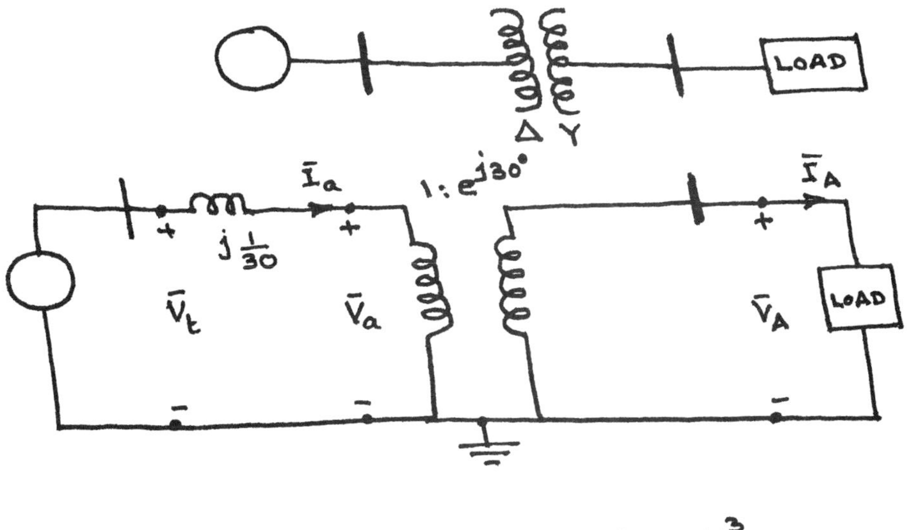

CURRENT SUPPLIED TO THE LOAD IS $\dfrac{240 \times 10^3}{\sqrt{3} \times 230} = 602.45$ A

BASE CURRENT AT THE LOAD IS $100{,}000 / (\sqrt{3} \times 230) = 251.02$ A

THE POWER-FACTOR ANGLE OF THE LOAD CURRENT IS $\theta = \cos^{-1} 0.9 = 25.84°$ LAG.

WITH $\bar{V}_A = 1.0\angle 0°$ AS REFERENCE, THE LINE CURRENTS DRAWN BY THE LOAD ARE

$$I_A = \frac{602.45}{251.02}\angle -25.84° = 2.4\angle -25.84° \text{ PER UNIT}$$

3.26 CONTD.

$$\bar{I}_B = 2.4 \angle -25.84^\circ - 120^\circ = 2.4 \angle -145.84^\circ \text{ PER UNIT}$$

$$\bar{I}_C = 2.4 \angle -25.84^\circ + 120^\circ = 2.4 \angle 94.16^\circ \text{ PER UNIT}$$

(b)

LOW-VOLTAGE SIDE CURRENTS FURTHER LAG BY 30° BECAUSE OF PHASE SHIFT

$\bar{I}_a = 2.4 \angle -55.84^\circ$; $\bar{I}_b = 2.4 \angle 175.84^\circ$; $\bar{I}_c = 2.4 \angle 64.16^\circ$

(c)

THE TRANSFORMER REACTANCE MODIFIED FOR THE CHOSEN BASE IS

$$X = 0.11 \times (100/330) = \frac{1}{30} \text{ PU}$$

THE TERMINAL VOLTAGE OF THE GENERATOR IS THEN GIVEN BY

$$\bar{V}_t = \bar{V}_A \angle -30^\circ + jX\bar{I}_a$$

$$= 1.0 \angle -30^\circ + j(1/30)(2.4 \angle -55.84^\circ)$$

$$= 0.9322 - j\,0.4551 = 1.0374 \angle -26.02^\circ \text{ PU}$$

TERMINAL VOLTAGE OF THE GENERATOR IS $23 \times 1.0374 = 23.86$ kV

THE REAL POWER SUPPLIED BY THE GENERATOR IS

$$\text{Re}[\bar{V}_t \bar{I}_a^*] = 1.0374 \times 2.4 \cos(-26.02^\circ + 55.84^\circ) = 2.16 \text{ PU}$$

WHICH CORRESPONDS TO 216 MW ABSORBED BY THE LOAD, SINCE THERE ARE NO I^2R LOSSES.

(d) BY OMITTING THE PHASE SHIFT OF THE TRANSFORMER ALTOGETHER, RECALCULATING $\bar{V}_t$ WITH THE REACTANCE $j(\frac{1}{30})$ ON THE HIGH-VOLTAGE SIDE, THE STUDENT WILL FIND THE SAME VALUE FOR V_t i.e. $|\bar{V}_t|$.

3.27

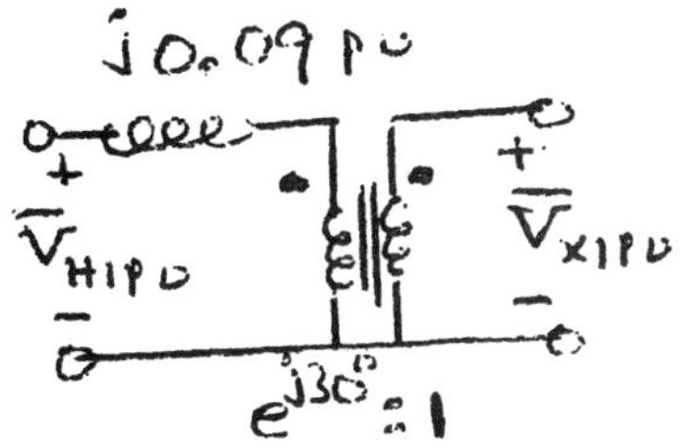

Positive Sequence

3.28

$$X_{pu\,new} = (0.09)\left(\frac{345}{360}\right)^2\left(\frac{100}{300}\right) = 0.02755 \text{ per unit}$$

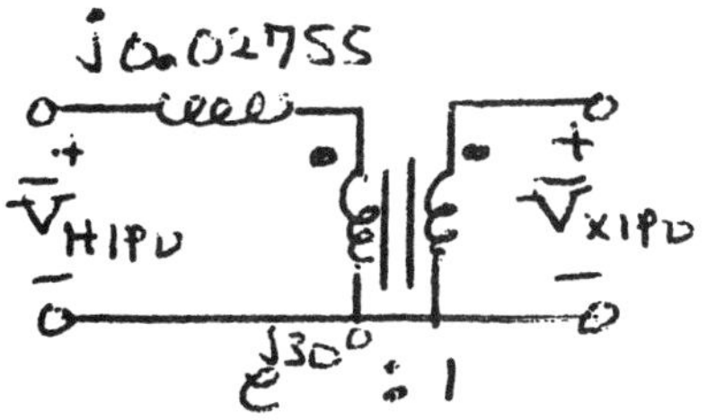

Positive Sequence

3.29

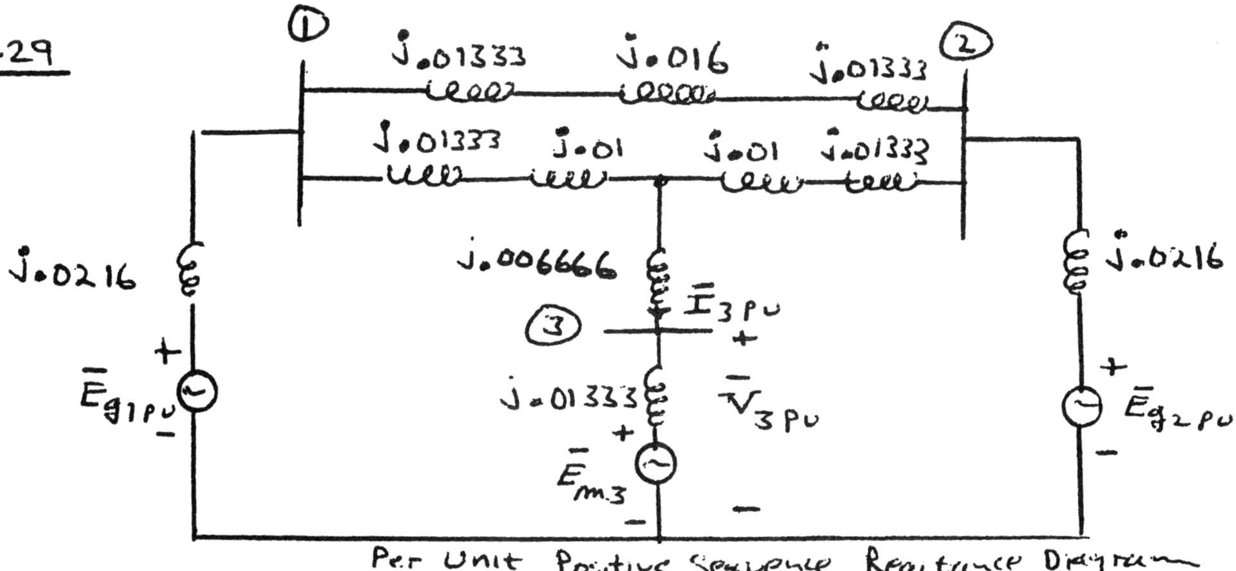

Per Unit Positive Sequence Reactance Diagram

$S_{base} = 100$ MVA

$V_{base\,H} = 500$ kV in transmission line zones.

$V_{base\,X} = 20$ kV in motor/generator zones.

3.29 CONTD.

$$X''_{g1} = X''_{g2} = (0.2)\left(\frac{18}{20}\right)^2\left(\frac{100}{750}\right) = 0.0216 \text{ per unit}$$

$$X''_{m3} = (0.2)\left(\frac{100}{1500}\right) = 0.01333 \text{ per unit}$$

$$X_{T1} = X_{T2} = X_{T3} = X_{T4} = (0.10)\left(\frac{100}{750}\right) = 0.01333$$

$$X_{T5} = (0.10)\left(\frac{100}{1500}\right) = 0.006666 \text{ per unit}$$

$$Z_{baseH} = \frac{(500)^2}{100} = 2500.\ \Omega$$

$$X_{Line\,40} = 40/2500 = 0.016 \text{ per unit}$$

$$X_{Line\,25} = 25/2500 = 0.01 \text{ per unit}$$

3.30

$$\bar{V}_{3pu} = \frac{18}{20}\angle 0^\circ = 0.9\angle 0^\circ \text{ per unit}$$

$$\bar{I}_3 = \frac{1200}{(\sqrt{3})(18)(0.8)}\angle \cos^{-1}(.8) = 48.11\angle 36.87^\circ \text{ kA}$$

$$I_{baseX} = \frac{100}{\sqrt{3}(20)} = 2.887 \text{ kA}$$

$$\bar{I}_{3pu} = \frac{48.11\angle 36.87^\circ}{2.887} = 16.67\angle 36.87^\circ \text{ per unit}$$

$$\bar{V}_{1pu} = \bar{V}_{2pu} = \bar{V}_{3pu} + \bar{I}_{3pu}(jX_{T5pu}) + \tfrac{1}{2}\bar{I}_{3pu}(jX_{Line25\,pu} + jX_{T3pu})$$

$$\bar{V}_{1pu} = \bar{V}_{2pu} = 0.9\angle 0^\circ + 16.67\angle 36.87^\circ(j)\left(.006666 + \frac{.01 + .01333}{2}\right)$$

$$= .9 + 0.30555\angle 126.87^\circ$$

$$= 0.7167 + j\,0.2444 = 0.7572\angle 18.83^\circ \text{ pu}$$

$$V_1 = V_2 = (0.7572)(20) = \underline{\underline{15.14 \text{ kV}}}$$

3.31

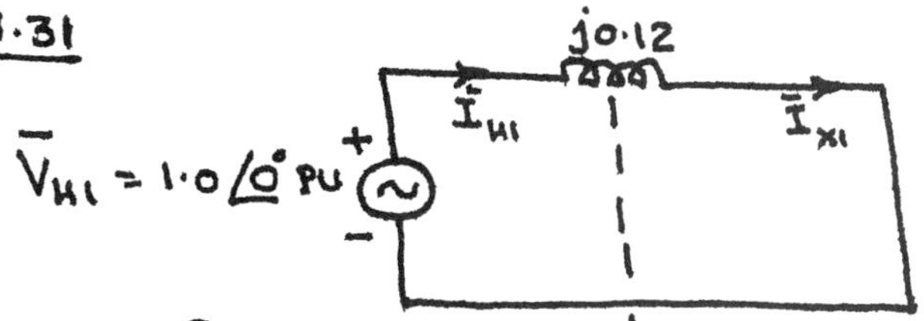

$S_{base\,3\phi} = 30$ MVA

$V_{base\,H} = 66.4\sqrt{3} = 115$ kV

$$\bar{I}_{H1} = \bar{I}_{X1} = \frac{1.0\angle 0°}{j0.12} = 8.333\angle -90° \text{ pu}$$

(a) $I_{base\,H} = \dfrac{30}{115\sqrt{3}} = 0.1506$ kA ; $V_{base\,X} = 12.5\sqrt{3} = 21.65$ kV

$I_{base\,X} = \dfrac{30}{21.65\sqrt{3}} = 0.8$ kA

$I_H = (8.333)(0.1506) = 1.255$ kA

$I_X = (8.333)(0.8) = 6.666$ kA

(b) $I_{base\,H} = 0.1506$ kA ; $V_{base\,X} = 12.5$ kV

$I_{base\,X} = \dfrac{30}{12.5\sqrt{3}} = 1.386$ kA

$I_H = (8.333)\,0.1506 = 1.255$ kA

$I_X = (8.333)\,1.386 = 11.55$ kA

3.32

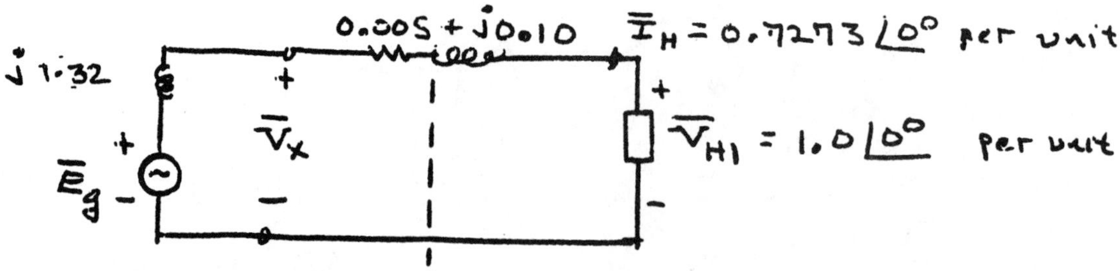

$S_{base} = 110$ MVA　|　$V_{BaseH} = 115$ kV

$V_{basex} = 13.2$ kV

(a) $x_{g1} = (1.2)\left(\frac{110}{100}\right) = 1.32$ per unit

(b)

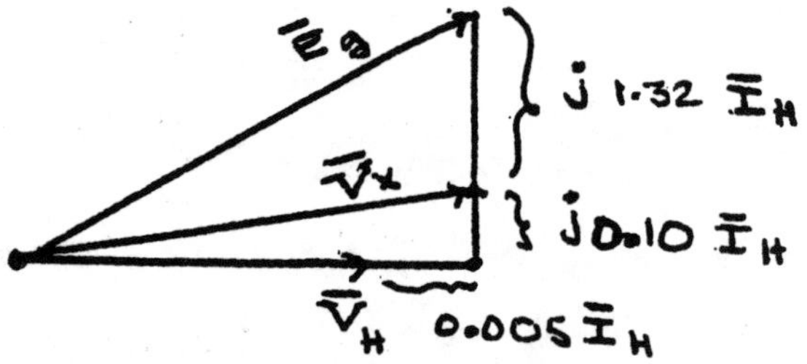

(c) $\bar{I}_H = \frac{80}{(115\sqrt{3})(1.0)}\angle 0^\circ = 0.4016\angle 0^\circ$ kA

$I_{baseH} = \frac{110}{115\sqrt{3}} = 0.5522$ kA

$\bar{I}_H = \frac{0.4016}{0.5522}\angle 0^\circ = 0.7273\angle 0^\circ$ per unit

$\bar{V}_x = 1.0\angle 0^\circ + (0.005 + j0.10)(0.7273\angle 0^\circ)$

$= 1.0036 + j\,0.07273 = 1.0063\angle 4.145^\circ$ per unit

$V_x = (1.0063)(13.2) = \underline{\underline{13.28}}$ kV

$\bar{E}_g = 1.0\angle 0^\circ + (0.005 + j\,1.42)(0.7273\angle 0^\circ) = 1.4402\angle 51.74^\circ$ PU

$E_g = 1.4402\,(13.2) = 19.01$ kV

$P_x + jQ_x = \bar{V}_x \bar{I}_x^* = (1.0063\angle 4.145^\circ)(0.7273\angle 0^\circ)$

$= 0.7318\angle 4.145^\circ$ PU $= 0.7318(110)\angle 4.145^\circ = 80.5\angle 4.145^\circ$ MVA

$= 80.29$ MW $+ j\,5.818$ MVAR

PF $= \cos(4.145^\circ) = 0.997$ LAGGING

3.33

THREE-PHASE RATING OF TRANSFORMER T_2 IS $3 \times 100 = 300$ MVA AND ITS LINE-TO-LINE VOLTAGE RATIO IS $\sqrt{3}(127) : 13.2$ OR $220 : 13.2$ kV. CHOOSING A COMMON BASE OF 300 MVA FOR THE SYSTEM, AND SELECTING A BASE OF 20 kV IN THE GENERATOR CIRCUIT,

THE VOLTAGE BASE IN THE TRANSMISSION LINE IS 230 kV

AND THE VOLTAGE BASE IN THE MOTOR CIRCUIT IS $230(13.2/220) = 13.8$ kV

TRANSFORMER REACTANCES CONVERTED TO THE PROPER BASE ARE GIVEN BY

T_1: $X = 0.1 \times \frac{300}{350} = 0.0857$; T_2: $0.1\left(\frac{13.2}{13.8}\right)^2 = 0.0915$

BASE IMPEDANCE FOR THE TRANSMISSION LINE IS $(230)^2/300 = 176.3\ \Omega$

THE REACTANCE OF THE LINE IN PER UNIT IS THEN $\frac{0.5 \times 64}{176.3} = 0.1815$

REACTANCE X''_d OF MOTOR M_1: $0.2\left(\frac{300}{200}\right)\left(\frac{13.2}{13.8}\right)^2 = 0.2745$

REACTANCE X''_d OF MOTOR M_2: $0.2\left(\frac{300}{100}\right)\left(\frac{13.2}{13.8}\right)^2 = 0.549$

NEGLECTING TRANSFORMER PHASE SHIFS, THE POSITIVE-SEQUENCE REACTANCE DIAGRAM IS SHOWN IN FIGURE BELOW:

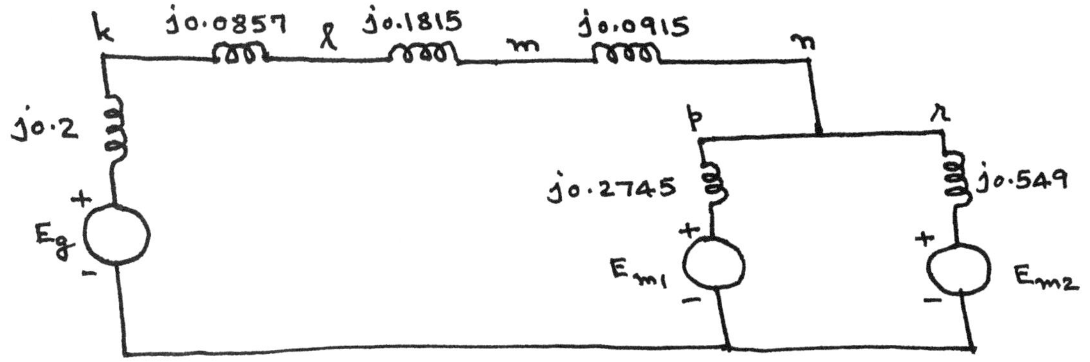

3.34

THE MOTORS TOGETHER DRAW 180 MW, OR $\frac{180}{300} = 0.6$ PU

WITH PHASE-a VOLTAGE AT THE MOTOR TERMINALS AS REFERENCE,

$$\bar{V} = \frac{13.2}{13.8} = 0.9565 \angle 0^\circ \text{ PU}$$

THE MOTOR CURRENT IS GIVEN BY

$$\bar{I} = \frac{0.6}{0.9565} \angle 0^\circ = 0.6273 \angle 0^\circ \text{ PU}$$

REFERRING TO THE REACTANCE DIAGRAM IN THE SOLUTION OF PR. 3-33, PHASE-a PER-UNIT VOLTAGES AT OTHER POINTS OF THE SYSTEM ARE

AT m: $\bar{V} = 0.9565 + 0.6273(j0.0915) = 0.9582 \angle 3.434^\circ$ PU

AT l: $\bar{V} = 0.9565 + 0.6273(j0.0915 + j0.1815) = 0.9717 \angle 10.154^\circ$ PU

AT k: $\bar{V} = 0.9565 + 0.6273(j0.0915 + j0.1815 + j0.0857) = 0.9826 \angle 13.237^\circ$ PU

THE VOLTAGE REGULATION OF THE LINE IS THEN

$$\frac{0.9826 - 0.9582}{0.9582} = 0.0255$$

THE MAGNITUDE OF THE VOLTAGE AT THE GENERATOR TERMINALS IS

$$0.9826 \times 20 = 19.652 \text{ kV}$$

NOTE THAT THE TRANSFORMER PHASE SHIFTS HAVE BEEN NEGLECTED HERE.

3.35

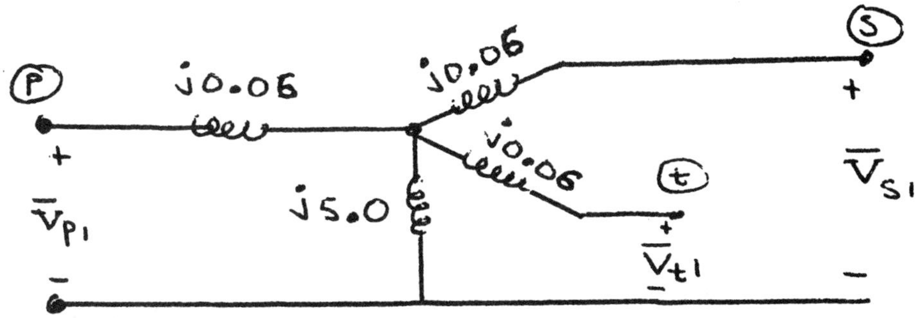

Per unit positive (or negative) sequence network
(Phase shift NOT shown)

p - primary
s - secondary
t - tertiary

3.36

(a) $X_{12} = 0.08$ per unit

$X_{13} = 0.10$ per unit

$X_{23} = 0.09\left(\frac{20}{15}\right) = 0.12$ per unit

$X_1 = \frac{1}{2}(0.08 + 0.10 - 0.12) = 0.03$ per unit

$X_2 = \frac{1}{2}(0.08 + 0.12 - 0.10) = 0.05$ per unit

$X_3 = \frac{1}{2}(0.10 + 0.12 - 0.08) = 0.07$ per unit

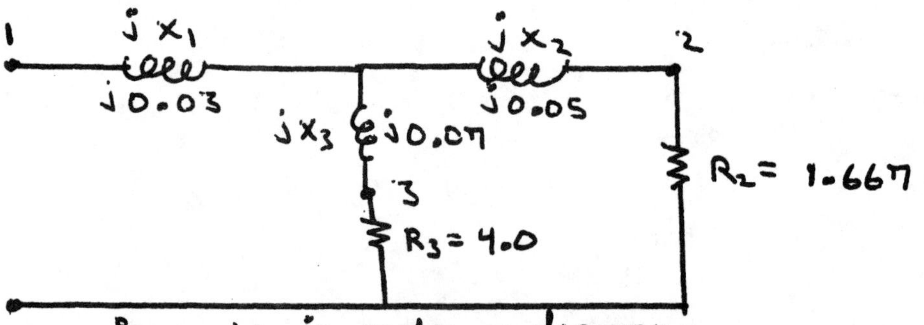

Per unit impedance diagram

Using $P_{3\phi} = \frac{3V_{LN}^2}{R} = \frac{V_{LL}^2}{R}$:

$R_2 = \frac{(13.2)^2}{12} = 14.52\ \Omega$ $\quad R_3 = \frac{(2.3)^2}{5} = 1.058\ \Omega$

$Z_{2base} = \frac{(13.2)^2}{20} = 8.712\ \Omega$ $\quad Z_{3base} = \frac{(2.3)^2}{20} = 0.2645\ \Omega$

$R_{2pu} = \frac{14.52}{8.712} = 1.667$ per unit $\quad R_{3pu} = \frac{1.058}{0.2645}$

$= 4.0$ per unit

3.37

NOTE PRINTING ERROR; FIG. 3.30 SHOULD BE REPLACED BY FIG. 3.31.

(a)

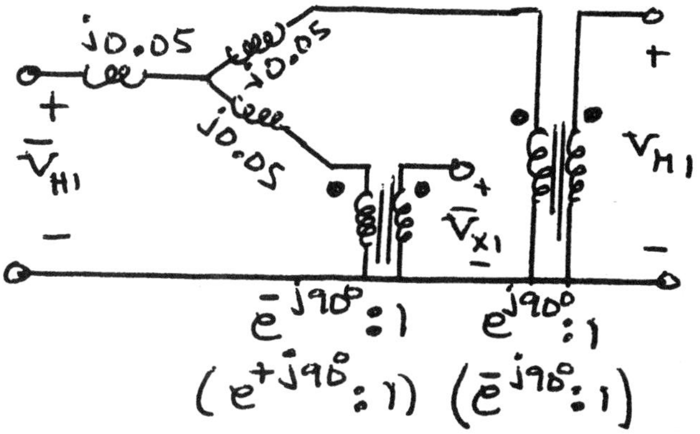

Per Unit Positive Sequence

$$X_1 = X_2 = X_3 = \tfrac{1}{2}(0.1 + 0.1 - 0.1)$$
$$= 0.05 \text{ per unit}$$

(b)

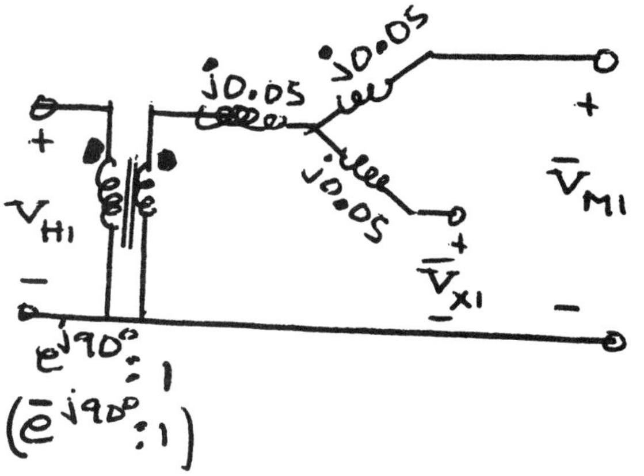

Per Unit Positive Sequence

(c)

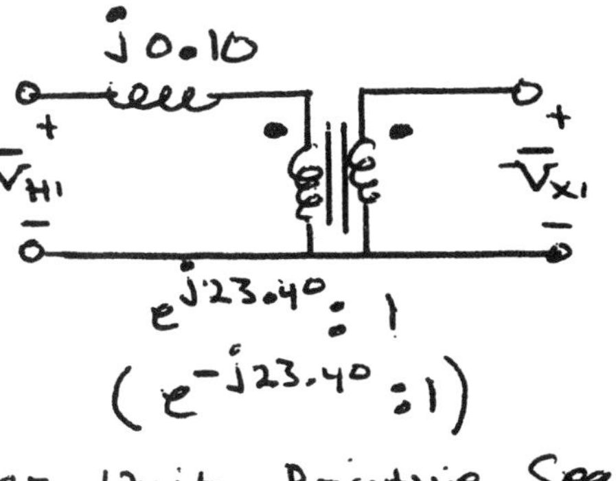

Per Unit Positive Sequence

3.38

WITH A BASE OF 15 MVA AND 66 kV IN THE PRIMARY CIRCUIT, THE BASE FOR SECONDARY CIRCUIT IS 15 MVA AND 13.2 kV, AND THE BASE FOR TERTIARY CIRCUIT IS 15 MVA AND 2.3 kV.

NOTE THAT X_{PS} AND X_{PT} NEED NOT BE CHANGED.

X_{ST} IS MODIFIED TO THE NEW BASE AS FOLLOWS:

$$X_{ST} = 0.08 \times \frac{15}{10} = 0.12$$

WITH THE BASES SPECIFIED, THE PER-UNIT REACTANCES OF THE PER-PHASE EQUIVALENT CIRCUIT ARE GIVEN BY

$$X_P = \frac{1}{2}(j0.07 + j0.09 - j0.12) = j0.02$$

$$X_S = \frac{1}{2}(j0.07 + j0.12 - j0.09) = j0.05$$

$$X_T = \frac{1}{2}(j0.09 + j0.12 - j0.07) = j0.07$$

3.39

THE CONSTANT VOLTAGE SOURCE IS REPRESENTED BY A GENERATOR HAVING NO INTERNAL IMPEDANCE. ON A BASE OF 5 MVA, 2.3 kV IN THE TERTIARY, THE RESISTANCE OF THE LOAD IS 1.0 PU. EXPRESSED ON A 15 MVA, 2.3 kV BASE, THE LOAD RESISTANCE IS $R = 1.0 \times \frac{15}{5} = 3.0$ PU

ON A BASE OF 15 MVA, 13.2 kV, THE REACTANCE OF THE MOTOR IS

$$X'' = 0.2 \times \frac{15}{7.5} = 0.4 \text{ PU}$$

THE IMPEDANCE DIAGRAM IS GIVEN BELOW:

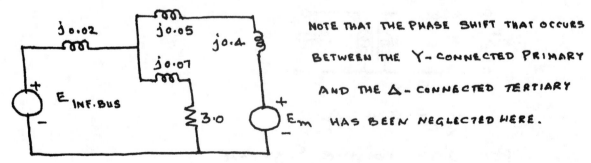

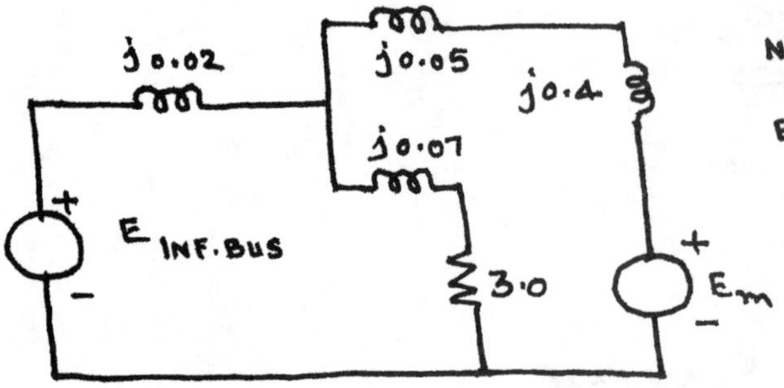

NOTE THAT THE PHASE SHIFT THAT OCCURS BETWEEN THE Y-CONNECTED PRIMARY AND THE Δ-CONNECTED TERTIARY HAS BEEN NEGLECTED HERE.

3.40 (a)

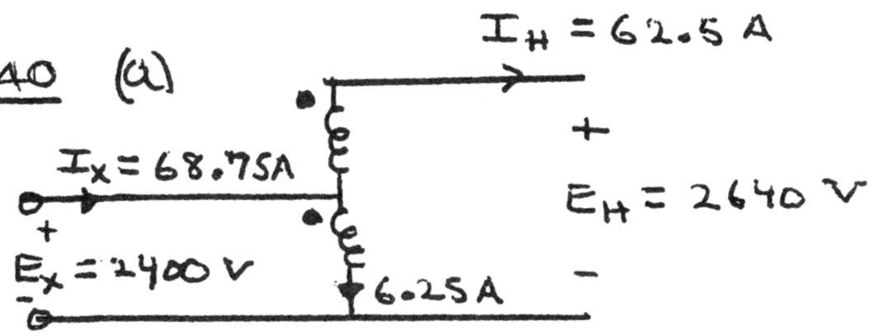

(b) $S_x = (2400)(68.75) = 165.$ kVA

$S_H = (2640)(62.5) = 165.$ kVA $= S_x$

15 kVA is transformed by magnetic induction.

150. kVA is transformed electrically

(c) At rated voltage: core losses = 105 W

At full load current: Winding losses = 330 W

Total losses = 105 + 330 = 435 W = 0.435 kW

$P_{out} = (2640)(62.5)(0.8) = 132.$ kW

$P_{in} = P_{out} + P_{Losses} = 132.435$ kW

% Efficiency $= \left(\frac{P_{out}}{P_{in}}\right) \times 100 = \left(\frac{132}{132.435}\right) \times 100 = \underline{99.67\%}$

3.41
(a)

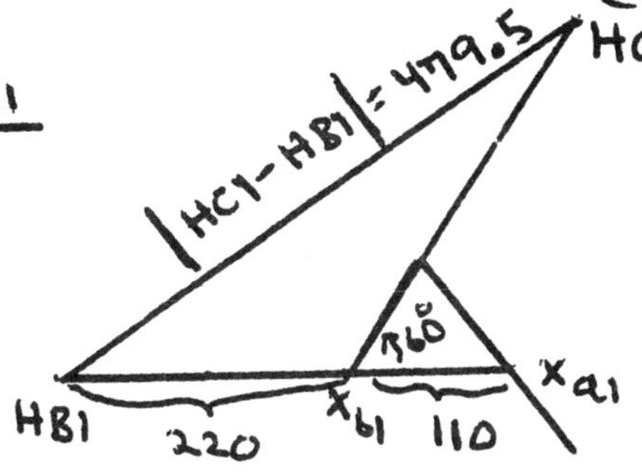

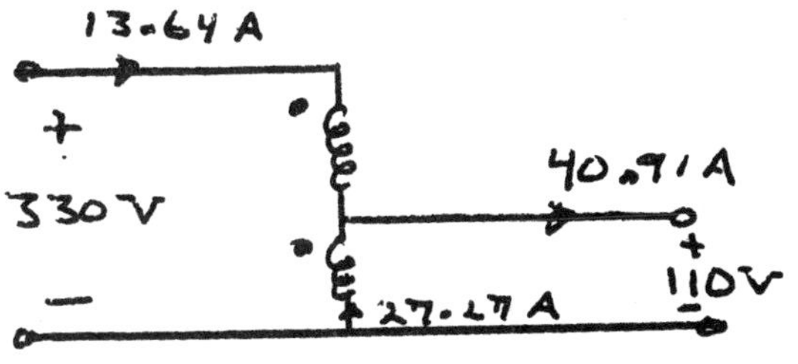

(b) As a normal, single-phase, two-winding transformer, rated: 3 kVA, 220/110 V, $X_{eq} = 0.10$ per unit.

$Z_{Base\,Hold} = (220)^2/3000 = 16.133\ \Omega$

3.41 (b)
CONTD.

As a single-phase autotransformer rated:

$330(13.64) = 4.50$ kVA , $330/110$ V ,

$Z_{BASEHnew} = (330)^2/4500 = 24.2\ \Omega$

$$X_{eq} = (0.10)\left(\frac{16.133}{24.2}\right) = 0.06667 \text{ per unit}$$

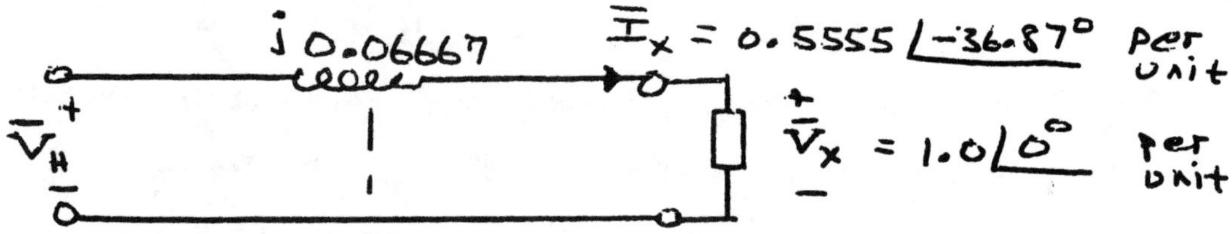

$S_{Base\,3\phi} = 13.5$ kVA $\qquad V_{Basex} = 110$ V

$V_{BaseH} = 479.5$ V $\qquad I_{Basex} = \dfrac{13.5\times10^3}{110\sqrt{3}} = 70.86$ A

$$I_{BaseH} = \frac{13.5\times10^3}{479.5\sqrt{3}}$$

$$= 16.256 \text{ A}$$

$$\bar{I}_x = \frac{6000\angle{-\cos^{-1}.8}}{(110\sqrt{3})(0.8)} = 39.36\angle{-36.87°} \text{ A}$$

$$\bar{I}_x = \frac{39.36}{70.86}\angle{-36.87°} = 0.5555\angle{-36.87°} \text{ per unit}$$

$I_H = I_x = 0.5555$ per unit

$I_H = (0.5555)(16.256) = \underline{\underline{9.031}}$ A

$$\bar{V}_H = \bar{V}_x + jX_{eq}\bar{I}_x = 1.0\angle{0°} + (j0.06667)(.5555\angle{-36.87°})$$

$$\bar{V}_H = 1.0 + 0.03704\angle{53.13°} = 1.0222 + j0.02963$$

$$\bar{V}_H = 1.0226\angle{1.66°} \text{ per unit}$$

$V_H = (1.0226)(479.5) = \underline{\underline{490.3}}$ V

3.42

RATED CURRENTS OF THE TWO-WINDING TRANSFORMER ARE

$$I_1 = \frac{60{,}000}{240} = 250\,A \quad \text{AND} \quad I_2 = \frac{60{,}000}{1200} = 50\,A$$

THE AUTOTRANSFORMER CONNECTION IS SHOWN BELOW:

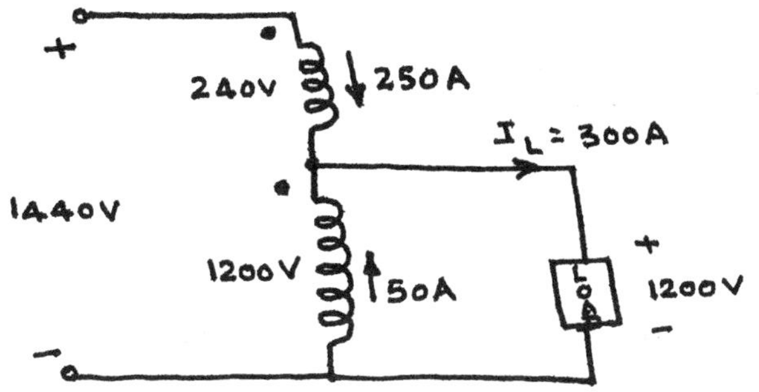

(a) THE AUTOTRANSFORMER SECONDARY CURRENT IS $I_L = 300\,A$

WITH WINDINGS CARRYING RATED CURRENTS, THE AUTOTRANSFORMER RATING IS $(1200)(300)\,10^{-3} = 360\,kVA$

(b) OPERATED AS A TWO-WINDING TRANSFORMER AT FULL-LOAD, 0.8 PF,

$$\text{Efficiency } \eta = \frac{60 \times 0.8}{(60 \times 0.8) + P_{LOSS}} = 0.96$$

FROM WHICH THE TOTAL TRANSFORMER LOSS $P_{LOSS} = \frac{48(1-0.96)}{0.96} = 2\,kW$

THE TOTAL AUTOTRANSFORMER LOSS IS SAME AS THE TWO-WINDING TRANSFORMER, SINCE THE WINDINGS ARE SUBJECTED TO THE SAME RATED VOLTAGES AND CURRENTS AS THE TWO-WINDING TRANSFORMER.

$$\therefore \eta_{AUTO.TR.} = \frac{360 \times 0.8}{(360 \times 0.8) + 2} = 0.9931$$

3.43

(a) THE AUTOTRANSFORMER CONNECTION IS SHOWN BELOW:

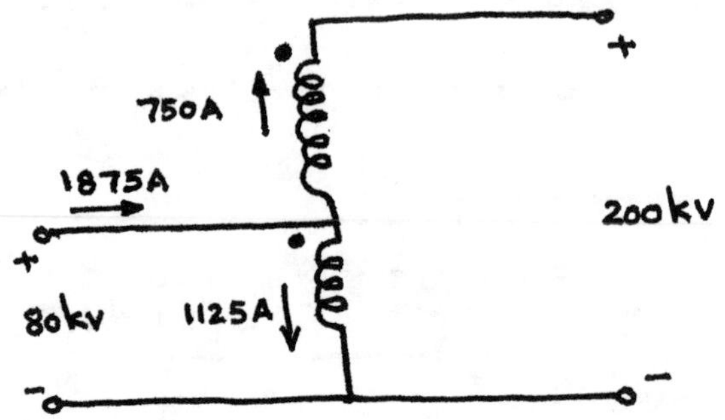

$$I_1 = \frac{90{,}000}{80} = 1125\text{A} \quad ; \quad I_2 = \frac{90{,}000}{120} = 750\text{A}$$

$$V_1 = 80\text{kV} \quad ; \quad V_2 = 120 + 80 = 200\text{ kV}$$

$$I_{in} = 1125 + 750 = 1875\text{ A}$$

(b) INPUT kVA IS CALCULATED AS $80 \times 1875 = 150{,}000$ kVA

WHICH IS SAME AS

OUTPUT kVA = $200 \times 750 = 150{,}000$

PERMISSIBLE kVA RATING OF THE AUTOTRANSFORMER IS 150,000.

THE kVA TRANSFERRED BY THE MAGNETIC INDUCTION IS SAME AS THE RATING OF THE TWO-WINDING TRANSFORMER, WHICH IS 90,000 kVA.

3.44

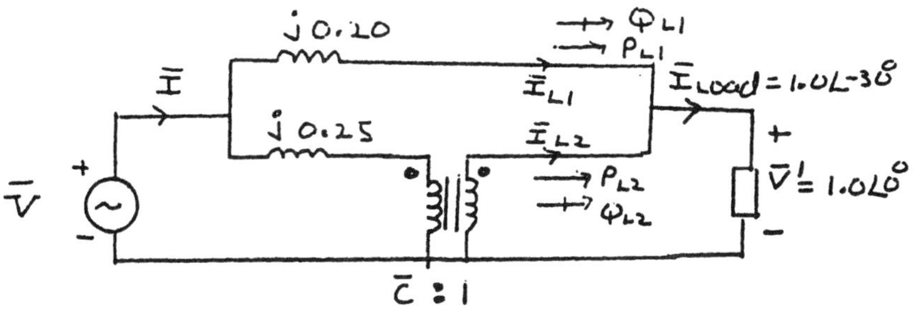

$$P_{Load} + jQ_{Load} = \bar{V}'\bar{I}^*_{Load} = (1.0\angle 0°)(1.0\angle -30°)^* = 1.0\angle 30° = 0.866 + j0.50$$ per unit

(a) No regulating transformer, $\bar{c} = 1.0$

Using current division:

$$\bar{I}_{L1} = \left(\frac{X_{L2}}{X_{L1}+X_{L2}}\right)\bar{I}_{Load} = \left(\frac{0.25}{0.45}\right)(1.0\angle -30°) = 0.5556\angle -30°$$ per unit

$$P_{L1} + jQ_{L1} = \bar{V}'\bar{I}^*_{L1} = 0.5556\angle +30° = \underline{0.4811 + j0.2778}$$ per unit

$$P_{L2} + jQ_{L2} = (P_{Load} + jQ_{Load}) - (P_{L1} + jQ_{L1}) = (0.866 + j0.5) - (.4811 + j.2778)$$
$$= \underline{0.3849 + j0.2222} \text{ per unit}$$

(b) Voltage magnitude regulating transformer, $c = 0.9524$

Using the admittance parameters from Example 4.14 (a)

$$\begin{bmatrix} \bar{I} \\ -1.0\angle -30° \end{bmatrix} = \begin{bmatrix} \bar{I} \\ -\bar{I}_{Load} \end{bmatrix} = \begin{bmatrix} \bar{Y}_{11} & \bar{Y}_{12} \\ \bar{Y}_{21} & \bar{Y}_{22} \end{bmatrix} \begin{bmatrix} \bar{V} \\ \bar{V}' \end{bmatrix} = \begin{bmatrix} -j9.0 & j8.810 \\ j8.810 & -j8.628 \end{bmatrix} \begin{bmatrix} \bar{V} \\ 1.0\angle 0° \end{bmatrix}$$

Solving the second equation above for $\bar{V}$:

$$-1.0\angle -30° = (j8.810)\bar{V} - (j8.628)(1.0\angle 0°)$$

$$\bar{V} = \frac{8.628\angle 90° - 1.0\angle -30°}{j8.810} = \frac{-.866 + j9.128}{j8.810} = 1.041\angle 5.42° \text{ per unit}$$

Then:

$$\bar{I}_{L1} = \frac{\bar{V} - \bar{V}'}{jX_{L1}} = \frac{1.041\angle 5.42° - 1.0\angle 0°}{j0.20} = \frac{0.0361 + j0.0983}{j0.20} = 0.5235\angle -20.14°$$

$$P_{L1} + jQ_{L1} = \bar{V}'\bar{I}^*_{L1} = 0.5235\angle 20.14° = \underline{0.4915 + j0.1802}$$ per unit

$$P_{L2} + jQ_{L2} = (P_{Load} + jQ_{Load}) - (P_{L1} + jQ_{L1}) = \underline{0.3745 + j0.3198}$$ per unit

3.44 CONTD.

The voltage magnitude regulating transformer increases the reactive power delivered by line L2 43.9% (from 0.2222 to 0.3198) with a relatively small change in the real power delivered by line L2.

(c) Phase angle regulating transformer, $\bar{C} = 1.0\angle{-3^\circ}$

Using $\bar{Y}_{21} = -0.2093 + j8.9945$ and $\bar{Y}_{22} = -j9.0$ per unit from Example 4.14 (b):

$$\bar{V} = \frac{-\bar{Y}_{22}\bar{V}' - \bar{I}_{Load}}{\bar{Y}_{21}} = \frac{(j9.0)(1.0\angle 0^\circ) - 1.0\angle{-30^\circ}}{-0.2093 + j8.9945}$$

$$= \frac{-0.8660 + j9.50}{-0.2093 + j8.9945} = \frac{9.539\angle 95.21^\circ}{8.997\angle 91.33^\circ} = 1.060\angle 3.879^\circ \text{ per unit}$$

$$\bar{I}_{L1} = \frac{\bar{V} - \bar{V}'}{jX_{L1}} = \frac{1.060\angle 3.879^\circ - 1.0\angle 0^\circ}{j0.20} = \frac{0.0578 + j0.0717}{j0.20}$$

$$= 0.4606\angle{-38.87^\circ} \text{ per unit}$$

$$P_{L1} + jQ_{L1} = \bar{V}'\bar{I}^*_{L1} = 0.4606\angle{+38.87^\circ} = \underline{\underline{0.3586 + j0.2890}}$$

$$P_{L2} + jQ_{L2} = (P_{Load} + jQ_{Load}) - (P_{L1} + jQ_{L1}) = \underline{\underline{0.5074 + j0.2110}}$$

The phase-angle regulating transformer increases the real power delivered by line L2 31.8% (from 0.3849 to 0.5074) with a relatively small change in the reactive power delivered by line L2.

Problem 3.45

A phase shift angle of 0° minimizes the system losses.

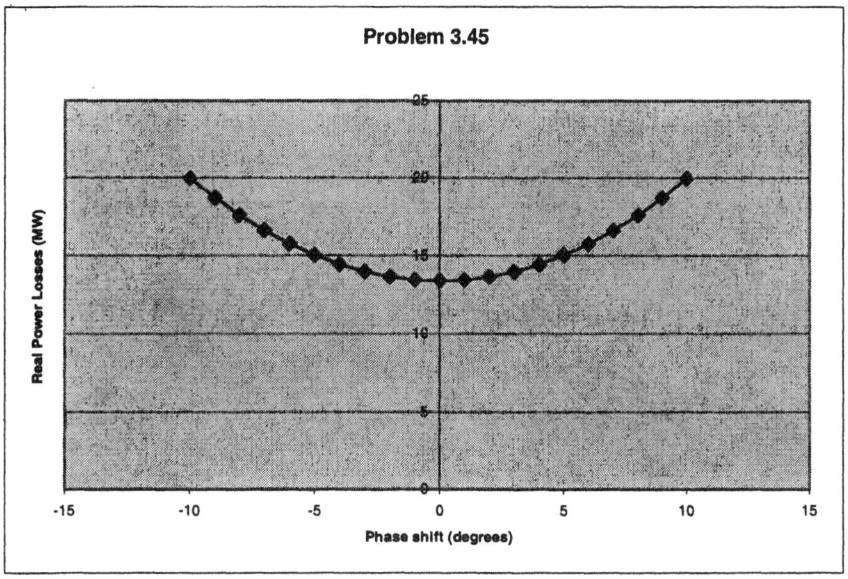

Problem 3.46

An LTC tap setting of 1.0 minimizes the real power losses to 13.489MW.

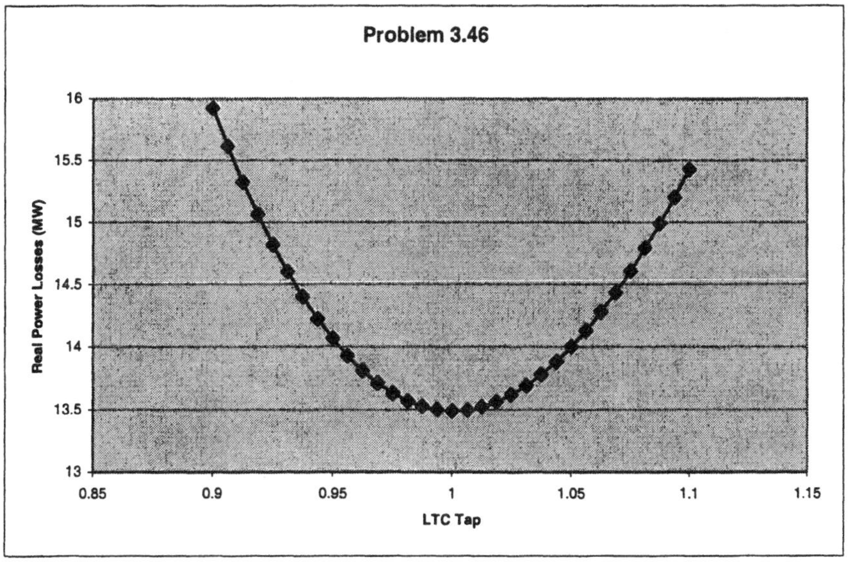

3.47

Using (3.8.1) and (3.8.2)

$$a_t = \frac{13.8}{345(1.1)} = 0.03636 \qquad b = \frac{13.8}{345} = 0.04$$

$$c = a_t / b = 0.03636/0.04 = 0.90909$$

From Figure 3.25 (d):

$$c\,\bar{Y}_{eq} = (0.90909)\left(\frac{1}{j0.05}\right) = -j18.18 \text{ per unit}$$

$$(1-c)\,\bar{Y}_{eq} = (0.0909)\left(\frac{1}{j0.05}\right) = -j1.818 \text{ per unit}$$

$$(|c|^2 - c)\,\bar{Y}_{eq} = (0.82645 - 0.90909)\left(\frac{1}{j0.05}\right) = +j1.6529 \text{ per unit}$$

The per-unit positive-sequence network is:

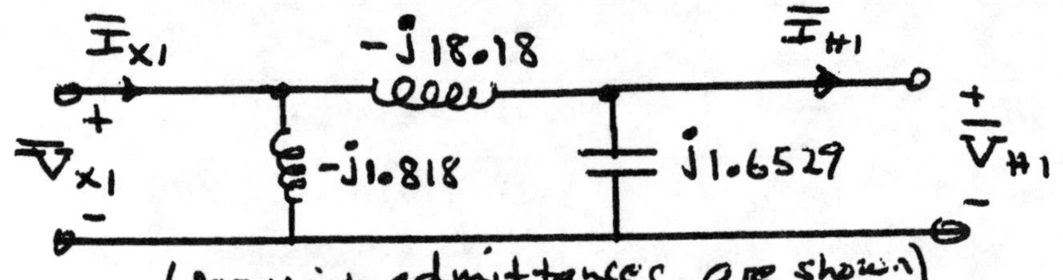

(Per unit admittances are shown)

3.48

A RADIAL LINE WITH TAP-CHANGING TRANSFORMERS AT BOTH ENDS IS SHOWN BELOW:

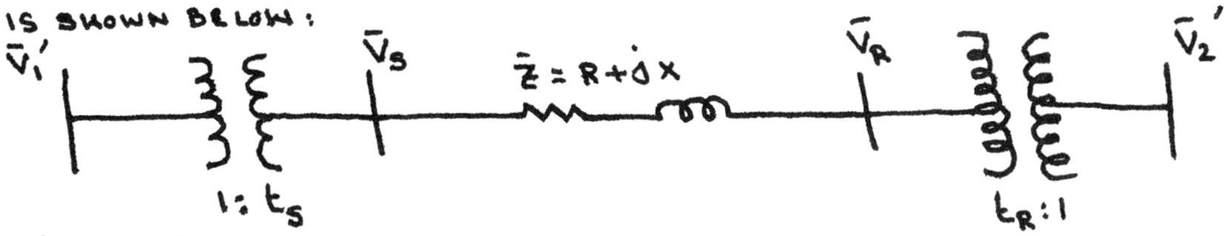

$\bar{V}_1'$ AND $\bar{V}_2'$ ARE THE SUPPLY PHASE VOLTAGE AND THE LOAD PHASE VOLTAGE, RESPECTIVELY, REFERRED TO THE HIGH-VOLTAGE SIDE. $\bar{V}_S$ AND $\bar{V}_R$ ARE THE PHASE VOLTAGES AT BOTH ENDS OF THE LINE. t_S AND t_R ARE THE TAP SETTINGS IN PER UNIT. THE IMPEDANCE $\bar{Z}$ INCLUDES THE LINE IMPEDANCE PLUS THE REFERRED IMPEDANCES OF THE SENDING END AND THE RECEIVING END TRANSFORMERS TO THE HIGH-VOLTAGE SIDE. AFTER DRAWING THE VOLTAGE PHASOR DIAGRAM FOR THE KVL $\bar{V}_S = \bar{V}_R + (R+jX)\bar{I}$, NEGLECTING THE PHASE SHIFT BETWEEN $\bar{V}_S$ AND $\bar{V}_R$ AS AN APPROXIMATION, AND NOTING THAT $\bar{V}_S = t_S \bar{V}_1'$ AND $\bar{V}_R = t_R \bar{V}_2'$, IT CAN BE SHOWN THAT

$$t_S = \sqrt{\frac{|\bar{V}_2'|/|\bar{V}_1'|}{1 - \dfrac{RP_\phi + XQ_\phi}{|\bar{V}_1'|\,|\bar{V}_2'|}}}$$

WHERE P_ϕ AND Q_ϕ ARE THE LOAD REAL AND REACTIVE POWERS PER PHASE AND IT IS ASSUMED THAT $t_S t_R = 1$.

IN OUR PROBLEM, $P_\phi = \frac{1}{3}(150 \times 0.8) = 40$ MW

AND $Q_\phi = \frac{1}{3}(150 \times 0.6) = 30$ MVAR

$$|\bar{V}_1'| = |\bar{V}_2'| = \frac{230}{\sqrt{3}} \text{ kV}$$

t_S IS CALCULATED AS

$$t_S = \sqrt{\frac{1}{1 - \dfrac{(18)(40) + (60)(30)}{(230/\sqrt{3})^2}}} = 1.08 \text{ PU}$$

AND $t_R = \frac{1}{1.08} = 0.926$ PU

3.49

WITH THE TAP SETTING $t = 1.05$, $\Delta V = t - 1 = 0.05$ PU

THE CURRENT SET UP BY $\Delta \bar{V} = 0.05 \angle 0^\circ$ CIRCULATES AROUND THE LOOP WITH SWITCH S OPEN; WITH S CLOSED, ONLY A VERY SMALL FRACTION OF THAT CURRENT GOES THROUGH THE LOAD IMPEDANCE, BECAUSE IT IS MUCH LARGER THAN THE TRANSFORMER IMPEDANCE, SO THE SUPERPOSITION PRINCIPLE CAN BE APPLIED TO $\Delta \bar{V}$ AND THE SOURCE VOLTAGE.

FROM $\Delta \bar{V}$ ALONE, $\bar{I}_{CIRC} = 0.05 / j0.2 = -j0.25$

WITH $\Delta \bar{V}$ SHORTED, THE CURRENT IN EACH PATH IS ONE-HALF THE LOAD CURRENT.

LOAD CURRENT IS $\dfrac{1.0}{0.8 + j0.6} = 0.8 - j0.6$

SUPERPOSITION YIELDS:

$$\bar{I}_{T_a} = 0.4 - j0.3 - (-j0.25) = 0.4 - j0.05$$

$$\bar{I}_{T_b} = 0.4 - j0.3 + (-j0.25) = 0.4 - j0.55$$

SO THAT $\bar{S}_{T_a} = 0.4 + j0.05$ PU AND $\bar{S}_{T_b} = 0.4 + j0.55$

THE TRANSFORMER WITH THE HIGHER TAP SETTING IS SUPPLYING MOST OF THE REACTIVE POWER TO THE LOAD. THE REAL POWER IS DIVIDED EQUALLY BETWEEN THE TRANSFORMERS.

<u>NOTE</u> AN ERROR IN PRINTING: IN THE FOURTH LINE OF THE PROBLEM STATEMENT, FIRST T_b SHOULD BE REPLACED BY T_a AND WITHIN BRACKETS, T_a SHOULD BE REPLACED BY T_b.

3.50

SAME PROCEDURE AS IN PR. 3.49 IS FOLLOWED.

NOW $t = 1.0 \angle 3^\circ$

SO $t - 1 = 1.0 \angle 3^\circ - 1 \angle 0^\circ = 0.0524 \angle 91.5^\circ$

$$\bar{I}_{CIRC} = \frac{0.0524 \angle 91.5^\circ}{0.2 \angle 90^\circ} = 0.262 + j0.0069$$

THEN $\bar{I}_{T_a} = 0.4 - j0.3 - (0.262 + j0.0069) = 0.138 - j0.307$

$\bar{I}_{T_b} = 0.4 - j0.3 + (0.262 + j0.0069) = 0.662 - j0.293$

SO

$$\bar{S}_{T_a} = 0.138 + j0.307 \; ; \; \bar{S}_{T_b} = 0.662 + j0.293$$

THE PHASE SHIFTING TRANSFORMER IS USEFUL TO CONTROL THE AMOUNT OF REAL POWER FLOW; BUT HAS LESS EFFECT ON THE REACTIVE POWER FLOW.

CHAPTER 4

4.1

$$R_{dc,20°C} = \frac{\rho_{20°C}\, l}{A} = \frac{(17.00)(1000 \times 1.016)}{1113 \times 10^3} = \underline{\underline{0.01552}} \ \frac{\Omega}{1000'}$$

$$R_{dc,50°C} = R_{dc,20°C}\left(\frac{50+T}{20+T}\right) = 0.01552\left(\frac{50+228.1}{20+228.1}\right)$$

$$R_{dc,50°C} = (0.01552)(1.1209) = \underline{\underline{0.01739}} \ \frac{\Omega}{1000'}$$

$$\frac{R_{60Hz,50°C}}{R_{dc,50°C}} = \frac{0.0951 \ \Omega/mi}{\left(0.01739 \frac{\Omega}{1000'}\right)\left(5.28 \frac{1000'}{mi}\right)} = \frac{0.0951}{0.0918} = \underline{\underline{1.035}}$$

The 60 Hz resistance is 3.5% larger than the dc resistance, due to skin effect.

4.2

(a) $$954 \text{ MCM} = (954 \times 10^3 \text{ cmil})\left(\frac{\frac{\pi}{4} \text{ sqmil}}{1 \text{ cmil}}\right)\left(\frac{1 \text{ in}}{1000 \text{ mil}}\right)^2\left(\frac{.0254 \text{ m}}{\text{in}}\right)^2$$

$$= \underline{\underline{4.834 \times 10^{-4}}} \text{ m}^2$$

(b) $$R_{60Hz,45°} = R_{60Hz,75°}\left(\frac{45+T}{75+T}\right)$$

$$= (0.0740)\left(\frac{45+228.1}{75+228.1}\right) = (0.0740)(0.9010)$$

$$= \underline{0.0667} \ \Omega/\text{km}$$

4.3 From Table A-4

$$R_{60Hz,50°C} = \left(0.0969 \frac{\Omega}{mi}\right)\left(\frac{1 \text{ mi}}{1.609 \text{ km}}\right) = 0.0602 \ \frac{\Omega}{\text{km}}$$

per conductor (at 75% current capacity)

For 4 conductors per phase:

$$R_{60Hz,50°C} = \frac{0.0602}{4} = \underline{\underline{0.0151}} \ \frac{\Omega}{\text{km}} \text{ per phase}$$

4.4

TOTAL TRANSMISSION LINE LOSS $P_L = \frac{2.5}{100}(190.5) = 4.7625$ MW

$$I = \frac{190.5 \times 10^3}{\sqrt{3}\,(220)} = 500\text{ A}$$

FROM $P_L = 3 I^2 R$, THE LINE RESISTANCE PER PHASE IS

$$R = \frac{4.7625 \times 10^6}{3\,(500)^2} = 6.35\ \Omega$$

THE CONDUCTOR CROSS-SECTIONAL AREA IS GIVEN BY

$$A = \frac{(2.84 \times 10^{-8})\,(63 \times 10^3)}{6.35} = 2.81764 \times 10^{-4}\ m^2$$

$\therefore\ d = 1.894$ cm $= 0.7456$ in $= 556{,}000$ cmil

4.5

(a) FROM EQ. (4.4.10)

$$L_{int} = \left(\frac{1}{2}\times10^{-7}\ \frac{H}{m}\right)\left(\frac{1000\,m}{1\,km}\right)\left(\frac{1000\,mH}{1\,H}\right) = 0.05\ mH/km$$

PER CONDUCTOR

(b) FROM EQ. (4.5.2)

$$L_x = L_y = 2\times10^{-7}\ \mathrm{Ln}\left(\frac{D}{r'}\right)\ \frac{H}{m}$$

$$D = 0.5\ m \qquad r' = e^{-\frac{1}{4}}\left(\frac{0.015}{2}\right) = 5.841\times10^{-3}\ m$$

$$L_x = L_y = 2\times10^{-7}\ \mathrm{Ln}\left(\frac{0.5}{5.841\times10^{-3}}\right)\frac{H}{m}\left(\frac{1000\,m}{km}\right)\left(\frac{1000\,mH}{H}\right)$$

$$= \underline{\underline{0.8899}}\ \frac{mH}{km} \text{ per conductor}$$

(c)

$$L = L_x + L_y = \underline{\underline{1.780}}\ \frac{mH}{km} \text{ per circuit}$$

4.6

(a) $L_{int} = 0.05\ mH/km$ PER CONDUCTOR

$$L_x = L_y = 2\times10^{-7}\ \ln\left(\frac{0.5}{1.2\times5.841\times10^{-3}}\right)10^6 = 0.8535\ mH/km$$

PER CONDUCTOR

$$L = L_x + L_y = 1.707\ mH/km \text{ PER CIRCUIT}$$

(b) $L_{int} = 0.05\ mH/km$ PER CONDUCTOR

$$L_x = L_y = 2\times10^{-7}\ \ln\left(\frac{0.5}{0.8\times5.841\times10^{-3}}\right)10^6 = 0.9346\ mH/km$$

PER CONDUCTOR

$$L = L_x + L_y = 1.869\ mH/km \text{ PER CIRCUIT.}$$

L_{int} IS INDEPENDENT OF CONDUCTOR DIAMETER.

THE TOTAL INDUCTANCE DECREASES 4.1 % (INCREASES 5 %)

AS THE CONDUCTOR DIAMETER INCREASES 20% (DECREASES 20%).

4.7

FROM EQ. (4.5.10)

$$L_1 = 2\times10^{-7}\ \mathrm{Ln}\left(\frac{D}{r'}\right)\ \frac{H}{m} \qquad D = 4\ \text{ft}$$

$$r' = e^{-\frac{1}{4}}\left(\frac{.5}{2}\right)\left(\frac{1\ \text{ft}}{12\ \text{in}}\right)$$

$$r' = 1.6225\times10^{-2}\ \text{ft}$$

$$L_1 = 2\times10^{-7}\ \mathrm{Ln}\left(\frac{4}{1.6225\times10^{-2}}\right)$$

$$L_1 = \underline{\underline{1.101\times10^{-6}}}\ \frac{H}{m}$$

$$X_1 = \omega L_1 = (2\pi 60)(1.101\times10^{-6})(1000) = \underline{\underline{0.4153}}\ \Omega/\text{km}$$

4.8

(a) $$L_1 = 2\times10^{-7}\ \ln\left(\frac{4.8}{1.6225\times10^{-2}}\right) = 1.138\times10^{-6}\ H/m$$

$$X_1 = \omega L_1 = 2\pi(60)(1.138\times10^{-6})(1000) = 0.4292\ \Omega/\text{km}$$

(b) $$L_1 = 2\times10^{-7}\ \ln\left(\frac{3.2}{1.6225\times10^{-2}}\right) = 1.057\times10^{-6}\ H/m$$

$$X_1 = 2\pi(60)(1.057\times10^{-6})(1000) = 0.3986\ \Omega/\text{km}$$

L_1 AND X_1 INCREASE BY 3.35% (DECREASE BY 4.02%) AS THE PHASE SPACING INCREASES BY 20% (DECREASES BY 20%).

4.9

FOR THIS CONDUCTOR, TABLE A.4 LISTS GMR TO BE 0.0217 ft.

$\therefore$ FOR ONE CONDUCTOR, $L_x = 2\times10^{-7} \ln \frac{20}{0.0217}$ H/m

THE INDUCTIVE REACTANCE IS THEN $[2\pi(60)L_x]$ Ω/m

OR $2.022\times10^{-3}(60)\ln\frac{20}{0.0217}$ Ω/mi

$= 0.828$ Ω/mi

FOR THE SINGLE-PHASE LINE, $2\times0.828 = 1.656$ Ω/mi

4.10

(a) THE TOTAL LINE INDUCTANCE IS GIVEN BY

$$L_T = \left[4\times10^{-4}\ln\frac{D}{r'}\right] \text{ mH/m}$$

$$= 4\times10^{-4}\ln\frac{3.6}{(0.7788)(0.025)} = 0.0209 \text{ mH/m}$$

(b) THE TOTAL LINE REACTANCE IS GIVEN BY

$$X_T = 2\pi(60)\,4\times10^{-4}\ln\frac{D}{r'}$$

$$= 0.1508\ln\frac{D}{r'}\ \Omega/\text{km}$$

OR $0.2426\ln\frac{D}{r'}\ \Omega/\text{mi}$

$\therefore X_T = 0.787$ Ω/km OR 1.266 Ω/mi

(c) $L_T = 4\times10^{-4}\ln\frac{7.2}{0.7788(0.025)} = 0.02365$ mH/m

DOUBLING THE SEPARATION BETWEEN THE CONDUCTORS CAUSES ONLY ABOUT a 13% RISE IN INDUCTANCE.

4.11

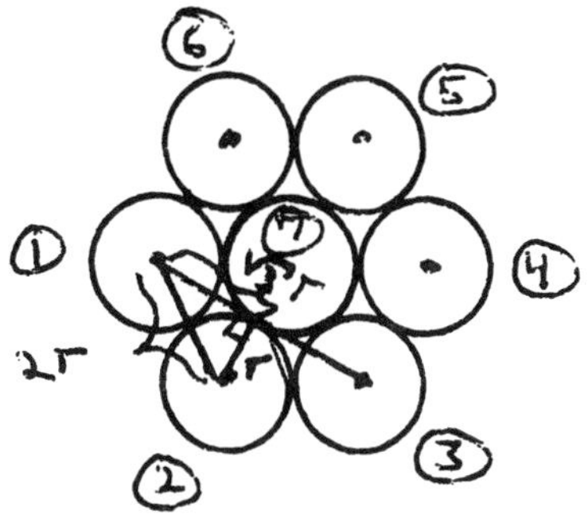

For each of six outer conductors:

$$D_{11} = r' = e^{-\frac{1}{4}} r$$

$$D_{12} = D_{16} = D_{17} = 2r$$

$$D_{13} = D_{15} = 2\sqrt{3}\, r$$

$$D_{14} = 4r$$

For the inner conductor:

$$D_{77} = r' = e^{-\frac{1}{4}} r$$

$$D_{71} = D_{72} = D_{73} = D_{74} = D_{75} = D_{76} = 2r$$

$$D_S = \text{GMR} = \sqrt[49]{\underbrace{\left[\left(e^{-\frac{1}{4}} r\right)(2r)^3\left(2\sqrt{3}\, r\right)^2(4r)\right]}_{\text{Distances for each outer conductor}}{}^{6}\ \underbrace{\left[\left(e^{-\frac{1}{4}} r\right)(2r)^6\right]}_{\text{Distances for inner conductor}}}$$

(exponent 6: six outer conductors)

$$D_S = \text{GMR} = r\sqrt[49]{\left(e^{-\frac{1}{4}}\right)^6 (2\ )^{18} \left(2\sqrt{3}\ \right)^{12} (4\ )^6 \left(e^{-\frac{1}{4}}\ \right)(2\ )^6}$$

$$D_S = \text{GMR} = r\sqrt[49]{\left(e^{-\frac{1}{4}}\right)^7 (2)^{24} \left(2\sqrt{3}\right)^{12} (4)^6} = \underline{\underline{2.177\ r}}$$

4.12

$$D_{SL} = \sqrt[N_b^2]{\left(D_{11} D_{12} \cdots D_{1N_b}\right)^{N_b}} = \left(D_{11} D_{12} \cdots D_{1N_b}\right)^{\frac{1}{N_b}}$$

$$D_{11} = D_S \qquad D_{1n} = 2A \sin\left[\frac{(n-1)\pi}{N_b}\right] \qquad n = 2, 3, \ldots N_b$$

$$D_{SL} = \left\{D_S\left[2A\sin\left(\frac{\pi}{N_b}\right)\right]\left[2A\sin\left(\frac{2\pi}{N_b}\right)\right]\left[2A\sin\left(\frac{3\pi}{N_b}\right)\right]\cdots\left[2A\sin\left(\frac{N_b-1}{N_b}\right)\pi\right]\right\}^{\frac{1}{N_b}}$$

4.12 CONTD.

Using the trigonometric identity;

$$D_{SL} = \left\{ D_S \, (A)^{(N_b-1)} \, N_b \right\}^{\frac{1}{N_b}}$$

which is the desired result.

Two-conductor bundle, $N_b = 2$

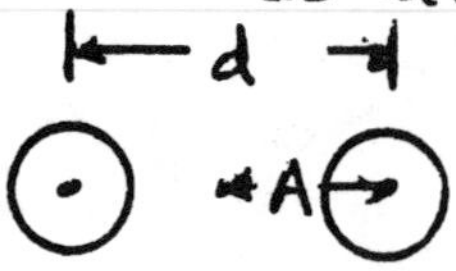

$A = \frac{d}{2}$ $\quad D_{SL} = \left[D_S \left(\frac{d}{2}\right)(2) \right]^{1/2}$

$$= \sqrt{D_S d} \quad \text{Eq } (4.6.19)$$

Three-conductor bundle, $N_b = 3$

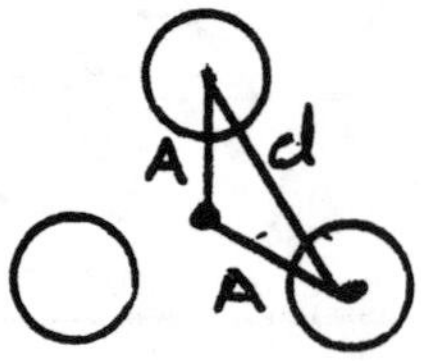

$A = \frac{d}{\sqrt{3}}$ $\quad D_{SL} = \left[D_S \left(\frac{d}{\sqrt{3}}\right)^2 3 \right]^{1/3}$

$$= \sqrt[3]{D_S d^2} \quad \text{Eq } (4.6.20)$$

Four-conductor bundle, $N_b = 4$

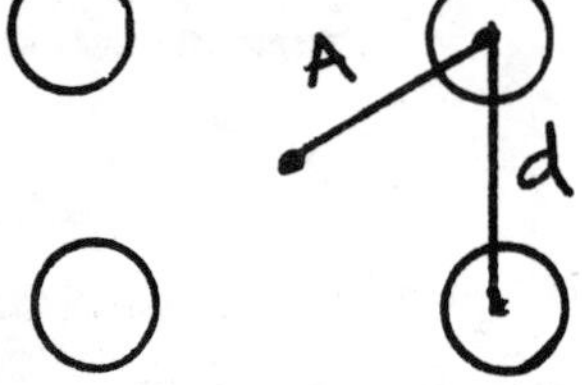

$A = \frac{d}{\sqrt{2}}$ $\quad D_{SL} = \left[D_S \left(\frac{d}{\sqrt{2}}\right)^3 4 \right]^{1/4}$

$$= \sqrt[4]{D_S d^3} \, \sqrt[4]{\left(\frac{4}{2\sqrt{2}}\right)}$$

$$= 1.0905 \sqrt[4]{D_S d^3}$$

Eq. (4.6.21)

4.13

(a) $$GMR = \sqrt[9]{\left[\left(e^{-\frac{1}{4}}r\right)(2r)(2r)\right]^3} = r\sqrt[3]{4e^{-\frac{1}{4}}}$$

$$= \underline{\underline{1.4605\ r}}$$

(b) $$GMR = \sqrt[16]{\underbrace{\left[\left(e^{-\frac{1}{4}}r\right)(2r)(4r)(6r)\right]^2}_{\text{Distances for each outer conductor}} \underbrace{\left[\left(e^{-\frac{1}{4}}r\right)(2r)(2r)(4r)\right]^2}_{\text{Distances for each inner conductor}}}$$

$$GMR = \sqrt[16]{\left(e^{-\frac{1}{4}}\right)^4(2)^6(4)^4(6)^2}\,(r) = \underline{\underline{2.1554\ r}}$$

(c) $$GMR = r\sqrt[81]{\underbrace{\left[\left(e^{-\frac{1}{4}}\right)(2)^2(4)^2\left(\sqrt{20}\right)^2\left(\sqrt{8}\right)\left(\sqrt{32}\right)\right]^4}_{\text{Distances for each corner conductor}} \times \underbrace{\left[\left(e^{-\frac{1}{4}}\right)(2)^3\left(\sqrt{8}\right)^2\left(\sqrt{20}\right)^2(4)\right]^4}_{\text{Distances for each outside non-corner conductor}} \times \underbrace{\left[\left(e^{-\frac{1}{4}}\right)(2)^4\left(\sqrt{8}\right)^4\right]}_{\text{Distances for the center conductor}}}$$

$$GMR = r\sqrt[81]{\left(e^{-\frac{1}{4}}\right)^9(2)^{24}\left(\sqrt{8}\right)^{16}\left(\sqrt{20}\right)^{16}(4)^{12}\left(\sqrt{32}\right)^4}$$

$$GMR = \underline{\underline{2.6374\ r}}$$

4.14 $D_{eq} = \sqrt[3]{8 \times 8 \times 16} = 10.079\ m$

FROM TABLE A.4, $D_S = (0.0403\ ft)\ \dfrac{1\ m}{3.28\ ft} = 0.0123\ m$

$$L_1 = 2 \times 10^{-7} \ln(D_{eq}/D_S) = 2 \times 10^{-7} \ln\left(\frac{10.079}{0.0123}\right) = 1.342 \times 10^{-6}\ H/m$$

$$X_1 = 2\pi(60) L_1 = 2\pi(60)\ 1.342 \times 10^{-6} \frac{\Omega}{m} \times \frac{1000\ m}{1\ km} = 0.506\ \Omega/km$$

4.15

(a) $L_1 = 2 \times 10^{-7} \ln\left(\dfrac{10.079 \times 1.1}{0.0123}\right) = 1.361 \times 10^{-6}\ H/m$

$X_1 = 2\pi(60)\ 1.361 \times 10^{-6}\ (1000) = 0.513\ \Omega/km$

(b) $L_1 = 2 \times 10^{-7} \ln\left(\dfrac{10.079 \times 0.9}{0.0123}\right) = 1.321 \times 10^{-6}\ H/m$

$X_1 = 2\pi(60)\ 1.321 \times 10^{-6}\ (1000) = 0.498\ \Omega/km$

THE POSITIVE SEQUENCE INDUCTANCE L_1 AND INDUCTIVE REACTANCE X_1 INCREASE 1.4% (DECREASE 1.6%) AS THE PHASE SPACING INCREASES 10% (DECREASES 10%).

4.16

$$D_{eq} = \sqrt[3]{10 \times 10 \times 20} = 12.6\ m$$

FROM TABLE A.4, $D_S = (0.0435\ ft)\ \dfrac{1\ m}{3.28\ ft} = 0.0133\ m$

$$X_1 = \omega L_1 = 2\pi(60)\ 2 \times 10^{-7} \ln\left(\frac{12.6}{0.149}\right) \frac{\Omega}{m} \times \frac{1000\ m}{1\ km}$$

$$= 0.335\ \Omega/km$$

4.17

(a) From Table A.4:

$$D_S = (0.0479)\left(\frac{1}{3.28}\right) = 0.0146 \text{ m}$$

$$D_{SL} = \sqrt[3]{(0.0146)(0.457)^2} = 0.145 \text{ m}$$

$$X_1 = (2\pi 60)\left[2\times10^{-7} \, \text{Ln}\left(\frac{12.60}{0.145}\right)\right]\times 1000 = \underline{\underline{0.337}} \ \frac{\Omega}{\text{km}}$$

(b) $$D_S = (0.0391)\left(\frac{1}{3.28}\right) = 0.0119 \text{ m}$$

$$D_{SL} = \sqrt[3]{(0.0119)(.457)(.457)} = 0.136 \text{ m}$$

$$X_1 = (2\pi 60)\left[2\times10^{-7} \, \text{Ln}\left(\frac{12.60}{0.136}\right)\right]\times 1000 = \underline{\underline{0.342}} \ \frac{\Omega}{\text{km}}$$

Results

ACSR Conductor	Aluminum Cross Section	X_1	
	kcmil	Ω/km	% Change
Canary	900	0.342	} 0.9%
Finch	1113	0.339	} 0.6%
Martin	1351	0.337	

4.18

APPLICATION OF EQ. (4.6.6) YIELDS THE GEOMETRIC MEAN DISTANCE THAT SEPERATES THE TWO BUNDLES:

$$D_{AB} = \sqrt[9]{(6.1)^2 (6.2)^2 (6.3)\, 6 (6.05)(6.15)(6.25)} = 6.15\text{m}$$

THE GEOMETRIC MEAN RADIUS OF THE EQUILATERAL ARRANGEMENT OF LINE A IS CALCULATED USING EQ. (4.6.7):

$$R_A = \sqrt[9]{(0.015576)^3 (0.1)^6} = 0.0538\text{ m}$$

IN WHICH THE FIRST TERM BENEATH THE RADICAL IS OBTAINED FROM

$$r' = 0.7788 r = 0.7788 (0.02) = 0.015576\text{ m}$$

THE GEOMETRIC MEAN RADIUS OF THE LINE B IS CALCULATED BELOW AS PER ITS CONFIGURATION:

$$R_B = \sqrt[9]{(0.015576)^3 (0.1)^4 (0.2)^2} = 0.0628\text{ m}$$

THE ACTUAL CONFIGURATION CAN NOW BE REPLACED BY THE TWO EQUIVALENT HOLLOW CONDUCTORS EACH WITH ITS OWN GEOMETRIC MEAN RADIUS AND SEPARATED BY THE GEOMETRIC MEAN DISTANCE AS SHOWN BELOW:

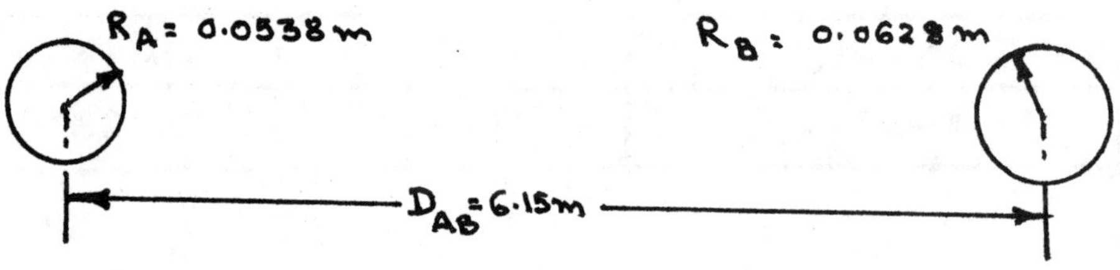

4.19

(a) THE GEOMETRIC MEAN RADIUS OF EACH PHASE IS CALCULATED AS

$$R = \sqrt[4]{(r')^2 (0.3)^2} \quad \text{WHERE } r' = 0.7788 \times 0.0074$$

$$= 0.0416 \text{ m}$$

THE GEOMETRIC MEAN DISTANCE BETWEEN THE CONDUCTORS OF PHASES A AND B IS GIVEN BY

$$D_{AB} = \sqrt[4]{6^2 (6.3)(5.7)} = 5.996 \simeq 6 \text{m}$$

SIMILARLY,

$$D_{BC} = \sqrt[4]{6^2 (6.3)(5.7)} = 5.996 \simeq 6 \text{m}$$

AND

$$D_{CA} = \sqrt[4]{12^2 (12.3)(11.7)} = 11.998 \simeq 12 \text{m}$$

THE GMD BETWEEN PHASES IS GIVEN BY THE CUBE ROOT OF THE PRODUCT OF THE THREE-PHASE SPACINGS.

$$D_{eq} = \sqrt[3]{6 \times 6 \times 12} = 7.56 \text{ m}$$

THE INDUCTANCE PER PHASE IS FOUND AS

$$L = 0.2 \ln \frac{7.56}{0.0416} = 1.041 \text{ mH/km}$$

OR

$$L = 1.609 \times 1.041 = 1.674 \text{ mH/mi}$$

(b) THE LINE REACTANCE FOR EACH PHASE THEN BECOMES

$$X = 2\pi f L = 2\pi (60)\, 1.674 \times 10^{-3} = 0.631 \ \Omega/\text{mi}$$

PER PHASE

4.20

$$C_n = \frac{2\pi\epsilon_0}{\ln\left(\frac{D}{r}\right)} = \frac{2\pi(8.854\times10^{-12})}{\ln\left(\frac{0.5}{0.015/2}\right)} = \underline{\underline{1.3246\times10^{-11}}}\ \frac{F}{m}$$

TO NEUTRAL

$$\bar{Y}_n = j\omega C_n = j(2\pi 60)(1.3246\times10^{-11})\ \frac{S}{m}\times 1000\ \frac{m}{km}$$

$$\bar{Y}_n = \underline{\underline{j\,4.994\times10^{-6}}}\ \frac{S}{km} \text{ to neutral}$$

4.21

(a) $C_n = \dfrac{2\pi(8.854\times10^{-12})}{\ln\left(\frac{0.5}{0.018/2}\right)} = 1.385\times10^{-11}$ F/m TO NEUTRAL

$\bar{Y}_n = j\,2\pi(60)\,1.385\times10^{-11}\,(1000) = j\,5.221\times10^{-6}$ S/km TO NEUTRAL

(b) $C_n = \dfrac{2\pi(8.854\times10^{-12})}{\ln\left(\frac{0.5}{0.012/2}\right)} = 1.258\times10^{-11}$ F/m TO NEUTRAL

$\bar{Y}_n = j\,2\pi(60)\,1.258\times10^{-11}\,(1000) = j\,4.742\times10^{-6}$ S/km TO NEUTRAL

BOTH THE CAPACITANCE AND ADMITTANCE-TO-NEUTRAL INCREASE 4.5% (DECREASE 5.1%) AS THE CONDUCTOR DIAMETER INCREASES 20% (DECREASES 20%).

4.22

$$C_1 = \frac{2\pi \epsilon_0}{\ln\left(\frac{D}{r}\right)} = \frac{2\pi(8.854\times10^{-12})}{\ln\left(\frac{4}{0.25/12}\right)} = \underline{\underline{1.058\times10^{-11}}}\ \frac{F}{m}$$

$$\bar{Y}_1 = j\omega C_1 = j(2\pi60)(1.058\times10^{-11})(1000)$$

$$= \underline{\underline{j\,3.989\times10^{-6}}}\ \frac{S}{km}$$

4.23

(a) $$C_1 = \frac{2\pi(8.854\times10^{-12})}{\ln\left(\frac{4.8}{0.25/12}\right)} = 1.023\times10^{-11}\ F/m$$

$$\bar{Y}_1 = j\,2\pi(60)\,1.023\times10^{-11}(1000) = j\,3.857\times10^{-6}\ S/km$$

(b) $$C_1 = \frac{2\pi(8.854\times10^{-12})}{\ln\left(\frac{3.2}{0.25/12}\right)} = 1.105\times10^{-11}\ F/m$$

$$\bar{Y}_1 = j\,2\pi(60)\,1.105\times10^{-11}(1000) = j\,4.167\times10^{-6}\ S/km$$

THE POSITIVE SEQUENCE SHUNT CAPACITANCE AND SHUNT ADMITTANCE BOTH DECREASE 3.3% (INCREASE 4.5%) AS THE PHASE SPACING INCREASES BY 20% (DECREASES BY 20%).

4.24

EQUATIONS (4.10.4) AND (4.10.5) APPLY.

FOR A 2-CONDUCTOR BUNDLE, THE GMR $D_{sc} = \sqrt{rd} = \sqrt{0.0074 \times 0.3}$

$= 0.0471$

THE GMD IS GIVEN BY $D_{eq} = \sqrt[3]{6 \times 6 \times 12} = 7.56\,m$

HENCE THE LINE-TO-NEUTRAL CAPACITANCE IS GIVEN BY

$$C_{an} = \frac{2\pi\epsilon}{\ln(D_{eq}/D_{sc})} \quad F/m$$

$$\text{OR} \quad \frac{55.63}{\ln(7.56/0.0471)} = 10.95\ nF/km$$

(WITH $\epsilon = \epsilon_0$)

$$\text{OR} \quad 1.609 \times 10.95 = 17.62\ nF/mi$$

(b) THE CAPACITIVE REACTANCE AT 60 HZ IS CALCULATED AS

$$X_c = \frac{1}{2\pi(60)C_{an}} = 29.63 \times 10^3 \ln \frac{D_{eq}}{D_{sc}} \quad \Omega\text{-mi}$$

$$= 29.63 \times 10^3 \ln \frac{7.56}{0.0471} = 150,500\ \Omega\text{-mi}$$

$$\text{OR} \quad \frac{150,500}{1.609} = 93,536\ \Omega\text{-km}$$

(c) WITH THE LINE LENGTH OF 100 mi, THE CAPACITIVE REACTANCE IS FOUND AS $\frac{150,500}{100} = 1505\ \Omega/\text{PHASE}$

4.25 $D_{eq} = \sqrt[3]{8\times8\times16} = 10.079\ m$

FROM TABLE A.4, $r = \frac{1.196}{2}\ in\left(\frac{0.0254\ m}{1\ in}\right) = 0.01519\ m$

$$C_1 = \frac{2\pi\varepsilon_0}{\ln\left(\frac{D}{r}\right)} = \frac{2\pi(8.854\times10^{-12})}{\ln\left(\frac{10.079}{0.01519}\right)} = 8.565\times10^{-12}\ F/m$$

$$\bar{Y}_1 = j\omega C_1 = j2\pi(60)\,8.565\times10^{-12}(1000) = j3.229\times10^{-6}\ S/km$$

FOR A 100 km LINE LENGTH

$$I_{chg} = Y_1 V_{LN} = (3.229\times10^{-6}\times100)(230/\sqrt{3}) = 4.288\times10^{-2}\ kA/PHASE$$

4.26

(a) $D_{eq} = \sqrt[3]{8.8\times8.8\times17.6} = 11.084\ m$

$$C_1 = \frac{2\pi(8.854\times10^{-12})}{\ln\left(\frac{11.084}{0.01519}\right)} = 8.442\times10^{-12}\ F/m$$

$$\bar{Y}_1 = j2\pi(60)\,8.442\times10^{-12}(1000) = j3.183\times10^{-6}\ S/km$$

$$I_{chg} = 3.183\times10^{-6}\times1000\,(230/\sqrt{3}) = 4.223\times10^{-2}\ \frac{kA}{PHASE}$$

(b) $D_{eq} = \sqrt[3]{7.2\times7.2\times14.4} = 9.069\ m$

$$C_1 = \frac{2\pi(8.854\times10^{-12})}{\ln\left(\frac{9.069}{0.01519}\right)} = 8.707\times10^{-12}\ F/m$$

$$\bar{Y}_1 = j2\pi(60)\,8.707\times10^{-12}(1000) = j3.284\times10^{-6}\ S/km$$

$$I_{chg} = 3.284\times10^{-6}\times100\,(230/\sqrt{3}) = 4.361\times10^{-2}\ \frac{kA}{PHASE}$$

C_1, Y_1, AND I_{chg} DECREASE 1.5% (INCREASE 1.7%)

AS THE PHASE SPACING INCREASES 10% (DECREASES 10%).

4.27 $D_{eq} = \sqrt[3]{10 \times 10 \times 20} = 12.6\ m$

FROM TABLE A.4, $r = \frac{1.293}{2}\ in \left(\frac{0.0254\ m}{1\ in}\right) = 0.01642\ m$

$$D_{SC} = \sqrt[3]{r d^2} = \sqrt[3]{0.01642(0.5)^2} = 0.16\ m$$

$$C_1 = \frac{2\pi\epsilon_0}{\ln \frac{D_{eq}}{D_{SC}}} = \frac{2\pi(8.854 \times 10^{-12})}{\ln\left(\frac{12.6}{0.16}\right)} = 1.275 \times 10^{-11}\ F/m$$

$$\bar{Y}_1 = j\omega C_1 = j2\pi(60)\,1.275 \times 10^{-11}(1000) = j4.807 \times 10^{-6}\ S/km$$

$$Q_1 = V_{LL}^2\, Y_1 = (500)^2\, 4.807 \times 10^{-6} = 1.2\ MVAR/km$$

4.28

(a) FROM TABLE A.4, $r = \frac{1.424}{2}(0.0254) = 0.0181\ m$

$$D_{SC} = \sqrt[3]{0.0181(0.5)^2} = 0.1654\ m$$

$$C_1 = \frac{2\pi(8.854 \times 10^{-12})}{\ln\left(\frac{12.6}{0.1654}\right)} = 1.284 \times 10^{-11}\ F/m$$

$$\bar{Y}_1 = j2\pi(60)(1.284 \times 10^{-11})(1000) = j4.842 \times 10^{-6}\ S/km$$

$$Q_1 = (500)^2\, 4.842 \times 10^{-6} = 1.21\ MVAR/km$$

(b) $r = \frac{1.162}{2}(0.0254) = 0.01476\ m$; $D_{SC} = \sqrt[3]{0.01476\ (0.5)^2} = 0.1546\ m$

$$C_1 = \frac{2\pi(8.854 \times 10^{-12})}{\ln\left(\frac{12.6}{0.1546}\right)} = 1.265 \times 10^{-11}\ F/m$$

$$\bar{Y}_1 = j2\pi(60)\,1.265 \times 10^{-11}(1000) = 4.77 \times 10^{-6}\ S/km$$

$$Q_1 = (500)^2\, 4.77 \times 10^{-6} = 1.192\ MVAR/km$$

C_1, Y_1, AND Q_1 INCREASE 0.8% (DECREASE 0.7%) FOR THE LARGER, 1351 kcmil CONDUCTORS (SMALLEL, 700 kcmil CONDUCTORS).

4.29

(a) FOR DRAKE, TABLE A.4 LISTS THE OUTSIDE DIAMETER AS 1.108 in

$$\therefore \; r = \frac{1.108}{2 \times 12} = 0.0462 \text{ ft}$$

$$D_{eq} = \sqrt[3]{20 \times 20 \times 38} = 24.8 \text{ ft}$$

$$C_{an} = \frac{2\pi \times 8.85 \times 10^{-12}}{\ln(24.8/0.0462)} = 8.8466 \times 10^{-12} \text{ F/m}$$

$$X_c = \frac{10^{12}}{2\pi(60)\, 8.8466 \times 1609} = 0.1864 \times 10^{6} \; \Omega\cdot\text{mi}$$

(b) FOR A LENGTH OF 175 mi

$$\text{CAPACITIVE REACTANCE} = \frac{0.1864 \times 10^{6}}{175} = 1065 \; \Omega$$

TO NEUTRAL

$$I_{chg} = \frac{220 \times 10^{3}}{\sqrt{3}} \frac{1}{X_c} = \frac{0.22}{\sqrt{3} \times 0.1864} = 0.681 \text{ A/mi}$$

OR $0.681 \times 175 = 119 \text{ A}$ FOR THE LINE

TOTAL THREE-PHASE REACTIVE POWER SUPPLIED BY THE LINE CAPACITANCE IS GIVEN BY $\sqrt{3} \times 220 \times 119 \times 10^{-3} = 43.5$ MVAR

4.30

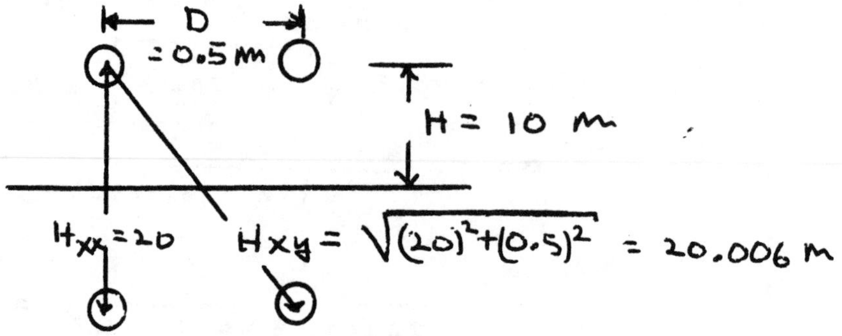

From Example 4.8,

$$C_{xn} = \frac{2\pi\varepsilon_0}{\ln\left(\frac{D}{r}\right) - \ln\left(\frac{H_{xy}}{H_{xx}}\right)} = \frac{2\pi\,(8.854\times10^{-12})}{\ln\left(\frac{0.5}{0.0075}\right) - \ln\left(\frac{20.006}{20}\right)}$$

$$C_{xn} = 1.3247\times10^{-11}\ \frac{F}{m}$$

which is 0.01% larger than in Problem 4.20

4.31

(a) $D_{eq} = \sqrt[3]{12 \times 12 \times 24} = 15.12\ m$

$r = 0.0328/2 = 0.0164\ m$

$X_c = \dfrac{1}{2\pi f C_{an}}$

WHERE $C_{an} = \dfrac{2\pi \times 8.85 \times 10^{-12}}{\ln(15.12/0.0164)}$

$\therefore\ X_c = \dfrac{2.86}{60} \times 10^9 \ln \dfrac{15.12}{0.0164} = 3.254 \times 10^8\ \Omega.m$

FOR 125 km, $X_c = \dfrac{3.254 \times 10^8}{125 \times 1000} = 2603\ \Omega$

(b)

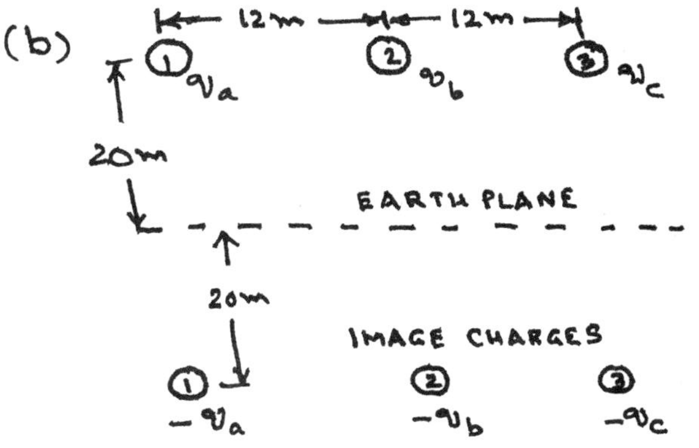

$H_1 = H_2 = H_3 = 40m$

$H_{12} = H_{23} = \sqrt{40^2 + 12^2} = 41.761\ m$

$H_{31} = \sqrt{40^2 + 24^2} = 46.648\ m$

$D_{eq} = 15.12\ m$ AND $r = 0.0164\ m$

$\therefore\ X_c = \dfrac{2.86}{60} \times 10^9 \left[\ln \dfrac{D_{eq}}{r} - \dfrac{1}{3} \ln \dfrac{H_{12} H_{23} H_{31}}{H_1 H_2 H_3}\right] \Omega.m$

$= 4.77 \times 10^7 \left[\ln \dfrac{15.12}{0.0164} - \dfrac{1}{3} \ln \dfrac{41.761 \times 41.761 \times 46.648}{40 \times 40 \times 40}\right]$

$= 3.218 \times 10^8\ \Omega.m$

FOR 125 km, $X_c = \dfrac{3.218 \times 10^8}{125 \times 10^3} = 2574\ \Omega$

4.32

From Problem 4.30

$$C_{xy} = \frac{1}{2} C_{xn} = \frac{1}{2}(1.3247 \times 10^{-11}) = 6.6235 \times 10^{-12} \ \frac{F}{m}$$

with $V_{xy} = 20 \text{ kV}$

$$q_x = C_{xy} V_{xy} = (6.6235 \times 10^{-12})(20 \times 10^{3}) = 1.3247 \times 10^{-7} \ \frac{C}{m}$$

From Eq (4.12.1) The conductor surface electric field strength is :

4.32 CONTD.

$$E_r = \frac{1.3247\times 10^{-7}}{(2\pi)(8.854\times 10^{-12})(0.0075)}$$

$$= 3.1750\times 10^{5}\ \frac{V}{m}\times\left(\frac{kV}{1000V}\right)\left(\frac{m}{100cm}\right)$$

$$= \underline{\underline{3.175}}\ \frac{kV_{rms}}{cm}$$

Using Eq(4.12.6), the ground level electric field strength directly under the conductor is:

$$E_k = \frac{1.3247\times 10^{-7}}{(2\pi)(8.854\times 10^{-12})}\left[\frac{(2)(10)}{(10)^2} - \frac{(2)(10)}{(10)^2+(0.5)^2}\right]$$

$$= 1.188\ \frac{V}{m}\times\left(\frac{kV}{1000V}\right) = \underline{\underline{0.001188}}\ \frac{kV}{m}$$

4.33 (a) From Problem 4.30,

$$C_{xn} = \frac{2\pi(8.854\times 10^{-12})}{Ln\left(\frac{0.5}{0.009375}\right) - Ln\left(\frac{20.006}{20}\right)} = 1.3991\times 10^{-11}\ \frac{F}{m}$$

$$C_{xy} = \frac{1}{2}C_{xn} = 6.995\times 10^{-12}\ \frac{F}{m}$$

$$q_x = C_{xy}V_{xy} = (6.995\times 10^{-12})(20\times 10^{3}) = 1.399\times 10^{-7}\ \frac{C}{m}$$

$$E_r = \frac{1.399\times 10^{-7}}{(2\pi)(8.854\times 10^{-12})(0.009375)}\times\left(\frac{1}{1000}\right)\left(\frac{1}{100}\right)$$

$$= \underline{\underline{2.682}}\ \frac{kV_{rms}}{cm}$$

4-33 CONTD.

$$E_k = \frac{1.399 \times 10^{-7}}{(2\pi)(8.854 \times 10^{-12})}\left[\frac{(2)(10)}{(10)^2} - \frac{(2)(10)}{(10)^2 + (0.5)^2}\right]$$

$$= 1.254 \frac{V}{m} \times \left(\frac{kV}{1000V}\right) = \underline{\underline{0.001254}} \frac{kV}{m}$$

(b) $$C_{xn} = \frac{2\pi(8.854 \times 10^{-12})}{\operatorname{Ln}\left(\frac{0.5}{.005625}\right) - \operatorname{Ln}\left(\frac{20.06}{20}\right)} = 1.2398 \times 10^{-11} \frac{F}{m}$$

$$C_{xy} = \frac{1}{2} C_{xn} = 6.199 \times 10^{-12} \frac{F}{m}$$

$$q_x = C_{xy} V_{xy} = (6.199 \times 10^{-12})(20 \times 10^3) = 1.2398 \times 10^{-7} \frac{C}{m}$$

$$E_r = \frac{1.2398 \times 10^{-7}}{(2\pi)(8.854 \times 10^{-12})(.005625)} \times \left(\frac{1}{1000}\right)\left(\frac{1}{100}\right)$$

$$E_r = \underline{\underline{3.962}} \frac{kV_{rms}}{cm}$$

$$E_k = \frac{1.2398 \times 10^{-7}}{(2\pi)(8.854 \times 10^{-12})}\left[\frac{(2)(10)}{(10)^2} - \frac{(2)(10)}{(10)^2 + (0.5)^2}\right]$$

$$E_k = 1.112 \frac{V}{m} \times \left(\frac{kV}{1000V}\right) = \underline{\underline{0.001112}} \frac{kV}{m}$$

The conductor surface electric field strength E_r decreases 15.5% (increases 24.8%) as the conductor diameter increases 25% (decreases 25%). The ground level electric field strength E_k increases 5.6% (decreases 6.4%).

CHAPTER 5

5.1

(a) $\bar{A} = \bar{D} = 1.0\angle 0°$ pu ; $\bar{C} = 0.0$ S

$\bar{B} = \bar{Z} = (0.19 + j0.34)(30) = 11.685\angle 60.8°\ \Omega$

(b) $\bar{V}_R = (33/\sqrt{3})\angle 0° = 19.05\angle 0°$ kV$_{LN}$

$$\bar{I}_R = \frac{S_R}{\sqrt{3}\,V_{R\,L\text{-}L}}\angle -\cos^{-1}(pf) = \frac{10}{\sqrt{3}\,(33)}\angle -\cos^{-1}0.9$$

$$= 0.1750\angle -25.84°\ \text{kA}$$

$$\bar{V}_S = \bar{A}\bar{V}_R + \bar{B}\bar{I}_R = 1.0(19.05) + (11.685\angle 60.8°)(0.175\angle -25.84°)$$

$$= 19.05 + 2.045\angle 34.96° = 20.73 + j1.172$$

$$= 20.76\angle 2.22°\ \text{kV}_{LN} \quad ; \quad V_S = 20.76\sqrt{3} = 35.96\ \text{kV}_{LL}$$

(c) $\bar{I}_R = 0.175\angle 25.84°$ kA

$$\bar{V}_S = 1.0(19.05) + (11.685\angle 60.8°)(0.175\angle 25.84°)$$

$$= 19.05 + 2.044\angle 86.64°$$

$$= 19.17 + j2.04$$

$$= 19.28\angle 4.07°\ \text{kV}_{LN}$$

$$V_S = 19.28\sqrt{3} = 33.39\ \text{kV}_{LL}$$

5.2

(a) $\bar{A} = \bar{D} = 1 + \frac{\bar{Y}\bar{Z}}{2} = 1 + \frac{1}{2}\left(3.33\times10^{-6}\times150\angle 90^\circ\right)(.08 + j.48)(150)$

$\bar{A} = \bar{D} = 1 + \frac{1}{2}\left(4.995\times10^{-4}\angle 90^\circ\right)\left(72.99\angle 80.54^\circ\right)$

$= 1 + 0.01823\angle 170.54^\circ = 0.9820 + j\,0.002997$

$= 0.9820\angle 0.175^\circ$ per unit

$\bar{B} = \bar{Z} = 72.99\angle 80.54^\circ\ \Omega$

$\bar{C} = \bar{Y}\left(1 + \frac{\bar{Y}\bar{Z}}{4}\right) = 4.995\times10^{-4}\angle 90^\circ\left(1 + .009115\angle 170.54^\circ\right)$

$\bar{C} = \left(4.995\times10^{-4}\angle 90^\circ\right)\left(0.991 + j\,0.00150\right)$

$= \left(4.995\times10^{-4}\angle 90^\circ\right)\left(0.991\angle 0.0867^\circ\right) = 4.950\times10^{-4}\angle 90.09^\circ\ \mho$

(b) $\bar{V}_R = \frac{220}{\sqrt{3}}\angle 0^\circ = 127.02\angle 0^\circ\ kV_{LN}$

$\bar{I}_R = \frac{P_R\ \angle -\cos^{-1}(\text{P.F.})}{\sqrt{3}\,V_{RLL}(\text{P.F.})} = \frac{250\ \angle -\cos^{-1}.99}{\sqrt{3}(220)(0.99)} = 0.6627\angle -8.11^\circ$

$\bar{V}_S = \bar{A}\bar{V}_R + \bar{B}\bar{I}_R = \left(0.9820\angle 0.175^\circ\right)\left(127.02\angle 0^\circ\right) + \left(72.99\angle 80.54^\circ\right)\times\left(.6627\angle -8.11^\circ\right)$

$\bar{V}_S = 124.73\angle 0.175^\circ + 48.37\angle 72.43^\circ$

$\bar{V}_S = 139.33 + j\,46.49 = 146.9\angle 18.45^\circ\ kV_{LN}$

$V_S = 146.9\sqrt{3} = \underline{\underline{254.4}}\ kV_{LL}$

$\bar{I}_S = \bar{C}\bar{V}_R + \bar{D}\bar{I}_R = \left(4.95\times10^{-4}\angle 90.09^\circ\right)(127.02) + \left(.9820\angle .175^\circ\right)\left(.6627\angle -8.11^\circ\right)$

$= 0.06287\angle 90.09^\circ + 0.6508\angle -7.935^\circ$

$\bar{I}_S = 0.6445 - j\,0.02697 = \underline{\underline{0.6450\angle -2.396^\circ}}\ kA$

5.2 CONTD. (C) $V_{RNL} = \frac{V_S}{A} = \frac{254.4}{0.9820} = 259.1 \text{ kV}_{LL}$

$\% V.R. = \frac{V_{RNL} - V_{RFL}}{V_{RFL}} \times 100 = \frac{259.1 - 220}{220} \times 100 = \underline{\underline{17.8\%}}$

5.3 $Z_{base} = \frac{V_{base}^2}{S_{base}} = \frac{(230)^2}{100} = 529.\ \Omega$

$Y_{base} = 1/Z_{base} = 1.890 \times 10^{-3}\ \mho$

(a) $\bar{A}_{pu} = \bar{D}_{pu} = 0.9820 \angle 0.175^\circ$ per unit

$\bar{B}_{pu} = \frac{\bar{B}}{Z_{base}} = \frac{72.99 \angle 80.54^\circ}{529.} = 0.1380 \angle 80.54^\circ$ per unit

$\bar{C}_{pu} = \frac{\bar{C}}{Y_{base}} = \frac{4.950 \times 10^{-4}}{1.890 \times 10^{-3}} \angle 90.09^\circ = 0.2619 \angle 90.09^\circ$ per unit

(b) $\bar{V}_{RPU} = \frac{220}{230} \angle 0^\circ = 0.9565 \angle 0^\circ$ per unit

$I_{base} = \frac{S_{base\,3\phi}}{\sqrt{3}\, V_{base\,LL}} = \frac{100}{\sqrt{3}(230)} = .2510$ kA

$\bar{I}_{RPU} = \frac{0.6627 \angle -8.11^\circ}{0.2510} = 2.640 \angle -8.11^\circ$ per unit

$\bar{V}_{SPU} = \bar{A}_{PU}\bar{V}_{RPU} + \bar{B}_{PU}\bar{I}_{RPU} = (.982 \angle .175^\circ)(.9565 \angle 0^\circ) + (.1380 \angle 80.54^\circ)(2.640 \angle -8.11^\circ)$

$= 0.9393 \angle 0.175^\circ + 0.3643 \angle 72.43^\circ = 1.049 + j0.3501$

$\bar{V}_{SPU} = \underline{\underline{1.106}} \angle 18.45^\circ$ per unit

$\bar{I}_{SPU} = \bar{C}_{PU}\bar{V}_{RPU} + \bar{D}_{PU}\bar{I}_{RPU} = (.2619 \angle 90.09^\circ)(.9565) + (.982 \angle .175^\circ)(2.64 \angle -8.11^\circ)$

$= 0.2505 \angle 90.09^\circ + 2.592 \angle -7.94^\circ = 2.567 - j0.1075$

$\bar{I}_{SPU} = \underline{\underline{2.569}} \angle -2.398^\circ$ per unit

(c) $V_{RNLPU} = V_{SPU}/A_{PU} = 1.106/0.982 = 1.1263$ per unit

$\% V.R. = \frac{V_{RNLPU} - V_{RFLPU}}{V_{RFLPU}} \times 100 = \frac{1.126 - .9565}{.9565} \times 100 = \underline{\underline{17.8}}\%$

5.4

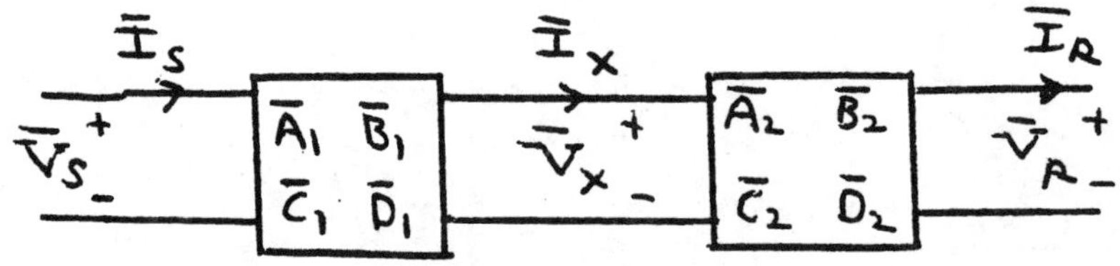

$$\begin{bmatrix}\bar{V}_S\\ \bar{I}_S\end{bmatrix} = \begin{bmatrix}\bar{A}_1 & \bar{B}_1\\ \bar{C}_1 & \bar{D}_1\end{bmatrix}\begin{bmatrix}\bar{V}_X\\ \bar{I}_X\end{bmatrix} = \begin{bmatrix}\bar{A}_1 & \bar{B}_1\\ \bar{C}_1 & \bar{D}_1\end{bmatrix}\begin{bmatrix}\bar{A}_2 & \bar{B}_2\\ \bar{C}_2 & \bar{D}_2\end{bmatrix}\begin{bmatrix}\bar{V}_R\\ \bar{I}_R\end{bmatrix}$$

$$\begin{bmatrix}\bar{V}_S\\ \bar{I}_S\end{bmatrix} = \begin{bmatrix}(\bar{A}_1\bar{A}_2+\bar{B}_1\bar{C}_2) & (\bar{A}_1\bar{B}_2+\bar{B}_1\bar{D}_2)\\ (\bar{C}_1\bar{A}_2+\bar{D}_1\bar{C}_2) & (\bar{C}_1\bar{B}_2+\bar{D}_1\bar{D}_2)\end{bmatrix}\begin{bmatrix}\bar{V}_R\\ \bar{I}_R\end{bmatrix}$$

5.5

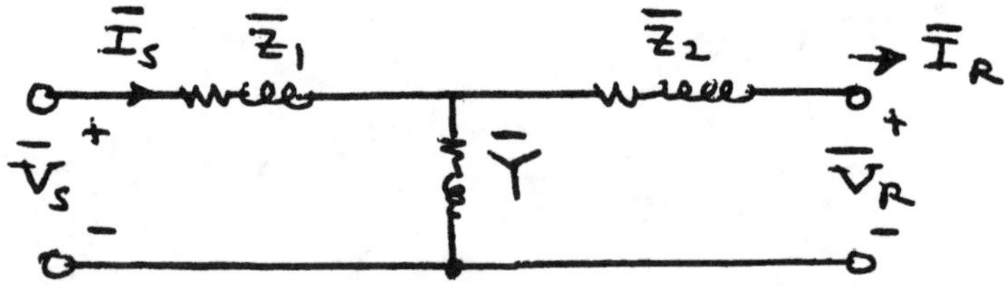

KCL: $\bar{I}_S = \bar{I}_R + \bar{Y}(\bar{V}_R + \bar{Z}_2\bar{I}_R) = \bar{Y}\bar{V}_R + (1+\bar{Y}\bar{Z}_2)\bar{I}_R$

KVL: $\bar{V}_S = \bar{V}_R + \bar{Z}_2\bar{I}_R + \bar{Z}_1\bar{I}_S$

$= \bar{V}_R + \bar{Z}_2\bar{I}_R + \bar{Z}_1\left[\bar{Y}\bar{V}_R + (1+\bar{Y}\bar{Z}_2)\bar{I}_R\right]$

$= (1+\bar{Y}\bar{Z}_1)\bar{V}_R + (\bar{Z}_1+\bar{Z}_2+\bar{Y}\bar{Z}_1\bar{Z}_2)\bar{I}_R$

In Matrix format:

$$\begin{bmatrix}\bar{V}_S\\ \bar{I}_S\end{bmatrix} = \begin{bmatrix}(1+\bar{Y}\bar{Z}_1) & (\bar{Z}_1+\bar{Z}_2+\bar{Y}\bar{Z}_1\bar{Z}_2)\\ \bar{Y} & (1+\bar{Y}\bar{Z}_2)\end{bmatrix}\begin{bmatrix}\bar{V}_R\\ \bar{I}_R\end{bmatrix}$$

5·6

(a) FROM TABLE A·4, $R = 0.1128 \frac{\Omega}{mi}\left(\frac{1\,mi}{1.609\,km}\right) = 0.0701\ \Omega/km$

$\bar{z} = 0.0701 + j0.506 = 0.511\angle 82.11°\ \Omega/km$; $\bar{y} = 3.229\times10^{-6}\angle 90°\ S/km$ FROM PROB. 4.14 & 4.25

$\bar{A} = \bar{D} = 1 + \frac{\bar{Y}\bar{Z}}{2} = 1 + \frac{1}{2}(3.229\times10^{-6}\times 100\angle 90°)(0.511\times100\angle 82.11°) = 0.9918\angle 0.0999°$ PER UNIT

$\bar{B} = \bar{Z} = \bar{z}\ell = 0.511\times100\angle 82.11° = 51.1\angle 82.11°\ \Omega$

$\bar{C} = \bar{Y}\left(1 + \frac{\bar{Y}\bar{Z}}{4}\right) = (3.229\times10^{-4}\angle 90°)[1 + 0.004125\angle 172.11°]$

$= 3.216\times10^{-4}\angle 90.033°\ S$

$\bar{V}_R = \frac{218}{\sqrt{3}}\angle 0° = 125.9\angle 0°\ kV_{LN}$

$\bar{I}_R = \frac{300}{218\sqrt{3}}\angle -\cos^{-1}0.9 = 0.7945\angle -25.84°\ kA$

$\bar{V}_S = \bar{A}\bar{V}_R + \bar{B}\bar{I}_R = 0.9918\angle 0.0999(125.9) + 51.1\angle 82.11°(0.7945\angle -25.84°)$

$= 151.3\angle 12.98°\ kV_{LN}$

$V_S = 151.3\sqrt{3} = 262\ kV_{LL}$

$V_{R\,NL} = V_S/A = 262/0.9918 = 264.2\ kV_{LL}$

$\%\ VR = \frac{V_{R\,NL} - V_{R\,FL}}{V_{R\,FL}}\times100 = \frac{264.2 - 218}{218}\times100 = 21.2\%$

(b) $\bar{I}_R = 0.7945\angle 0°\ kA$

$\bar{V}_S = 0.9918\angle 0.0999°(125.9) + 51.1\angle 82.11°(0.7945\angle 0°)$

$= 136.6\angle 17.2°\ kV_{LN}$; $V_S = 136.6\sqrt{3} = 236.6\ kV_{LL}$

$V_{R\,NL} = V_S/A = 236.6/0.9918 = 238.6\ kV_{LL}$

$\%\ VR = \frac{238.6 - 218}{218}\times100 = 9.43\%$

(c) $\bar{I}_R = 0.7945\angle 25.84°\ kA$

$\bar{V}_S = 124.9\angle 0.0999° + 40.6\angle 107.95° = 118.9\angle 19.1°\ kV_{LN}$

$V_S = 118.9\sqrt{3} = 205.9\ kV_{LL}$

$\%\ VR = \frac{205.9 - 218}{218}\times100 = -5.6\%$

5.7 FROM TABLE A.4, $R = \frac{1}{3}(0.0969)\frac{\Omega}{mi}\left(\frac{1\,mi}{1.609\,km}\right) = 0.0201\ \Omega/km$

FROM PROB. 4.16 & 4.27, $\bar{z} = 0.0201 + j0.335 = 0.336\angle 86.6^\circ\ \Omega/km$

$$\bar{y} = 4.807\times 10^{-6}\angle 90^\circ\ S/km$$

(a) $\bar{A} = \bar{D} = 1 + \frac{\bar{Y}\bar{Z}}{2} = 1 + \frac{1}{2}(0.336\times 180\angle 86.6^\circ)(4.807\times 10^{-6}\times 180\angle 90^\circ)$

$$= 0.9739\angle 0.0912^\circ\ \text{PU}$$

$\bar{B} = \bar{Z} = \bar{z}\ell = 0.336(180)\angle 86.6^\circ = 60.48\angle 86.6^\circ\ \Omega$

$\bar{C} = \bar{Y}\left(1 + \frac{\bar{Y}\bar{Z}}{4}\right) = (4.807\times 10^{-6}\times 180\angle 90^\circ)(1 + 0.0131\angle 176.6^\circ)$

$$= 8.54\times 10^{-4}\angle 90.05^\circ\ S$$

(b) $\bar{V}_R = \frac{475}{\sqrt{3}}\angle 0^\circ = 274.24\angle 0^\circ\ kV_{LN}$

$\bar{I}_R = \frac{P_R\ \angle \cos^{-1}(pf)}{\sqrt{3}\,V_{RLL}(pf)} = \frac{1600\angle \cos^{-1}0.95}{\sqrt{3}\,475(0.95)} = 2.047\angle 18.19^\circ\ kA$

$\bar{V}_S = \bar{A}\bar{V}_R + \bar{B}\bar{I}_R = (0.9739\angle 0.0912)(274.24) + (60.48\angle 86.6^\circ)(2.047\angle 18.19^\circ)$

$$= 264.4\angle 27.02^\circ\ kV_{LN}\ ;\ V_S = 264.4\sqrt{3} = 457.9\ kV_{LL}$$

$\bar{I}_S = \bar{C}\bar{V}_R + \bar{D}\bar{I}_R = (8.54\times 10^{-4}\angle 90.05^\circ)(274.24) + (0.9739\angle 0.0912^\circ)(2.047\angle 18.19^\circ)$

$$= 2.079\angle 24.42^\circ\ kA$$

(c) $P_S = \sqrt{3}V_{SLL}I_S(pf) = \sqrt{3}\,457.9(2.079)\cos(27.02^\circ - 24.42^\circ) = 1647\,MW$

$pf = \cos(27.02^\circ - 24.42) = 0.999$ LAGGING

(d) FULL-LOAD LINE LOSSES $= P_S - P_R = 1647 - 1600 = 47$ MW

EFFICIENCY $= (P_R/P_S)100 = (1600/1647)100 = 97.1\%$

(e) $V_{RNL} = V_S/A = 457.9/0.9739 = 470.2\ kV_{LL}$

$$\%\ VR = \frac{V_{RNL} - V_{RFL}}{V_{RFL}}\times 100 = \frac{470.2 - 475}{475}\times 100 = -1\%$$

5.8

(a) THE SERIES IMPEDANCE PER PHASE $\bar{Z} = (r + j\omega L)\ell$

$$= (0.15 + j\,2\pi(60)\,1.3263\times10^{-3})\,40 = 6 + j20\ \Omega$$

THE RECEIVING END VOLTAGE PER PHASE $\bar{V}_R = \frac{220}{\sqrt{3}}\angle 0^\circ = 127\angle 0^\circ$ kV

COMPLEX POWER AT THE RECEIVING END $\bar{S}_{R(3\phi)} = 381\angle \cos^{-1}0.8$ MVA $= 304.8 + j228.6$ MVA

THE CURRENT PER PHASE IS GIVEN BY $\bar{S}^*_{R(3\phi)} / 3\bar{V}^*_R$

$$\therefore\ \bar{I}_R = \frac{(381\angle -36.87^\circ)\,10^3}{3\times 127\angle 0^\circ} = 1000\angle -36.87^\circ\ \text{A}$$

THE SENDING END VOLTAGE, AS PER KVL, IS GIVEN BY

$$\bar{V}_S = \bar{V}_R + \bar{Z}\,\bar{I}_R = 127\angle 0^\circ + (6+j20)(1000\angle -36.87^\circ)\,10^{-3}$$

$$= 144.33\angle 4.93^\circ\ \text{kV}$$

THE SENDING END LINE-TO-LINE VOLTAGE MAGNITUDE IS THEN

$$V_{S(L-L)} = \sqrt{3}\,(144.33) = 250\ \text{kV}$$

THE SENDING END POWER IS $\bar{S}_{S(3\phi)} = 3\bar{V}_S\bar{I}_S^* = 3(144.33\angle 4.93^\circ)(1000\angle 36.87^\circ)\,10^{-3}$

$$= 322.8\ \text{MW} + j\,288.6\ \text{MVAR} = 433\angle 41.8^\circ\ \text{MVA}$$

VOLTAGE REGULATION IS $\frac{250-220}{220} = 0.136$

TRANSMISSION LINE EFFICIENCY IS $\eta = \frac{P_{R(3\phi)}}{P_{S(3\phi)}} = \frac{304.8}{322.8} = 0.944$

(b) WITH 0.8 LEADING POWER FACTOR, $\bar{I}_R = 1000\angle 36.87^\circ$ A

THE SENDING END VOLTAGE IS $\bar{V}_S = \bar{V}_R + \bar{Z}\,\bar{I}_R = 121.39\angle 9.29^\circ$ kV

THE SENDING END LINE-TO-LINE VOLTAGE MAGNITUDE $V_{S(L-L)} = \sqrt{3}\times 121.39$
$= 210.26$ kV

THE SENDING END POWER $\bar{S}_{S(3\phi)} = 3\bar{V}_S\bar{I}_S^*$

$$= 3(121.39\angle 9.29^\circ)(1\angle -36.87^\circ) = 322.8\ \text{MW} - j\,168.6\ \text{MVAR}$$

$$= 3618\angle -27.58^\circ\ \text{MVA}$$

VOLTAGE REGULATION $= \frac{210.26-220}{220} = -0.0443$

TRANSMISSION LINE EFFICIENCY $\eta = \frac{P_{R(3\phi)}}{P_{S(3\phi)}} = \frac{304.8}{322.8} = 0.944$

5.9

(a) THE NOMINAL π CIRCUIT IS SHOWN BELOW:

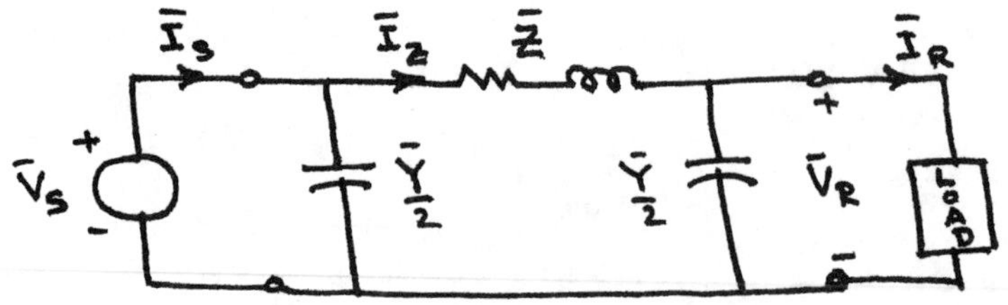

THE TOTAL LINE IMPEDANCE $\bar{Z} = (0.1826 + j\,0.784)100 = 18.26 + j\,78.4$
$= 80.5 \angle 76.89^\circ\ \Omega/\text{ph.}$

THE LINE ADMITTANCE FOR 100 mi IS

$$\bar{Y} = \frac{1}{X_C}\angle 90^\circ = \frac{1}{\frac{185.5 \times 10^3}{100}}\angle 90^\circ = 0.5391 \times 10^{-3}\angle 90^\circ\ \text{S/ph.}$$

(b) $\bar{V}_R = \frac{230}{\sqrt{3}}\angle 0^\circ = 132.8\angle 0^\circ$ kV

$\bar{I}_R = \frac{200 \times 10^3}{\sqrt{3}(230)}\angle 0^\circ = 502\angle 0^\circ$ A (∵ UNITY POWERFACTOR)

$\bar{I}_Z = \bar{I}_R + \bar{V}_R\left(\frac{\bar{Y}}{2}\right) = 502\angle 0^\circ + (132{,}800\angle 0^\circ)(0.27 \times 10^{-3}\angle 90^\circ)$
$= 502 + j\,35.86 = 503.3\angle 4.09^\circ$ A

THE SENDING END VOLTAGE $\bar{V}_S = 132.8\angle 0^\circ + (0.5033\angle 4.09^\circ)(80.5\angle 76.89^\circ)$

$= 139.152 + j\,40.01 = 144.79\angle 16.04^\circ$ kV

THE LINE-TO-LINE VOLTAGE MAGNITUDE AT THE SENDING END IS $\sqrt{3}(144.79)$
$= 250.784$ kV

$\bar{I}_S = \bar{I}_Z + \bar{V}_S\left(\frac{\bar{Y}}{2}\right) = 502 + j\,35.86 + (144.79\angle 16.04^\circ)(0.27\angle 90^\circ)$
$= 491.2 + j\,73.46 = 496.7\angle 8.5^\circ$ A

SENDING END POWER $\bar{S}_{S(3\phi)} = 3(144.79)(0.4967)\angle 16.04^\circ - 8.5^\circ$
$= 213.88 + j\,28.31$ MVA

So $P_{S(3\phi)} = 213.88$ MW ; $Q_{S(3\phi)} = 28.31$ MVAR

(c)

$$\text{REGULATION} = \frac{V_S - V_R}{V_R} = \frac{144.79 - 132.8}{132.8} = 0.09$$

5.10 $\bar{\gamma}\ell = 0.45\angle 87° = 0.023551 + j\,0.449383$

$$e^{\bar{\gamma}\ell} = e^{0.023551}\,e^{j0.449383} = 1.023831\angle 0.449383 \text{ radians}$$

$$= 0.922180 + j\,0.444763$$

$$e^{-\bar{\gamma}\ell} = e^{-0.023551}\,e^{-j0.449383} = 0.9767239\angle -0.449383 \text{ radians}$$

$$= 0.87975 - j\,0.4242987$$

$$\cosh(\bar{\gamma}\ell) = \frac{e^{\bar{\gamma}\ell} + e^{-\bar{\gamma}\ell}}{2} = \frac{(.922180 + j.444763) + (.87975 - j.4242987)}{2}$$

$$\cosh(\bar{\gamma}\ell) = 0.900965 + j\,0.010232 = \underline{\underline{0.9010\angle 0.6507°}} \text{ per unit}$$

Alternatively:

$$\cosh(.023551 + j.449383) = \cosh(.023551)\cos(.449383 \text{ radians}) + j\sinh(.023551)\sin(.449383)$$

$$\cosh(\bar{\gamma}\ell) = (1.000277)(.9007153) + j(.023553)(.434410)$$

$$= 0.900965 + j\,0.010232 = \underline{\underline{0.9010\angle 0.6507°}} \text{ per unit}$$

$$\sinh(\bar{\gamma}\ell) = \frac{e^{\bar{\gamma}\ell} - e^{-\bar{\gamma}\ell}}{2} = \frac{(.922180 + j.444763) - (.87975 - j.4242987)}{2}$$

$$= 0.021215 + j.4345308 = 0.4350\angle 87.20°$$

$$\tanh(\bar{\gamma}\ell/2) = \frac{\cosh(\bar{\gamma}\ell) - 1}{\sinh(\bar{\gamma}\ell)} = \frac{(.900965 + j.010232) - 1}{0.4350\angle 87.20°}$$

$$= \frac{-0.099035 + j0.010232}{0.4350\angle 87.20°} = \frac{0.099562\angle 174.10°}{0.4350\angle 87.20°}$$

$$\tanh(\bar{\gamma}\ell/2) = \underline{\underline{0.2289\angle 86.90°}} \text{ per unit}$$

5.11

(a)

$$\bar{Z}_c = \sqrt{\frac{\bar{z}}{\bar{y}}} = \sqrt{\frac{0.03 + j.35}{j\,4.4\times10^{-6}}} = \sqrt{\frac{0.3513\angle 85.10^\circ}{4.4\times10^{-6}\angle 90^\circ}}$$

$$\bar{Z}_c = \sqrt{79837.\angle -4.899^\circ} = \underline{\underline{282.6\angle -2.450^\circ\ \Omega}}$$

(b) $\bar{\gamma}\ell = \sqrt{\bar{z}\bar{y}}\,(\ell) = \sqrt{(.3513\angle 85.10^\circ)(4.4\times10^{-6}\angle 90^\circ)}\,(500)$

$$\bar{\gamma}\ell = \underline{\underline{0.6216\angle 87.55^\circ}} = 0.02657 + j\,0.62105$$

(c) $\bar{A} = \bar{D} = \cosh(\bar{\gamma}\ell) = \cosh(.02657 + j.62105)$

$= \cosh(.02657)\cos(.62105) + j\sinh(.02657)\sin(.62105)$ ← radians →

$= (1.000353)(0.813268) + j(.0265731)(.581889)$

$= 0.813555 + j0.015463 = \underline{\underline{0.8137\angle 1.089^\circ}}$

per unit

$\sinh(\bar{\gamma}\ell) = \sinh(.02657 + j.62105)$ radians

$= \sinh(.02657)\cos(.62105) + j\cosh(.02657)\sin(.62105)$

$= (.02657)(.81327) + j(1.000353)(.581889)$

$= 0.021609 + j\,0.582094 = 0.5825\angle 87.87^\circ$

$\bar{B} = \bar{Z}_c \sinh(\bar{\gamma}\ell) = (282.6\angle -2.450^\circ)(.5825\angle 87.87^\circ)$

$$\bar{B} = \underline{\underline{164.6\angle 85.42^\circ\ \Omega}}$$

$$\bar{C} = \left(\frac{1}{\bar{Z}_c}\right)\sinh(\bar{\gamma}\ell) = \frac{0.5825\angle 87.87^\circ}{282.6\angle -2.450^\circ}$$

$$\bar{C} = \underline{\underline{2.061\times10^{-3}\angle 90.32^\circ\ S}}$$

5.12 $\bar{V}_R = \frac{480}{\sqrt{3}} \angle 0° = 277.1 \angle 0°$ kV_{LN}

$$\bar{I}_R = \frac{P_R}{\sqrt{3}\, V_{R\,LL}\,(pf)} \angle 0° = \frac{1000 \angle 0°}{\sqrt{3}\; 480\,(1)} = 1.202 \angle 0° \text{ kA}$$

(a) $\bar{V}_S = \bar{A}\bar{V}_R + \bar{B}\bar{I}_R = 0.8137 \angle 1.089° (277.1) + 164.6 \angle 85.42° (1.202)$

$= 314.4 \angle 39.9°$ kV_{LN} ; $V_S = 314.4\sqrt{3} = 544.5$ kV_{LL}

(b) $\bar{I}_S = \bar{C}\bar{V}_R + \bar{D}\bar{I}_R = 2.061 \times 10^{-3} \angle 90.32° (277.1) + 0.8137 \angle 1.089° (1.202)$

$= 1.139 \angle 31.17°$ kA ; $I_S = 1.139$ kA

(c) $(pf)_S = \cos(39.9° - 31.17°) = \cos(8.73°) = 0.9884$ LAGGING

(d) $P_S = \sqrt{3}\, V_{S\,LL}\, I_S\, (pf)_S = \sqrt{3}\; 544.5\,(1.139)\,0.9884$

$= 1061.7$ MW

FULL-LOAD LINE LOSSES = $P_S - P_R = 1061.7 - 1000 = 61.7$ MW

(e) $V_{R\,NL} = V_S / A = 544.5 / 0.8137 = 669.2$ kV

$$\% \, VR = \frac{V_{R\,NL} - V_{R\,FL}}{V_{R\,FL}} \times 100$$

$$= \frac{669.2 - 480}{480} \times 100 = 39.4\%$$

5.13 TABLE A.4 THREE ACSR FINCH CONDUCTORS PER PHASE

$$r = \frac{0.0969}{3}\ \frac{\Omega}{\text{mi}}\ \frac{1\ \text{mi}}{1.609\ \text{km}} = 0.02\ \Omega/\text{km}$$

(a) $$\bar{Z}_c = \sqrt{\bar{z}/\bar{y}} = \sqrt{\frac{0.336\angle 86.6^\circ}{4.807\times 10^{-6}\angle 90^\circ}} = 264.4\angle -1.7^\circ\ \Omega$$

(b) $$\bar{\gamma} l = \sqrt{\bar{z}\,\bar{y}}\ l = \sqrt{0.336\times 4.807\times 10^{-6}\angle 86.6^\circ + 90^\circ}\ (300)$$

$$= 0.0113 + j0.381\ \text{PU}$$

(c) $$\bar{A} = \bar{D} = \cosh(\bar{\gamma} l) = \cosh(0.0113 + j0.381)$$

$$= \cosh 0.0113\ \cos \underset{\text{rad.}}{0.381} + j \sinh 0.0113\ \sin \underset{\text{rad.}}{0.381}$$

$$= 0.9285 + j0.00418 = 0.9285\angle 0.258^\circ\ \text{PU}$$

$$\sinh \bar{\gamma} l = \sinh(0.0113 + j0.381)$$

$$= \sinh 0.0113\ \cos \underset{\text{rad.}}{0.381} + j \cosh 0.0113\ \sin \underset{\text{rad.}}{0.381}$$

$$= 0.01045 + j0.3715 = 0.3716\angle 88.39^\circ$$

$$\bar{B} = \bar{Z}_c \sinh \bar{\gamma} l = 264.4\angle -1.7^\circ\ (0.3716\angle 88.39^\circ)$$

$$= 98.25\angle 86.69^\circ\ \Omega$$

$$\bar{C} = \sinh \bar{\gamma} l / \bar{Z}_c = 0.3716\angle 88.39^\circ / (264.4\angle -1.7^\circ)$$

$$= 1.405\times 10^{-3}\angle 90.09^\circ\ \text{S}$$

5.14

$$\bar{V}_R = (480/\sqrt{3}) \angle 0° = 277.1 \angle 0° \ kV_{LN}$$

(a) $$\bar{I}_R = \frac{1500}{480\sqrt{3}} \angle -\cos^{-1} 0.9 = 1.804 \angle -25.84° \ kA$$

$$\bar{V}_S = \bar{A}\bar{V}_R + \bar{B}\bar{I}_R = 0.9285 \angle 0.258° (277.1) + 98.25 \angle 86.69° (1.804 \angle -25.84°)$$

$$= 377.4 \angle 24.42° \ kV_{LN} \ ; \ V_S = 377.4\sqrt{3} = 653.7 \ kV_{LL}$$

$$V_{R\,NL} = V_S / A = 653.7/0.9285 = 704 \ kV_{LL}$$

$$\% \ VR = \frac{V_{R\,NL} - V_{R\,FL}}{V_{R\,FL}} \times 100 = \frac{704 - 480}{480} \times 100 = 46.7\%$$

(b) $$\bar{V}_S = 0.9285 \angle 0.258° (277.1) + 98.25 \angle 86.69° (1.804 \angle 0°)$$

$$= 321.4 \angle 33.66° \ kV_{LN} \ ; \ V_S = 321.4\sqrt{3} = 556.7 \ kV_{LL}$$

$$V_{R\,NL} = V_S / A = 556.7/0.9285 = 599.5 \ kV_{LL}$$

$$\% \ VR = \frac{599.5 - 480}{480} \times 100 = 24.9\%$$

(c) $$\bar{V}_S = 257.3 \angle 0.258° + 177.24 \angle 112.5°$$

$$= 251.2 \angle 41.03° \ kV_{LN}$$

$$V_S = 251.2\sqrt{3} = 435.1 \ kV_{LL}$$

$$V_{R\,NL} = V_S / A = 435.1/0.9285 = 468.6 \ kV_{LL}$$

$$\% \ VR = \frac{468.6 - 480}{480} \times 100 = -2.4\%$$

5.15

$$\bar{\gamma}\ell = \ell\sqrt{\bar{y}\bar{z}} = 230\left(\sqrt{0.8431 \times 5.105 \times 10^{-6}}\right)\angle(79.04^\circ + 90^\circ)/2$$

$$= 0.4772\angle 84.52^\circ = 0.0456 + j0.475 = (\alpha + j\beta)\ell$$

$$\bar{Z}_c = \sqrt{\frac{\bar{z}}{\bar{y}}} = \sqrt{\frac{0.8431}{5.105 \times 10^{-6}}}\angle(79.04^\circ - 90^\circ)/2 = 406.4\angle -5.48^\circ\ \Omega$$

$$\bar{V}_R = \frac{215}{\sqrt{3}} = 124.13\angle 0^\circ \text{ kV/ph.}\ ; \quad \bar{I}_R = \frac{125 \times 10^3}{\sqrt{3} \times 215}\angle 0^\circ = 335.7\angle 0^\circ \text{ A}$$

$$\cosh\bar{\gamma}\ell = \tfrac{1}{2}e^{0.0456}\angle 27.22^\circ + \tfrac{1}{2}e^{-0.0456}\angle -27.22^\circ = 0.8904\angle 1.34^\circ$$

$$\sinh\bar{\gamma}\ell = \tfrac{1}{2}e^{0.0456}\angle 27.22^\circ - \tfrac{1}{2}e^{-0.0456}\angle -27.22^\circ = 0.4597\angle 84.93^\circ$$

$$\bar{V}_S = \bar{V}_R\cosh\bar{\gamma}\ell + \bar{I}_R\bar{Z}_c\sinh\bar{\gamma}\ell =$$

$$= (124.13 \times 0.8904\angle 1.34^\circ) + (0.3357 \times 406.4\angle -5.48^\circ \times 0.4597\angle 84.93^\circ)$$

$$= 137.86\angle 27.77^\circ \text{ kV}$$

LINE-TO-LINE VOLTAGE MAGNITUDE AT THE SENDING END IS $\sqrt{3}\,137.86 = 238.8$ kV

$$\bar{I}_S = \bar{I}_R\cosh\bar{\gamma}\ell + \frac{\bar{V}_R}{\bar{Z}_c}\sinh\bar{\gamma}\ell = (335.7 \times 0.8904\angle 1.34^\circ) + \frac{124{,}130}{406.4\angle -5.48^\circ} \times 0.4597\angle 84.93^\circ$$

$$= 332.31\angle 26.33^\circ \text{ A}$$

SENDING END LINE CURRENT MAGNITUDE IS 332.31 A

$$P_{S(3\phi)} = \sqrt{3}\,(238.8)(332.31)\cos(27.77^\circ - 26.33^\circ) = 137{,}433 \text{ kW}$$

$$Q_{R(3\phi)} = \sqrt{3}\,(238.8)(332.31)\sin(27.77^\circ - 26.33^\circ) = 3454 \text{ kVAR}$$

$$\text{VOLTAGE REGULATION} = \frac{(137.86/0.8904) - 124.13}{124.13} = 0.247$$

(NOTE THAT AT NO LOAD, $\bar{I}_R = 0$; $\bar{V}_R = \bar{V}_S/\cosh\bar{\gamma}\ell$)

SINCE $\beta = 0.475/230 = 0.002065$ rad/mi

THE WAVELENGTH $\lambda = \dfrac{2\pi}{\beta} = \dfrac{2\pi}{0.002065} = 3043$ mi

AND THE VELOCITY OF PROPAGATION $= f\lambda = 60 \times 3043$

$= 182{,}580$ mi/s

5.16

CHOOSING A BASE OF 125 MVA AND 215 kV,

BASE IMPEDANCE $= \dfrac{(215)^2}{125} = 370\,\Omega$; BASE CURRENT $= \dfrac{125 \times 10^3}{\sqrt{3} \times 215} = 335.7$ A

SO $\bar{Z}_c = \dfrac{406.4 \angle -5.48°}{370} = 1.098 \angle -5.48$ PU ; $\bar{V}_R = 1 \angle 0°$ PU

THE LOAD BEING AT UNITY PF, $\bar{I}_R = 1.0 \angle 0°$ PU

$$\therefore\ \bar{V}_S = \bar{V}_R \cosh \bar{\gamma} l + \bar{I}_R \bar{Z}_c \sinh \bar{\gamma} l =$$

$$= (1 \angle 0° \times 0.8904 \angle 1.34°) + (1 \angle 0° \times 1.098 \angle -5.48° \times 0.4597 \angle 84.93°)$$

$$= 1.1102 \angle 27.75° \text{ PU}$$

$$\bar{I}_S = \bar{I}_R \cosh \bar{\gamma} l + \frac{\bar{V}_R}{\bar{Z}_c} \sinh \bar{\gamma} l$$

$$= (1 \angle 0° \times 0.8904 \angle 1.34°) + \left(\frac{1.0 \angle 0°}{1.098 \angle -5.48°} \times 0.4597 \angle 84.93° \right)$$

$$= 0.99 \angle 26.35° \text{ PU}$$

AT THE SENDING END

LINE-TO-LINE VOLTAGE MAGNITUDE $= 1.1102 \times 215$

$= 238.7$ kV

LINE CURRENT MAGNITUDE $= 0.99 \times 335.7$

$= 332.3$ A

5.17 EQUIVALENT π CIRCUIT:

$$\bar{Z}' = \bar{B} = 164.6\angle 85.42^\circ = 13.14 + j164.1 \ \Omega$$

ALTERNATIVELY:
$$\bar{Z}' = \bar{Z}F_1 = \bar{z}\ell \frac{\sinh \bar{\gamma}\ell}{\bar{\gamma}\ell}$$

$$= 0.3513\angle 85.1^\circ (500) \frac{0.5825\angle 87.87^\circ}{0.6216\angle 87.55^\circ}$$

$$= 164.6\angle 85.42^\circ \ \Omega$$

$$\frac{\bar{Y}'}{2} = \left(\frac{\bar{Y}}{2}\right)\bar{F}_2 = \frac{4.4\times10^{-6}\times 500\angle 90^\circ}{2} \quad \frac{\tanh(\bar{\gamma}\ell/2)}{(\bar{\gamma}\ell/2)}$$

$$= (1.1\times10^{-3}\angle 90^\circ)\left[\frac{\cosh(\bar{\gamma}\ell)-1}{\frac{\bar{\gamma}\ell}{2}\sinh\bar{\gamma}\ell}\right]$$

$$= (1.1\times10^{-3}\angle 90^\circ)\left[\frac{(0.813555 + j0.015463) - 1}{\frac{0.6216}{2}\angle 87.55^\circ(0.5825\angle 87.87^\circ)}\right]$$

$$= 1.1\times10^{-3}\angle 90^\circ \left[1.0337\angle -0.16^\circ\right]$$

$$\frac{\bar{Y}'}{2} = \frac{G' + jB'}{2} = 1.137\times10^{-3}\angle 89.84^\circ = 3.18\times10^{-6} + j1.137\times10^{-3} \ S$$

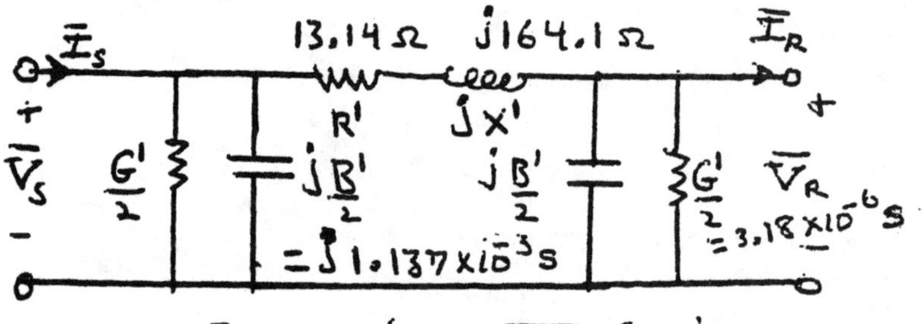

Equivalent π Circuit

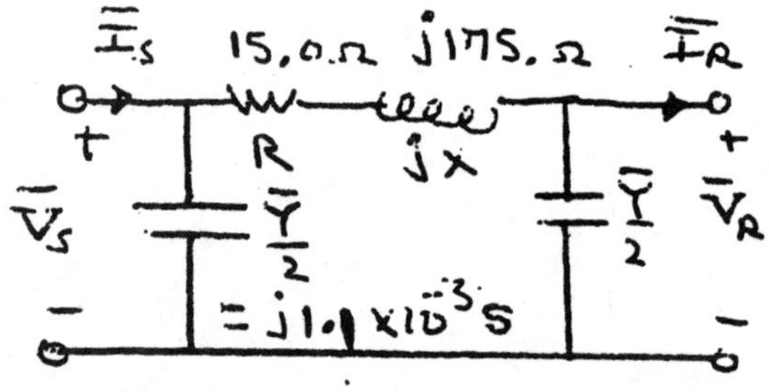

Nominal π Circuit

$R' = 13.14\ \Omega$ is 12.4% smaller than $R = 15.0\ \Omega$

$X' = 164.1\ \Omega$ is 6.2% smaller than $X = 175.\ \Omega$

$B'/2 = 1.137\times10^{-3}$ S is 3.4% larger than $Y/2 = 1.1\times10^{-3}$ S

$G'/2 = 3.18\times10^{-6}$ S is introduced into the equivalent π circuit.

5.18

$$\bar{Z}' = \bar{B} = 98.25\angle 86.69^\circ\ \Omega = 5.673 + j98.09\ \Omega$$

$$\frac{\bar{Y}'}{2} = \left(\frac{\bar{Y}}{2}\right)\bar{F}_2 = \left(\frac{4.807}{2}\times 10^{-6}\angle 90^\circ \times 300\right)\left[\frac{\cosh \bar{\gamma}l - 1}{\frac{\bar{\gamma}l}{2}\sinh \bar{\gamma}l}\right]$$

$$= \left(\frac{1.442}{2}\times 10^{-3}\angle 90^\circ\right)\left[\frac{0.9285 + j0.00418 - 1}{\frac{0.3812}{2}\angle 88.3^\circ(0.3716\angle 88.39^\circ)}\right]$$

$$= 7.21\times 10^{-4}\angle 90^\circ\left[\frac{-0.0715 + j0.00418}{0.0708\angle 176.7^\circ}\right]$$

$$= 6.37\times 10^{-7} + j7.294\times 10^{-4}\ \text{S}$$

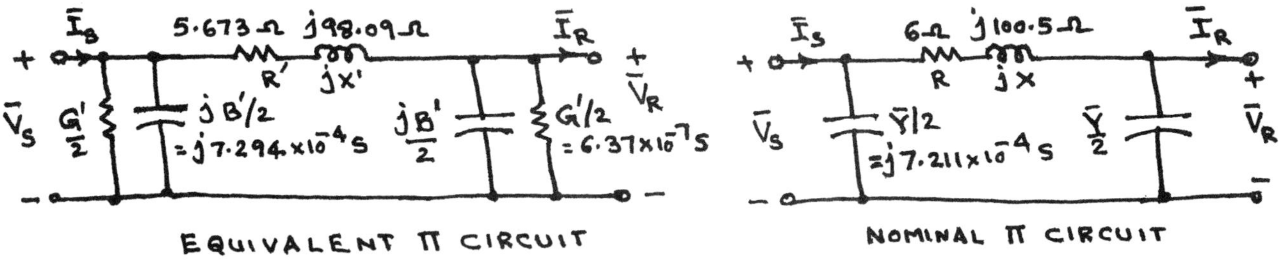

$R' = 5.673\ \Omega$ IS 5.5% SMALLER THAN $R = 6\ \Omega$

$X' = 98.09\ \Omega$ IS 2.4% SMALLER THAN $X = 100.5\ \Omega$

$B'/2 = 7.294\times 10^{-4}$ S IS 1.2% LARGER THAN $Y/2 = 7.211\times 10^{-4}$ S

$G'/2 = 6.37\times 10^{-7}$ S IS INTRODUCED INTO THE EQUIVALENT Π CIRCUIT.

5.19

THE LONG LINE π-EQUIVALENT CIRCUIT IS SHOWN BELOW:

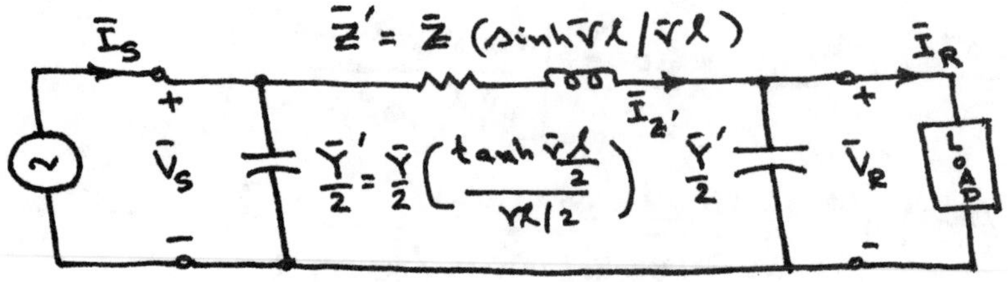

$\bar{z} = (0.1826 + j0.784)\,\Omega/\text{mi}$ PER PHASE

$\bar{y} = \dfrac{1}{X_c \angle -90^\circ} = \dfrac{1}{185.5 \times 10^3 \angle -90^\circ} = 5.391 \times 10^{-6} \angle 90^\circ$ S/mi PER PHASE

$\bar{\gamma} = \sqrt{\bar{y}\bar{z}}$; $\bar{Z} = \bar{z}l = 160.99\angle 76.89^\circ\,\Omega$; $\bar{Y} = \bar{y}l = 1.078 \times 10^{-3}\angle 90^\circ$ S

$\bar{F}_1 = (\sinh\bar{\gamma}l)/\bar{\gamma}l = 0.972\angle 0.37^\circ$; $\bar{F}_2 = \dfrac{\tanh(\bar{\gamma}l/2)}{\bar{\gamma}l/2} = 1.0144\angle -0.19^\circ$

$\therefore\ \bar{Z}' = \bar{Z}\dfrac{\sinh\bar{\gamma}l}{\bar{\gamma}l} = 156.48\angle 77.26^\circ\,\Omega$

$\dfrac{\bar{Y}'}{2} = \dfrac{\bar{Y}}{2}\left(\dfrac{\tanh(\bar{\gamma}l/2)}{\bar{\gamma}l/2}\right) = 0.5476 \times 10^{-3}\angle 89.81^\circ$ S

$\bar{I}_{Z'} = \bar{I}_R + \bar{V}_R\dfrac{\bar{Y}'}{2} = 502\angle 0^\circ + (132{,}800\angle 0^\circ)(0.5476 \times 10^{-3}\angle 89.81^\circ)$

$= 507.5\angle 8.24^\circ$ A

$\bar{V}_S = \bar{V}_R + \bar{I}_{Z'}\bar{Z}' = 132{,}800\angle 0^\circ + 507.5\angle 8.24^\circ(156.48\angle 77.26^\circ)$

$= 160{,}835\angle 29.45^\circ$ V

(a) SENDING END LINE-TO-LINE VOLTAGE MAGNITUDE $= \sqrt{3}\,160.835 = 278.6$ kV

(b) $\bar{I}_S = \bar{I}_{Z'} + \bar{V}_S\left(\dfrac{\bar{Y}'}{2}\right) = 507.5\angle 8.24^\circ + 160.835(0.5476)\angle 29.45 + 89.81^\circ$

$= 482.93\angle 18.04^\circ$ A ; $I_S = 482.93$ A

(c) $\bar{S}_{S(3\phi)} = 3\bar{V}_S\bar{I}_S^* = 3(160.835)(0.48293)\angle 29.45^\circ - 18.04^\circ$

$= 228.41$ MW $+ j46.1$ MVAR

(d) PERCENT VOLTAGE REGULATION $= \dfrac{160.835 - 132.8}{132.8} \times 100 = 21.1\%$

5.20

(a) $\bar{Z}_c = \sqrt{\dfrac{\bar{z}}{\bar{y}}} = \sqrt{\dfrac{j0.34}{j4.5\times10^{-6}}} = 274.9\ \Omega$

(b) $\bar{\gamma}\ell = \sqrt{\bar{z}\bar{y}}\,\ell = \sqrt{(j0.34)(j4.5\times10^{-6})}\,(320) = j0.3958$ PU

(c) $\bar{\gamma}\ell = j\beta\ell \quad ; \quad \beta\ell = 0.3958$ PU

$\bar{A} = \bar{D} = \cos\beta\ell = \cos(0.3958 \text{ radians}) = 0.9227\angle 0°$ PU

$\bar{B} = j\bar{Z}_c \sin\beta\ell = j(274.9)\sin(0.3958 \text{ radians})$

$= j108.81\ \Omega$

$\bar{C} = j\left(\dfrac{1}{Z_c}\right)\sin\beta\ell = j\,\dfrac{1}{274.9}\sin(0.3958 \text{ radians})$

$= j1.44\times10^{-3}$ S

(d) $\beta = \beta\ell/\ell = 0.3958/300 = 1.319\times10^{-3}$ radians/km

$\lambda = 2\pi/\beta = 4766$ km

(e) $SIL = \dfrac{V^2_{\text{rated L-L}}}{Z_c} = \dfrac{(500)^2}{274.9} = 909.4$ MW (3ϕ)

5.21

$$\bar{Z}' = \bar{B} = j\,108.81\ \Omega$$

ALTERNATIVELY:

$$\bar{Z}' = \bar{Z}F_1 = (\bar{z}l)\frac{\sin\beta l}{\beta l} = (j0.34\times 320)\ \frac{\sin(0.3958 \text{ radians})}{0.3958}$$

$$= j\,108.8\ (0.9741) = j\,105.98\ \Omega$$

$$\frac{\bar{Y}'}{2} = \frac{\bar{Y}}{2}F_2 = \left(\frac{y}{2}l\right)\ \frac{\tan(\beta l/2)}{\beta l/2} = j\,\frac{4.5\times 10^{-6}}{2}\times 320\ \frac{\tan(0.1979 \text{ radians})}{0.1979}$$

$$= j\,7.2\times 10^{-4}\ (1.0133) = j\,7.295\times 10^{-4}\ S$$

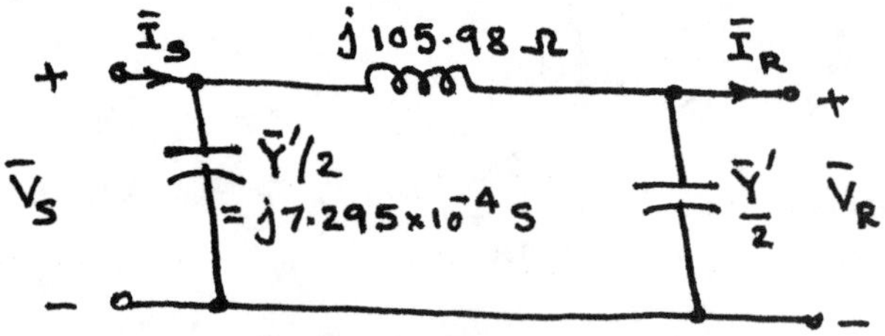

EQUIVALENT Π CIRCUIT

5.22

(a) $V_R = V_S / A = 500/0.9227 = 541.9$ kV

(b) $V_R = V_S = 500$ kV

(c) $$\bar{V}_S = \cos\beta l\ \bar{V}_R + j Z_c \sin\beta l\left[\bar{V}_R / (\tfrac{1}{2}Z_c)\right]$$

$$= \left[\cos\beta l + j\,2\sin\beta l\right]\bar{V}_R$$

$$V_S = \left|\cos\beta l + j\,2\sin\beta l\right| V_R$$

$$= \frac{500}{\left|\cos \underset{\text{rad.}}{0.3958} + j\,2\sin \underset{\text{rad.}}{0.3958}\right|} = \frac{500}{1.202} = 416\ \text{kV}$$

(d) $$P_{max\,3\phi} = \frac{V_S V_R}{X'} = \frac{500\times 500}{105.98} = 2359\ \text{MW}$$

5-23 REWORKING PROB. 5.6:

(a) $\bar{z} = j\,0.506\ \Omega/\text{km}$

$$\bar{A} = \bar{D} = 1 + \frac{\bar{Y}\bar{Z}}{2} = 1 + \tfrac{1}{2}(3.229\times10^{-4}\angle 90^\circ)(50.6\angle 90^\circ) = 0.9918 \text{ PU}$$

$$\bar{B} = \bar{Z} = \bar{z}\ell = j\,50.6\ \Omega$$

$$\bar{C} = \bar{Y}\left(1 + \frac{\bar{Y}\bar{Z}}{4}\right) = 3.229\times10^{-4}\angle 90^\circ\,(1 - 0.004085)$$

$$= 3.216\times10^{-4}\angle 90^\circ \text{ S}$$

$$\bar{V}_S = \bar{A}\bar{V}_R + \bar{B}\bar{I}_R = 0.9918(125.9) + j\,50.6(0.7945\angle -25.84^\circ)$$

$$= 146.9\angle 14.26^\circ \text{ kV}_{LN}$$

$$V_S = 146.9\sqrt{3} = 254.4 \text{ kV}_{LL}$$

$$V_{R\,NL} = V_S/A = 254.4/0.9918 = 256.5 \text{ kV}_{LL}$$

$$\%\ VR = \frac{V_{R\,NL} - V_{R\,FL}}{V_{R\,FL}}\times100 = \frac{256.5 - 218}{218}\times100 = 17.7\%$$

(b) $\bar{V}_S = 0.9918(125.9) + j\,50.6(0.7945\angle 0^\circ)$

$$= 124.86 + j\,40.2 = 131.2\angle 17.85^\circ \text{ kV}_{LN}$$

$$V_S = 131.2\sqrt{3} = 227.2 \text{ kV}_{LL}$$

$$V_{R\,NL} = V_S/A = 227.2/0.9918 = 229.1 \text{ kV}$$

$$\%\ VR = \frac{229.1 - 218}{218}\times100 = 5.08\%$$

(c) $\bar{V}_S = 0.9918(125.9) + j\,50.6(0.7945\angle 25.84^\circ)$

$$= 107.34 + j\,36.18 = 113.3\angle 18.63^\circ$$

$$V_S = 113.3\sqrt{3} = 196.2 \text{ kV}_{LL}$$

$$V_{R\,NL} = V_S/A = 196.2/0.9918 = 197.9 \text{ kV}$$

$$\%\ VR = \frac{197.9 - 218}{218}\times100 = -9.22\%$$

5.23 CONTD. NEXT, REWORKING PROB. 5.13:

(a) $Z_c = \sqrt{\bar{z}/\bar{y}} = \sqrt{j0.335/j4.807\times10^{-6}} = 264\ \Omega$

(b) $\bar{\gamma}l = \sqrt{\bar{z}\bar{y}}\ l = \sqrt{j0.335(j4.807\times10^{-6})}\ (300) = j0.3807$ PU

(c) $A = D = \cos\beta l = \cos(0.3807 \text{ radians}) = 0.9284$ PU

$\bar{B} = jZ_c\sin\beta l = j264\sin(0.3807 \text{ radians}) = j98.1\ \Omega$

$\bar{C} = j\left(\frac{1}{Z_c}\right)\sin\beta l = j\frac{1}{264}\sin(0.3807 \text{ radians}) = j1.408\times10^{-3}$ S

5.24 $Z_c = \sqrt{\dfrac{\bar{z}}{\bar{y}}} = \sqrt{\dfrac{L_1}{C_1}} = \sqrt{\dfrac{\frac{\mu_0}{2\pi}\operatorname{Ln}(D_{eq}/D_{SL})}{2\pi\varepsilon_0/\operatorname{Ln}\left(\frac{D_{eq}}{D_{SC}}\right)}}$

$$\bar{Z}_c = \underbrace{\sqrt{\frac{\mu_0}{\varepsilon_0}}}_{\text{characteristic impedance of free space}}\ \underbrace{\left[\frac{\sqrt{\operatorname{Ln}\left(\frac{D_{eq}}{D_{SL}}\right)\operatorname{Ln}\left(\frac{D_{eq}}{D_{SC}}\right)}}{2\pi}\right]}_{\text{Geometric Factors}}$$

where $\sqrt{\dfrac{\mu_0}{\varepsilon_0}} = \sqrt{\dfrac{4\pi\times10^{-7}}{\left(\frac{1}{36\pi}\right)\times10^{-9}}} = 377.\ \Omega$

$$v = \sqrt{\frac{1}{L_1C_1}} = \sqrt{\frac{1}{\frac{\mu_0}{2\pi}\operatorname{Ln}\left(\frac{D_{eq}}{D_{SL}}\right)2\pi\varepsilon_0/\operatorname{Ln}\left(\frac{D_{eq}}{D_{SC}}\right)}}$$

$$v = \underbrace{\left(\frac{1}{\sqrt{\mu_0\varepsilon_0}}\right)}_{\text{Free space velocity of propagation}}\underbrace{\left(\sqrt{\frac{\operatorname{Ln}(D_{eq}/D_{SC})}{\operatorname{Ln}(D_{eq}/D_{SL})}}\right)}_{\text{Geometric Factors}}$$

where $\sqrt{\dfrac{1}{\mu_0\varepsilon_0}} = \sqrt{\dfrac{1}{(4\pi\times10^{-7})\left(\frac{1}{36\pi}\times10^{-9}\right)}} = 3.0\times10^{8}\ \frac{m}{s}$

5.24 CONTD.

For the 765 kV line in Example 5.10,

$$D_{eq} = \sqrt[3]{(14)(14)(28)} = 17.64 \text{ m}$$

$$D_{SL} = 1.091 \sqrt[4]{\left(\frac{.0403}{3.28}\right)(0.457)^3} = 0.202 \text{ m}$$

$$D_{SC} = 1.091 \sqrt[4]{\left(\frac{1.196}{2}\right)(.0254)(0.457)^3} = 0.213 \text{ m}$$

$$Z_c = 377\left[\frac{\sqrt{\ln\left(\frac{17.64}{0.202}\right)\ln\left(\frac{17.64}{0.213}\right)}}{2\pi}\right] = \underline{\underline{267.\ \Omega}}$$

$$v = 3\times10^8 \sqrt{\frac{\ln(17.64/.213)}{\ln(17.64/.202)}} = \underline{\underline{2.98\times10^8}}\ \frac{\text{m}}{\text{s}}$$

5.25

(a) FOR A LOSSLESS LINE, $\beta = \omega\sqrt{LC} = 2\pi(60)\sqrt{0.97 \times 0.0115 \times 10^{-9}}$

$= 0.001259$ rad/km

$$\bar{Z}_c = \sqrt{L/C} = \sqrt{\frac{0.97 \times 10^{-3}}{0.0115 \times 10^{-6}}} = 290.43\ \Omega$$

VELOCITY OF PROPAGATION $v = \frac{1}{\sqrt{LC}} = \frac{1}{\sqrt{0.97 \times 0.0115 \times 10^{-9}}} = 2.994 \times 10^5$ km/s

AND THE LINE WAVE LENGTH IS $\lambda = v/f = \frac{1}{60}(2.994 \times 10^5) = 4990$ km

(b) $\bar{V}_R = \frac{500}{\sqrt{3}} \angle 0°$ kV $= 288.675 \angle 0°$ kV

$\bar{S}_{R(3\phi)} = \frac{800}{0.8} \angle \cos^{-1} 0.8 = 800 + j600$ MVA $= 1000 \angle 36.87°$ MVA

$$\bar{I}_R = \bar{S}^*_{R(3\phi)} / 3\bar{V}^*_R = \frac{(1000 \angle -36.87°)\, 10^3}{3 \times 288.675 \angle 0°} = 1154.7 \angle -36.87°\ \text{A}$$

SENDING END VOLTAGE $\bar{V}_S = \cos\beta l\, \bar{V}_R + j\,\bar{Z}_c \sin\beta l\, \bar{I}_R$

$\beta l = 0.001259 \times 300 = 0.3777$ rad $= 21.641°$

$\therefore \bar{V}_S = 0.9295(288.675 \angle 0°) + j(290.43)\, 0.3688\, (1154.7 \angle -36.87°)(10^{-3})$

$= 356.53 \angle 16.1°$ kV

SENDING END LINE-TO-LINE VOLTAGE MAGNITUDE $= \sqrt{3}\ 356.53$

$= 617.53$ kV

$$\bar{I}_S = j\,\frac{1}{\bar{Z}_c} \sin\beta l\, \bar{V}_R + \cos\beta l\, \bar{I}_R$$

$$= j\,\frac{1}{290.43}\, 0.3688\,(288.675 \angle 0°)\, 10^3 + 0.9295(1154.7 \angle -36.87°)$$

$= 902.3 \angle -17.9°$ A ; LINE CURRENT $= 902.3$ A

$$\bar{S}_{S(3\phi)} = 3\bar{V}_S \bar{I}^*_S = 3(356.53 \angle 16.1°)(902.3 \angle -17.9°)\, 10^{-3}$$

$= 800$ MW $+ j\,539.672$ MVAR

PERCENT VOLTAGE REGULATION $= \frac{(356.53/0.9295) - 288.675}{288.675} \times 100$

$= 32.87\%$

5.26

(a) THE LINE PHASE CONSTANT IS $\beta l = \frac{2\pi}{\lambda} l \text{ rad} = \frac{360}{\lambda} l = \frac{360}{5000} 315$

FROM THE PRACTICAL LINE LOADABILITY, $= 22.68^\circ$

$$P_{3\phi} = \frac{V_{S\,pu} V_{R\,pu} (SIL)}{\sin \beta l} \sin \delta \; ; \; 700 = \frac{(1.0)(0.9)(SIL)}{\sin 22.68^\circ} \sin 36.87^\circ$$

$\therefore$ SIL $= 499.83$ MW

SINCE $SIL = \frac{(kV_{L\,rated})^2}{Z_c}$ MW, $kV_L = \sqrt{Z_c (SIL)} = \sqrt{(320)(499.83)}$

$= 400$ kV

(b) THE EQUIVALENT LINE REACTANCE FOR A LOSSLESS LINE IS

$$X' = Z_c \sin \beta l = 320(\sin 22.68^\circ) = 123.39\ \Omega$$

FOR A LOSSLESS LINE, THE MAXIMUM POWER THAT CAN BE TRANSMITTED UNDER STEADY-STATE CONDITION OCCURS FOR A LOAD ANGLE OF 90°.

WITH $V_S = 1$ PU $= 400$ kV (L-L), $V_R = 0.9$ PU $= 0.9(400)$ kV (L-L)

THEORETICAL MAXIMUM POWER $= \frac{(400)(0.9 \times 400)}{123.39} \times 1$

$= 1167$ MW

5.27

From Problem 5.11

$\bar{A} = 0.8137 \angle 1.089^\circ$ per unit $A = 0.8137$ $\theta_A = 1.089^\circ$

$\bar{B} = \bar{Z}' = 164.6 \angle 85.42^\circ \Omega$ $Z' = 164.6\ \Omega$ $\theta_Z = 85.42^\circ$

Using Eq (5.5.6)

$$P_{R\,MAX} = \frac{(500)(500)}{164.6} - \frac{(0.8137)(500)^2}{164.6}\cos(85.42^\circ - 1.089^\circ)$$

$$P_{RMAX} = 1518.8 - 122.1 = \underline{\underline{1397.}}\ \text{MW} \quad (3\text{-phase})$$

For this loading at unity power factor:

$$I_R = \frac{P_{RMAX}}{\sqrt{3}\, V_{RLL}\,(\text{P.F.})} = \frac{1397}{\sqrt{3}\,(500)\,(1.0)} = 1.613\ \text{kA/phase}$$

From Table A.3, the thermal limit for three ACSR 1113 kcmil conductors is $3(1.11) = 3.33$ kA/phase. The current 1.613 kA corresponding to the theoretical steady-state stability limit is well below the thermal limit of 3.33 kA.

5.28

LINE LENGTH :	200 km	550 km
$\bar{Z}_c$ (Ω) :	$282.6\angle -2.45^\circ$	$282.6\angle -2.45^\circ$
$\bar{\gamma}\ell$ (PU) :	$0.2486\angle 87.55^\circ$	$0.6838\angle 87.55^\circ$
$\bar{A} = \bar{D}$ (PU) :	$0.9694\angle 0.1544^\circ$	$0.7761\angle 1.36^\circ$
$\bar{B}$ (Ω) :	$69.54\angle 85.15^\circ$	$178.6\angle 85.5^\circ$
$\bar{C}$ (S) :	$8.710\times10^{-4}\angle 90.05^\circ$	$2.236\times10^{-3}\angle 90.39^\circ$
$P_{R\,MAX}$ (MW) :	3291	1289

THE THERMAL LIMIT OF 3.33 kA/PHASE CORRESPONDS TO

$\sqrt{3}(500)(3.33) = 2884$ MW AT 500 kV AND UNITY POWER FACTOR.

5.29

$\bar{A} = 0.9285\angle 0.258^\circ$ PU ; $A = 0.9285$, $\theta_A = 0.258^\circ$

$\bar{B} = \bar{Z}' = 98.25\angle 86.69^\circ\,\Omega$; $Z' = 98.25$, $\theta_Z = 86.69^\circ$

(a) USING EQ. (5.5.6)

$$P_{R\,MAX} = \frac{500\times500}{98.25} - \frac{0.9285(500)^2}{98.25}\cos(86.69^\circ - 0.258^\circ)$$

$$= 2544.5 - 147 = 2397.5 \text{ MW}$$

(b) USING EQ. (5.5.4) WITH $\delta = \theta_Z$:

$$Q_R = \frac{-AV_R^2}{Z'}\sin(\theta_Z - \theta_A) = \frac{-0.9285(500)^2}{98.25}\sin(86.69^\circ - 0.258^\circ)$$

$Q_R = -2358$ MVAR DELIVERED TO RECEIVING END

$Q_R = +2358$ MVAR ABSORBED BY LINE AT THE RECEIVING END

$$\text{RECEIVING END PF} = \cos\left(\tan^{-1}\frac{Q_R}{P_R}\right) = \cos\left[\tan^{-1}\frac{2358}{2397.5}\right]$$

$= 0.713$ LEADING

5.30

(a) $\bar{Z} = \bar{z}\ell = (0.088 + j0.465)100 = 8.8 + j46.5 \ \Omega$

$\frac{\bar{Y}}{2} = \frac{\bar{y}\ell}{2} = (j3.524 \times 10^{-6})100/2 = j0.1762 \text{ mS}$

$Z_{base} = V_{L\,base}^2 / S_{3\phi\,base} = \frac{(230)^2}{100} = 529 \ \Omega$

$\therefore \bar{Z} = (8.8 + j46.5)/529 = 0.0166 + j0.088 \text{ pu}$

$\frac{\bar{Y}}{2} = j0.1762/(1/0.529) = j0.09321 \text{ pu}$

THE NOMINAL π CIRCUIT FOR THE MEDIUM LINE IS SHOWN BELOW:

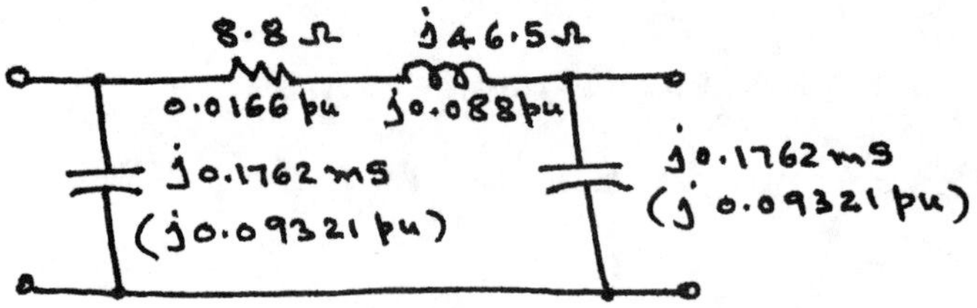

(b) $S_{3\phi\,rated} = V_{L\,rated} I_{L\,rated} \sqrt{3} = 230(0.9)\sqrt{3} = 358.5 \text{ MVA}$

(c) $\bar{A} = \bar{D} = 1 + \frac{\bar{Z}\bar{Y}}{2} = 1 + (8.8 + j46.5)(0.1762 \times 10^{-3}) = 0.9918 \angle 0.1^\circ$

$\bar{B} = \bar{Z} = 8.8 + j46.5 = 47.32 \angle 79.3^\circ \ \Omega$

$\bar{C} = \bar{Y} + \frac{\bar{Z}\bar{Y}^2}{4} = 0.1755 \angle 90.04^\circ \text{ mS}$

(d) $SIL = V_{L\,rated}^2 / Z_c$

$$\bar{Z}_c = \sqrt{\frac{\bar{z}}{\bar{y}}} = \sqrt{\frac{0.088 + j0.465}{j3.524}} \times 10^3 = 366.6 \angle -5.36^\circ \ \Omega$$

$\therefore SIL = (230)^2 / 366.6 = 144.3 \text{ MVA}$

Problem 5.31

The maximum amount of real power that can be transferred to the load at unity pf with a bus voltage greater than 0.9 pu (688.5 kV) is 2950 MW.

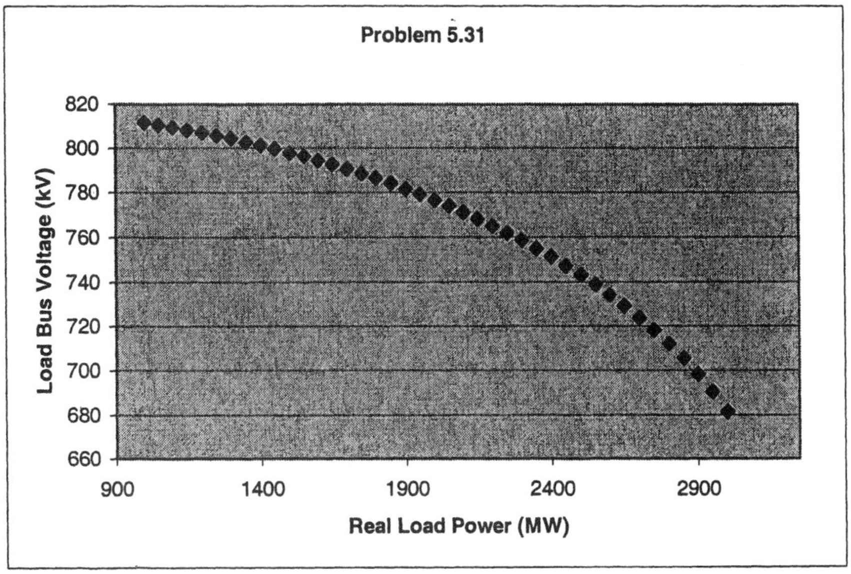

Problem 5.32

The maximum about of reactive power transfer that can be transferred to the load with a bus voltage greater than 0.9 pu is 650 Mvar.

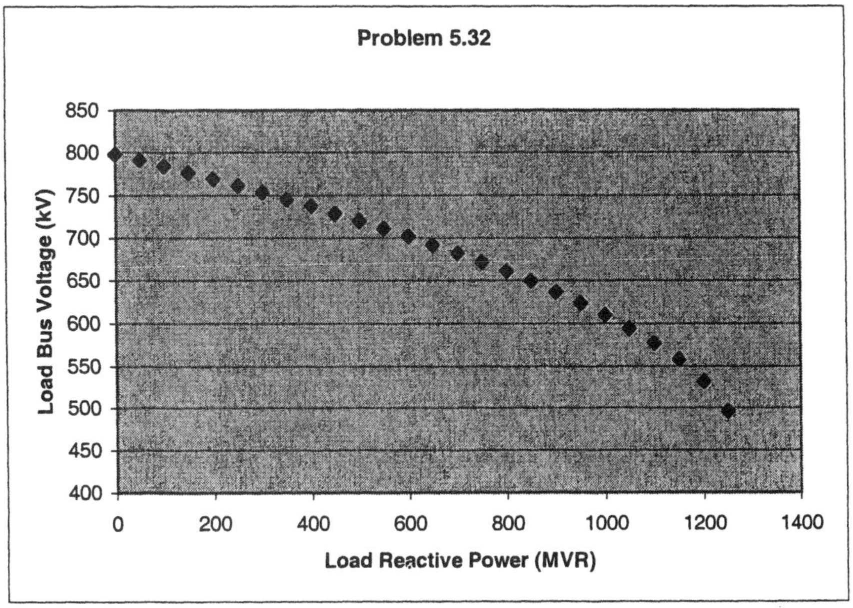

5.33 (a) Using Eq(5.5.3) with $\delta = 35°$:

$$P_R = \frac{(500)(.95 \times 500)}{164.6}\cos(85.42° - 35°) - \frac{(.8137)(.95\times 500)^2}{164.6}\cos(85.42° - 1.09°)$$

$$P_R = 919.3 - 110.2 = \underline{\underline{809.\ \text{MW}}} \quad \text{(three-phase)}$$

$P_R = 809.$ MW is the practical line loadability provided that the voltage drop limit and thermal limit are not exceeded.

(b) $$I_{RFL} = \frac{P_R}{\sqrt{3}\,V_{RLL}\,(\text{P.F.})} = \frac{809}{\sqrt{3}(0.95\times 500)(0.99)} = \underline{\underline{0.993\ \text{kA}}}$$

(c) $$\bar{V}_S = \bar{A}\bar{V}_{RFL} + \bar{B}\bar{I}_{RFL}$$

$$\frac{500}{\sqrt{3}}\angle\delta = (0.8137\angle 1.089°)(V_{RFL}\angle 0°) + (164.6\angle 85.42°)(0.993\angle 8.11°)$$

$$288.68\angle\delta = .8137\,V_{RFL}\angle 1.089° + 163.45\angle 93.53°$$

$$288.68\angle\delta = (0.8136\,V_{RFL} - 10.06) + j\,(0.01546\,V_{RFL} + 163.14)$$

Taking the squared magnitude of the above equation:

$$83{,}333. = 0.6622\,V_{RFL}^2 - 11.33\,V_{RFL} + 26716.$$

Solving the above quadradic equation:

$$V_{RFL} = \frac{11.33 + \sqrt{(11.33)^2 + 4(.6622)(56617)}}{2(0.6622)} = 301.1\ \text{kV}_{LN}$$

$$V_{RFL} = 301.1\sqrt{3} = \underline{\underline{521.5\ \text{kV}_{LL}}} = 1.043 \text{ per unit}$$

(d) $$V_{RNL} = V_S/A = \frac{500}{0.8137} = 614.5\ \text{kV}_{LL}$$

$$\%\text{V.R.} = \frac{614.5 - 521.5}{521.5}\times 100 = \underline{\underline{17.8\ \%}}$$

5.33 CONTD.

(e)

From Problem 5.27, the thermal limit is 3.33 kA. Since $V_{RFL}/V_S = 521.5/500 = 1.043$ is greater than 0.95 and the thermal limit = 3.33 kA is greater than I_{RFL} = 0.993 kA, the voltage drop limit and thermal limit are not exceeded at $P_R = 809.$ MW. therefore, loadability is determined by stability.

5.34 $\bar{A} = 0.9739\angle 0.0912°$ PU; $A = 0.9739$, $\theta_A = 0.0912°$

$\bar{B} = \bar{Z} = 60.48\angle 86.6°\ \Omega$; $Z = 60.48$, $\theta_Z = 86.6°$

(a) USING EQ. (5.5.3) WITH $\delta = 35°$:

$$P_R = \frac{500\,(0.95\times500)}{60.48}\cos(86.6° - 35°) - \frac{0.9739\,(0.95\times500)^2}{60.48}\cos(86.6° - 0.0912°)$$

$$= 2439.2 - 221.2 = 2218 \text{ MW } (3\phi)$$

$P_R = 2218$ MW IS THE LINE LOADABILITY IF THE VOLTAGE DROP AND THERMAL LIMITS ARE NOT EXCEEDED.

(b) $$I_{R\,FL} = \frac{P_R}{\sqrt{3}\,V_{R\,LL}\,(pf)} = \frac{2218}{\sqrt{3}(0.95\times500)(0.99)} = 2.723 \text{ kA}$$

(c) $$\bar{V}_S = \bar{A}\bar{V}_R + \bar{B}\bar{I}_R$$

$$\frac{500}{\sqrt{3}}\angle\delta = (0.9739\angle 0.0912°)\,V_{R\,FL}\angle 0° + 60.48\angle 86.6°\,(2.723\angle 8.11°)$$

$$288.68\angle\delta = (0.9739\,V_{R\,FL} - 13.55) + j\,(0.0016\,V_{R\,FL} + 164.14)$$

TAKING THE SQUARED MAGNITUDE OF THE ABOVE

$$83{,}333 = 0.93664\,V_{R\,FL}^2 - 25.6\,V_{R\,FL} + 27{,}126$$

SOLVING THE ABOVE QUADRATIC EQUATION:

5.3A CONTD.

$$V_{RFL} = \frac{25.60 + \sqrt{(25.60)^2 + 4(.93664)(56{,}207)}}{2(0.9678)} = 250.68 \text{ kV}_{LN}$$

$V_{RFL} = 250.68\sqrt{3} = \underline{\underline{434.18}}$ kV$_{LL}$ = 0.868 per unit

For this load current, 2.723 kA, the voltage drop limit $V_R/V_S = 0.95$ is exceeded. The thermal limit, 3.33 kA is not exceeded. Therefore the voltage drop limit determines loadability for this line. Based on $V_{RFL} = .95$ per unit, I_{RFL} is calculated as follows:

$$\bar{V}_S = \bar{A}\bar{V}_{RFL} + \bar{B}\bar{I}_{RFL}$$

$$\frac{500}{\sqrt{3}}\angle\delta = 0.9739\angle 0.0912^\circ \left(\frac{0.95 \times 500}{\sqrt{3}}\angle 0^\circ\right) + 60.48\angle 86.6^\circ \left(I_{RFL}\angle 8.11^\circ\right)$$

$$288.68\angle\delta = 267.09\angle 0.0912^\circ + 60.48\, I_{RFL}\angle 94.71^\circ$$

$$= (-4.966\, I_{RFL} + 267.09) + j(60.28\, I_{RFL} + 0.4251)$$

TAKING SQUARED MAGNITUDES:

$$83{,}333 = 3658\, I_{RFL}^2 - 2601\, I_{RFL} + 71{,}337$$

SOLVING THE QUADRATIC:

$$I_{RFL} = \frac{2601 + \sqrt{(2601)^2 + 4(3658)(11{,}996)}}{2(3658)} = 2.2 \text{ kA}$$

AT 0.99 pf LEADING, THE PRACTICAL LINE LOADABILITY FOR THE LINE IS

$$P_R = \sqrt{3}\,(0.95 \times 500)\; 2.2\,(0.99) = 1792 \text{ MW}$$

WHICH IS BASED ON THE VOLTAGE DROP LIMIT $V_R/V_S = 0.95$.

5.34 CONTD.

(d) $V_{RNL} = V_S/A = 500/0.9739 = 513.4\ kV_{LL}$

$$\%\ VR = \frac{513.4 - (500\times 0.95)}{500\times 0.95}\times 100 = 8.08\%$$

5.35 (a) $\ell = 200$ km. The steady-state stability limit is:

$$P_R = \frac{(500)(.95)(500)}{69.54}\cos(85.15^\circ - 35^\circ) - \frac{(.9694)(.95\times 500)^2}{69.54}\cos(85.15^\circ - 0.154^\circ)$$

$P_R = 2188. - 274. = 1914.$ MW

$$I_{RFL} = \frac{P_R}{\sqrt{3}\,V_{RFL}\,(P.F.)} = \frac{1914}{(\sqrt{3})(.95\times 500)(.99)} = 2.35\ kA$$

$\bar{V}_S = \bar{A}\bar{V}_{RFL} + \bar{B}\bar{I}_{RFL}$

$$\frac{500}{\sqrt{3}}\angle\delta_S = (.9694\angle 0.154^\circ)(V_{RFL}\angle 0^\circ) + (69.54\angle 85.15^\circ)(2.35\angle 8.11^\circ)$$

$288.675\angle\delta_S = (.9694\,V_{RFL} - 9.293) + j(0.0026\,V_{RFL} + 163.15)$

Taking the squared magnitude:

$83{,}333. = .9397\,V_{RFL}^2 - 17.17\,V_{RFL} + 26704.$

Solving

$$V_{RFL} = \frac{17.17 + \sqrt{(17.17)^2 + 4(.9397)(56629)}}{2(.9397)} = 254.8\ kV_{LN}$$

$V_{RFL} = 254.8\sqrt{3} = 441.3\ kV_{LL} = 0.8826$ per unit

The voltage drop limit $|V_R/V_S| \geq 0.95$ is not satisfied.

At the voltage drop limit:

$\bar{V}_S = \bar{A}\bar{V}_{RFL} + \bar{B}\bar{I}_{RFL}$

$$\frac{500}{\sqrt{3}}\angle\delta_S = (0.9694\angle 0.154^\circ)\left(\frac{.95\times 500}{\sqrt{3}}\angle 0^\circ\right) + (69.54\angle 85.15^\circ)(I_{RFL}\angle 8.109^\circ)$$

5.35 CONTD.

$$288.675\angle\delta_S = (265.85 - 3.953 I_{RFL}) + j(0.7146 + 69.43 I_{RFL})$$

squared magnitudes:

$$83,333 = 4836 I_{RFL}^2 - 2003.\ I_{RFL} + 70677.$$

Solving

$$I_{RFL} = \frac{2003 + \sqrt{(2003)^2 + (4)(4836)(12656)}}{2(4836)} = 1.84\ kA$$

The practical line loadability for this 200 km line is:

$$P_{RFL} = \sqrt{3}(.95 \times 500)(1.84)(.99) = \underline{\underline{1497.\ MW}}$$

at $V_{RFL}/V_S = 0.95$ per unit and at 0.99 p.f. leading

(b) $\ell = 600$ km ; CORRESPONDING $\bar{B} = 191.8\angle 85.57°$; $\bar{A} = \bar{D} = 0.7356\angle 1.685°$

$$P_R = \frac{(500)(.95 \times 500)}{191.8}\cos(85.57° - 35°) - \frac{(.7356)(.95 \times 500)^2}{191.8}\cos(85.57° - 1.685°)$$

$$P_R = 786.5 - 92.2 = \underline{\underline{694.3\ MW}}$$

The practical line loadability for this 600 km line is 694.3 MW corresponding to the steady-state stability limit

5.36 (a) $SIL = \frac{(345)^2}{300} = 396.8$ MW

Neglecting losses and using Eq (5.4.29):

$$P = \frac{(1)(.95)(SIL)\sin(35°)}{\sin\left(\frac{2\pi\ 300}{5000}\ radians\right)} = 1.480(SIL) = 1.480(396.8)$$

$$P = 587.3\ MW/line$$

5.36 CONTD.

$$\# \text{ 345-kV LINES} = \frac{2200}{587.3} + 1 = 3.7 + 1 \simeq 5 \text{ LINES}$$

(b) FOR 500 kV LINES, $\text{SIL} = \dfrac{(500)^2}{275} = 909.1 \text{ MW}$

$$P = 1.48 \text{ SIL}$$

$$= 1.48(909.1) = 1345.5 \text{ MW/LINE}$$

$$\# \text{ 500-kV LINES} = \frac{2200}{1345.5} + 1 = 1.6 + 1 \simeq 3 \text{ LINES}$$

(c) FOR 765-kV LINES, $\text{SIL} = \dfrac{(765)^2}{260} = 2250.9 \text{ MW}$

$$P = 1.48(\text{SIL}) = 1.48(2250.9) = 3331.3 \text{ MW/LINE}$$

$$\# \text{ 765-kV LINES} = \frac{2200}{3331.3} + 1 = 0.66 + 1 \simeq 2 \text{ LINES}$$

5.37

(a) USING EQ. (5.4.29):

$$P = \frac{1 \times 0.95\,(SIL)\sin 35^\circ}{\sin\left(\frac{2\pi(300)}{5000}\text{ radians}\right)} = 1.48\,(SIL)$$

$P = 1.48(396.8) = 587.3$ MW/345-kV LINE

$\#$ 345-kV LINES $= \frac{3200}{587.3} + 1 = 5.4 + 1 \simeq 7$ LINES

$P = 1.48\,(909.1) = 1345.5$ MW/500-kV LINE

$\#$ 500-kV LINES $= \frac{3200}{1345.5} + 1 = 2.4 + 1 \simeq 4$ LINES

$P = 1.48\,(2250.9) = 3331.3$ MW/765-kV LINE

$\#$ 765-kV LINES $= \frac{3200}{3331.3} + 1 = 0.96 + 1 \simeq 2$ LINES

(b) $$P = \frac{(1)(.95)(SIL)(\sin 35^\circ)}{\sin\left(\frac{2\pi \times 400}{5000}\text{ radians}\right)} = 1.131\,(SIL)$$

$P = 1.131(396.8) = 448.8$ MW/345-kV Line

$\#$ 345-kV Lines $= \frac{2000}{448.8} + 1 = 4.5 + 1 = \underline{\underline{6 \text{ Lines}}}$

$P = (1.131)(909.1) = 1028.3$ MW/500kV Line

$\#$ 500-kV Lines $= \frac{2000}{1028.3} + 1 = 1.94 + 1 = \underline{\underline{3 \text{ Lines}}}$

$P = (1.131)(2250.9) = 2545.9$ MW/765 kV Line

$\#$ 765-kV Lines $= \frac{2000}{2545.9} + 1 = 0.79 + 1 = \underline{\underline{2 \text{ Lines}}}$

5.38

$$\beta l = (9.46\times10^{-4})(300)(180/\pi) = 16.26°$$

REAL POWER FOR ONE TRANSMISSION CIRCUIT $P = 3600/4 = 900$ MW

FROM THE PRACTICAL LINE LOADABILITY, $P_{3\phi} = \dfrac{V_{S\,pu} V_{R\,pu}(SIL)}{\sin \beta l} \sin\delta$

OR $$900 = \frac{(1.0)(0.9)(SIL)}{\sin 16.26°} \sin(36.87°)$$

FROM WHICH $SIL = 466.66$ MW

SINCE $SIL = \left[(kV_{L\,rated})^2/Z_c\right]$ MW

$$kV_L = \sqrt{Z_c(SIL)} = \sqrt{(343)(466.66)} = 400\text{kV}$$

5.39

(a) NOTE: ERROR IN PRINTING: $P_R + jQ_R = \dfrac{|\bar{V}_R||\bar{V}_S| \angle \beta-\delta}{|\bar{B}|} - \dfrac{|A||\bar{V}_R|^2 \angle \beta-\alpha}{|\bar{B}|}$

THE PHASOR DIAGRAM CORRESPONDING TO THE ABOVE EQUATION IS SHOWN BELOW:

FIG. (a)

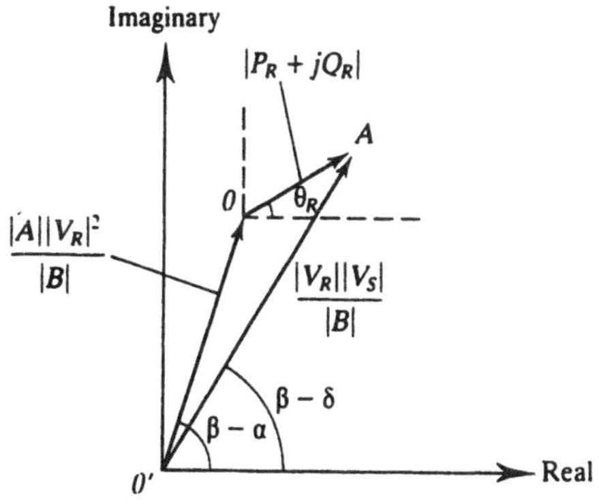

(a)

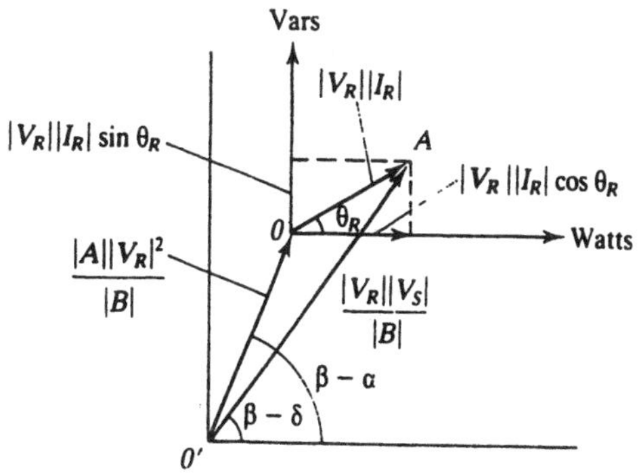

(b)

(b) BY SHIFTING THE ORIGIN FROM O' TO O, THE POWER DIAGRAM IS SHOWN IN FIG. (b) ABOVE.

5·39 CONTD.

FOR A GIVEN LOAD AND A GIVEN VALUE OF $|\bar{V}_R|$, $O'A = |\bar{V}_R||\bar{V}_S|/|\bar{B}|$ THE LOCI OF POINT A WILL BE A SET OF CIRCLES OF RADII $O'A$, ONE FOR EACH OF THE SET OF VALUES OF $|\bar{V}_S|$. PORTIONS OF TWO SUCH CIRCLES (KNOWN AS RECEIVING-END CIRCLES) ARE SHOWN BELOW:

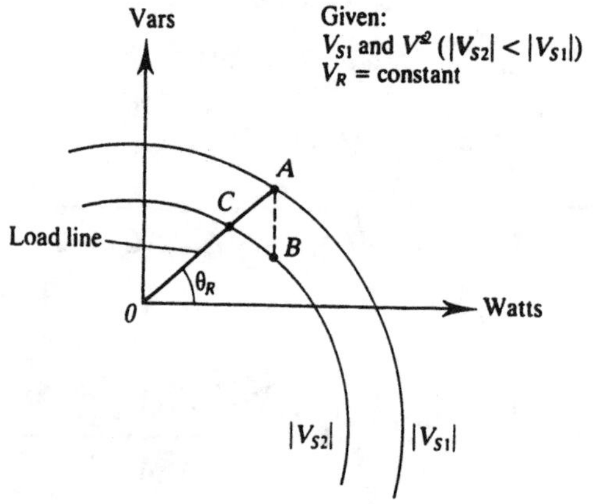

(c) LINE OA IN THE FIGURE ABOVE IS THE LOAD LINE WHOSE INTERSECTION WITH THE POWER CIRCLE DETERMINES THE OPERATING POINT. THUS, FOR A LOAD (WITH A LAGGING POWER-FACTOR ANGLE θ_R) A AND C ARE THE OPERATING POINTS CORRESPONDING TO SENDING-END VOLTAGES $|\bar{V}_{S1}|$ AND $|\bar{V}_{S2}|$, RESPECTIVELY. THESE OPERATING POINTS DETERMINE THE REAL AND REACTIVE POWER RECEIVED FOR THE TWO SENDING-END VOLTAGES.

THE REACTIVE POWER THAT MUST BE SUPPLIED AT THE RECEIVING END IN ORDER TO MAINTAIN CONSTANT $|\bar{V}_R|$ WHEN THE SENDING-END VOLTAGE DECREASES FROM $|\bar{V}_{S1}|$ TO $|\bar{V}_{S2}|$ IS GIVEN BY AB, WHICH IS PARALLEL TO THE REACTIVE-POWER AXIS.

Problem 5.40
The maximum power that can be delivered to the load is 10250MW.

Problem 5.41
For 8800MW at the load the load bus voltage is maintained above 720kV even if 2 lines are taken out of service (8850 MW may be OK since the voltage is 719.9 kV).

5.42 From Problem 5-17, the shunt admittance of the equivalent π circuit without compensation is:

$$\bar{Y}' = 2\left(3.18\times10^{-6} + j\,1.137\times10^{-3}\right) = 6.36\times10^{-6} + j\,2.274\times10^{-3}\ S$$

$$\bar{Y}' = G' + j\,B'$$

With 70% shunt reactive compensation, the equivalent shunt admittance is:

$$\bar{Y}_{eq} = 6.36\times10^{-6} + j\,(2.274\times10^{-3})\left(1-\frac{70}{100}\right)$$

$$\bar{Y}_{eq} = 6.36\times10^{-6} + j\,6.822\times10^{-4}\ S \quad = 6.822\times10^{-4}\angle 89.47^{\circ}\ S$$

Since there is no series compensation,

$$\bar{Z}_{eq} = \bar{Z}' = 164.6\angle 85.42^{\circ}\ \Omega$$

The equivalent $\bar{A}$ parameter of the compensated lines

$$\bar{A}_{eq} = 1 + \frac{\bar{Y}_{eq}\bar{Z}_{eq}}{2} = 1 + \left(\frac{6.822\times10^{-4}}{2}\angle 89.47^{\circ}\right)(164.6\angle 85.42^{\circ})$$

$$\bar{A}_{eq} = 1 + 0.0561\angle 174.89^{\circ} = 0.9441 + j.005 = .9441\angle 0.3^{\circ}\ \text{pu}$$

The no-Load voltage is

$$V_{RNL} = \frac{V_S}{A_{eq}} = \frac{544.5}{0.9441} = 576.7\ \text{kV}_{LL}$$

where V_S is obtained from Problem 5.12

$V_{RFL} = 480\ \text{kV}_{LL}$ is the same as given in Problem 5.12, since the shunt reactors are removed at full load. Therefore,

$$\%\ V.R. = \frac{V_{RNL} - V_{RFL}}{V_{RFL}}\times100 = \frac{576.7-480}{480}\times100 = \underline{\underline{20.15\ \%}}$$

The impedance of each shunt reactor is:

$$\bar{Z}_{reactor} = j\left[\frac{B'}{2}(.70)\right]^{-1} = j\left[\frac{2.274\times10^{-3}}{2}(.70)\right]^{-1} = \underline{\underline{j1256.5\ \Omega}}$$

At each end of the line.

5.43

(a) $V_S = 653.7 \ kV_{LL}$ (SAME AS PROB. 5.14)

$\bar{Y}_{eq} = 2 \left[6.37 \times 10^{-7} + j \ 7.294 \times 10^{-4} (1-0.5) \right]$ FROM PROB. 5.18

$= 1.274 \times 10^{-6} + j \ 7.294 \times 10^{-4} = 7.294 \times 10^{-4} \ \underline{/87.5°} \ S$

$\bar{Z}_{eq} = \bar{Z}' = 98.25 \ \underline{/86.69°} \ \Omega$

$\bar{A}_{eq} = 1 + \dfrac{\bar{Y}_{eq} \ \bar{Z}_{eq}}{2} = 1 + \frac{1}{2} (7.294 \times 10^{-4} \ \underline{/87.5°})(98.25 \ \underline{/86.69°})$

$= 1 + 0.0358 \ \underline{/174.19°} = 0.9644 + j0.0036 = 0.9644 \ \underline{/0.21°}$

$V_{RNL} = V_S / A_{eq} = 653.7 / 0.9644 = 677.8 \ kV_{LL}$

$\% \ VR = \dfrac{677.8 - 480}{480} \times 100 = 41.2 \%$

(b) $V_S = 556.7 \ kV_{LL}$ (SAME AS PROB. 5.14)

$V_{RNL} = V_S / A = 556.7 / 0.9644 = 577.3 \ kV_{LL}$

$\% \ VR = \dfrac{577.3 - 480}{480} \times 100 = 20.3 \%$

(c) $V_S = 435.1 \ kV_{LL}$ (SAME AS PROB. 5.14)

$V_{RNL} = V_S / A = 435.1 / 0.9644 = 451.2 \ kV_{LL}$

$\% \ VR = \dfrac{451.2 - 480}{480} \times 100 = -6 \%$

5.44

From Problem 5.17,

$\bar{Z}' = R' + jX' = 13.14 + j\,164.1\ \Omega$

Based on 40% series compensation, half at each end of the line, the impedance of each series capacitor is:

$\bar{Z}_{CAP} = -jX_{CAP} = -j\frac{1}{2}(.40)(164.1) = \underline{\underline{-j\,32.82}}\ \Omega/\text{phase}$ (at each end)

Using the ABCD parameters from Problem 5.11, the equivalent ABCD parameters of the compensated line are:

$$\begin{bmatrix} \bar{A}_{eq} & \bar{B}_{eq} \\ \bar{C}_{eq} & \bar{D}_{eq} \end{bmatrix} = \begin{bmatrix} 1 & -j32.82 \\ 0 & 1 \end{bmatrix} \begin{bmatrix} 0.8137\angle 1.089^\circ & 164.6\angle 85.42^\circ \\ 2.061\times10^{-3}\angle 90.32^\circ & 0.8137\angle 1.089^\circ \end{bmatrix} \begin{bmatrix} 1 & -j32.82 \\ 0 & 1 \end{bmatrix}$$

compensated line; sending end series capacitors; uncompensated line (from Pr. 5.11); Receiving End Series Capacitors

$$\begin{bmatrix} \bar{A}_{eq} & \bar{B}_{eq} \\ \bar{C}_{eq} & \bar{D}_{eq} \end{bmatrix} = \begin{bmatrix} 1 & -j32.82 \\ 0 & 1 \end{bmatrix} \begin{bmatrix} 0.8137\angle 1.089^\circ & 138.05\angle 84.32^\circ \\ 2.061\times10^{-3}\angle 90.32^\circ & 0.8813\angle 1.03^\circ \end{bmatrix}$$

$$= \begin{bmatrix} 0.8813\angle 1.03^\circ & 109.4\angle 82.55^\circ \\ 2.061\times10^{-3}\angle 90.32^\circ & 0.8813\angle 1.03^\circ \end{bmatrix}$$

5.45

FROM PROB. 5.13:

(a) $\bar{Z}' = \bar{B} = 98.25 \angle 86.69° = 5.673 + j98.09 \ \Omega$

IMPEDANCE OF EACH SERIES CAPACITOR IS

$$\bar{Z}_{CAP} = -jX_{CAP} = -j(\tfrac{1}{2})\,0.3\,(98.09) = -j14.71 \ \Omega$$

EQUIVALENT ABCD PARAMETERS OF THE COMPENSATED LINE ARE

$$\begin{bmatrix} \bar{A}_{eq} & \bar{B}_{eq} \\ \bar{C}_{eq} & \bar{D}_{eq} \end{bmatrix} = \underbrace{\begin{bmatrix} 1 & -j14.71 \\ 0 & 1 \end{bmatrix}}_{\text{SENDING END SERIES CAPACITORS}} \underbrace{\begin{bmatrix} 0.9285\angle 0.258° & 98.25\angle 86.69° \\ 1.405\times 10^{-3}\angle 90.09° & 0.9285\angle 0.258° \end{bmatrix}}_{\text{UNCOMPENSATED LINE FROM PR. 5.13}} \underbrace{\begin{bmatrix} 1 & -j14.71 \\ 0 & 1 \end{bmatrix}}_{\text{RECEIVING END SERIES CAPACITORS}}$$

$$= \begin{bmatrix} 1 & -j14.71 \\ 0 & 1 \end{bmatrix} \begin{bmatrix} 0.9285\angle 0.258° & 84.62\angle 86.12° \\ 1.405\times 10^{-3}\angle 90.19° & 0.9492\angle 0.2535° \end{bmatrix}$$

$$= \begin{bmatrix} 0.9492\angle 0.2553° & 71.45\angle 80.5° \\ 1.405\times 10^{-3}\angle 90.09° & 0.9492\angle 0.2535° \end{bmatrix}$$

(b) $A_{eq} = 0.9492$, $\theta_A = 0.2553°$

$B_{eq} = Z'_{eq} = 71.45 \ \Omega$, $\theta_{Z\,eq} = 80.5°$

FROM EQ.(5.5.6) WITH $V_S = V_R = 500 \ kV_{LL}$

$$P_{R\,MAX} = \frac{500\times 500}{71.45} - \frac{(0.9492)(500)^2}{71.45} \cos(80.5° - 0.2553°)$$

$$= 3499 - 563 = 2936 \ \text{MW} \ (3\phi)$$

WHICH IS 22.5% LARGER THAN THE VALUE

$P_{MAX} = 2397.5$ MW CALCULATED IN PROB. 5.29

FOR THE UNCOMPENSATED LINE.

5.46

From Problem 5.44:

$A_{eq} = 0.8813 \qquad \theta_A = 1.03°$

$B_{eq} = Z'_{eq} = 109.4 \qquad \theta_Z = 82.55°$

From Eq(5.5.6) with $V_S = V_R = 500$ kV$_{LL}$:

$$P_{RMAX} = \frac{(500)(500)}{109.4} - \frac{(.8813)(500)^2}{109.4}\cos(82.55° - 1.03°)$$

$P_{RMAX} = 2285. - 297. = \underline{\underline{1988.\ MW}}$ (three-phase)

which is $\underline{\underline{42.3\%\ \text{larger}}}$ than the value $P_{RMAX} = 1397.$ MW calculated in Problem 5.27 for the uncompensated line.

5.47

Let X_{eq} be the equivalent series reactance of one 765-kV, 500 km, series compensated line. The equivalent series reactance of four lines with two intermediate substations and one line section out-of-service is then:

$$\frac{1}{4}\left(\frac{2}{3}X_{eq}\right) + \frac{1}{3}\left(\frac{1}{3}X_{eq}\right) = 0.2778\, X_{eq}$$

From Eq (5.4.26) with $\delta = 35°$, $V_R = 0.95$ per unit, and $P = 9000$ MW;

$$P = \frac{(765)(.95 \times 765)\sin(35°)}{.2778\, X_{eq}} = 9000.$$

Solving for X_{eq}:

$$X_{eq} = 127.54\ \Omega = X'\left(1 - \frac{N_C}{100}\right) = 156.35\left(1 - \frac{N_C}{100}\right)$$

Solving: $N_C = 18.4\%$ series capacitive compensation ($N_C = 21.6\%$ including 4% line losses).

5.48

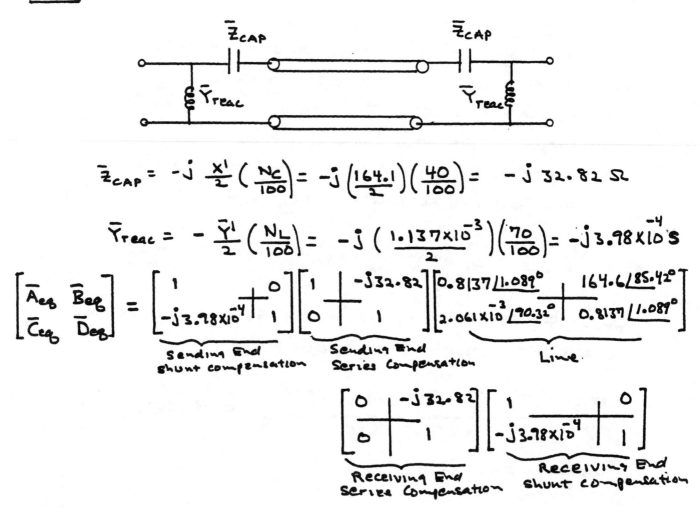

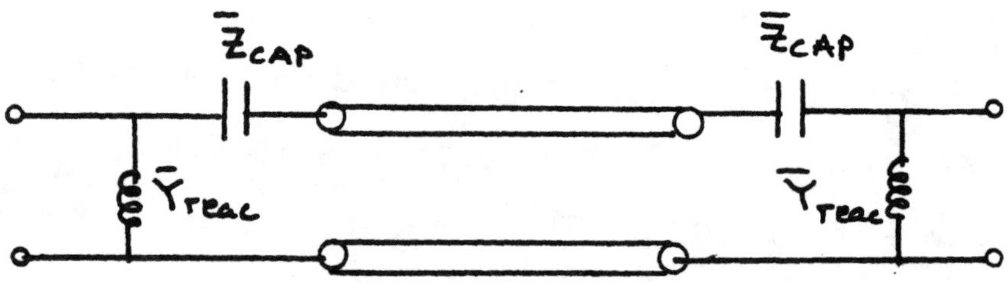

$$\bar{Z}_{CAP} = -j\,\frac{X'}{2}\left(\frac{N_C}{100}\right) = -j\left(\frac{164.1}{2}\right)\left(\frac{40}{100}\right) = -j\,32.82\ \Omega$$

$$\bar{Y}_{reac} = -\frac{\bar{Y}'}{2}\left(\frac{N_L}{100}\right) = -j\left(\frac{1.137\times10^{-3}}{2}\right)\left(\frac{70}{100}\right) = -j\,3.98\times10^{-4}\ S$$

$$\begin{bmatrix}\bar{A}_{eq} & \bar{B}_{eq}\\ \bar{C}_{eq} & \bar{D}_{eq}\end{bmatrix} = \underbrace{\begin{bmatrix}1 & 0\\ -j3.98\times10^{-4} & 1\end{bmatrix}}_{\text{Sending End shunt compensation}} \underbrace{\begin{bmatrix}1 & -j32.82\\ 0 & 1\end{bmatrix}}_{\text{Sending End Series Compensation}} \underbrace{\begin{bmatrix}0.8137\angle 1.089^\circ & 164.6\angle 85.42^\circ\\ 2.061\times10^{-3}\angle 90.32^\circ & 0.8137\angle 1.089^\circ\end{bmatrix}}_{\text{Line}}$$

$$\underbrace{\begin{bmatrix}0 & -j32.82\\ 0 & 1\end{bmatrix}}_{\text{Receiving End Series Compensation}} \underbrace{\begin{bmatrix}1 & 0\\ -j3.98\times10^{-4} & 1\end{bmatrix}}_{\text{Receiving End shunt compensation}}$$

After multiplying the above five matrices:

$$\begin{bmatrix}\bar{A}_{eq} & \bar{B}_{eq}\\ \bar{C}_{eq} & \bar{D}_{eq}\end{bmatrix} = \begin{bmatrix}0.9244\angle 0.632^\circ & 109.4\angle 82.55^\circ\\ 8.021\times10^{-4}\angle 89.96^\circ & 0.9244\angle 0.632^\circ\end{bmatrix}$$

5.49

SEE SOLUTION OF PR. 5.15 FOR $\bar{\gamma}\ell$, $\bar{Z}_c$, $\cosh\bar{\gamma}\ell$, AND $\sinh\bar{\gamma}\ell$.

FOR THE UNCOMPENSATED LINE:

$$\bar{A} = \bar{D} = \cosh\bar{\gamma}\ell = 0.8904\angle 1.34^\circ$$

$$\bar{B} = \bar{Z}' = \bar{Z}_c \sinh\bar{\gamma}\ell = 186.78\angle 79.46^\circ\ \Omega$$

$$\bar{C} = \frac{\sinh\bar{\gamma}\ell}{\bar{Z}_c} = \frac{0.4596\angle 84.94^\circ}{406.4\angle -5.48^\circ} = 0.001131\angle 90.42^\circ\ \text{S}$$

NOTING THAT THE SERIES COMPENSATION ONLY ALTERS THE SERIES ARM OF THE EQUIVALENT π-CIRCUIT, THE NEW SERIES ARM IMPEDANCE IS

$$\bar{Z}'_{new} = \bar{B}_{new} = 186.78\angle 79.46^\circ - j0.7\times 230(0.8277) = 60.88\angle 55.85^\circ\ \Omega$$

IN WHICH 0.8277 IS THE IMAGINARY PART OF $\bar{z} = 0.8431\angle 79.04^\circ\ \Omega/\text{mi}$

NOTING THAT $\bar{A} = \frac{\bar{Z}'\bar{Y}'}{2} + 1$ AND $\frac{\bar{Y}'}{2} = \frac{1}{\bar{Z}_c}\frac{\cosh\bar{\gamma}\ell - 1}{\sinh\bar{\gamma}\ell} = 0.000599\angle 89.82^\circ\ \text{S}$

$$\bar{A}_{new} = (60.88\angle 55.85^\circ \times 0.000599\angle 89.81^\circ) + 1 = 0.97\angle 1.24^\circ$$

$$\bar{C}_{new} = \bar{Y}'\left(1 + \frac{\bar{Z}'\bar{Y}'}{4}\right) = \bar{Y}' + \frac{\bar{Z}'\bar{Y}'^2}{4}$$

$$= 2\times 0.000599\angle 89.81^\circ + 60.88\angle 55.85^\circ(0.000599\angle 89.81^\circ)^2$$

$$= 0.00118\angle 90.41^\circ\ \text{S}$$

THE SERIES COMPENSATION HAS REDUCED THE PARAMETER $\bar{B}$ TO ABOUT ONE-THIRD OF ITS VALUE FOR THE UNCOMPENSATED LINE, WITHOUT AFFECTING THE $\bar{A}$ AND $\bar{C}$ PARAMETERS APPRECIABLY.

THUS, THE MAXIMUM POWER THAT CAN BE TRANSMITTED IS INCREASED BY ABOUT 300%.

5.50

THE SHUNT ADMITTANCE OF THE ENTIRE LINE IS

$$\bar{Y} = \bar{y}\ell = -j\,5.105 \times 10^{-6} \times 230 = -j\,0.001174\ \text{S}$$

WITH 70% COMPENSATION, $\bar{Y}_{new} = 0.7 \times (-j0.001174) = -j\,0.000822\ \text{S}$

FROM FIG. 5.4 OF THE TEXT, FOR THE CASE OF 'SHUNT ADMITTANCE',

$$A = D = 1\ ;\quad B = 0\ ;\quad \bar{C} = \bar{Y}$$

$$\therefore\ \bar{C} = \bar{Y}_{new} = -j\,0.000822\ \text{S}$$

FOR THE UNCOMPENSATED LINE, THE $\bar{A}, \bar{B}, \bar{C}, \bar{D}$ PARAMETERS ARE CALCULATED IN THE SOLUTION OF PR. 5.49.

FOR 'SERIES NETWORKS', SEE FIG. 5.4 OF THE TEXT TO MODIFY THE PARAMETERS.

SO FOR THE LINE WITH A SHUNT INDUCTOR,

$$\bar{A}_{eq} = 0.8904\angle 1.34^\circ + 186.78\angle 79.46^\circ\,(0.000822\angle -90^\circ)$$

$$= 1.0411\angle -0.4^\circ$$

THE VOLTAGE REGULATION WITH THE SHUNT REACTOR CONNECTED AT NO LOAD IS GIVEN BY

$$\frac{(137.86/1.0411) - 124.13}{124.13} = 0.0667$$

WHICH IS A CONSIDERABLE REDUCTION COMPARED TO 0.247 FOR THE REGULATION OF THE UNCOMPENSATED LINE. (SEE SOLUTION OF PR. 5.15)

5.51

(a) FROM THE SOLUTION OF PR. 5.25,

$$Z_c = 290.43\ \Omega\ ;\quad \beta\ell = 21.641^\circ$$

FOR A LOSSLESS LINE, THE EQUIVALENT LINE REACTANCE IS GIVEN BY

$$X' = Z_c \sin\beta\ell = (290.43)\sin 21.641^\circ = 107.11\ \Omega$$

5.51 CONTD.

THE RECEIVING END POWER $\bar{S}_{R(3\phi)} = 1000 \angle \cos^{-1} 0.8 = 800 + j600$ MVA

SINCE $P_{3\phi} = \dfrac{V_{S(L-L)} V_{R(L-L)}}{X'} \sin\delta$, THE POWER ANGLE δ

IS OBTAINED FROM $800 = (500 \times 500 / 107.11) \sin\delta$

OR $\delta = 20.044°$

THE RECEIVING END REACTIVE POWER IS GIVEN BY (APPROXIMATELY)

$$Q_{R(3\phi)} = \frac{V_{S(L-L)} V_{R(L-L)}}{X'} \cos\delta - \frac{V^2_{R(L-L)}}{X'} \cos\beta l$$

$$= \frac{500 \times 500}{107.11} \cos(20.044°) - \frac{(500)^2}{107.11} \cos(21.641°)$$

$$= 23.15 \text{ MVAR}$$

THEN THE REQUIRED CAPACITOR MVAR IS $\bar{S}_C = j23.15 - j600 = -j576.85$

THE CAPACITIVE REACTANCE IS GIVEN BY (SEE EQ. 2.3.5 IN TEXT)

$$X_C = \frac{-jV_L^2}{\bar{S}_C} = \frac{-j500^2}{-j576.85} = 433.38\ \Omega$$

$$\text{OR} \quad C = \frac{10^6}{2\pi(60)\,433.38} = 6.1\ \mu F$$

(b) FOR 40% COMPENSATION, THE SERIES CAPACITOR REACTANCE PER PHASE IS

$$X_{ser} = 0.4X' = 0.4(107.1) = 42.84\ \Omega$$

THE NEW EQUIVALENT π-CIRCUIT PARAMETERS ARE GIVEN BY

$$\bar{Z}' = j(X' - X_{ser}) = j\,64.26\ \Omega\ ; \quad \bar{Y}' = j\frac{2}{\bar{Z}_c}\tan\left(\frac{\beta l}{2}\right) = j0.001316\ \text{S}$$

$$\bar{B}_{new} = j\,64.26\ \Omega\ ; \quad \bar{A}_{new} = 1 + \frac{\bar{Z}'\bar{Y}'}{2} = 0.9577$$

THE RECEIVING END VOLTAGE PER PHASE $\bar{V}_R = \dfrac{500}{\sqrt{3}} \angle 0°$ kV $= 288.675 \angle 0°$ kV

THE RECEIVING END CURRENT IS $\bar{I}_R = \bar{S}^*_{R(3\phi)} / 3\bar{V}^*_R$

$$\text{THUS} \quad \bar{I}_R = \frac{1000 \angle -36.87°}{3 \times 288.675 \angle 0°} = 1.1547 \angle -36.87°\ \text{kA}$$

THE SENDING END VOLTAGE IS THEN GIVEN BY

$$\bar{V}_S = \bar{A}\bar{V}_R + \bar{B}\bar{I}_R = 326.4 \angle 10.47°\ \text{kV}\ ; \quad V_{S(L-L)} = \sqrt{3}\ 326.4 = 565.4\ \text{kV}$$

$$\text{PERCENT VOLTAGE REGULATION} = \frac{(565.4/0.958) - 500}{500} \times 100 = 18\%$$

Problem 5.52

The maximum amount of real power which can be transferred to the load at unity pf with a bus voltage greater than 0.9 pu is 3900MW.

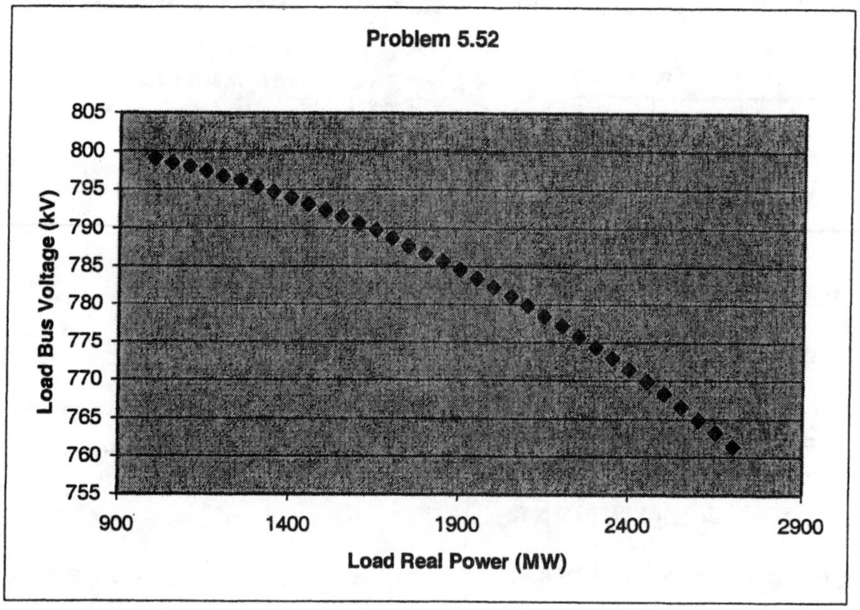

Problem 5.53

The maximum amount of real power which can be transferred to the load at unity pf with a bus voltage greater than 0.9 pu is 3400MW (3450 MW may be OK since pu voltage is 0.8985).

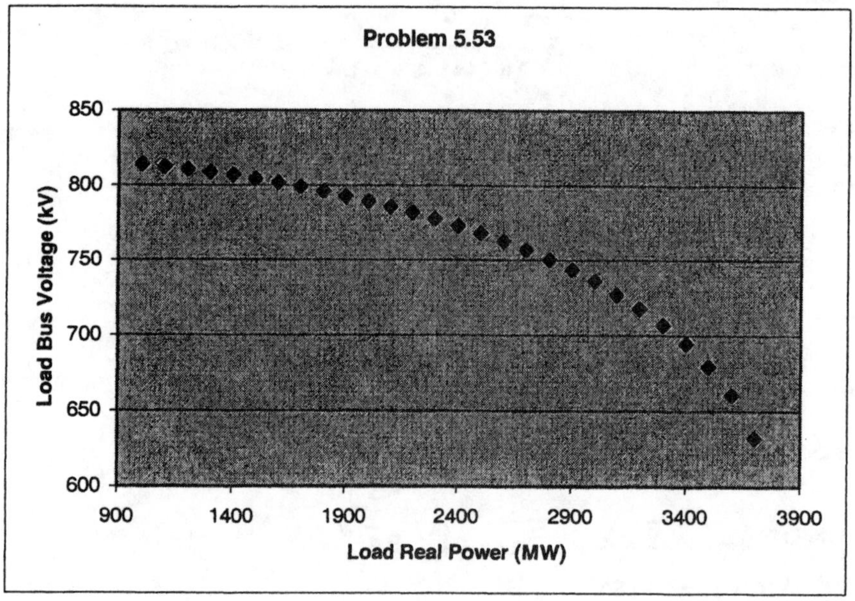

CHAPTER 6

6.1

$$\begin{bmatrix} 5 & -2 & -3 \\ -5 & 7 & -2 \\ -3 & -3 & 8 \end{bmatrix} \begin{bmatrix} x_1 \\ x_2 \\ x_3 \end{bmatrix} = \begin{bmatrix} 4 \\ -10 \\ 6 \end{bmatrix}$$

THERE ARE $N-1 = 2$ GAUSS ELIMINATION STEPS.

DURING STEP 1, SUBTRACT $A_{21}/A_{11} = -5/5 = -1$ TIMES EQ. 1 FROM EQ. 2, AND SUBTRACT $A_{31}/A_{11} = -3/5$ TIMES EQ. 1 FROM EQ. 3.

$$\begin{bmatrix} 5 & -2 & -3 \\ 0 & 5 & -5 \\ 0 & -\frac{21}{5} & \frac{31}{5} \end{bmatrix} \begin{bmatrix} x_1 \\ x_2 \\ x_3 \end{bmatrix} = \begin{bmatrix} 4 \\ -6 \\ \frac{42}{5} \end{bmatrix}$$ WHICH IS $A^{(1)}x = y^{(1)}$

DURING STEP 2, SUBTRACT $A_{32}^{(1)} / A_{22}^{(1)} = \dfrac{-21/5}{5} = -\dfrac{21}{25}$ TIMES EQ. 2 FROM EQ. 3.

$$\begin{bmatrix} 5 & -2 & -3 \\ 0 & 5 & -5 \\ 0 & 0 & 2 \end{bmatrix} \begin{bmatrix} x_1 \\ x_2 \\ x_3 \end{bmatrix} = \begin{bmatrix} 4 \\ -6 \\ \frac{84}{25} \end{bmatrix}$$ WHICH IS TRIANGULARIZED.

VIA BACK SUBSTITUTION, $x_3 = 1.68$; $x_2 = 0.48$; $x_1 = 2$

BY CRAMER'S RULE,

$$\Delta = \begin{vmatrix} 5 & -2 & -3 \\ -5 & 7 & -2 \\ -3 & -3 & 8 \end{vmatrix} = 50 \; ; \; \Delta_1 = \begin{vmatrix} 4 & -2 & -3 \\ -10 & 7 & -2 \\ 6 & -3 & 8 \end{vmatrix} = 100$$ (EXPANDING Δ_1 ABOUT THE FIRST COLUMN)

$$\Delta_2 = \begin{vmatrix} 5 & 4 & -3 \\ -5 & -10 & -2 \\ -3 & 6 & 8 \end{vmatrix} = 24 \; ; \; \Delta_3 = \begin{vmatrix} 5 & -2 & 4 \\ -5 & 7 & -10 \\ -3 & -3 & 6 \end{vmatrix} = 84$$

6.1 CONTD.

$x_1 = \frac{\Delta_1}{\Delta} = 2$; $x_2 = \frac{\Delta_2}{\Delta} = 0.48$; $x_3 = \frac{\Delta_3}{\Delta} = 1.68$

BY MATRIX METHOD

$AX = Y$; $A^{-1}AX = A^{-1}Y$; $X = A^{-1}Y$ WHERE $A^{-1} = \frac{1}{50}\begin{bmatrix} 50 & 25 & 25 \\ 46 & 31 & 25 \\ 36 & 21 & 25 \end{bmatrix}$

$x_1 = 2$; $x_2 = 0.48$; $x_3 = 1.68$

6.2

1st GE Step

$$\begin{bmatrix} 10 & 3 & 0 \\ 0 & 18.8 & 2 \\ 0 & 0.5 & 14 \end{bmatrix} \begin{bmatrix} x_1 \\ x_2 \\ x_3 \end{bmatrix} = \begin{bmatrix} 1 \\ 1.6 \\ 2.5 \end{bmatrix}$$

2nd GE step

$$\begin{bmatrix} 10 & 3 & 0 \\ 0 & 18.8 & 2 \\ 0 & 0 & 13.94681 \end{bmatrix} \begin{bmatrix} x_1 \\ x_2 \\ x_3 \end{bmatrix} = \begin{bmatrix} 1 \\ 1.6 \\ 2.45745 \end{bmatrix}$$

Back substitution:

$$x_3 = \frac{2.45745}{13.94681} = 0.17620$$

$$x_2 = \frac{1.6 - 2(0.17620)}{18.8} = 0.06636$$

$$x_1 = \frac{1 - 3(.06636)}{10} = 0.08009$$

6.3

1ST GE STEP

$$\begin{bmatrix} 10 & 3 & 0 \\ 0 & 18.8 & 2 \\ 0 & 0.5 & 1.4 \end{bmatrix} \begin{bmatrix} x_1 \\ x_2 \\ x_3 \end{bmatrix} = \begin{bmatrix} 1 \\ 1.6 \\ 2.5 \end{bmatrix}$$

2ND GE STEP

$$\begin{bmatrix} 10 & 3 & 0 \\ 0 & 18.8 & 2 \\ 0 & 0 & 1.3468085 \end{bmatrix} \begin{bmatrix} x_1 \\ x_2 \\ x_3 \end{bmatrix} = \begin{bmatrix} 1 \\ 1.6 \\ 2.457447 \end{bmatrix}$$

BACK SUBSTITUTION YIELDS:

$$x_3 = 2.457447 / 1.3468085 = 1.8246$$

$$x_2 = \frac{1.6 - 2(1.8246)}{18.8} = -0.109$$

$$x_1 = \frac{1 - 3(-0.109)}{10} = 0.1327$$

6.4

Summary – Gauss Elimination

	# Divisions	# Multiplications	# Subtractions
1st GE step	$N-1$	$N(N-1)$	$N(N-1)$
2nd GE step	$(N-2)$	$(N-1)(N-2)$	$(N-1)(N-2)$
3rd GE step	$(N-3)$	$(N-2)(N-3)$	$(N-2)(N-3)$
⋮	⋮	⋮	⋮
$(N-1)^{th}$ GE step	1	$(2)(1)$	$(2)(1)$
Totals	$\sum_{i=1}^{N-1} i = \frac{N(N-1)}{2}$	$\sum_{i=1}^{N-1} i(i+1) = \frac{N^3-N}{3}$	$\sum_{i=1}^{N-1} i(i+1) = \frac{N^3-N}{3}$

6.5 From Eq (7.1.6), back substitution is given by:

$$x_k = \frac{y_k - A_{k,k+1}x_{k+1} - A_{k,k+2}x_{k+2} \cdots - A_{k,N}x_N}{A_{kk}}$$

which requires <u>one</u> division, $(N-k)$ multiplications and $(N-k)$ subtractions for each $k = N, (N-1) \cdots 1$.

Summary – Back Substitution

Solving for	# Divisions	# Multiplications	# Subtractions
x_N	1	0	0
x_{N-1}	1	1	1
x_{N-2}	1	2	2
	⋮		
x_1	1	$(N-1)$	$(N-1)$
Totals	N	$\sum_{i=1}^{N-1} i = \frac{N(N-1)}{2}$	$\sum_{i=1}^{N-1} i = \frac{N(N-1)}{2}$

6.6 Using the results of Problems 6.4 and 6.5 with $N = 100$:

$$\text{Time for G.E.} = \left[\frac{100(99)}{2}\right]10^{-6} + \left[\frac{(100)^3 - 100}{3}\right]\left[10^{-6} + 10^{-7}\right] = 0.3716$$

$$\text{Time for back substitution} = [100]\,10^{-6} + \left[\frac{(100)(99)}{2}\right]\left[10^{-6} + 10^{-7}\right] = 0.0055$$

Total time = 0.3771 s

Note: Additional time is required for indexing and managing DO loops.

6.7 The y vector has $N = 10^3$ elements and the A matrix has $N^2 = 10^6$ elements. Storage requirements are:

$$(N^2 + N)\,4 = (10^3 + 10^6)\,4 = 4.004 \times 10^6 \text{ bytes}$$

$$= 4004.\ \text{k bytes}$$

6.8

$$x_1(i+1) = \frac{1}{A_{11}}\left[y_1 - A_{12}x_2(i) - A_{13}x_3(i)\right] = \frac{1}{10}\left[1 - 3x_2(i)\right]$$

$$x_2(i+1) = \frac{1}{A_{22}}\left[y_2 - A_{21}x_1(i) - A_{23}x_3(i)\right] = \frac{1}{20}\left[2 - 4x_1(i) - 2x_3(i)\right]$$

$$x_3(i+1) = \frac{1}{A_{33}}\left[y_3 - A_{31}x_1(i) - A_{32}x_2(i)\right] = \frac{1}{14}\left[3 - 5x_1(i) - 2x_2(i)\right]$$

i	0	1	2	3	4	5	6
$x_1(i)$	0	0.10000	0.07000	0.08243	0.07913	0.08037	0.08000
$x_2(i)$	0	0.10000	0.05857	0.06957	0.06542	0.06668	0.06626
$x_3(i)$	0	0.21429	0.16439	0.18092	0.17491	0.17668	0.17606

Stop after 6 iterations

$$\left|\frac{x_1(6) - x_1(5)}{x_1(5)}\right| = \left|\frac{0.08000 - 0.08037}{.08037}\right| = 0.005$$

$$\left|\frac{x_2(6) - x_2(5)}{x_2(5)}\right| = \left|\frac{0.06626 - 0.06668}{0.06668}\right| = 0.006 \quad \left|\frac{x_3(6) - x_3(5)}{x_3(5)}\right| = 0.004$$

6.9

$$x_1(i+1) = \frac{1}{10}\left[1 - 3x_2(i)\right] \quad x_2(i+1) = \frac{1}{20}\left[2 - 4x_1(i+1) - 2x_3(i)\right]$$

$$x_3(i+1) = \frac{1}{14}\left[3 - 5x_1(i+1) - 2x_2(i+1)\right]$$

i	0	1	2	3	4
$x_1(i)$	0	0.10000	0.07600	0.07957	0.08010
$x_2(i)$	0	0.08000	0.06809	0.06634	0.06634
$x_3(i)$	0	0.16714	0.17742	0.17639	0.17620

Stop after four iterations. Gauss-Seidel converges more rapidly for this problem.

$$\left|\frac{x_1(4) - x_1(3)}{x_1(3)}\right| = \left|\frac{0.08010 - 0.07957}{0.07957}\right| = 0.007$$

$$\left|\frac{x_2(4) - x_2(3)}{x_2(3)}\right| = 0$$

$$\left|\frac{x_3(4) - x_3(3)}{x_3(3)}\right| = 0.001$$

6.10 Jacobi:

$$x_1(i+1) = \frac{1}{10}\left[1-3x_2(i)\right] \qquad x_2(i+1) = \frac{1}{20}\left[2-4x_1(i)-2x_3(i)\right]$$

$$x_3(i+1) = \frac{1}{0.14}\left[3-5x_1(i)-2x_2(i)\right]$$

i	0	1	2	3	4	5	6
$x_1(i)$	0	0.100	0.0700	0.71887	0.56707	1.56331	0.6439
$x_2(i)$	0	0.100	-2.0629	-1.5569	-4.8777	-1.8130	-7.2984
$x_3(i)$	0	21.429	16.429	48.399	17.996	70.8575	-8.5039

i	7	8	9	10	11	12	13
$x_1(i)$	2.2895	-0.14648	3.2884	-2.101	5.6218	-6.0809	11.191
$x_2(i)$	0.82161	-10.6279	7.3373	-18.406	20.603	-36.97	48.684
$x_3(i)$	102.70	-72.08	178.48	-200.83	359.41	-473.68	766.75

Gauss Seidel:

$$x_1(i+1) = \frac{1}{10}\left[1-3x_2(i)\right] \qquad x_2(i+1) = \frac{1}{20}\left[2-4x_1(i+1)-2x_3(i)\right]$$

$$x_3(i+1) = \frac{1}{0.14}\left[3-5x_1(i+1)-2x_2(i+1)\right]$$

i	0	1	2	3	4	5	6
$x_1(i)$	0	0.100	0.0760	0.57598	1.3460	1.9564	2.0402
$x_2(i)$	0	0.080	-1.5866	-4.1532	-6.1881	-6.4672	-4.7026
$x_3(i)$	0	16.714	41.380	60.189	61.759	43.946	15.744

i	7	8	9	10	11	12	13
$x_1(i)$	1.51078	0.63278	-0.10646	-0.26666	0.28712	1.28311	2.1724
$x_2(i)$	-1.7766	0.68819	1.2222	-0.62374	-3.9437	-6.9079	-7.7632
$x_3(i)$	-7.1479	-11.009	7.7707	39.863	67.513	74.2875	54.75

Neither the Jacobi nor Gauss-Seidel iterative methods converge to the unique solution (given in the Problem 7.2 solution)

G.11

[NOTE ERROR IN PRINTING OF PROB. STATEMENT:

THE SECOND EQUATION SHOULD BE $x_2 + x_1^2 - 1.8 = 0$]

REWRITING THE GIVEN EQUATIONS,

$$x_1 = \frac{x_2}{3} + 0.633 \quad ; \quad x_2 = 1.8 - x_1^2$$

WITH AN INITIAL GUESS OF $x_1(0) = 1.$ AND $x_2(0) = 1.$,

UPDATE x_1 WITH THE FIRST EQ. ABOVE, AND x_2 WITH THE SECOND EQUATION.

THUS $\quad x_1 = \dfrac{x_2(0)}{3} + 0.633 = \dfrac{1}{3} + 0.633 = 0.9663$

AND $\quad x_2 = 1.8 - x_1(0)^2 = 1.8 - 1 = 0.8$

IN SUCCEEDING ITERATIONS, COMPUTE MORE GENERALLY AS

$$x_1(n+1) = \frac{x_2(n)}{3} + 0.633$$

AND $$x_2(n+1) = 1.8 - x_1^2(n)$$

AFTER SEVERAL ITERATIONS, $x_1 = 0.938$ AND $x_2 = 0.917$.

AFTER A FEW MORE ITERATIONS, $x_1 = 0.93926$ AND $x_2 = 0.9178$.

HOWEVER, NOTE THAT AN 'UNEDUCATED GUESS' OF INITIAL VALUES, SUCH AS $x_1(0) = x_2(0) = 100$, WOULD HAVE CAUSED THE SOLUTION TO DIVERGE.

6.12

REWRITING THE GIVEN EQUATION, FOR THE GAUSS-SEIDEL METHOD:

$$x_1 = \frac{1}{6} x_1^2 + \frac{1}{3} = F(x_1)$$

USE THE INITIAL ESTIMATE $x_1(0) = 1$

THEN, IN SUCCEEDING ITERATIONS

ITERATION 1: $x_1(1) = F(1) = \frac{1}{6} + \frac{1}{3} = 0.5$

ITERATION 2: $x_1(2) = F(0.5) = \frac{1}{6}(0.5)^2 + \frac{1}{3} = 0.375$

ITERATION 3: $x_1(3) = F(0.375) = \frac{1}{6}(0.375)^2 + \frac{1}{3} = 0.3568$

ITERATION 4: $x_1(4) = F(0.3568) = \frac{1}{6}(0.3568)^2 + \frac{1}{3} = 0.3545$

SINCE $|x_1(n+1)| - |x_1(n)| < \epsilon = 0.0023$, WHICH SEEMS TO BE SUFFICIENTLY SMALL, ONE MAY NOW STOP.

THE QUADRATIC FORMULA GIVES THIS ROOT AS

$x_1 = 0.35425$ TO FIVE PLACES.

6.13 Eq(6.2.6) is : $\underline{x}(i+1) = \underline{M}\,\underline{x}(i) + \underline{D}^{-1}\underline{y}$

Taking the z transform (assume zero initial conditions):

$$z\,\underline{X}(z) = \underline{M}\,\underline{X}(z) + \underline{D}^{-1}\underline{Y}(z)$$

$$(z\underline{U} - \underline{M})\,\underline{X}(z) = \underline{D}^{-1}\underline{Y}(z)$$

$$\underline{X}(z) = (z\underline{U} - \underline{M})^{-1}\,\underline{D}^{-1}\,\underline{Y}(z) = \underline{G}(z)\,\underline{Y}(z)$$

6.14 For Example 6.3,

$$\text{Det}\,(z\underline{U} - \underline{M}) = \text{Det}\begin{bmatrix} z & 5/10 \\ 2/9 & z \end{bmatrix} = z^2 - \frac{1}{9} = 0$$

$$z = +\frac{1}{3},\ -\frac{1}{3}.$$

For Example 7.5,

$$\underline{D} = \begin{bmatrix} 5 & 0 \\ 9 & 2 \end{bmatrix} \qquad \underline{M} = \underline{D}^{-1}(\underline{D} - \underline{A}) = \begin{bmatrix} \frac{2}{10} & 0 \\ -\frac{9}{10} & \frac{5}{10} \end{bmatrix}\begin{bmatrix} 0 & -10 \\ 0 & 0 \end{bmatrix} = \begin{bmatrix} 0 & -2 \\ 0 & 9 \end{bmatrix}$$

$$\text{Det}\,(z\underline{U} - \underline{M}) = \text{Det}\begin{bmatrix} z & 2 \\ 0 & z-9 \end{bmatrix} = z\,(z-9) = 0$$

$$z = 0,\ 9$$

6.15 For Jacobi,

$$\underline{M} = \underline{D}^{-1}(\underline{D} - \underline{A}) = \begin{bmatrix} A_{11} & 0 \\ 0 & A_{22} \end{bmatrix}^{-1}\begin{bmatrix} 0 & -A_{12} \\ -A_{21} & 0 \end{bmatrix} = \begin{bmatrix} 0 & -\frac{A_{12}}{A_{11}} \\ -\frac{A_{21}}{A_{22}} & 0 \end{bmatrix}$$

$$\text{Det}(z\underline{U} - \underline{M}) = \text{Det}\begin{bmatrix} z & \frac{A_{12}}{A_{11}} \\ \frac{A_{21}}{A_{22}} & z \end{bmatrix} = z^2 - \frac{A_{12}A_{21}}{A_{11}A_{22}} = 0$$

$$z = \pm\sqrt{\left(\frac{A_{12}A_{21}}{A_{11}A_{22}}\right)}$$

For Gauss-Seidel,

$$\underline{M} = \underline{D}^{-1}(\underline{D} - \underline{A}) = \begin{bmatrix} A_{11} & 0 \\ A_{21} & A_{22} \end{bmatrix}^{-1}\begin{bmatrix} 0 & -A_{12} \\ 0 & 0 \end{bmatrix} = \begin{bmatrix} 0 & \frac{-A_{12}}{A_{11}} \\ 0 & \frac{A_{12}A_{21}}{A_{11}A_{22}} \end{bmatrix}$$

6.15 CONTD.

$$\mathrm{Det}(z\underline{U}-\underline{M}) = \mathrm{Det}\begin{bmatrix} z & +\frac{A_{12}}{A_{11}} \\ 0 & z-\frac{A_{12}A_{21}}{A_{11}A_{22}} \end{bmatrix} = z\left(z-\frac{A_{12}A_{21}}{A_{11}A_{22}}\right)=0$$

$$z = 0,\ \frac{A_{12}A_{21}}{A_{11}A_{22}}$$

When $N=2$, Both Jacobi and Gauss-Seidel converge if and only if $\left|\frac{A_{12}A_{21}}{A_{11}A_{22}}\right| < 1$

6.16 Gauss-Seidel, from Eq (6.2.9) is given by

$$x_k(i+1) = \frac{1}{A_{kk}}\left[y_k - \sum_{n=1}^{k-1} A_{kn}x_n(i+1) - \sum_{n=k+1}^{N} A_{kn}x_n(i)\right]$$

$$k = 1,2,3\ldots N$$

For each k, the above equation requires $(N-1)$ multiplications one division, and $(N-1)$ subtractions. Thus for N equations, each iteration requires $N(N-1)$ multiplications N divisions, and $N(N-1)$ subtractions. For $N = 100$, computer time per iteration is

$$N(N-1)(10^{-6}) + N(10^{-6}) + N(N-1)(10^{-7})$$

$$= (100)(99)(10^{-6}) + (100)(10^{-6}) + 100(99)(10^{-7}) = \underline{0.011\ \text{s}}$$

plus some additional time for indexing and managing DO loops.

6.17 $J = \frac{df}{dx} = 9x^2 + 8x + 5$ From Eq (6.3.9):

$$x(i+1) = x(i) + [9x^2(i) + 8x(i) + 5]^{-1}\{0 - [3x^3(i) + 4x^2(i) + 5x(i) + 8]\}$$

i	0	1	2	3	4	5
x(i)	1	0.090909	−1.3724426	−1.4559933	−1.451163	−1.4511453

$$\left|\frac{x(5) - x(4)}{x(4)}\right| = \left|\frac{-1.4511453 + 1.451163}{-1.451163}\right| = 0.000012$$

Stop after 5 iterations. Note that $x = -1.4511453$ is one solution. The other two solutions are $x = 0.0589059 \pm j1.3543113$

6.18 $J = \frac{df}{dx} = 4x^3 + 36x^2 + 108x + 108$ From Eq (6.3.9):

$$x(i+1) = x(i) + [4x^3(i) + 36x^2(i) + 108x(i) + 108]\{0 - [x^4(i) + 12x^3(i) + 54x^2(i) + 108x(i) + 81]\}$$

i	0	1	2	3	4	...	17	18	19
x(i)	−1	−1.5	−1.875	−2.15625	−2.3671875	...	−2.9848614	−2.989901	−2.9923223

$$\left|\frac{x(19) - x(18)}{x(18)}\right| = \left|\frac{-2.9923223 + 2.989901}{-2.989901}\right| = 0.0008$$

Stop after 19 iterations. $x(19) = -2.9923223$. Note that $x = -3$ is one of four solutions to this 4th degree polynomial. The other three solutions are $x = -3$, $x = -3$, and $x = -3$.

6.19

$$\begin{bmatrix} x_1(i+1) \\ x_2(i+1) \end{bmatrix} = \begin{bmatrix} x_1 \\ x_2 \end{bmatrix} + \begin{bmatrix} x_2 e^{x_1x_2} & x_1 e^{x_1x_2} \\ -\sin(x_1+x_2) & -\sin(x_1+x_2) \end{bmatrix}^{-1} \begin{bmatrix} y_1 - e^{x_1x_2} \\ y_2 - \cos(x_1+x_2) \end{bmatrix}$$

$$\begin{bmatrix} x_1(i+1) \\ x_2(i+1) \end{bmatrix} = \begin{bmatrix} x_1 \\ x_2 \end{bmatrix} + \frac{\begin{bmatrix} -\sin(x_1+x_2) & -x_1 e^{x_1x_2} \\ \sin(x_1+x_2) & x_2 e^{x_1x_2} \end{bmatrix}}{(x_1-x_2)e^{x_1x_2}\sin(x_1+x_2)} \begin{bmatrix} 1.2 - e^{x_1x_2} \\ 0.5 - \cos(x_1+x_2) \end{bmatrix}$$

$$x_1(i+1) = x_1 + \frac{-\sin(x_1+x_2)\left[1.2 - e^{x_1x_2}\right] - x_1 e^{x_1x_2}\left[0.5 - \cos(x_1+x_2)\right]}{(x_1-x_2)e^{x_1x_2}\sin(x_1+x_2)}$$

$$x_2(i+1) = x_2 + \frac{\sin(x_1+x_2)\left[1.2 - e^{x_1x_2}\right] + x_2 e^{x_1x_2}\left[0.5 - \cos(x_1+x_2)\right]}{(x_1-x_2)e^{x_1x_2}\sin(x_1+x_2)}$$

where the right side of the equations are evaluated at i.

(a) $x_1(0) = 1 \quad x_2(0) = 0.5$

i	0	1	2	3	4	5
$x_1(i)$	1.0	0.68364	0.89557	0.83155	0.82667	0.82664
$x_2(i)$	0.5	0.38601	0.15176	0.21565	0.22053	0.22056

$$\left|\frac{x_1(5) - x_1(4)}{x_1(4)}\right| = 4\times10^{-5} \qquad \left|\frac{x_2(5) - x_2(4)}{x_2(4)}\right| = 1.4\times10^{-4}$$

(b) $x_1(0) = 1 \quad x_2(0) = 2$

i	0	1	2
$x_1(i)$	1	10.7207	1.7×10^{38}
$x_2(i)$	2	-18.279	-1.7×10^{38}

which is Diverging

6.20

WITH THE STARTING POINT $x_1(0) = 1$ AND $x_2(0) = -1$ FOR THE FIRST ITERATION IN THE NEWTON-RAPHSON METHOD,

$$f_1(x_1(0), x_2(0)) = 1 + 4 - 4 = 1$$

$$f_2(x_1(0), x_2(0)) = 2 + 1 - 2 = 1$$

THE PARTIAL DERIVATIVES EVALUATED AT $x_1(0)$ AND $x_2(0)$ ARE

$$\frac{\partial f_1}{\partial x_1} = 2x_1 = 2 \quad ; \quad \frac{\partial f_2}{\partial x_1} = 2$$

$$\frac{\partial f_1}{\partial x_2} = -4 \quad ; \quad \frac{\partial f_2}{\partial x_2} = -1$$

NEGLECTING DERIVATIVES OF ORDER GREATER THAN ONE IN TAYLOR-SERIES EXPANSION,

$$f_1(x_1(0), x_2(0)) + \Delta x_1(0) \left.\frac{\partial f_1}{\partial x_1}\right|_{x_1(0)} + \Delta x_2(0) \left.\frac{\partial f_1}{\partial x_2}\right|_{x_2(0)} = 0$$

$$f_2(x_1(0), x_2(0)) + \Delta x_1(0) \left.\frac{\partial f_2}{\partial x_1}\right|_{x_1(0)} + \Delta x_2(0) \left.\frac{\partial f_2}{\partial x_2}\right|_{x_2(0)} = 0$$

SUBSTITUTION YIELDS: $1 + 2\Delta x_1 - 4\Delta x_2 = 0$

AND $1 + 2\Delta x_1 - \Delta x_2 = 0$

SIMULTANEOUS SOLUTION YIELDS: $\Delta x_1(0) = -0.5$ AND $\Delta x_2(0) = 0$

THUS, BETTER ESTIMATES OF x_1 AND x_2 ARE

$x_1(1) = x_1(0) + \Delta x_1 = 1 - 0.5 = 0.5$; $x_2(1) = x_2(0) + \Delta x_2 = -1 + 0 = -1$

PROCEEDING AS ABOVE WITH THESE NEW ESTIMATES, SECOND AND THIRD ITERATIONS YIELD:

$x_1(2) = 0.5357$ AND $x_2(2) = -0.9286$

$x_1(3) = 0.5359$ AND $x_2(3) = -0.9282$

NOTE THAT SUCH PROBLEMS ARE SOLVED MOST CONVENIENTLY WITH A DIGITAL COMPUTER.

6.21

LET $p(y) = y \sin y + 4$

USING THE INITIAL GUESS $y^0 = 4$, $p(y^0) = p(4) = 4 \sin 4 + 4 = 0.9728$

$p'(y) = \dfrac{dp}{dy} = y \cos y + \sin y$ SO THAT $p'(y^0) = p'(4) = -3.3714$

AND $\Delta y^0 = p(y^0)/p'(y^0) = 0.9728/(-3.3714) = -0.289$

FOR THE FIRST ITERATION, $y^1 = y^0 - \Delta y^0 = y^0 - \dfrac{p(y^0)}{\left(\dfrac{dp}{dy}\right)^0}$

SO $y^1 = y^0 - \Delta y^0 = 4 + 0.289 = 4.289$; $p(y^1) = p(4.289) = 0.0897$

$p'(y^2) = p'(4.289) = -2.6738$; $\Delta y^1 = \dfrac{0.0897}{-2.6738} = -0.0335$

2ND ITERATION: $y^2 = y^1 - \Delta y^1 = 4.289 + 0.0335 = 4.3225$

$\therefore$ $p(y^2) = p(4.3225) = 0.0019$; $p'(y^2) = p'(4.3225) = -2.5679$

$$\Delta y^2 = 0.0019/(-2.5679) = -0.00074$$

3RD ITERATION: $y^3 = y^2 - \Delta y^2 = 4.3225 + 0.00074 = 4.32324$

$$p(y^3) = -0.000001$$

SINCE $p(y^3)$ DIFFERS FROM ZERO BY ONE PART IN A MILLION, ONE SOLUTION TO THIS NONLINEAR EQUATION CAN BE SAID TO BE

$$y = y^3 = 4.32324 \text{ rad}.$$

OFCOURSE, THE PRESENCE OF THE TRIGONOMETRIC FUNCTION MEANS THAT THERE ARE OTHER SOLUTIONS TO THE PROBLEM.

6.22

(a) $\bar{Y}_{11} = 5 - j10 = 11.18 \angle -63.43^\circ$; $\bar{Y}_{22} = 2 - j4 = 4.47 \angle -63.43^\circ$

$\bar{Y}_{33} = 3 - j6 = 6.71 \angle -63.43^\circ$; $\bar{Y}_{12} = -2 + j4 = 4.47 \angle 116.57^\circ$

$\bar{Y}_{13} = -3 + j6 = 6.71 \angle 116.57^\circ$; $\bar{Y}_{23} = 0$

(b) AT BUS 2, $P_2 = V_2 \left[Y_{12} V_1 \cos(\delta_2 - \delta_1 - \theta_{12}) + Y_{22} V_2 \cos(\delta_2 - \delta_2 - \theta_{22}) + \right.$
$\left. + Y_{23} V_3 \cos(\delta_2 - \delta_3 - \theta_{23}) \right]$

THUS $1.6 = 1.1 \left[4.47(1) \cos(\delta_2 - 116.57^\circ) + 4.47(1.1) \cos(-63.43^\circ) \right]$

WHICH YIELDS $\cos(\delta_2 - 116.57^\circ) = -0.16669$; $\delta_2 - 116.57^\circ = \pm 99.59535^\circ$

OR $\delta_2 = 216.16^\circ$ OR 16.97465° ; TAKE $\delta_2 = 16.97465^\circ$

(c) FOR BUS 3, $P_3 = V_3 \left[Y_{31} V_1 \cos(\delta_3 - \delta_1 - \theta_{31}) + Y_{33} V_3 \cos(-\theta_{33}) \right]$

SUBSTITUTING, $-2 = V_3 \left[6.71(1) \cos(\delta_3 - 116.57^\circ) + 6.71 V_3 \cos 63.43^\circ \right]$

THUS $\frac{-2}{6.71} = V_3^2 \left[\cos 63.43^\circ \right] + V_3 \cos(\delta_3 - 116.57^\circ)$ — EQ. 1

ALSO, $Q_3 = V_3 \left[Y_{31} V_1 \sin(\delta_3 - \delta_1 - \theta_{31}) + Y_{33} V_3 \sin(-\theta_{33}) \right]$

$1 = V_3 \left[6.71 \sin(\delta_3 - 116.57^\circ) + 6.71 V_3 \sin 63.43^\circ \right]$

$\frac{1}{6.71} = V_3^2 \sin 63.43^\circ + V_3 \sin(\delta_3 - 116.57^\circ)$ — EQ. 2

COMBINING EQ. 1 AND EQ. 2 ABOVE,

$$\left[\frac{2}{6.71} + V_3^2 \cos 63.43^\circ \right]^2 + \left[\frac{1}{6.71} - V_3^2 \sin 63.43^\circ \right]^2 = V_3^2$$

OR $V_3^4 + \frac{4}{6.71} V_3^2 \left[\cos 63.43^\circ - 0.5 \sin 63.43^\circ \right] + \frac{5}{(6.71)^2} = V_3^2$

WHICH GIVES $V_3^4 - V_3^2 + \frac{1}{9} = 0$

THE SOLUTION OF WHICH IS $V_3^2 = \frac{1 \pm \sqrt{5}/3}{2}$

TAKING THE POSITIVE SIGN, $V_3^2 = 0.8727$

OR $V_3 = 0.9342$

6.22 CONTD.

SUBSTITUTING IN EQ. 1

$$\frac{-2}{6.71} = 0.8727 \cos 63.43^\circ + 0.9342 \cos(\delta_3 - 116.57^\circ)$$

WHICH YIELDS $\cos(\delta_3 - 116.57^\circ) = -0.7369$

OR $\delta_3 - 116.57^\circ = \pm 137.468$

OR $\delta_3 = -20.898^\circ$

(d) $$P_1 = V_1 \left[Y_{11} V_1 \cos(-\theta_{11}) + Y_{12} V_2 \cos(\delta_1 - \delta_2 - \theta_{12}) + Y_{13} V_3 \cos(\delta_1 - \delta_3 - \theta_{13}) \right]$$

$$= 0.9937$$

(e) TOTAL REAL POWER LOSS IN THE SYSTEM IS CALCULATE AS

$$0.9937 + 1.6 - 2 = 0.5937$$

6.23

$\bar{Y}_{31} = \bar{Y}_{32} = \bar{Y}_{35} = 0 \qquad \bar{Y}_{34} = \frac{-1}{0.003 + j0.04} = 24.93\underline{/94.29^\circ}$ per unit

$\bar{Y}_{33} = -\bar{Y}_{34} = 24.93\underline{/-85.71^\circ}$ per unit

6.24

In Example 6.9, as shown in Figure 6.3, buses 1 and 3 are not directly connected to bus 2. Therefore,

$$Y_{21} = Y_{23} = 0$$

Also, Y_{24} is the same as in Example 6.9,

$$Y_{24} = 9.95972/95.143^\circ \text{ per unit}$$

Using (6.4.2) with the impedance of the line between buses 2 and 5 (Line 2) doubled,

$$Y_{25} = \frac{-1}{R'_{25} + jX'_{25}} = \frac{-1}{2(0.0045 + j0.05)} =$$

$$= 9.95972/95.143^\circ \text{ per unit}$$

$$Y_{22} = \frac{1}{R'_{24} + jX'_{24}} + \frac{1}{R'_{25} + jX'_{25}} + jB'_{24}/2 + j B'_{25}/2$$

$$= (0.89276 - j9.91964) + (0.89276 - j9.91964) + j1.72/2 + j0.88/2$$

$$= 1.78552 - j18.539 = 18.625/-84.523^\circ \text{ per unit}$$

The above results can be verified using PowerWorld simulator.

6.25 (a) By inspection:

$$\bar{Y}_{BUS} = \begin{bmatrix} -j12.5 & +j10. & +j2.5 \\ +j10. & -j15. & +j5. \\ +j2.5 & +j5. & -j7.5 \end{bmatrix} \quad \text{per unit}$$

(b)

Bus	Type	Input Data	Unknowns
1	Swing	$V_1 = 1.0$ per unit $\delta_1 = 0°$	P_1, Q_1
2	Load	$P_2 = P_{G2} - P_{L2} = -2.0$ per unit $Q_2 = Q_{G2} - Q_{L2} = -0.5$ per unit	V_2, δ_2
3	Constant voltage	$V_3 = 1.0$ per $P_3 = P_{G3} - P_{L3} = 1.0$ per unit	Q_3, δ_3

6.26 Bus 3 is voltage controlled. First calculate Q_3 from Eq (6.5.3).

$$Q_3 = V_3(0)\Big\{Y_{31}V_1 \sin[\delta_3(0)-\delta_1(0)-\theta_{31}] + Y_{32}V_2(1)\sin[\delta_3(0)-\delta_2(0)-\theta_{32}]$$

$$+ Y_{33}V_3(0)\sin[-\theta_{33}] + Y_{34}V_4(0)\sin[\delta_3(0)-\delta_4(0)-\theta_{34}]$$

$$+ Y_{35}V_5(0)\sin[\delta_3(0)-\delta_5(0)-\theta_{35}]\Big\}$$

$$Q_3 = 1.05\{0+0+24.93(1.05)\sin[85.711^\circ] + 24.93(1.0)\sin[-94.289^\circ] + 0\}$$

$$= 1.305 \text{ per unit}$$

Also $Q_{G3} = Q_3 + Q_{L3} = 1.305 + 0.1 = 1.405$ per unit

Next check generator 3 var limits. Since $Q_{G3} = 1.405$ exceeds $Q_{G3max} = 1.0$ (as given in Table 6.1), set $Q_{G3} = Q_{G3max} = 1.0$ per unit.

Then $Q_3 = Q_{G3} - Q_{L3} = 1.0 - 0.1 = 0.9$ per unit.

Bus 3 is now a load bus for this iteration.

Next compute $\bar{V}_3(1)$ from Eq (6.5.2).

$$\bar{V}_3(1) = \frac{1}{\bar{Y}_{33}}\left\{\frac{P_3 - jQ_3}{V_3^*(0)} - [\bar{Y}_{34}\bar{V}_4(0)]\right\}$$

$$= \frac{1}{24.93\angle -85.711^\circ}\left\{\frac{1.1-j0.9}{1.05\angle 0^\circ} - [(24.93\angle 94.289^\circ)(1.0\angle 0^\circ)]\right\}$$

$$= \frac{1}{24.93\angle -85.711^\circ}\{1.0476 - j0.8571 - [-1.8644 + j24.86]\}$$

$$= \frac{2.912 - j25.717}{24.93\angle -85.711^\circ} = \frac{25.88\angle -83.54^\circ}{24.93\angle -85.711^\circ} = 1.0382\angle 2.171^\circ \text{ per unit}$$

Finally, one more pass through Eq (7.5.2),

$$\bar{V}_3(1) = \frac{1}{24.93\angle -85.711^\circ}\left\{\frac{1.1-j0.9}{1.0382\angle -2.171^\circ} - [-1.8644 + j24.86]\right\}$$

$$= \frac{2.9560 - j25.686}{24.93\angle -85.711^\circ} = \frac{25.856\angle -83.435^\circ}{24.93\angle -85.711^\circ} = \underline{\underline{1.0371\angle 2.276^\circ}}$$

per unit

6.27 Bus 2 is a load bus. Using the input data and bus admittance values from Problem 6.25 in Eq (6.5.2):

$$\bar{V}_2(1) = \frac{1}{\bar{Y}_{22}}\left\{\frac{P_2 - jQ_2}{\bar{V}_2^*(0)} - \left[\bar{Y}_{21}\bar{V}_1 + \bar{Y}_{23}\bar{V}_3(0)\right]\right\}$$

$$\bar{V}_2(1) = \frac{1}{-j15}\left\{\frac{-2.0 - j(-0.5)}{1.0\angle 0^\circ} - \left[(j10)(1.0\angle 0^\circ) + (j5)\,1.0\angle 0^\circ\right]\right\}$$

$$\bar{V}_2(1) = \frac{1}{15\angle -90^\circ}\left\{-2.0 + j0.5 - [j15]\right\}$$

$$\bar{V}_2(1) = \frac{-2.0 - j14.5}{15\angle -90^\circ} = \frac{14.637\angle 262.15^\circ}{15\angle -90^\circ} = 0.9758\angle -7.853^\circ$$

Next, the above value is used in Eq (6.5.2) to re-calculate $\bar{V}_2(1)$:

$$\bar{V}_2(1) = \frac{1}{15\angle -90^\circ}\left\{\frac{-2.0 + j0.5}{0.9758\angle +7.853^\circ} - [j15]\right\}$$

$$\bar{V}_2(1) = \frac{1}{15\angle -90^\circ}\left\{\frac{2.06155\angle 165.96^\circ}{0.9758\angle 7.853^\circ} - [j15]\right\}$$

$$\bar{V}_2(1) = \frac{1}{15\angle -90^\circ}\left\{2.1127\angle 158.11^\circ - j15\right\} = \frac{-1.9603 - j14.2122}{15\angle -90^\circ}$$

$$\bar{V}_2(1) = \frac{14.3468\angle 262.15^\circ}{15\angle -90^\circ} = \underline{\underline{0.9565\angle -7.853^\circ}} \text{ per unit}$$

Bus 3 is a voltage controlled bus. First calculate Q_3 from Eq (6.5.3).

$$Q_3 = V_3(0)\left\{Y_{31}V_1 \sin[\delta_3(0) - \delta_1 - \theta_{31}] + Y_{32}V_2(1)\sin[\delta_3(0) - \delta_2(0) - \theta_{32}] + Y_{33}V_3 \sin[-\theta_{33}]\right\}$$

6.27 CONTD.

$$Q_3 = 1.0\{(2.5)(1.0)\sin(0^\circ - 0^\circ - 90^\circ) + (5)(0.9565)\sin(0^\circ + 7.853^\circ - 90^\circ) + (7.5)(1.0)\sin(90^\circ)\}$$

$Q_3 = 0.2624$ per unit

Also $Q_{G3} = Q_3 + Q_{L3} = 0.2624$ ($Q_{L3} = 0$ from Table 6.12)

Since $Q_{G3} = 0.2624$ does not exceed $Q_{G3max} = +5.0$ per unit, as given in Table 6.12, the generator var limits at bus 3 are not exceeded.

Computing $\bar{V}_3(1)$ from Eq (6.5.2):

$$\bar{V}_3(1) = \frac{1}{\bar{Y}_{33}}\left\{\frac{P_3 - jQ_3}{V_3^*(0)} - [\bar{Y}_{31}\bar{V}_1 + \bar{Y}_{32}\bar{V}_2(1)]\right\}$$

$$\bar{V}_3(1) = \frac{1}{-j7.5}\left\{\frac{1.0 - j0.2624}{1.0\angle 0^\circ} - [(j2.5)(1.0\angle 0^\circ) + (j5)(.9565\angle -7.853^\circ)]\right\}$$

$$\bar{V}_3(1) = \frac{1}{7.5\angle -90^\circ}\{(1.0 - j0.2624) - [j2.5 + 4.7825\angle 82.147^\circ]\}$$

$$\bar{V}_3(1) = \frac{0.3466 - j7.5}{7.5\angle -90^\circ} = \frac{7.508\angle -87.35^\circ}{7.5\angle -90^\circ}$$

$$\bar{V}_3(1) = 1.001\angle 2.646^\circ$$

Eq (7.5.2) has been used above to compute $\delta_3(1) = 2.646^\circ$. The bus voltage magnitude $V_3 = 1.0$ per unit is input data, as given in Table 6.12. Therefore, $\bar{V}_3(1) = 1.0\angle 2.646^\circ$ per unit.

$$V_2^1 = \frac{1}{Y_{22}}\left[\frac{P_2 - jQ_2}{(V_2^0)^*} - Y_{21}V_1 - Y_{23}V_3^0 - Y_{24}V_4^0\right]$$

$$= \frac{1}{Y_{22}}\left[\frac{0.5 + j0.2}{1 - j0} - 1.04(-2+j6) - (-0.666+j2) - (-1+j3)\right]$$

$$= \frac{4.246 - j11.04}{3.666 - j11} = 1.019 + j0.046 = 1.02\,\angle 2.58^\circ \text{ PU}$$

$$V_2^2 = \frac{1}{Y_{22}}\left[\frac{P_2 - jQ_2}{(V_2^1)^*} - Y_{21}V_1 - Y_{23}V_3^1 - Y_{24}V_4^1\right]$$

DETERMINE V_3^1 AND V_4^1 IN THE SAME WAY AS V_2^1. THEN

$$V_2^2 = \frac{1}{Y_{22}}\left[\frac{0.5 + j0.2}{1.019 + j0.046} - 1.04(-2+j6) - (-0.666+j2.0)(1.028 - j0.087) - (-1+j3)(1.025 - j0.0093)\right]$$

$$= \frac{4.0862 - j11.6119}{3.666 - j11.0} = 1.061 + j0.0179 = 1.0616\,\angle 0.97^\circ \text{ PU}$$

Problem 6.29

The maximum mismatches corresponding to the first three iterations are 171.55, 56.76, and 73.6MVA. 38 iterations are necessary in order to have the maximum mismatch be less than 0.5MVA.

Problem 6.30

The maximum mismatches corresponding to the first three iterations are 199.67, 83.51, and 64.62MVA. 33 iterations are necessary in order for the maximum mismatch value to be less than 0.5 MVA.

Problem 6.31

(Note: Typo in problem: load increase should be at bus 2; also increase maximum number of iterations from 50 to 200)

Bus 2 Load (MW)	Iterations required
800	49
810	49
820	50
830	50
840	51
850	120
860	No solution - diverges

6.32 $\Delta P_4(0) = P_4 - P_4(x)$ Using Eq (6.6.2):

$$\Delta P_4(0) = P_4 - V_4(0)\left\{ Y_{41} V_1 \cos[\delta_4(0) - \delta_1 - \theta_{41}] + Y_{42} V_2(0) \cos[\delta_4(0) - \delta_2(0) - \theta_{42}] + Y_{43} V_3 \cos[\delta_4(0) - \delta_3(0) - \theta_{43}] + Y_{44} V_4(0) \cos[-\theta_{44}] + Y_{45} V_5(0) \cos[\delta_4(0) - \delta_5(0) - \theta_{45}] \right\}$$

Using Eq (6.4.2):

$$\bar{Y}_{41} = 0 \qquad \bar{Y}_{42} = \bar{Y}_{24} = \frac{-1}{R'_{24} + jX'_{24}} = \frac{-1}{0.036 + j0.40} = 2.4899\underline{/95.143^\circ} \text{ per unit}$$

$$\bar{Y}_{43} = \frac{-1}{R_{34} + jX_{34}} = \frac{-1}{0.003 + j0.04} = 24.93\underline{/94.289^\circ} \text{ per unit}$$

$$\bar{Y}_{45} = \frac{-1}{R'_{45} + jX'_{45}} = \frac{-1}{0.009 + j0.10} = 9.9597\underline{/95.143^\circ} \text{ per unit}$$

$$\bar{Y}_{44} = \frac{1}{R'_{24} + jX'_{24}} + \frac{1}{R_{34} + jX_{34}} + \frac{1}{R'_{45} + jX'_{45}} + j\frac{B'_{24}}{2} + j\frac{B'_{45}}{2}$$

$$\bar{Y}_{44} = (0.2232 - j2.4799) + (1.8644 - j24.860) + (0.8928 - j9.9196) + j\frac{0.43}{2} + j\frac{0.11}{2}$$

$$\bar{Y}_{44} = 2.9804 - j36.99 = 37.11\underline{/-85.39^\circ} \text{ per unit}$$

Using these admittance values in Eq (6.6.2) above

$$\Delta P_4(0) = 0 - 1.0\left\{0 + 2.4899(1.0)\cos[-95.143^\circ] + 24.93(1.05)\cos[-94.289^\circ] + 37.11(1.0)\cos[85.39^\circ] + 9.9597(1.0)\cos[-95.143^\circ]\right\}$$

$$\Delta P_4(0) = -1.0\{-0.09104\} = \underline{\underline{+0.09104}} \text{ per unit}$$

6.32 CONTD. Using the equation for J1 in Table 6.5

$$J1_{44}^{(0)} = -V_4(0)\left\{Y_{41}V_1\sin[\delta_4(0)-\delta_1-\theta_{41}] + Y_{42}V_2(0)\sin[\delta_4(0)-\delta_2(0)-\theta_{42}] + Y_{43}V_3\sin[\delta_4(0)-\delta_3(0)-\theta_{43}] + Y_{45}V_5(0)\sin[\delta_4(0)-\delta_5(0)-\theta_{45}]\right\}$$

$$J1_{44}(0) = -1.0\left\{0 + 2.4899(1.0)\sin(-95.143^\circ) + 24.93(1.05)\sin(-94.289^\circ) + 9.9597(1.0)\sin[-95.143^\circ]\right\}$$

$$J1_{44}(0) = -1.0\{-38.503\} = \underline{\underline{+38.503}} \text{ per unit}$$

6.33 Using Eq (6.6.2)

$$k=2 \quad P_2 = V_2[Y_{21}V_1\cos(\delta_2-\delta_1-\theta_{21}) + Y_{22}V_2\cos(-\theta_{22}) + Y_{23}V_3\cos(\delta_2-\delta_3-\theta_{23})]$$

$$k=3 \quad P_3 = V_3[Y_{31}V_1\cos(\delta_3-\delta_1-\theta_{31}) + Y_{32}V_2\cos(\delta_3-\delta_2-\theta_{32}) + Y_{33}V_3\cos(-\theta_{33})]$$

Using Eq (6.6.3)

$$k=2 \quad Q_2 = V_2[Y_{21}V_1\sin(\delta_2-\delta_1-\theta_{21}) + Y_{22}V_2\sin(-\theta_{22}) + Y_{23}V_3\sin(\delta_2-\delta_3-\theta_{23})]$$

Knowns: Unknowns:

$$\underline{y} = \begin{bmatrix} P_2 \\ P_3 \\ Q_2 \end{bmatrix} = \begin{bmatrix} P_{G2}-P_{L2} \\ P_{G3}-P_{L3} \\ Q_{G2}-Q_{L2} \end{bmatrix} = \begin{bmatrix} -2.0 \\ 1.0 \\ -0.5 \end{bmatrix} \text{per unit} \qquad \underline{x} = \begin{bmatrix} \delta_2 \\ \delta_3 \\ V_2 \end{bmatrix}$$

Also $V_1 = V_3 = 1.0$ per unit and $\delta_1 = 0^\circ$.

Using the above known values and admittances from Problem 7.18 in the above three equations:

$$-2.0 = V_2[10.\cos(\delta_2-90^\circ) + 5.\cos(\delta_2-\delta_3-90^\circ)] \quad (1)$$

$$1.0 = 2.5\cos(\delta_3-90^\circ) + 5.V_2\cos(\delta_3-\delta_2-90^\circ) \quad (2)$$

$$-0.5 = V_2[10.\sin(\delta_2-90^\circ) + 15.V_2 + 5.\sin(\delta_2-\delta_3-90^\circ)] \quad (3)$$

6.33 CONTD. (a) Step 1 $\quad \delta_2(0) = \delta_3(0) = 0^\circ \quad V_2(0) = 1.0$

Compute $\Delta \underline{y}(0)$

$$P_2(\underline{x}) = 1.0\left[10\cos(-90^\circ) + 5\cos(-90^\circ)\right] = 0$$

$$P_3(\underline{x}) = 2.5\cos(-90^\circ) + 5\cos(-90^\circ) = 0$$

$$Q_3(\underline{x}) = 1.0\left[10\sin(-90^\circ) + 15 + 5\sin(-90^\circ)\right] = 0$$

$$\Delta \underline{y}(0) = \begin{bmatrix} P_2 - P_2(\underline{x}) \\ P_3 - P_3(x) \\ Q_2 - Q_2(x) \end{bmatrix} = \begin{bmatrix} -2.0 - 0 \\ 1.0 - 0 \\ -0.5 - 0 \end{bmatrix} = \begin{bmatrix} -2.0 \\ 1.0 \\ -0.5 \end{bmatrix}$$

(b) Step 2 $\quad$ Compute $\underline{J}(0)$ (see Table 6.5 Text)

$$J1_{22} = \frac{\partial P_2}{\partial \delta_2} = -V_2\left[Y_{21}V_1\sin(\delta_2 - \delta_1 - \theta_{21}) + Y_{23}V_3\sin(\delta_2 - \delta_3 - \theta_{23})\right]$$
$$= -1.0\left[10(1)\sin(-90^\circ) + 5(1)\sin(-90^\circ)\right] = 15.$$

$$J1_{23} = \frac{\partial P_2}{\partial \delta_3} = V_2Y_{23}V_3\sin(\delta_2 - \delta_3 - \theta_{23}) = (1.0)(5)\sin(-90^\circ) = -5.$$

$$J1_{32} = \frac{\partial P_3}{\partial \delta_2} = V_3Y_{32}V_2\sin(\delta_3 - \delta_2 - \theta_{32}) = (1)(5)(1)\sin(-90^\circ) = -5$$

$$J1_{33} = \frac{\partial P_3}{\partial \delta_3} = -V_3\left[Y_{31}V_1\sin(\delta_3 - \delta_1 - \theta_{31}) + Y_{32}V_2\sin(\delta_3 - \delta_2 - \theta_{32})\right]$$
$$= -1.0\left[(2.5)(1)\sin(-90^\circ) + (5)(1)\sin(-90^\circ)\right] = 7.5$$

$$J2_{22} = \frac{\partial P_2}{\partial V_2} = V_2Y_{22}\cos(\theta_{22}) + \left[Y_{21}V_1\cos(\delta_2 - \delta_1 - \theta_{21}) + Y_{22}V_2\cos(-\theta_{22}) + Y_{23}V_3\cos(\delta_2 - \delta_3 - \theta_{23})\right] = 0$$

$$J2_{32} = \frac{\partial P_3}{\partial V_2} = V_3Y_{32}\cos(\delta_3 - \delta_2 - \theta_{32}) = 0$$

$$J3_{22} = \frac{\partial Q_2}{\partial \delta_2} = V_2\left[Y_{21}V_1\cos(\delta_2 - \delta_1 - \theta_{21}) + Y_{23}V_3\cos(\delta_2 - \delta_3 - \theta_{23})\right] = 0$$

$$J3_{23} = \frac{\partial Q_2}{\partial \delta_3} = -V_2Y_{23}V_3\cos(\delta_2 - \delta_3 - \theta_{23}) = 0$$

6.34

$$J4_{22} = \frac{\partial Q_2}{\partial V_2} = -V_2 Y_{22} \sin\theta_{22} + \left[Y_{21} V_1 \sin(\delta_2-\delta_1-\theta_{21}) + Y_{22} V_2 \sin(-\theta_{22}) + Y_{23} V_3 \sin(\delta_2-\delta_3-\theta_{23})\right]$$

$$J4_{22} = (-1)(15)\sin(-90°) + [(10)(1)\sin(-90°) + 15(1)\sin(90°) + 5(1)\sin(-90°)]$$
$$= 15$$

$$\underline{J}(0) = \left[\begin{array}{c|c} \underline{J1} & \underline{J2} \\ \hline \underline{J3} & \underline{J4} \end{array}\right] = \left[\begin{array}{cc|c} 15 & -5 & 0 \\ -5 & 7.5 & 0 \\ \hline 0 & 0 & 15 \end{array}\right] \text{ per unit}$$

Step 3 solve $\underline{J}\,\underline{\Delta x} = \underline{\Delta y}$

$$\begin{bmatrix} 15 & -5 & 0 \\ -5 & 7.5 & 0 \\ 0 & 0 & 15 \end{bmatrix} \begin{bmatrix} \Delta\delta_2 \\ \Delta\delta_3 \\ \Delta V_2 \end{bmatrix} = \begin{bmatrix} -2.0 \\ 1.0 \\ -0.5 \end{bmatrix}$$

Using Gauss elimination, multiply the first equation by (-5/15) and subtract from the second equation:

$$\begin{bmatrix} 15 & -5 & 0 \\ 0 & 5.833333 & 0 \\ 0 & 0 & 15 \end{bmatrix} \begin{bmatrix} \Delta\delta_2 \\ \Delta\delta_3 \\ \Delta V_2 \end{bmatrix} = \begin{bmatrix} -2.0 \\ 0.33333 \\ -0.5 \end{bmatrix}$$

Back substitution:

$$\Delta V_2 = -0.5/15 = -0.033333$$
$$\Delta\delta_3 = 0.33333/5.833333 = 0.05714285$$
$$\Delta\delta_2 = [-2.0 + 5(0.05714285)]/15 = -0.1142857$$

$$\underline{\Delta x} = \begin{bmatrix} \Delta\delta_2 \\ \Delta\delta_3 \\ \Delta V_2 \end{bmatrix} = \begin{bmatrix} -0.1142857 \\ 0.05714285 \\ -0.033333 \end{bmatrix}$$

6.34 CONTD.

Step 4 compute $\underline{x}(1)$

$$\underline{x}(1) = \begin{bmatrix} \delta_2(1) \\ \delta_3(1) \\ V_2(1) \end{bmatrix} = x(0) + \Delta x = \begin{bmatrix} 0 \\ 0 \\ 1 \end{bmatrix} + \begin{bmatrix} -.1142857 \\ .05714285 \\ -.0333333 \end{bmatrix} = \begin{bmatrix} -0.1142857 \\ 0.05714285 \\ 0.96666667 \end{bmatrix} \begin{matrix} \} \text{ radians} \\ \\ \text{per unit} \end{matrix}$$

Check Q_{G3} using Eq (6.5.3)

$$Q_3 = V_3 \left[Y_{31} V_1 \sin(\delta_3 - \delta_1 - \theta_{31}) + Y_{32} V_2 \sin(\delta_3 - \delta_2 - \theta_{32}) + Y_{33} V_3 \sin(-\theta_{33}) \right]$$

$$= 1 \left[(2.5)(1) \sin\left(\underbrace{0.05714}_{\text{radians}} - \frac{\pi}{2}\right) + 5(.966666) \sin\left(.05714 + .11429 - \frac{\pi}{2}\right) + 7.5(1) \sin\left(\frac{\pi}{2}\right) \right]$$

$$Q_3 = 1 \left[-2.4959 - 4.7625 + 7.5 \right] = 0.2416 \text{ per unit}$$

$$Q_{G3} = Q_3 + Q_{L3} = 0.2416 + 0 = 0.2416 \text{ per unit}$$

Since $Q_{G3} = 0.2416$ is within the limits $[-5.0, +5.0]$, Bus 3 remains a voltage-controlled bus. This completes the first Newton-Raphson iteration.

6.35

THE $\bar{Y}$-BUS FOR THE SYSTEM IS GIVEN BY

$$\bar{Y}_{BUS} = \begin{bmatrix} -j19.98 & j10 & j10 \\ j10 & -j19.98 & j10 \\ j10 & j10 & -j19.98 \end{bmatrix}$$

BUS 1 IS THE SWING BUS; BUS 2 IS THE VOLTAGE-CONTROLLED BUS; BUS 3 IS THE LOAD BUS. THE UNKNOWN VARIABLES ARE δ_2, δ_3, AND V_3. THUS THE JACOBIAN WILL BE A 3×3 MATRIX. VALUES OF δ_1, Y_{ij}, V_1 AND V_2 ARE KNOWN. THUS,

$$P_2 = V_2 V_1 Y_{21} \sin(\delta_2 - \delta_1) + V_2 V_3 Y_{23} \sin(\delta_2 - \delta_3)$$
$$= 10.5 \sin \delta_2 + 10.5 V_3 \sin(\delta_2 - \delta_3)$$

$$P_3 = V_3 V_1 Y_{31} \sin(\delta_3 - \delta_1) + V_3 V_2 Y_{32} \sin(\delta_3 - \delta_2)$$
$$= 10 V_3 \sin \delta_3 + 10.5 V_3 \sin(\delta_3 - \delta_2)$$

SINCE V_2 IS GIVEN, THE EQUATION FOR Q_2 CAN BE ELIMINATED.

$$Q_3 = -\left[V_3 V_1 Y_{31} \cos(\delta_3 - \delta_1) + V_3 V_2 Y_{32} \cos(\delta_3 - \delta_2) + V_3^2 Y_{23}\right]$$
$$= -\left[10 V_3 \cos \delta_3 + 10.5 V_3 \cos(\delta_3 - \delta_2) - 19.98 V_3^2\right]$$

THE UNKNOWN VECTOR AND JACOBIAN MATRIX ARE GIVEN BY

$$\bar{X} = \begin{bmatrix} \delta_2 \\ \delta_3 \\ V_3 \end{bmatrix} ; \quad \bar{J}(\bar{x}) = \begin{bmatrix} \frac{\partial P_2}{\partial \delta_2} & \frac{\partial P_2}{\partial \delta_3} & \frac{\partial P_2}{\partial V_3} \\ \frac{\partial P_3}{\partial \delta_2} & \frac{\partial P_3}{\partial \delta_3} & \frac{\partial P_3}{\partial V_3} \\ \frac{\partial Q_3}{\partial \delta_2} & \frac{\partial Q_3}{\partial \delta_3} & \frac{\partial Q_3}{\partial V_3} \end{bmatrix}$$

THE PARTIAL DERIVATIVES ARE GIVEN BY

$$\frac{\partial P_2}{\partial \delta_2} = V_2 V_1 Y_{21} \cos(\delta_2 - \delta_1) + V_2 V_3 Y_{23} \cos(\delta_2 - \delta_3)$$
$$= 10.5 \cos \delta_2 + 10.5 V_3 \cos(\delta_2 - \delta_3)$$

6.35 CONTD.

$$\frac{\partial P_2}{\partial \delta_2} = -V_2 V_3 Y_{23}\cos(\delta_2-\delta_3) = -10.5\, V_3 \cos(\delta_2-\delta_3)$$

$$\frac{\partial P_2}{\partial V_3} = V_2 Y_{23} \sin(\delta_2-\delta_3) = 10.5 \sin(\delta_2-\delta_3)$$

$$\partial P_3/\partial \delta_2 = -10.5\, V_3 \cos(\delta_3-\delta_2)$$

$$\partial P_3/\partial \delta_3 = 10\, V_3 \cos\delta_3 + 10.5\, V_3 \cos(\delta_3-\delta_2)$$

$$\partial P_3/\partial V_3 = 10 \sin\delta_3 + 10.5 \sin(\delta_3-\delta_2)$$

$$\partial Q_3/\partial \delta_2 = -10\, V_3 V_2 \sin(\delta_3-\delta_2) = -10.5\, V_3 \sin(\delta_3-\delta_2)$$

$$\partial Q_3/\partial \delta_3 = 10\, V_3 \sin\delta_3 + 10 V_3 V_2 \sin(\delta_3-\delta_2) = 10\, V_3 \sin\delta_3 + 10.5\, V_3 \sin(\delta_3-\delta_2)$$

$$\partial Q_3/\partial V_3 = -\left[10\cos\delta_3 + 10.5\cos(\delta_3-\delta_2) - 39.96\, V_3\right]$$

NOTE THAT $P_2 = P_{G2} = 0.6661$, $P_3 = -P_{L3} = -2.8653$, AND $Q_3 = -Q_{L3} = -1.2244$,

AND THESE WILL REMAIN CONSTANT THROUGH THE ENTIRE ITERATIVE PROCESS.

WITH AN INITIAL GUESS $\delta_2^0 = \delta_3^0 = 0$ AND $V_3 = 1.0$,

$$\begin{bmatrix} \Delta P_2 \\ \Delta P_3 \\ \Delta Q_3 \end{bmatrix}^0 = \begin{bmatrix} P_2 \\ P_3 \\ Q_3 \end{bmatrix} - \begin{bmatrix} P_2(\bar{x}^0) \\ P_3(\bar{x}^0) \\ Q_3(\bar{x}^0) \end{bmatrix} = \begin{bmatrix} 0.6661 \\ -2.8653 \\ -1.2244 \end{bmatrix} - \begin{bmatrix} 0 \\ 0 \\ -0.52 \end{bmatrix} = \begin{bmatrix} 0.6661 \\ -2.8653 \\ -0.7044 \end{bmatrix}$$

$$\bar{J}^0 = \begin{bmatrix} 21 & -10.5 & 0 \\ -10.5 & 20.5 & 0 \\ 0 & 0 & 19.46 \end{bmatrix}$$

NOTE THAT $\bar{J}_{12}^0$ AND $\bar{J}_{21}^0$ ARE BOTH ZERO.

$$\bar{J}_0^{-1} = \begin{bmatrix} \bar{J}_{11} & 0 \\ 0 & \bar{J}_{22} \end{bmatrix}^{-1} = \begin{bmatrix} \bar{J}_{11}^{-1} & 0 \\ 0 & \bar{J}_{22}^{-1} \end{bmatrix} = \begin{bmatrix} 0.0640 & 0.0328 & 0 \\ 0.0328 & 0.0656 & 0 \\ 0 & 0 & 0.0514 \end{bmatrix}$$

6.35 CONTD.

$$\Delta \bar{x}^0 \begin{bmatrix} \Delta\delta_2 \\ \Delta\delta_3 \\ \Delta V_3 \end{bmatrix} = \begin{bmatrix} -0.0513 \text{ rad} \\ -0.1660 \text{ rad} \\ -0.0362 \end{bmatrix} = \begin{bmatrix} -2.9395^\circ \\ -9.5111^\circ \\ -0.0362 \end{bmatrix}$$

$$\bar{x}^1 = \bar{x}^0 + \Delta\bar{x}^0 = \begin{bmatrix} 0 \\ 0 \\ 1 \end{bmatrix} + \begin{bmatrix} -2.9395^\circ \\ -9.5111^\circ \\ -0.0362 \end{bmatrix} = \begin{bmatrix} -2.9395^\circ \\ -9.5111^\circ \\ 0.9638 \end{bmatrix}$$

USING THE NEW VALUES $\delta_2^1 = -2.9395^\circ$, $\delta_3^1 = -9.5111^\circ$, AND $V_3^1 = 0.9638$,

$P_2(\bar{x}^1) = 0.6198$ AND $\Delta P_2^1 = 0.6661 - 0.6198 = 0.0463$.

UPDATED MISMATCH VECTOR: $\begin{bmatrix} \Delta P_2 \\ \Delta P_3 \\ \Delta Q_3 \end{bmatrix}^1 = \begin{bmatrix} 0.0463 \\ -0.1145 \\ -0.2251 \end{bmatrix}$

THUS $\bar{J}^1 = \begin{bmatrix} 20.5396 & -10.0534 & 1.2017 \\ -10.0534 & 19.5589 & -2.8541 \\ 1.1582 & -2.7508 & 18.2199 \end{bmatrix}$

THE UPDATED INVERSE: $\bar{J}_1^{-1} = \begin{bmatrix} 0.0651 & 0.0336 & 0.0010 \\ 0.0336 & 0.0696 & 0.0087 \\ 0.0009 & 0.0084 & 0.0561 \end{bmatrix}$

THEN $\bar{x}^2 = \begin{bmatrix} \delta_2 \\ \delta_3 \\ V_3 \end{bmatrix}^2 = \begin{bmatrix} -3.0023^\circ \\ -9.9924^\circ \\ 0.9502 \end{bmatrix}$

THEN $\begin{bmatrix} \Delta P_2 \\ \Delta P_3 \\ \Delta Q_3 \end{bmatrix} = \begin{bmatrix} 0.0019 \\ -0.0023 \\ -0.0031 \end{bmatrix}$

THE MISMATCH BEING SMALL ENOUGH, $\delta_2 = -3.0023^\circ$; $\delta_3 = -9.9924^\circ$; $V_3 = 0.9502$

THEN $P_{G1} = P_1 = V_1 V_2 Y_{12} \sin(\delta_1 - \delta_2) + V_1 V_3 Y_{13} \sin(\delta_1 - \delta_3)$

$$= 10.5 \sin 3.0023^\circ + 9.502 \sin 9.9924^\circ = 2.1987$$

$Q_{G1} = Q_1 = -[V_1 V_2 Y_{12} \cos(\delta_1 - \delta_2) + V_1 V_3 Y_{13} \cos(\delta_1 - \delta_3) + V_1^2 Y_{11}]$

6.35 CONTD..

$$Q_{G1} = Q_1 = -\left[10.5 \cos 3.0023^\circ + 9.502 \cos 9.9924^\circ - 19.98\right]$$

$$= 0.1365$$

$$Q_{G2} = Q_2 = -\left[V_2 V_1 Y_{21} \cos(\delta_2 - \delta_1) + V_2 V_3 Y_{23} \cos(\delta_2 - \delta_3) + V_2^2 Y_{22}\right]$$

$$= -\left[10.5 \cos(-3.0023^\circ) + 9.977 \cos 6.9901^\circ - 22.028\right]$$

$$= -1.6395$$

Problem 6.36

After the first three iterations J_{22}= 28.72, 23.87, 22.61; and with the next iteration it converges to 22.58.

Problem 6.37

(Note typo: Problem reads "...loadings an...." but an should be "loadings and")

261 Mvar will increase V_2 to 1.0. Adding the 261 Mvar decreases losses from 34.84 to 23.95MW.

Problem 6.38

	Before new line	After new line
Bus voltage V2 (p.u)	0.834	0.964
Total real power losses (MW)	34.84	19.62
Branch between buses 1 and 5 (%loading)	68.5	64.1
Branch between buses 2 and 4 (%loading)	26.9	19.5 (both lines)
Branch between buses 2 and 5 (%loading)	43.9	32.8
Branch between buses 3 and 4 (%loading)	53.1	44.9
Branch between buses 4 and 5 (%loading)	16.8	11.8

Problem 6.39

G3 voltage (p.u)	Mvar at bus 3	Bus 2 voltage (p.u)	Real power losses (MW)
1.00	279	0.777	39.88

6.39 CONTD.

1.005	284	0.783	39.21
1.01	289	0.789	38.6
1.015	294	0.795	38.03
1.02	300	0.801	37.48
1.025	306	0.807	36.97
1.03	312	0.812	36.49
1.035	318	0.818	36.04
1.04	324	0.823	35.61
1.045	331	0.829	35.21
1.05	337	0.834	34.83
1.055	344	0.839	34.48
1.06	351	0.844	34.15
1.065	359	0.849	33.83
1.07	366	0.854	33.54
1.075	374	0.854	33.27
1.08	381	0.864	33.02

Problem 6.40

Tap setting	Mvar @ G1	V5 (p.u)	V2 (p.u)	P losses
0.975	94	0.954	0.806	37.64
0.98125	90	0.961	0.817	36.63
0.9875	98	0.965	0.823	36
0.99375	106	0.97	0.828	35.4
1.0	114	0.974	0.834	34.84
1.00625	123	0.979	0.839	34.31
1.0125	131	0.983	0.845	33.81
1.01875	140	0.987	0.850	33.33
1.025	149	0.992	0.855	32.89
1.03125	158	0.996	0.86	32.47
1.0375	167	1.0	0.865	32.08
1.04375	176	1.004	0.87	31.72
1.05	185	1.008	0.874	31.38
1.05625	195	1.012	0.879	31.06
1.0625	204	1.016	0.884	30.76
1.06875	214	1.02	0.888	30.49
1.075	224	1.024	0.893	30.23
1.08125	233	1.028	0.897	30
1.0875	243	1.031	0.901	29.79
1.09375	253	1.035	0.906	29.59
1.1	263	1.039	0.910	29.42

Problem 6.41

Tap setting	Mvar @ G1	XFMR1(MW/MVR)	XFMR 2(MW/MVR)	P losses(MW)
0.9	170	193 / -172	210 / 342.4	42.61
0.9063	152	192.2 / -164.8	209.2 / 316.8	41.37

6.41 CONTD.

0.9125	135	192.2 / -156.9	208 / 291.9	40.23
0.9188	119	192.3 / -148.4	206.9 / 267.6	39.2
.925	104	192.3 / -139.5	205.9 / 243.9	38.24
.9313	91	192.5 / -130.1	204.9 / 220.7	37.35
.9375	79	192.6 / -119.7	203.9 / 198.5	36.55
.9438	82	192.9 / -101.8	203 / 183.6	35.96
.95	85	193.2 / -83.9	202.2 / 168.9	35.41
.9563	88	193.5 / -66	201.4 / 154.4	34.89
.9625	92	193.8 / -48	200.6 / 140.2	34.41
.9688	96	194.2 / -30.1	199.8 / 126.2	33.95
.975	100	194.5 / -12.1	199 / 112.5	33.53
.9813	105	194.9 / 5.8	198.2 / 98.9	33.14
.9875	109	195.3 / 23.7	197.5 / 85.6	32.78
.9938	114	195.7 / 41.7	196.8 / 72.5	32.45
1.0	119	196.1 / 59.6	196.1 / 59.6	32.14
1.0063	124	196.5 / 77.5	195.4 / 46.9	31.86
1.0125	130	196.9 / 95.3	194.7 / 34.4	31.61
1.0188	135	197.3 / 113.1	194 / 22	31.31
1.025	141	197.7 / 131	193.4 / 9.9	31.12
1.0313	147	198.2 / 148.7	192.7 / -2	30.94
1.0375	153	198.7 / 166.5	192.1 / -13.7	30.79
1.0438	159	199.1 / 184.2	191.5 / -25.2	30.66
1.05	165	199.6 / 201.9	190.9 / -36.6	30.55
1.0563	172	200.1 / 219.6	190.4 / -47.7	30.47
1.0625	178	200.6 / 237.2	189.8 / -58.7	30.4
1.0688	185	201.1 / 254.8	189.3 / -69.5	30.36
1.075	192	201.6 / 272.3	188.7 / -80.2	30.33
1.0813	199	202.1 / 289.8	188.2 / -90.6	30.32
1.0875	206	202.6 / 307.2	187.7 / -100.9	30.34
1.0938	214	203.1 / 324.6	187.2 / -111.1	30.36
1.1	221	203.7 / 342	186.7 / -121.1	30.41

Problem 6.42
31.4 Mvar nominal = 28.4 Mvar actual at 0.95 p.u.

Problem 6.43
Real power loses are minimized when BLT138 generation is 360MW (the non-convex behavior is due to the other generators being on economic dispatch control – to pickup all the generation change at the slack bus, turn the area off of AGC control using the Case Information, Areas display).

6.43 CONTD.

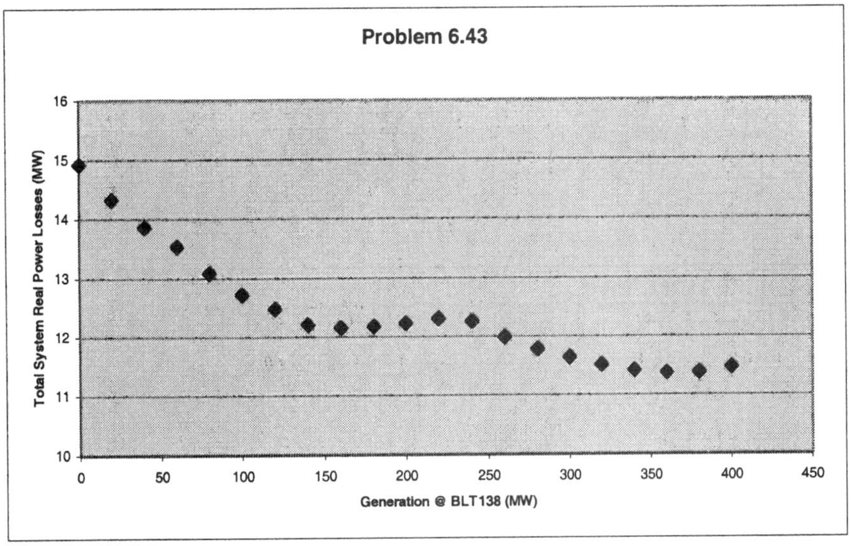

Problem 6.44

Total real power losses are minimized when generation at BLT138 is 140MW.

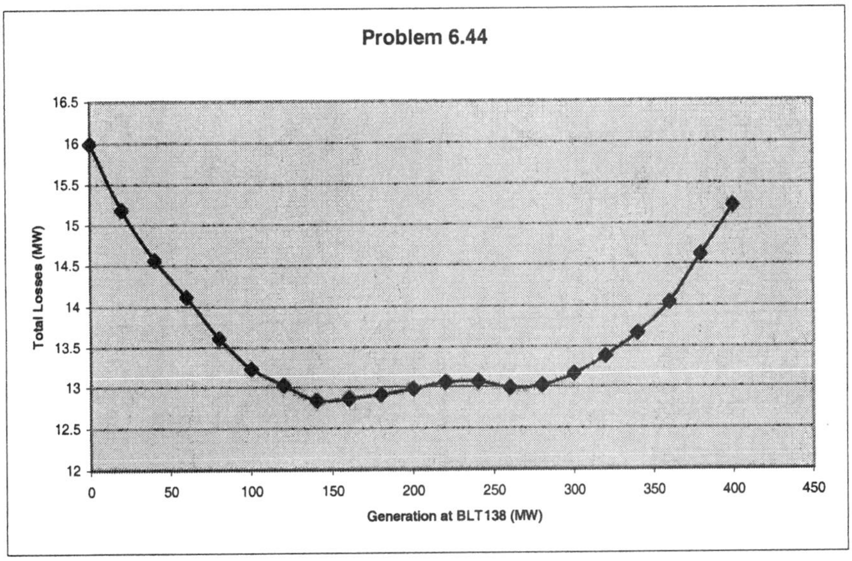

Problem 6.45

Device taken out of service	System Losses (MW)
Branch between Slack345 and Ray345	14.46
Branch between Tim345 and Slack 345	15.53
Branch between Slack 345 and JO345	14.90
Transformer between JO345 and JO138 (ckt 1)	12.12
Transformer between JO345 and JO138 (ckt 2)	12.12
Transformer between Slack138 and Slack345	12.05
Transformer between Ray138 and Ray345 (ckt 1)	12.28
Transformer between Ray138 and Ray345 (ckt 2)	12.28

6.45 CONTD

Transformer between Tim345 and Tim138	15.53

The largest impact on system losses occurs when either the line or transformer connected to bus Tim345 is taken out of service.

6.46 DIAG = [17 25 9 2 14 15]

OFFDIAG = [−9.1 −2.1 −7.1 −9.1 −8.1 −1.1 −6.1 −8.1 −1.1 −2.1 −6.1 −5.1 −7.1 −5.1]

COL = [2 5 6 1 3 4 5 2 2 1 2 6 1 5]

ROW = [3 4 1 1 3 2]

6.47

With Compact Storage	Without Compact Storage
DIAG = 24 bytes	
OFF DIAG = 56 bytes	$(6)^2 \times 4 = 144$ bytes
COL = 28 bytes	
ROW = 12 bytes	
TOTAL = 120 bytes	

6.48 Reordering the matrix such that the rows with the fewest off-diagonal elements are at the top, one solution is

$$\underline{S}_{reordered} = \begin{bmatrix} 9 & 0 & 0 & 0 & 0 & -8.1 \\ 0 & 2 & 0 & 0 & 0 & -1.1 \\ 0 & 0 & 15 & -7.1 & -5.1 & 0 \\ 0 & 0 & -7.1 & 17 & -2.1 & -9.1 \\ 0 & 0 & -5.1 & -2.1 & 14 & -6.1 \\ -8.1 & -1.1 & 0 & -9.1 & -6.1 & 25 \end{bmatrix} \begin{matrix} x_3 \\ x_4 \\ x_6 \\ x_1 \\ x_5 \\ x_2 \end{matrix}$$

which has 12 zeroes in colums 2-6

After the first Gauss-elimination step

$$S^{(1)}_{reordered} = \begin{bmatrix} 9 & 0 & 0 & 0 & 0 & -8.1 \\ 0 & 2 & 0 & 0 & 0 & -1.1 \\ 0 & 0 & 15 & -7.1 & -5.1 & 0 \\ 0 & 0 & -7.1 & 17 & -2.1 & -9.1 \\ 0 & 0 & -5.1 & -2.1 & 14 & -6.1 \\ 0 & -1.1 & 0 & -9.1 & -6.1 & 17.71 \end{bmatrix}$$

which also has 12 zeroes in columns 2-6

6.49

BY THE PROCESS OF NODE ELIMINATION AND ACTIVE BRANCH DESIGNATION, IN FIG. 6.9:

STEP NO.	1	2	3	4	5	6	7	8	9	10
NODE ELIMINATED	(h)	(e)	(j)	(i)	(d)	(c)	(a)	(b)	(f)	(g)
NO. OF ACTIVE BRANCHES	1	1	2	1	1	2	2	2	1	0
RESULTING FILL-INS	0	0	0	0	0	0	2	0	0	0

THE FILL-IN (DASHED) BRANCH AFTER STEP 6 IS SHOWN BELOW:

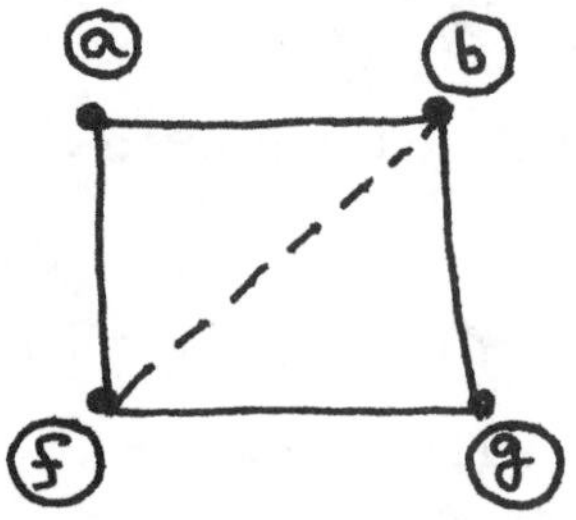

NOTE THAT TWO FILL-INS ARE UNAVOIDABLE.

WHEN THE BUS NUMBERS ARE ASSIGNED TO FIG. 6.9 IN ACCORDANCE WITH THE STEP NUMBERS ABOVE, THE ROWS AND COLUMNS OF $\bar{Y}_{BUS}$ WILL BE OPTIMALLY ORDERED FOR GAUSSIAN ELIMINATION, AND AS A RESULT, THE TRIANGULAR FACTORS $\bar{L}$ AND $\bar{U}$ WILL REQUIRE MINIMUM STORAGE AND COMPUTING TIME FOR SOLVING THE NODAL EQUATIONS.

6.50

COMBINING IN PAIRS THE P AND Q MISMATCH EQUATIONS FOR EACH OF THE LOAD BUSES ② AND ③ :

$$\underbrace{\begin{array}{c} \\ ② \\ \\ ③ \\ \\ ④ \end{array}\left[\begin{array}{cc|cc|c} \overset{②}{45.443} & 8.882 & \overset{③}{0} & 0 & \overset{④}{-26.365} \\ -9.089 & 44.229 & 0 & 0 & 5.273 \\ \hline 0 & 0 & 41.269 & 8.133 & -15.421 \\ 0 & 0 & -8.254 & 40.459 & 3.084 \\ \hline -26.365 & -5.273 & -15.421 & -3.084 & 41.786 \end{array}\right]}_{\text{JACOBIAN}} \underbrace{\left[\begin{array}{c} \Delta\delta_2 \\ \Delta V_2/V_2 \\ \hline \Delta\delta_3 \\ \Delta V_3/V_3 \\ \hline \Delta\delta_4 \end{array}\right]}_{\text{CORRECTIONS}} = \underbrace{\left[\begin{array}{c} -1.597 \\ -0.447 \\ \hline -1.94 \\ -0.835 \\ \hline 2.213 \end{array}\right]}_{\text{MISMATCHES}}$$

THE ROWS AND COLUMNS OF THE ABOVE EQUATION ARE OPTIMALLY ORDERED FOR GAUSSIAN ELIMINATION. THE ELEMENTS IN THE FIRST COLUMN OF THE JACOBIAN CONSTITUTE THE FIRST COLUMN OF THE LOWER TRIANGULAR FACTOR L ; THE ELEMENTS OF THE FIRST ROW, WHEN DIVIDED BY THE INITIAL PIVOT 45.443, CONSTITUTE THE FIRST ROW OF THE UPPER-TRIANGULAR FACTOR U. THEN, ELIMINATING THE FIRST ROW AND COLUMN FROM THE JACOBIAN AND THEREBY OBTAINING THE SECOND COLUMN OF L AND THE SECOND ROW OF U, THE FOLLOWING IS OBTAINED:

$$\underbrace{\begin{bmatrix} 45.443 & \cdot & \cdot & \cdot & \cdot \\ -9.089 & 46.005 & \cdot & \cdot & \cdot \\ 0 & 0 & 41.269 & \cdot & \cdot \\ 0 & 0 & -8.254 & 42.086 & \cdot \\ -26.365 & -0.120 & -15.421 & -0.045 & 20.727 \end{bmatrix}}_{L} \underbrace{\begin{bmatrix} x_1 \\ x_2 \\ x_3 \\ x_4 \\ x_5 \end{bmatrix}}_{X} = \begin{bmatrix} -1.597 \\ -0.447 \\ -1.940 \\ -0.835 \\ 2.213 \end{bmatrix}$$

6.50 CONTD.

HERE THE x'S DENOTE THE INTERMEDIATE RESULTS TO BE CALCULATED BY FORWARD SUBSTITUTION. THE UPPER TRIANGULAR MATRIX U AND THE SOLVED VALUES OF x'S ARE SHOWN BELOW:

$$\underbrace{\begin{bmatrix} 1 & 0.195 & 0 & 0 & -0.580 \\ \cdot & 1 & 0 & 0 & 0.000 \text{ (TRUNCATED)} \\ \cdot & \cdot & 1 & 0.197 & -0.374 \\ \cdot & \cdot & \cdot & 1 & 0.000 \text{ (TRUNCATED)} \\ \cdot & \cdot & \cdot & \cdot & 1 \end{bmatrix}}_{U} \begin{bmatrix} \Delta\delta_2 \\ \Delta V_2/V_2 \\ \Delta\delta_3 \\ \Delta V_3/V_3 \\ \Delta\delta_4 \end{bmatrix} = \underbrace{\begin{bmatrix} -0.035 \\ -0.017 \\ -0.047 \\ -0.029 \\ 0.027 \end{bmatrix}}_{x}$$

BACK SUBSTITUTION YIELDS THE VOLTAGE CORRECTIONS OF THE FIRST ITERATION:

	②	③	④
$\Delta\delta$ (rad.)	−0.016	−0.031	0.027
$\Delta V/V$ (PU)	−0.017	−0.029	—

ADDING THESE CORRECTIONS TO THE ORIGINAL VALUES, OBTAIN THE UPDATED VOLTAGES:

	②	③	④
δ (DEG.)	−0.931	−1.788	1.544
V (PU)	0.983	0.971	—

FROM WHICH THE NEW JACOBIAN ELEMENTS AND THE POWER MISMATCHES OF THE SECOND ITERATION ARE CALCULATED.

NOTE: NO FILL-INS HAVE OCCURED AND THE ZERO ELEMENTS OF THE ORIGINAL JACOBIAN ARE REPEATED IN L AND U, BECAUSE OF THE ORDER IN WHICH THE MISMATCH EQUATIONS ARE SOLVED.

Design Projects 1 and 2

The solutions given below solve the problems, but lower cost solutions may be available. For simplicity both designs assume the use of Rook conductor with 5 ft equilateral spacing. For such a line the resistance and reactance, in ohms per mile, are 0.148 and 0.609 respectively. Using the short line approximation, C is assumed to be zero. Converting to per unit (100 MVA base, 69 kV gives Zbase = 47.61 ohm). Therefore the 69kV per unit values are R = 0.0031 and X = 0.0128 per mile. For a 138 kV the values are R = 0.00078 and X = 0.0032.

Design Project 1

Initially the case has three problem contingencies: Tim69 to Hana69 (5 violations), Tim69 to Hisky69 (1 violation), and Robin69 to Lauf69 (1 violation). One design constraint is imposed by the Tim69 to Hisky69 contingency. During this contingency the load at Pete69 and Hisky69 is feed radially from UIUC69, causing an overload of the UIUC69 to PETE69 line. Therefore, as a minimum at least one new line must connect to either PETE69 or HISKY69. One solution is to build a new line 69 kV line from AMANS69 to UIUC69 and a second line from HANA69 to HISKY69. The total new 69 kV line mileage is 12.7 miles. Total construction cost is $50,000 fixed cost for each line, plus 12.7 * $120,000/mile = $1,624,000. Since the addition of the new lines causes the losses to decrease from about 12.92 to about 12.17 MW, the savings in losses over five years is 5 years * 8760 hrs/yr * 0.75 MWh * 50$/MWh = $1,642,500, so there is an actual savings of $18,500 over five years (assuming zero cost of money).

Design Project 2

Without the new load the case has two problem contingencies: Ray 138 to Ray 69 and Ray 69 to FERNA 69. Both contingencies cause overloads on the BLT69 to DEMAR69 kV line, requiring that the upgrades include additions at either DEMAR69 and/or FERNA69. One solution is to install a 138/69 kV substation at ABC, with a 138 kV line coming from Ray138 and a 69 kV line coming from FERNA69. Construction costs are $400,000 for the new ABC substation, $870,000 for the ABC 101 MVA transformer, $100,000 + 11.9 * $180,000 = $ 2,242,000 for the new 138 kV line and $50,000 + 4.2 * $120.000 = $ 554,000 for the new 69 kV line. Total construction cost is $4,066,000.

CHAPTER 7

7.1

(a) $\bar{Z} = R + j\omega L = 0.5 + j\,2\pi(60)\,3\times10^{-3} = 0.5 + j\,1.131$

$= 1.2366\,\angle 66.15^\circ\ \Omega\ ;\quad Z = 1.2366\ \Omega,\quad \theta = 66.15^\circ$

$I_{ac} = V/Z = 220/1.2366 = 177.9\ \text{A}$

(b) $I_{rms}(0) = I_{ac}K(0) = 177.9\sqrt{3} = 308\,\text{A}$

(c) USING EQ. (7.1.11) AND (7.1.12)

$X/R = 1.131/0.5 = 2.262\ ;\quad K(\tau = 5\,\text{cycles}) = \sqrt{1 + 2e^{\frac{-4\pi(5)}{2.262}}}$

$K(5\ \text{cycles}) \simeq 1.0$

$I_{rms}(5\,\text{cycles}) = I_{ac}\,K(5\,\text{cycles}) = 177.9\ \text{A}$

(d) USING EQ. (7.1.1)

$V(0) = \sqrt{2}\,V\sin\alpha = 244\ \text{VOLTS}$

$\alpha = \sin^{-1}\left(\frac{244}{\sqrt{2}\,277}\right) = 38.53^\circ$

USING EQ. (7.1.4)

$i_{dc}(t) = -\frac{\sqrt{2}\,V}{Z}\sin(\alpha - \theta)\,e^{-t/T}$

$i_{dc}(t) = -\frac{\sqrt{2}\,(220)}{1.2366}\sin(38.53^\circ - 66.15^\circ)\,e^{-t/T}$

$= 116.62\,e^{-t/T}$

$T = L/R = 3\times10^{-3}/0.5 = 6\times10^{-3}\ \text{seconds}$

$i_{dc}(t) = 116.62\ e^{-t/(6\times10^{-3})}\ \text{A}$

7.2

(a) $\bar{Z} = 1 + j3 = 3.1623 \angle 71.57^\circ \ \Omega$

$$I_{ac} = \frac{V}{Z} = \frac{4000}{3.1623} = \underline{\underline{1265.\ A}}$$

(b) $I_{rms}(0) = 1265\sqrt{3} = \underline{\underline{2191.\ A}}$

(c) $\frac{X}{R} = 3 \qquad K(5) = \sqrt{1 + 2e^{-4\pi(5)/3}} \simeq 1.0$

$$I_{rms}(5) = K(5)\, I_{ac} = 1.0\,(1265) = \underline{\underline{1265.\ A}}$$

(d) $\alpha = \sin^{-1}\left(\frac{300}{4000\sqrt{2}}\right) = 3.04^\circ$

$$T = \frac{L}{R} = \frac{X}{\omega R} = \frac{3}{(2\pi 60)(1)} = 7.958 \times 10^{-3}\ \text{s}$$

$$i_{dc}(t) = \frac{-\sqrt{2}\,(4000)}{3.1623} \sin(3.04^\circ - 71.57^\circ)\, e^{-t/T}$$

$$i_{dc}(t) = \underline{\underline{1665.\, e^{-t/(7.958\times 10^{-3})}}} \quad \text{A}$$

7.3

$$\bar{Z} = 0.125 + j\,2\pi(60)\,0.01 = 0.125 + j\,3.77 = 3.772\angle 88.1^\circ\ \Omega$$

$$I_{ac\,rms} = \frac{151}{\sqrt{2}}\,\frac{1}{3.772} = \frac{40}{\sqrt{2}}\ \text{A}$$

$$T = L/R = 0.08\ \text{Sec.}$$

THE RESPONSE IS THEN GIVEN BY

$$i(t) = 40\sin(\omega t + \alpha - 88.1^\circ) - 40\,e^{-t/0.08}\sin(\alpha - 88.1^\circ)$$

(a) NO DC OFFSET, IF SWITCH IS CLOSED WHEN $\alpha = 88.1^\circ$.

(b) MAXIMUM DC OFFSET, WHEN $\alpha = 88.1^\circ - 90^\circ = -1.9^\circ$

CURRENT WAVEFORMS WITH NO DC OFFSET (a), AND WITH MAX. DC OFFSET (b) ARE SHOWN BELOW:

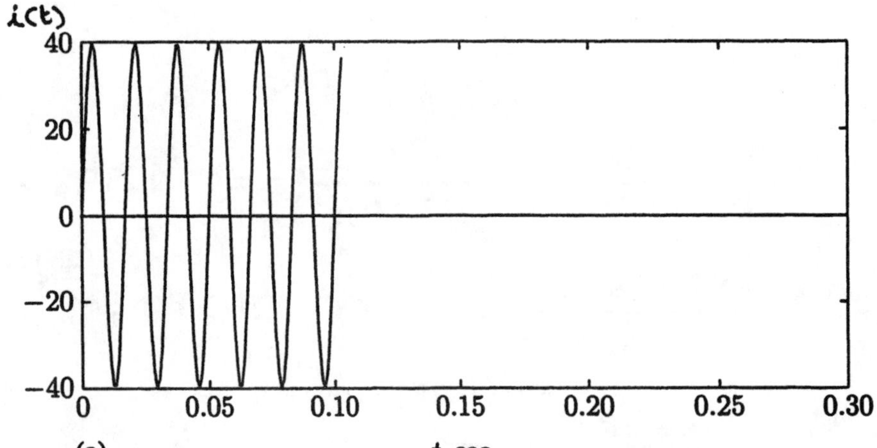

(a)

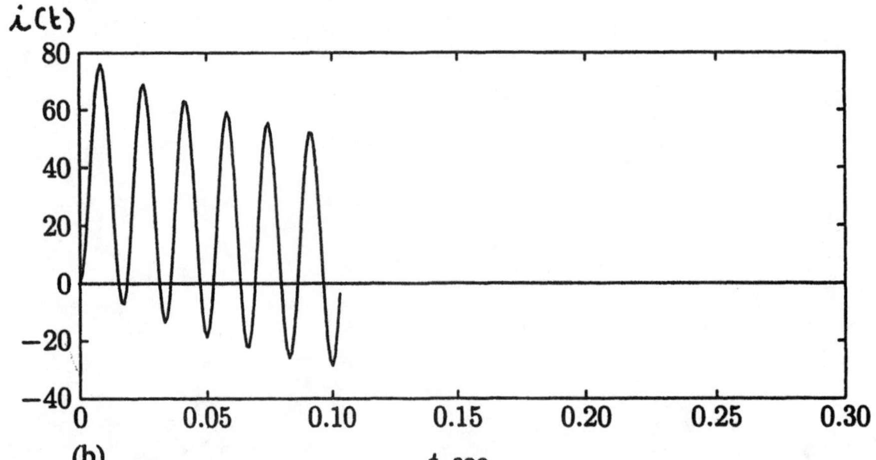

(b)

7.4 (a) Neglecting the transformer winding resistance,

$$I'' = \frac{E_g}{X''_d + X_{TR}} = \frac{1.0}{0.17+0.10} = \underline{\underline{3.704}} \text{ per unit}$$

The base current on the high-voltage side of the transformer is:

$$I_{base\,H} = \frac{S_{rated}}{\sqrt{3}\, V_{H\,rated}} = \frac{1500}{\sqrt{3}\,(500)} = 1.732 \text{ kA}$$

$$I'' = (3.704)(1.732) = \underline{\underline{6.415}} \text{ kA}$$

(b) Using Eq(7.2.1) at t = 3 cycles = 0.05 s with the transformer reactance included:

$$I_{ac}(0.05) = 1.0\left[\left(\frac{1}{0.27} - \frac{1}{0.40}\right) e^{\frac{-0.05}{0.05}} + \left(\frac{1}{0.40} - \frac{1}{1.6}\right) e^{\frac{-0.05}{1.0}} + \frac{1}{1.6}\right]$$

$$= 2.851 \text{ per unit}$$

Using Eq(7.2.5),

$$i_{dc}(t) = \sqrt{2}\,(3.704)\, e^{-t/0.10} = 5.238\, e^{-t/0.10} \text{ per unit}$$

The rms asymmetrical current that the breaker interrupts is

$$I_{rms}(0.05\text{ s}) = \sqrt{I_{ac}^2(0.05) + i_{dc}^2(0.05)}$$

$$= \sqrt{(2.851)^2 + (5.238)^2\, e^{-\frac{2(0.05)}{0.10}}}$$

$$= 4.269 \text{ per unit} = (4.269)(1.732) = \underline{\underline{7.394}} \text{ kA}$$

7.5

(a) Using Eq(7.2.1) with the transformer reactance included, and with $\alpha = 0°$ for maximum dc offset

$$i_{ac}(t) = \sqrt{2}(1.0)\left[\left(\frac{1}{0.27} - \frac{1}{0.40}\right)e^{-t/0.05} + \left(\frac{1}{.40} - \frac{1}{1.6}\right)e^{-t/1.0} + \frac{1}{1.6}\right]\sin(\omega t - \frac{\pi}{2})$$

$$= \sqrt{2}\left[1.204\, e^{-t/0.05} + 1.875\, e^{-t/1.0} + 0.625\right]\sin(\omega t - \frac{\pi}{2}) \text{ per unit}$$

The generator base current is :

$$I_{base\,L} = \frac{S_{rated}}{\sqrt{3}\,V_{rated\,L}} = \frac{1500}{\sqrt{3}(20)} = 43.3 \text{ kA}$$

Therefore :

$$i_{ac}(t) = 61.23\left[1.204\, e^{\frac{-t}{0.05}} + 1.875\, e^{\frac{-t}{1.0}} + 0.625\right]\sin(\omega t - \frac{\pi}{2}) \text{ kA}$$

where the effect of the transformer on the time constants has been neglected.

(b) From Eq (7.2.5) and the results of Problem 7.4,

$$i_{dc}(t) = \sqrt{2}\, I''\, e^{-t/T_A} = \sqrt{2}\,(3.704)\, e^{-t/0.10}$$

$$= 5.238\, e^{\frac{-t}{0.10}} \text{ per unit} = \underline{\underline{226.8\, e^{\frac{-t}{0.10}}}} \text{ kA}$$

7.6

(a) $i_{ac}(t) = 10\left(1 + e^{-t/200} + 6e^{-t/15}\right)$, t IN ms AND i IN kA.

THE PLOT IS SHOWN BELOW:

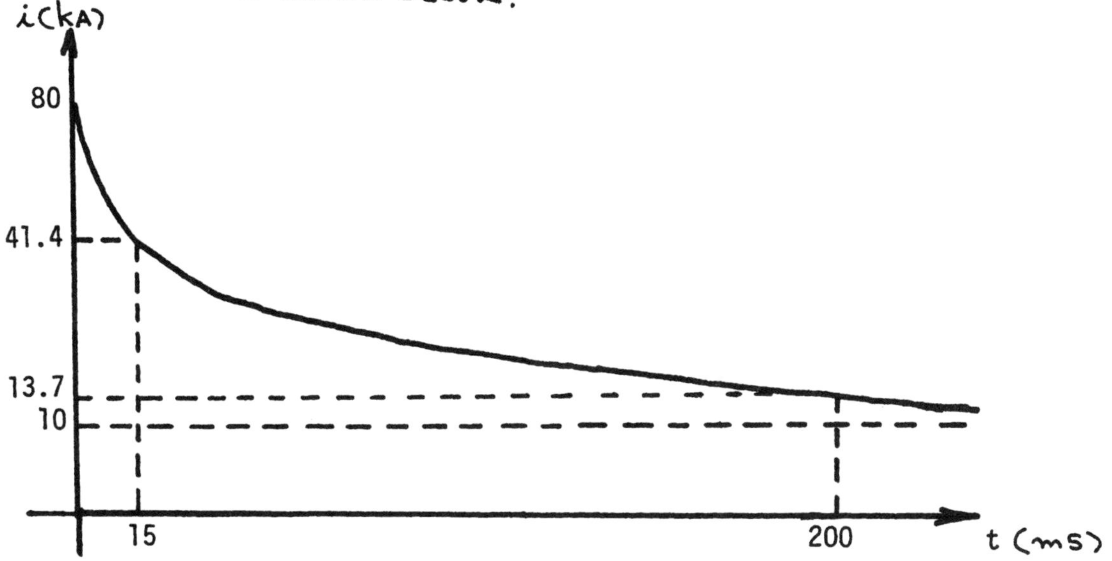

(b) $I_{base} = \dfrac{300}{0.0138\sqrt{3}} = 12551\text{A}$; $Z_{base} = \dfrac{(13.8)^2}{300} = 0.635\,\Omega$

$i(t) = 0.797\left(1 + e^{-t/\tau_1} + 6e^{-t/\tau_2}\right)$ PU

$\lim_{t\to\infty} i(t) = 0.797$; $\therefore X_d = \dfrac{1}{0.797} = 1.255$ PU

$\lim_{t\to 0} i(t) = 8\times 0.797$; $\therefore X_d'' = \dfrac{1}{8\times 0.797} = 0.157$ PU

(c) $X_d = 1.255 \times 0.635 = 0.797\,\Omega$

$X_d'' = 0.157 \times 0.635 = 0.0996\,\Omega$

7.7

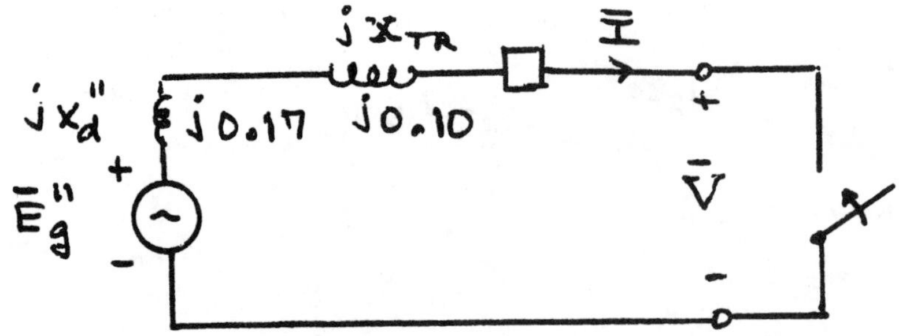

The prefault load current in per unit is:

$$\bar{I}_L = \frac{S_{pu}}{V_{pu}} \underline{/ -\cos^{-1}(\text{P.F.})} = \frac{1.0}{1.0} \underline{/ -\cos^{-1}(0.8)} = 1.0 \underline{/-36.86^\circ} \text{ per unit}$$

The internal generator voltage behind the subtransient reactance is

$$E_g'' = \bar{V} + j(X_d'' + X_{TR})\bar{I}_L = 1.0\underline{/0^\circ} + j(0.27)(1.0\underline{/-36.86^\circ})$$
$$= 1.162 + j\,0.216 = 1.182 \underline{/10.53^\circ} \text{ per unit}$$

The subtransient fault current is:

$$\bar{I}'' = \frac{E_g''}{j(X_d'' + X_{TR})} = \frac{1.182 \underline{/10.53^\circ}}{j(0.27)} = 4.378 \underline{/-79.47^\circ} \text{ per unit}$$

$$\bar{I}'' = 4.378\,(1.732) \underline{/-79.47^\circ} = \underline{\underline{7.583 \underline{/-79.47^\circ} \text{ kA}}}$$

Alternatively, using superposition:

$$\bar{I}'' = \bar{I}_1'' + \bar{I}_2'' = \bar{I}_1'' + \bar{I}_L = \underbrace{3.704 \underline{/-90^\circ}}_{\text{From Problem 8.3 (a)}} + 1.0 \underline{/-36.86^\circ}$$

$$\bar{I}'' = 0.80 - j\,4.304 = 4.378 \underline{/-79.47^\circ} \text{ per unit}$$

$$\bar{I}'' = 7.583 \underline{/-79.47^\circ} \text{ kA}$$

7.8

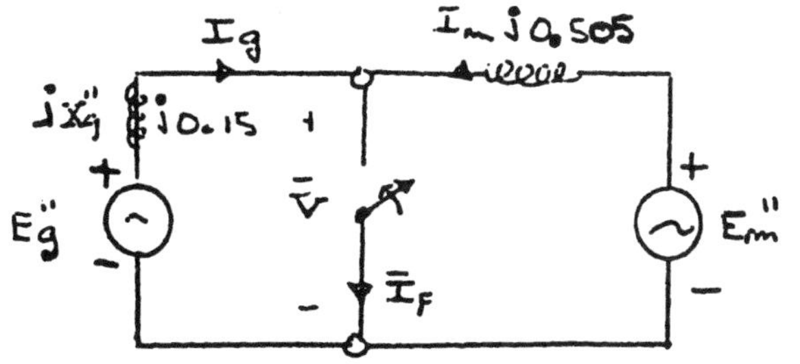

The prefault load current in per unit is:

$$\bar{I}_L = \frac{S}{V} \angle -\cos^{-1}(\text{p.f.}) = \frac{1.0}{1.05} \angle -\cos^{-1} 0.95 = 0.9524 \angle -18.195^\circ \text{ per unit}$$

The internal machine voltages are:

$$\bar{E}_g'' = \bar{V} + jX_g'' \bar{I}_L = 1.05\angle 0^\circ + (j0.15)(0.9524\angle -18.195^\circ)$$

$$= 1.05 + 0.1429 \angle 71.81^\circ = 1.0946 + j0.1358 = 1.1030 \angle 7.072^\circ \text{ per unit}$$

$$\bar{E}_m'' = \bar{V} - j(X_{T1} + X_{Line} + X_{T2} + X_m'')\bar{I}_L$$

$$= 1.05\angle 0^\circ - (j0.505)(0.9524 \angle -18.195^\circ)$$

$$= 1.05 + 0.48095 \angle -18.195^\circ = 0.8798 - j0.4569 = 1.0092 \angle -26.92^\circ \text{ per unit}$$

The short circuit currents are:

$$\bar{I}_g'' = \frac{\bar{E}_g''}{jX_g''} = \frac{1.1030 \angle 7.072^\circ}{j0.15} = 7.353 \angle -82.93^\circ \text{ per unit}$$

$$\bar{I}_m'' = \frac{\bar{E}_m''}{j(X_{T1} + X_{Line} + X_{T2} + X_m'')} = \frac{1.0092 \angle -26.92^\circ}{j0.505} = 1.998 \angle 243.1^\circ \text{ per unit}$$

$$\bar{I}_F'' = \bar{I}_g'' + \bar{I}_m'' = 7.353 \angle -82.93^\circ + 1.998 \angle 243.1^\circ = -j9.079 \text{ per unit}$$

7.9

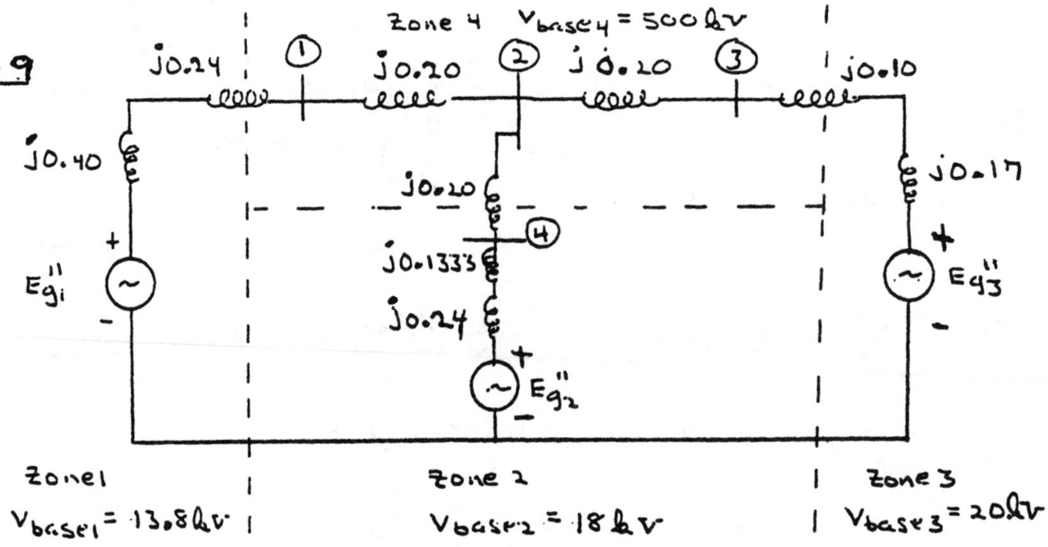

Per Unit Positive Sequence Reactance Diagram

$X''_{g1} = (0.20)\left(\frac{1000}{500}\right) = 0.40$ per unit $\quad X_{T1} = (0.12)(1000/500) = 0.24$ per unit

$X''_{g2} = (0.18)(1000/750) = 0.24$ per unit $\quad X_{T2} = (0.10)(1000/750) = 0.1333$ per unit

$X''_{g3} = 0.17$ per unit $\quad X_{T3} = 0.10$ per unit

$$Z_{base4} = \frac{V_{base4}}{S_{base}} = \frac{(500)^2}{1000} = 250\ \Omega \quad X_{Line1\text{-}2} = X_{Line2\text{-}3} = X_{Line2\text{-}4} = \frac{50}{250} = 0.20 \text{ per unit}$$

(a) $X_{Th} = (0.40 + 0.24) // [0.20 + (0.20 + 0.10 + 0.17) // (0.20 + 0.1333 + 0.24)]$

$= 0.64 // [0.20 + 0.47 // 0.5733] = 0.64 // 0.4583$

$= \underline{\underline{0.2670}}$ per unit

(b) $\bar{V}_F = \frac{525}{500} = 1.05\angle 0^\circ$ per unit $\qquad I_{base4} = \frac{S_{base}}{\sqrt{3}\,V_{base4}} = \frac{1000}{(\sqrt{3})(500)} = 1.155$ kA

$I''_F = \frac{\bar{V}_F}{Z_{Th}} = \frac{1.05\angle 0^\circ}{j\,0.2670} = \underline{\underline{-j3.933}}$ per unit $= (-j3.933)(1.155) = \underline{\underline{-j4.541 \text{ kA}}}$

(c) Using current division:

$I''_{g1} = I''_F \frac{0.4583}{(0.4583 + 0.64)} = (-j3.933)(0.4173) = \underline{\underline{-j1.641}}$ per unit $= \underline{\underline{-j1.896}}$ kA

$I''_{Line1\text{-}2} = I''_F\left(\frac{0.64}{0.4583 + 0.64}\right) = (-j3.933)(0.5827) = \underline{\underline{-j2.292}}$ per unit $= \underline{\underline{-j2.647}}$ kA

7.10

(a) $X_{Th} = (0.20+0.24+0.40) \| (0.20+0.10+0.17) \| (0.20+0.1333+0.24)$

$$X_{Th} = 0.84 \| 0.47 \| 0.5733 = \frac{1}{\frac{1}{0.84}+\frac{1}{0.47}+\frac{1}{0.5733}} = 0.1975 \text{ per unit}$$

(b) $$I_F'' = \frac{\bar{V}_F}{\bar{Z}_{Th}} = \frac{1.05\angle 0°}{j0.1975} = -j5.3155 \text{ per unit}$$

$$I_F'' = (-j5.3155)(1.155) = -j6.1379 \text{ kA}$$

(c) $$I_{12}'' = \frac{1.05\angle 0°}{j0.84} = -j1.25 \text{ per unit} = (-j1.25)(1.155) = -j1.443 \text{ kA}$$

$$I_{32}'' = \frac{1.05\angle 0°}{j0.47} = -j2.234 \text{ per unit} = (-j2.234)(1.155) = -j2.580 \text{ kA}$$

$$I_{42}'' = \frac{1.05\angle 0°}{j0.5733} = -j1.8315 \text{ per unit} = (-j1.8315)(1.155) = -j2.115 \text{ kA}$$

7.11

(a)

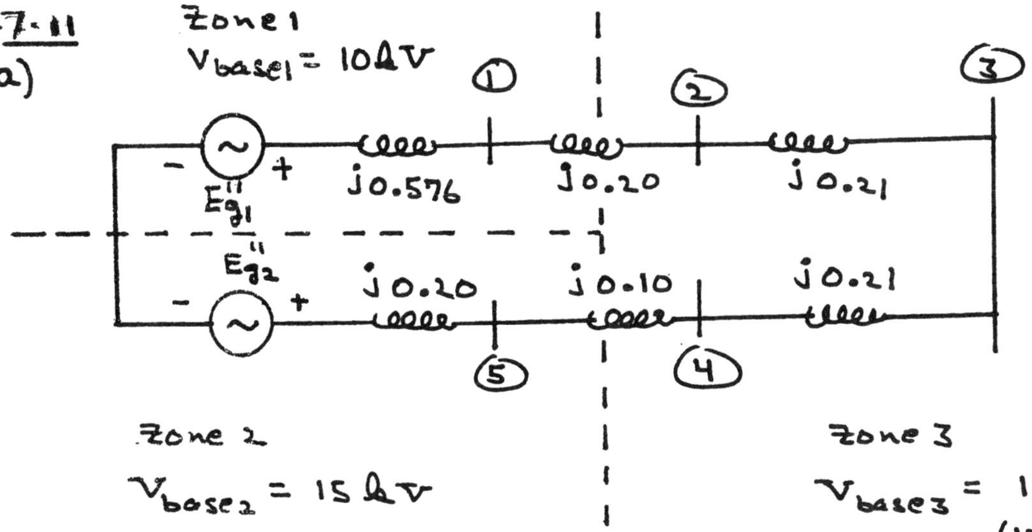

$$Z_{base3} = \frac{(138)^2}{100} = 190.44\,\Omega$$

$$X_{g1}'' = (0.20)\left(\frac{12}{10}\right)^2\left(\frac{100}{50}\right) = 0.576 \text{ per unit}$$

$$X_{g2}'' = 0.20 \text{ per unit}$$

$$X_{T1} = (0.10)\left(\frac{100}{50}\right) = 0.20 \text{ per unit}$$

$$X_{T2} = 0.10 \text{ per unit} \qquad X_{Line} = 40/190.44 = 0.21 \text{ per unit}$$

7.11 CONTD.

(b) $X_{Th} = (0.20)\|(0.576 + 0.20 + 0.21 + 0.21 + 0.10)$

$= 0.20 \| 1.296 = \underline{\underline{0.1733}}$ per unit

$V_F = \underline{\underline{1.0}}$ per unit

(c) $I_F'' = \dfrac{V_F}{Z_{Th}} = \dfrac{1.0\angle 0^\circ}{j0.1733} = \underline{\underline{-j5.772}}$ per unit

$I_{base2} = \dfrac{100}{15\sqrt{3}} = 3.849$ kA

$I_F'' = (-j5.772)(3.849) = \underline{\underline{-j22.21}}$ kA

(d) $I_{g2}'' = \dfrac{1.0\angle 0^\circ}{j0.20} = \underline{\underline{-j5.0}}$ per unit $= (-j5.0)(3.849) = \underline{\underline{-j19.245}}$ kA

$I_{T2}'' = \dfrac{1.0\angle 0^\circ}{j1.296} = \underline{\underline{-j0.7716}}$ per unit $= (-j0.7716)(3.849) = \underline{\underline{-j2.970}}$ kA

7.12

(a) $X_{Th} = (0.20 + 0.10)\|(0.576 + 0.20 + 0.21 + 0.21)$

$= 0.30 \| 1.196 = \underline{\underline{0.2398}}$ per unit

(b) $I_F'' = \dfrac{1.0\angle 0^\circ}{j0.2398} = \underline{\underline{-j4.1695}}$ per unit

$I_{base3} = \dfrac{100}{138\sqrt{3}} = 0.4184$ kA

$I_F'' = (-j4.1695)(0.4184) = \underline{\underline{-j1.744}}$ kA

(c) $I_{T2}'' = \dfrac{1.0\angle 0^\circ}{j0.30} = \underline{\underline{-j3.333}}$ per unit $= (-j3.333)(0.4184) = \underline{\underline{-j1.395}}$ kA

$I_{34}'' = \dfrac{1.0\angle 0^\circ}{j1.196} = \underline{\underline{-j0.836}}$ per unit $= (-j0.836)(0.4184) = \underline{\underline{-j0.350}}$ kA

7.13

CHOOSING BASE MVA AS 30 MVA AND THE BASE LINE VOLTAGE AT THE HV-SIDE OF THE TRANSFORMER TO BE 33kV,

$X_{G1} = \frac{30}{20} \times 0.15 = 0.225$ PU ; $X_{G2} = \frac{30}{10} \times 0.1 = 0.3$ PU ; $X_{TRANS} = \frac{30}{30} \times 0.05 = 0.05$ PU

$\bar{Z}_{LINE} = (3 + j15)\ \frac{30}{33^2} = (0.0826 + j0.4132)$ PU

THE SYSTEM WITH PU-VALUES IS SHOWN BELOW:

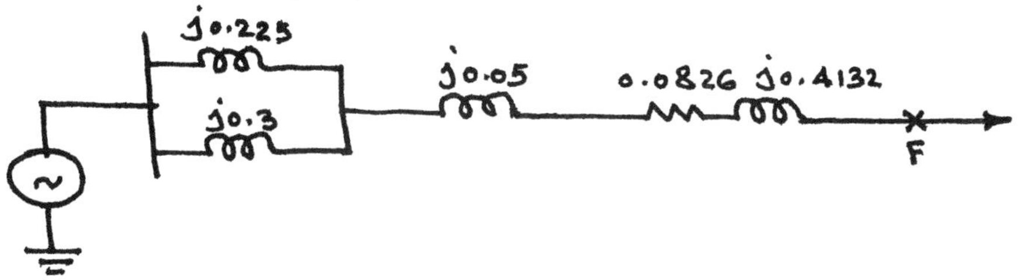

THE ABOVE IS REDUCED TO:

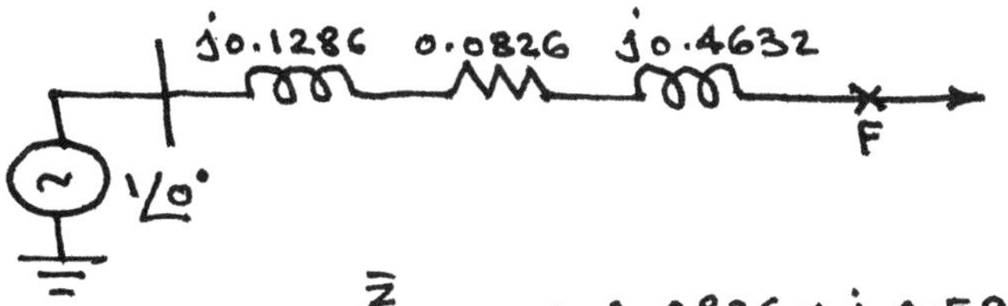

$$\bar{Z}_{TOTAL} = 0.0826 + j\,0.5918 = 0.5975\angle 82^\circ \text{ PU}$$

THEN $$\bar{I}_F = \frac{1.0}{0.5975\angle 82^\circ} = 1.674\angle -82^\circ \text{ PU}$$

$$I_{base} = \frac{30 \times 10^6}{\sqrt{3}\ 33 \times 10^3} = 524.8 \text{ A}$$

$$I_F = 1.674 \times 524.8 = 878.6 \text{ A}$$

7.14

NOTE: TRANSFORMERS ARE RATED 25 MVA. (DATA MISSING IN THE PROB. STATEMENT)

CHOOSING BASE VALUES OF 25 MVA AND 13.8 kV ON THE GENERATOR SIDE

GENERATOR REACTANCE = 0.15 PU

TRANSFORMER REACTANCE = $\frac{25}{25}\left(\frac{13.2}{13.8}\right)^2 0.11 = 0.101$ PU

BASE VOLTAGE AT THE TRANSMISSION LINE IS $13.8 \times \frac{69}{13.2} = 72.136$ kV

PER-UNIT LINE REACTANCE: $65 \frac{25}{(72.136)^2} = 0.312$

$$X_M = 0.15 \times \frac{25}{15} \times \left(\frac{13}{13.8}\right)^2 = 0.222 \text{ PU}$$

THE REACTANCE DIAGRAM IS SHOWN BELOW; SWITCH SW SIMULATES THE SHORT CIRCUIT, AND $\bar{E}_g''$ AND $\bar{E}_m''$ ARE THE MACHINE PREFAULT INTERNAL VOLTAGES.

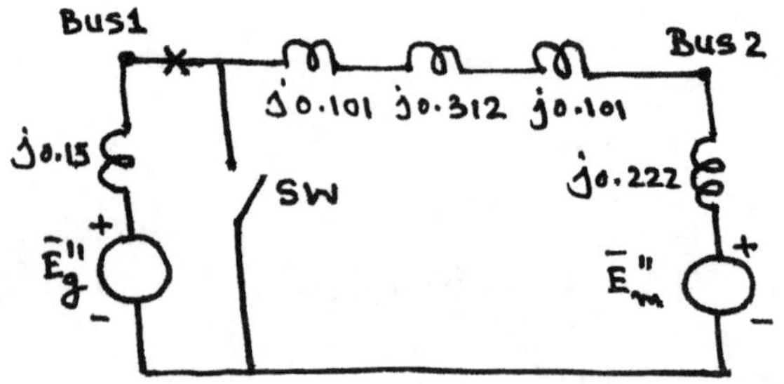

(a)

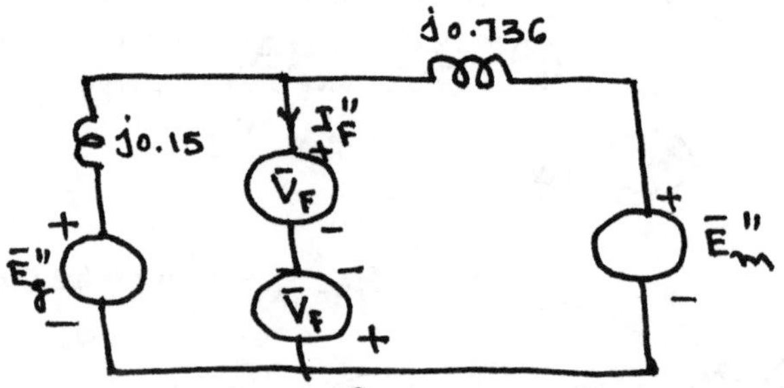

(b)

VOLTAGES V_F IN PHASE OPPOSITION REPLACE THE SWITCH

USING SUPERPOSITION:

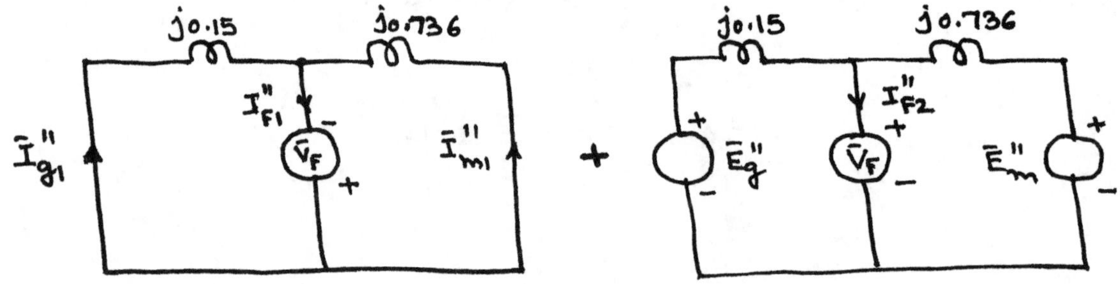

(c)

CHOOSE $\bar{V}_F$ TO BE EQUAL TO THE VOLTAGE AT THE FAULT POINT PRIOR TO THE OCCURENCE OF THE FAULT; THEN $\bar{V}_F = \bar{E}_m'' = \bar{E}_g''$; PREFAULT CURRENTS ARE NEGLECTED; $\bar{I}_{F2}'' = 0$; SO $\bar{V}_F$ MAY BE OPEN CIRCUITED AS SHOWN BELOW:

7.14 CONTD.

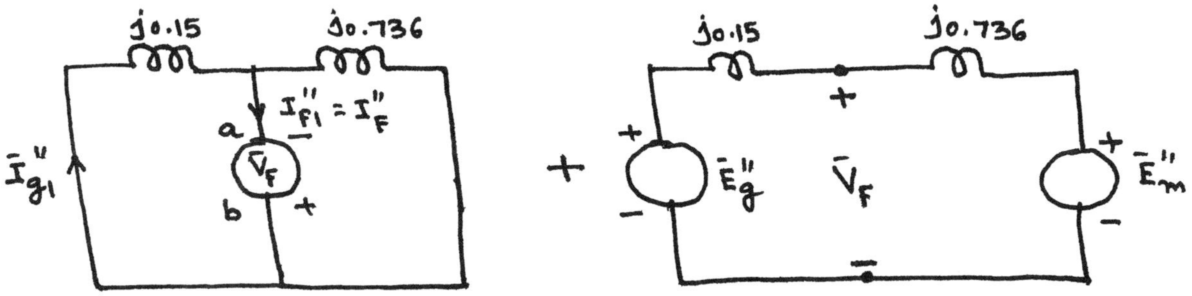

(d)

EQUIVALENT IMPEDANCE BETWEEN TERMINALS a & b IS

$$\frac{j0.15 \times j0.736}{j0.15 + j0.736} = j0.1246$$

NEGLECTING PREFAULT CURRENTS,

$$\bar{E}''_g = \bar{E}''_m = \bar{V}_F = 1\angle 0° \text{ PU}$$

$$\therefore \quad \bar{I}''_F = \bar{I}''_{F1} = \frac{1\angle 0°}{j0.1246} = -j\,8.025 \text{ PU}$$

7-15

(a)

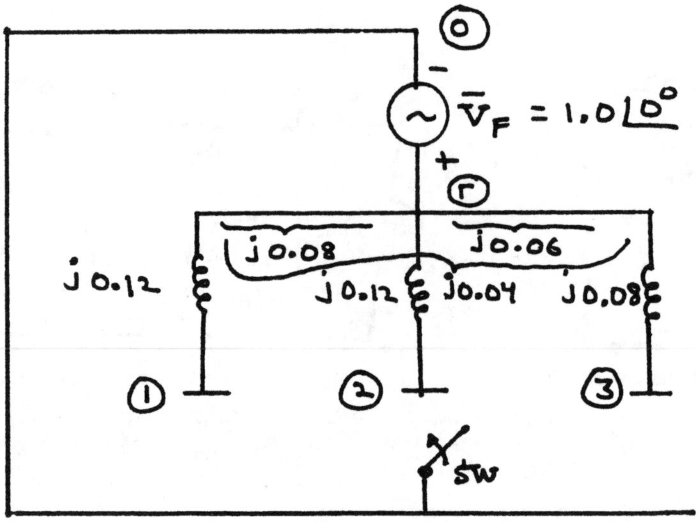

Rake Equivalent

(b) $\bar{I}''_{F2} = \dfrac{\bar{V}_F}{\bar{Z}_{22}} = \dfrac{1.0\angle 0°}{j0.12} = \underline{\underline{-j8.333}}$ per unit

Using Eq (8.4.7):

$\bar{E}_1 = \left(1 - \dfrac{\bar{Z}_{12}}{\bar{Z}_{22}}\right)\bar{V}_F = \left(1 - \dfrac{0.08}{0.12}\right)1.0\angle 0° = \underline{\underline{0.3333\angle 0°}}$ per unit

$\bar{E}_2 = \left(1 - \dfrac{\bar{Z}_{22}}{\bar{Z}_{22}}\right)\bar{V}_F = 0$

$\bar{E}_3 = \left(1 - \dfrac{\bar{Z}_{23}}{\bar{Z}_{22}}\right)\bar{V}_F = \left(1 - \dfrac{0.06}{0.12}\right)1.0\angle 0° = \underline{\underline{0.50\angle 0°}}$ per unit

7.16

$$\bar{Y}_{BUS} = -j\begin{bmatrix} 6.5625 & -5 & 0 & 0 \\ -5 & 15 & -5 & -5 \\ 0 & -5 & 8.7037 & 0 \\ 0 & -5 & 0 & 7.6786 \end{bmatrix} \text{ per unit}$$

Using the personal computer subroutine:

$$\bar{Z}_{bus} = j\begin{bmatrix} 0.2671 & 0.1505 & 0.0865 & 0.098 \\ 0.1505 & 0.1975 & 0.1135 & 0.1286 \\ 0.0865 & 0.1135 & 0.1801 & 0.0739 \\ 0.098 & 0.1286 & 0.0739 & 0.214 \end{bmatrix} \text{ per unit}$$

7.17

$$\bar{Y}_{bus} = -j\begin{bmatrix} 6.7361 & -5 & 0 & 0 & 0 \\ -5 & 9.7619 & -4.7619 & 0 & 0 \\ 0 & -4.7619 & 9.5238 & -4.7619 & 0 \\ 0 & 0 & -4.7619 & 14.7619 & -10 \\ 0 & 0 & 0 & -10 & 15 \end{bmatrix} \text{ per unit}$$

Using the personal computer subroutine:

$$\bar{Z}_{bus} = j\begin{bmatrix} 0.3542 & 0.2772 & 0.1964 & 0.1155 & 0.077 \\ 0.2772 & 0.3735 & 0.2645 & 0.1556 & 0.1037 \\ 0.1964 & 0.2645 & 0.3361 & 0.1977 & 0.1318 \\ 0.1155 & 0.1556 & 0.1977 & 0.2398 & 0.1599 \\ 0.077 & 0.1037 & 0.1318 & 0.1599 & 0.1733 \end{bmatrix} \text{ per unit.}$$

7.18

(a) THE ADMITTANCE DIAGRAM IS SHOWN BELOW:

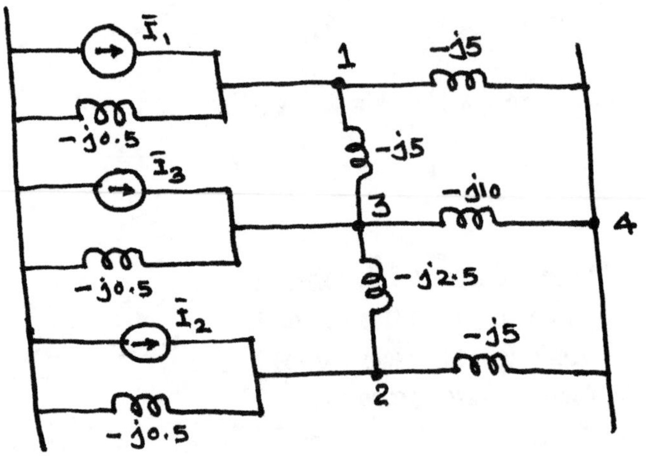

(b) $\bar{Y}_{11} = -j0.5 - j5 - j5 = -j10.5$; $\bar{Y}_{22} = -j0.5 - j2.5 - j5 = -j8.0$

$\bar{Y}_{33} = -j0.5 - j5 - j10 - j2.5 = -j18.0$; $\bar{Y}_{44} = -j5 - j10 - j5 = -j20.0$

$\bar{Y}_{12} = \bar{Y}_{21} = 0$; $\bar{Y}_{13} = \bar{Y}_{31} = j5.0$; $\bar{Y}_{14} = \bar{Y}_{41} = j5.0$

$\bar{Y}_{23} = \bar{Y}_{32} = j2.5$; $\bar{Y}_{24} = \bar{Y}_{42} = j5$; $\bar{Y}_{34} = \bar{Y}_{43} = j10.0$

HENCE THE BUS ADMITTANCE MATRIX IS GIVEN BY

$$\bar{Y}_{BUS} = \begin{bmatrix} -j10.5 & 0 & j5.0 & j5.0 \\ 0 & -j8.0 & j2.5 & j5.0 \\ j5.0 & j2.5 & -j18.0 & j10.0 \\ j5.0 & j5.0 & j10.0 & -j20.0 \end{bmatrix}$$

(c) THE BUS IMPEDANCE MATRIX $\bar{Z}_{BUS} = \bar{Y}_{BUS}^{-1}$ IS GIVEN BY

$$\bar{Z}_{BUS} = \begin{bmatrix} j0.724 & j0.620 & j0.656 & j0.644 \\ j0.620 & j0.738 & j0.642 & j0.660 \\ j0.656 & j0.642 & j0.702 & j0.676 \\ j0.644 & j0.660 & j0.676 & j0.719 \end{bmatrix}$$

7.19

(a)

$$\tilde{Y}_{BUS} = \begin{array}{c} \textcircled{1} \\ \textcircled{2} \\ \textcircled{3} \\ \textcircled{4} \end{array} \begin{bmatrix} j1.5 & -j0.25 & 0 & 0 \\ -j0.25 & j0.775 & -j0.4 & -j0.125 \\ 0 & -j0.4 & j1.85 & -j0.2 \\ 0 & -j0.125 & -j0.2 & j0.325 \end{bmatrix} \begin{array}{c} \textcircled{1} \;\; \textcircled{2} \;\; \textcircled{3} \;\; \textcircled{4} \end{array}$$

(b)

$$\bar{Z}_{BUS} = \begin{array}{c} \textcircled{1} \\ \textcircled{2} \\ \textcircled{3} \\ \textcircled{4} \end{array} \begin{bmatrix} j0.71660 & j0.60992 & j0.53340 & j0.58049 \\ j0.60992 & j0.73190 & j0.64008 & j0.69659 \\ j0.53340 & j0.64008 & j0.71660 & j0.66951 \\ j0.58049 & j0.69659 & j0.66951 & j0.76310 \end{bmatrix} \begin{array}{c} \textcircled{1} \;\; \textcircled{2} \;\; \textcircled{3} \;\; \textcircled{4} \end{array}$$

NOTE: $\bar{Z}_{BUS}$ MAY BE FORMULATED DIRECTLY (INSTEAD OF INVERTING $\tilde{Y}_{BUS}$) BY ADDING THE BRANCHES IN THE ORDER OF THEIR LABELS, AND NUMBERED SUBSCRIPTS ON $\bar{Z}_{BUS}$ WILL INDICATE THE INTERMEDIATE STEPS OF THE SOLUTION.

FOR DETAILS OF THIS STEP-BY-STEP METHOD OF FORMULATING $\bar{Z}_{BUS}$, PLEASE REFER TO THE 2ND EDITION OF THE TEXT.

Problem 7.20

Generator	Current supplied (Amps)
5	52296
6	58745
7	64491

Bus	Voltage (p.u)
1	0.25
2	0
3	0.447
4	0.367
5	0.55
6	0.610
7	0.670

Problem 7.21

Generator	Current supplied (Amps)
5	31435
6	90219
7	38765

Bus	Voltage (p.u)
1	0.569
2	0.419
3	0.687
4	0
5	0.749
6	0.375
7	0.822

Problem 7.22

(Note: Place fault between buses 1 and 2. Also, the nominal voltage at bus 4 should be 345kV)

Generator	Current supplied (Amps)
5	59363
6	42348
7	46490

Bus	Voltage (p.u)
1	0.142
2	0.293
3	0.615
4	.5571
5	0.482

7.22 CONTD.

6	0.73313
7	0.77622

Problem 7.23

In order to limit the fault current at G1 to 1.5 p.u. the reactance should be raised to 0.7 per unit (from 0.4 per unit) Therefore, the reactance should be 0.3 per unit. The fault that causes the highest G1 current occurs at bus 5 (i.e., G1's terminal bus).

Problem 7.24

Generator	Current (p.u)	Current (Amps)
14	0	0
28	3.273	548
28	3.273	548
31	4.613	772
44	8.328	6968
48	0	0
50	2.067	1732
53	4.833	2022
54	3.814	3191

73% of buses have voltage magnitudes below 0.75 p.u.

Problem 7.25

Generator	Current (p.u)	Current (Amps)
14	0	0
28	1.951	327
28	1.951	327
31	3.388	559
44	2.193	1835
48	0	0
50	0.851	712
53	2.871	1201
54	2.091	1750

13.5% of buses have voltage magnitudes below 0.75 p.u.

Problem 7.26

Fault Bus	Fault Current (p.u)
1	23.333
2	10.426
3	10.889
4	12.149
5	16.154

7.27 (a) The symmetrical interrupting capability is:

at 10 kV : $(9.0)\left(\frac{15.5}{10}\right) = \underline{\underline{13.95\ kA}}$

$$V_{min} = \frac{V_{max}}{K} = \frac{15.5}{2.67} = 5.805\ kV$$

at 5 kV : $I_{max} = K\,I = (2.67)(9.0) = \underline{\underline{24.0\ kA}}$

(b) The symmetrical interrupting capability at 13.8 kV is:

$$9.0\left(\frac{15.5}{13.8}\right) = 10.11\ kA$$

Since the interrupting capability of 10.11 kA is greater than the 10 kA symmetrical fault current and the (X/R) ratio is less than 15, the answer is <u>yes</u>. This breaker can be safely installed at the bus.

7.28 From Table 7.10, select the 500 kV (nominal voltage class) breaker with a 40 kA rated short circuit current. This breaker has a 3 kA rated continuous current.

9.1

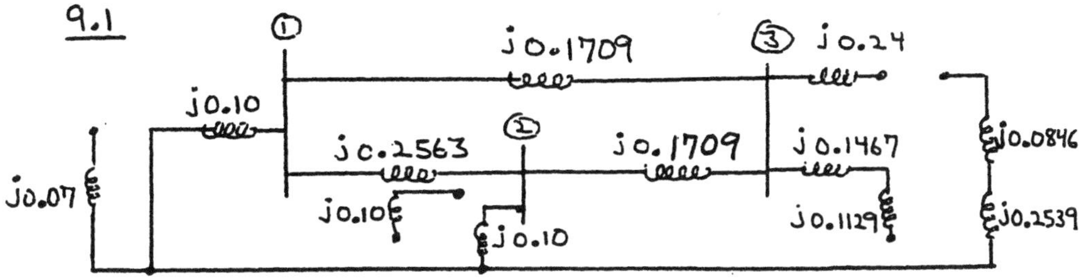

Per Unit Zero Sequence Network

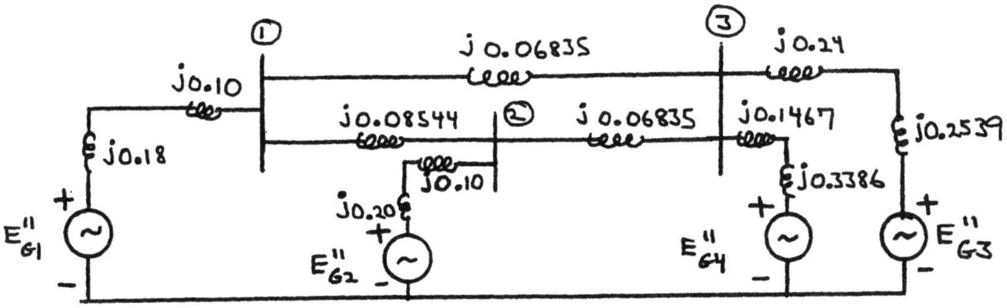

Per Unit Positive Sequence Network

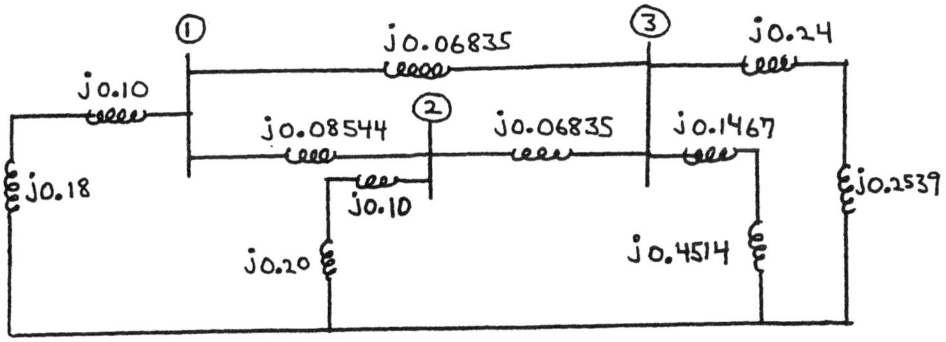

Per Unit Negative Sequence Network

7.29

THE MAXIMUM SYMMETRICAL INTERRUPTING CAPABILITY IS

K x RATED SHORT-CIRCUIT CURRENT = 1.21 x 19,000 = 22,990 A

WHICH MUST NOT BE EXCEEDED.

$$\text{LOWER LIMIT OF OPERATING VOLTAGE} = \frac{\text{RATED MAXIMUM VOLTAGE}}{K}$$

$$= \frac{72.5}{1.21} = 60 \text{ kV}$$

HENCE, IN THE OPERATING VOLTAGE RANGE 72.5 – 60 kV, THE SYMMETRICAL INTERRUPTING CURRENT MAY EXCEED THE RATED SHORT-CIRCUIT CURRENT OF 19,000 A, BUT IS LIMITED TO 22,990 A. FOR EXAMPLE, AT 66 kV THE INTERRUPTING CURRENT CAN BE

$$\frac{72.5}{60} \times 19{,}000 = 20{,}871 \text{ A}$$

7.30

(a) FOR A BASE OF 25 MVA, 13.8 kV IN THE GENERATOR CIRCUIT, THE BASE FOR MOTORS IS 25 MVA, 6.9 kV. FOR EACH OF THE MOTORS,

$$X_d'' = 0.2 \ \frac{25000}{5000} = 1.0 \text{ PU}$$

THE REACTANCE DIAGRAM IS SHOWN BELOW:

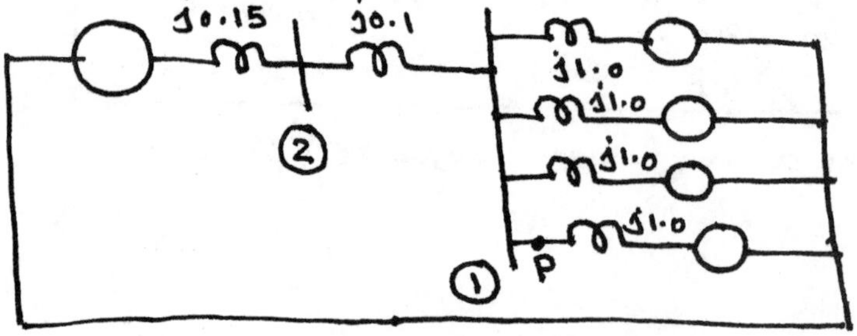

FOR A FAULT AT P, $\bar{V}_F = 1\angle 0^\circ$ PU ; $\bar{Z}_{Th} = j0.125$ PU

$$\bar{I}_f'' = 1\angle 0^\circ / j0.125 = -j8.0 \text{ PU}$$

THE BASE CURRENT IN THE 6.9 kV CIRCUIT IS $\dfrac{25000}{\sqrt{3} \times 6.9} = 2090$ A

7.30 CONTD.

SO, SUBTRANSIENT FAULT CURRENT = $8 \times 2090 = 16{,}720$ A

(b) CONTRIBUTIONS FROM THE GENERATOR AND THREE OF THE FOUR MOTORS COME THROUGH BREAKER A.

THE GENERATOR CONTRIBUTES A CURRENT OF $-j8.0 \times \frac{0.25}{0.50} = -j4.0$ PU

EACH MOTOR CONTRIBUTES 25% OF THE REMAINING FAULT CURRENT, OR $-j1.0$ PU AMPERES EACH. FOR BREAKER A

$$\bar{I}'' = -j4.0 + 3(-j1.0) = -j7.0 \text{ PU} \quad \text{OR} \quad 7 \times 2090 = 14{,}630 \text{ A}$$

(c) TO COMPUTE THE CURRENT TO BE INTERRUPTED BY BREAKER A, LET US REPLACE THE SUBTRANSIENT REACTANCE OF $j1.0$ BY THE TRANSIENT REACTANCE, SAY $j1.5$, IN THE MOTOR CIRCUIT. THEN

$$\bar{Z}_{Th} = j\frac{0.375 \times 0.25}{0.375 + 0.25} = j0.15 \text{ PU}$$

THE GENERATOR CONTRIBUTES A CURRENT OF

$$\frac{1.0}{j0.15} \times \frac{0.375}{0.625} = -j4.0 \text{ PU}$$

EACH MOTOR CONTRIBUTES A CURRENT OF $\frac{1}{4} \times \frac{1}{j0.15} \times \frac{0.25}{0.625} = -j0.67$ PU

THE SYMMETRICAL SHORT-CIRCUIT CURRENT TO BE INTERRUPTED IS

$$(4.0 + 3 \times 0.67) \times 2090 = 12{,}560 \text{ A}$$

SUPPOSING THAT ALL THE BREAKERS CONNECTED TO THE BUS ARE RATED ON THE BASIS OF THE CURRENT INTO A FAULT ON THE BUS, THE SHORT-CIRCUIT CURRENT INTERRUPTING RATING OF THE BREAKERS CONNECTED TO THE 6.9 kV BUS MUST BE AT LEAST

$4 + 4 \times 0.67 = 6.67$ PU, OR $6.67 \times 2090 = 13{,}940$ A.

A 14.4-kV CIRCUIT BREAKER HAS A RATED MAXIMUM VOLTAGE OF 15.5 kV AND A K OF 2.67. AT 15.5 kV ITS RATED SHORT-CIRCUIT INTERRUPTING CURRENT IS 8900 A. THIS BREAKER IS RATED FOR A SYMMETRICAL SHORT-CIRCUIT INTERRUPTING CURRENT OF $2.67 \times 8900 = 23{,}760$ A, AT A VOLTAGE OF $15.5/2.67 = 5.8$ kV.

7.30 CONTD.

THIS CURRENT IS THE MAXIMUM THAT CAN BE INTERRUPTED EVEN THOUGH THE BREAKER MAY BE IN A CIRCUIT OF LOWER VOLTAGE.

THE SHORT-CIRCUIT INTERRUPTING CURRENT RATING AT 6.9 kV IS

$$\frac{15.5}{6.9} \times 8900 = 20{,}000 \text{ A}$$

THE REQUIRED CAPABILITY OF 13,940 A IS WELL BELOW 80% OF 20,000 A, AND THE BREAKER IS SUITABLE WITH RESPECT TO SHORT-CIRCUIT CURRENT.

Chapter 8

8.1 Using the identities given in Table 8.1:

(a) $$\frac{a+1}{1+a-a^2} = \frac{1\angle 60^\circ}{\underbrace{(1+a+a^2)}_{0}-2a^2} = \frac{1\angle 60^\circ}{(-2)(1\angle 240^\circ)} = -\frac{1}{2}\angle -180^\circ$$

$$= +\frac{1}{2}\angle 0^\circ = \underline{\underline{\frac{1}{2}}}$$

(b) $$\frac{(a^2+a)+j}{(ja-a^2)} = \frac{-1+j}{a(j-a)} = \frac{\sqrt{2}\angle 135^\circ}{(1\angle 120^\circ)\left(j+\frac{1}{2}-j\frac{\sqrt{3}}{2}\right)}$$

$$= \frac{\sqrt{2}\angle 15^\circ}{\frac{1}{2}+j\left(1-\frac{\sqrt{3}}{2}\right)} = \frac{\sqrt{2}\angle 15^\circ}{0.5177\angle 15^\circ} = \underline{\underline{2.732\angle 0^\circ}}$$

(c) $$(1-a)(1+a^2) = (\sqrt{3}\angle -30^\circ)(1\angle -60^\circ) = \underline{\underline{\sqrt{3}\angle -90^\circ}}$$

(d) $$(a+a^2)(a^2+1) = (-1)(1\angle -60^\circ) = \underline{\underline{1\angle 120^\circ}} = a$$

8.2 (a) $$(a)^{10} = a(a^3)^3 = a = -\frac{1}{2}+j\frac{\sqrt{3}}{2}$$

(b) $$(ja)^{10} = (j)^{10}(a)^{10} = (j)^4(j)^4(j)^2(a) = -a = \frac{1}{2}-j\frac{\sqrt{3}}{2}$$

(c) $$(1-a)^3 = (\sqrt{3}\angle -30^\circ)^3 = (\sqrt{3})^3\angle -90^\circ = 0-j3\sqrt{3}$$

$$= 0-j5.196$$

(d) $$e^a = e^{-\frac{1}{2}+j\frac{\sqrt{3}}{2}} = e^{-\frac{1}{2}}\angle \tfrac{\sqrt{3}}{2}\text{ radians}$$

$$= 0.6065\angle 49.62^\circ = \underline{\underline{0.3929+j0.4620}}$$

8.3

(a)
$$\begin{bmatrix}\bar{I}_0\\ \bar{I}_1\\ \bar{I}_2\end{bmatrix} = \frac{1}{3}\begin{bmatrix}1 & 1 & 1\\ 1 & a & a^2\\ 1 & a^2 & a\end{bmatrix}\begin{bmatrix}10\angle 90^\circ\\ 10\angle 340^\circ\\ 10\angle 200^\circ\end{bmatrix} = \frac{10}{3}\begin{bmatrix}1\angle 90^\circ + 1\angle 340^\circ + 1\angle 200^\circ\\ 1\angle 90^\circ + 1\angle 100^\circ + 1\angle 80^\circ\\ 1\angle 90^\circ + 1\angle 220^\circ + 1\angle 320^\circ\end{bmatrix}$$

$$= \frac{10}{3}\begin{bmatrix}0 + j0.316\\ 0 + j2.9696\\ 0 - j0.2856\end{bmatrix} = \begin{bmatrix}1.0533\angle 90^\circ\\ 9.8987\angle 90^\circ\\ 0.9520\angle -90^\circ\end{bmatrix} \text{ A}$$

(b)
$$\begin{bmatrix}\bar{I}_0\\ \bar{I}_1\\ \bar{I}_2\end{bmatrix} = \frac{1}{3}\begin{bmatrix}1 & 1 & 1\\ 1 & a & a^2\\ 1 & a^2 & a\end{bmatrix}\begin{bmatrix}100\angle 0^\circ\\ 100\angle 90^\circ\\ 0\end{bmatrix} = \frac{100}{3}\begin{bmatrix}1\angle 0^\circ + 1\angle 90^\circ\\ 1\angle 0^\circ + 1\angle 210^\circ\\ 1\angle 0^\circ + 1\angle 330^\circ\end{bmatrix}$$

$$= \frac{100}{3}\begin{bmatrix}\sqrt{2}\angle 45^\circ\\ 0.5176\angle -75^\circ\\ 1.9319\angle -15^\circ\end{bmatrix} = \begin{bmatrix}47.13\angle 45^\circ\\ 17.253\angle -75^\circ\\ 64.4\angle -15^\circ\end{bmatrix} \text{ A}$$

8.4

$$\begin{bmatrix}\bar{V}_{an}\\ \bar{V}_{bn}\\ \bar{V}_{cn}\end{bmatrix} = \begin{bmatrix}1 & 1 & 1\\ 1 & a^2 & a\\ 1 & a & a^2\end{bmatrix}\begin{bmatrix}20\angle 80^\circ\\ 100\angle 0^\circ\\ 30\angle 180^\circ\end{bmatrix} = \begin{bmatrix}20\angle 80^\circ + 100\angle 0^\circ + 30\angle 180^\circ\\ 20\angle 80^\circ + 100\angle 240^\circ + 30\angle 300^\circ\\ 20\angle 80^\circ + 100\angle 120^\circ + 30\angle 60^\circ\end{bmatrix}$$

$$= \begin{bmatrix}73.47 + j19.70\\ -31.53 - j92.89\\ -31.53 + j132.3\end{bmatrix} = \begin{bmatrix}76.07\angle 15.01^\circ\\ 98.09\angle 251.3^\circ\\ 135.98\angle 103.4^\circ\end{bmatrix} \text{ V}$$

8.5

$$\begin{bmatrix}\bar{I}_0\\ \bar{I}_1\\ \bar{I}_2\end{bmatrix} = \frac{1}{3}\begin{bmatrix}1 & 1 & 1\\ 1 & a & a^2\\ 1 & a^2 & a\end{bmatrix}\begin{bmatrix}0\\ 1500\angle 90^\circ\\ 1500\angle -30^\circ\end{bmatrix} = \frac{1500}{3}\begin{bmatrix}1\angle 90^\circ + 1\angle -30^\circ\\ 1\angle 210^\circ + 1\angle 210^\circ\\ 1\angle 330^\circ + 1\angle 90^\circ\end{bmatrix}$$

$$= 500\begin{bmatrix}0.866 + j0.5\\ 2\angle 210^\circ\\ 0.866 + j0.5\end{bmatrix} = \begin{bmatrix}166.7\angle 30^\circ\\ 333.3\angle 210^\circ\\ 166.7\angle 30^\circ\end{bmatrix} \text{ A}$$

CURRENT INTO GROUND $\bar{I}_n = 3\bar{I}_0 = 500\angle 30^\circ$ A

8.6

(a)

$$\begin{bmatrix}\bar{V}_{Lg0}\\ \bar{V}_{Lg1}\\ \bar{V}_{Lg2}\end{bmatrix} = \frac{1}{3}\begin{bmatrix}1 & 1 & 1\\ 1 & a & a^2\\ 1 & a^2 & a\end{bmatrix}\begin{bmatrix}280\angle 0^\circ\\ 290\angle -130^\circ\\ 260\angle 110^\circ\end{bmatrix}$$

$$= \frac{1}{3}\begin{bmatrix}280\angle 0^\circ + 290\angle -130^\circ + 260\angle 110^\circ\\ 280\angle 0^\circ + 290\angle -10^\circ + 260\angle -10^\circ\\ 280\angle 0^\circ + 290\angle 110^\circ + 260\angle 230^\circ\end{bmatrix} = \begin{bmatrix}1.555 + j7.389\\ 273.9 - j31.84\\ 4.563 + j24.45\end{bmatrix}$$

$$= \begin{bmatrix}7.551\angle 78.12^\circ\\ 275.7\angle -6.631^\circ\\ 24.87\angle 79.43^\circ\end{bmatrix} \text{ V}$$

(b)

$$\begin{bmatrix}\bar{V}_{ab}\\ \bar{V}_{bc}\\ \bar{V}_{ca}\end{bmatrix} = \begin{bmatrix}\bar{V}_{ag} - \bar{V}_{bg}\\ \bar{V}_{bg} - \bar{V}_{cg}\\ \bar{V}_{cg} - \bar{V}_{ag}\end{bmatrix} = \begin{bmatrix}280\angle 0^\circ - 290\angle -130^\circ\\ 290\angle -130^\circ - 260\angle 110^\circ\\ 260\angle 110^\circ - 280\angle 0^\circ\end{bmatrix}$$

$$= \begin{bmatrix}466.4 + j222.2\\ -97.48 - j466.5\\ -368.9 + j244.3\end{bmatrix} = \begin{bmatrix}516.6\angle 25.47^\circ\\ 476.6\angle 258.2^\circ\\ 442.5\angle 146.5^\circ\end{bmatrix} \text{ V}$$

(c)

$$\begin{bmatrix}V_{LL0}\\ V_{LL1}\\ V_{LL2}\end{bmatrix} = \frac{1}{3}\begin{bmatrix}1 & 1 & 1\\ 1 & a & a^2\\ 1 & a^2 & a\end{bmatrix}\begin{bmatrix}516.6\angle 25.47^\circ\\ 476.6\angle 258.2^\circ\\ 442.5\angle 146.5^\circ\end{bmatrix}$$

$$= \frac{1}{3}\begin{bmatrix}516.6\angle 25.47^\circ + 476.6\angle 258.2^\circ + 442.5\angle 146.5\\ 516.6\angle 25.47^\circ + 476.6\angle 378.2 + 442.5\angle 26.5^\circ\\ 516.6\angle 25.47^\circ + 476.6\angle 138.2^\circ + 442.5\angle 266.5^\circ\end{bmatrix}$$

$$= \begin{bmatrix}0 + j0\\ 438.4 + j189.5\\ 28.03 + j32.72\end{bmatrix} = \begin{bmatrix}0\\ 477.6\angle 23.37^\circ\\ 43.08\angle 49.41^\circ\end{bmatrix} \text{V} = \begin{bmatrix}0\\ \sqrt{3}\,\bar{V}_{Lg1}\angle +30^\circ\\ \sqrt{3}\,\bar{V}_{Lg2}\angle -30^\circ\end{bmatrix}$$

8.7

THE CIRCUIT IS SHOWN BELOW:

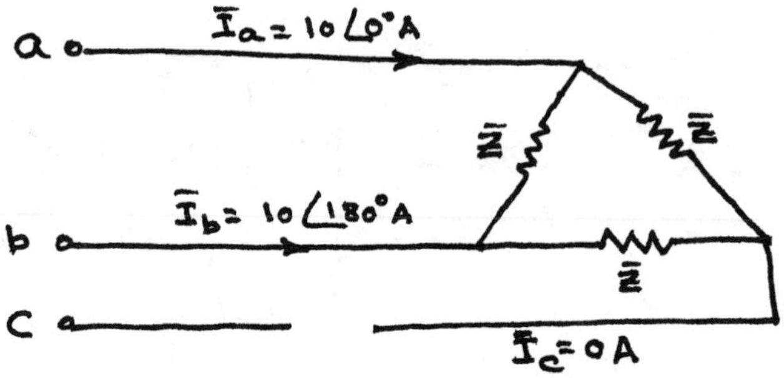

$$\bar{I}_{a0} = \frac{1}{3}\left(10\angle 0° + 10\angle 180° + 0\right) = 0$$

$$\bar{I}_{a1} = \frac{1}{3}\left(10\angle 0° + 10\angle 180°+120° + 0\right) = 5 - j2.89 = 5.78\angle -30° \text{ A}$$

$$\bar{I}_{a2} = \frac{1}{3}\left(10\angle 0° + 10\angle 180°+240° + 0\right) = 5 + j2.89 = 5.78\angle 30° \text{ A}$$

THEN

$\bar{I}_{b0} = \bar{I}_{a0} = 0$ A ; $\bar{I}_{c0} = \bar{I}_{a0} = 0$ A

$\bar{I}_{b1} = a^2\bar{I}_{a1} = 5.78\angle -150°$ A ; $\bar{I}_{c1} = a\bar{I}_{a1} = 5.78\angle 90°$ A

$\bar{I}_{b2} = a\bar{I}_{a2} = 5.78\angle 150°$ A ; $\bar{I}_{c2} = a^2\bar{I}_{a2} = 5.78\angle -90°$ A

8.8

NOTE AN ERROR IN PRINTING: $\bar{V}_{ab}$ SHOULD BE $1840\angle 82.8°$

SELECTING A BASE OF 2300V AND 500kVA, EACH RESISTOR HAS AN IMPEDANCE OF $1\angle 0°$ PU; $V_{ab} = 0.8$; $V_{bc} = 1.2$; $V_{ca} = 1.0$

THE SYMMETRICAL COMPONENTS OF THE LINE VOLTAGES ARE:

$$\bar{V}_{ab1} = \frac{1}{3}\left(0.8\angle 82.8° + 1.2\angle 120° - 41.4° + 1.0\angle 240°+180°\right) = 0.2792 + j0.9453$$
$$= 0.9857\angle 73.6°$$

$$\bar{V}_{ab2} = \frac{1}{3}\left(0.8\angle 82.8° + 1.2\angle 240° - 41.4° + 1.0\angle 120°+180°\right) = -0.1790 - j0.1517$$
$$= 0.2346\angle 220.3°$$

(THESE ARE IN PU ON LINE-TO-LINE VOLTAGE BASE.)

PHASE VOLTAGES IN PU ON THE BASE OF VOLTAGE TO NEUTRAL ARE GIVEN BY

$$\bar{V}_{an1} = 0.9857\angle 73.6° - 30° = 0.9857\angle 43.6°$$

$$\bar{V}_{an2} = 0.2346\angle 220.3° + 30° = 0.2346\angle 250.3°$$

[NOTE: AN ANGLE OF 180° IS ASSIGNED TO $\bar{V}_{ca}$]

8.8 CONTD.

ZERO-SEQUENCE CURRENTS ARE NOT PRESENT DUE TO THE ABSENCE OF A NEUTRAL CONNECTION.

$$\bar{I}_{a1} = \bar{V}_{a1} / 1\angle 0° = 0.9857 \angle 43.6° \text{ PU}$$

$$\bar{I}_{a2} = \bar{V}_{a2} / 1\angle 0° = 0.2346 \angle 250.3° \text{ PU}$$

THE POSITIVE DIRECTION OF CURRENT IS FROM THE SUPPLY TOWARD THE LOAD.

8.9

(a)

$$\begin{bmatrix} \bar{I}_{\Delta 0} \\ \bar{I}_{\Delta 1} \\ \bar{I}_{\Delta 2} \end{bmatrix} = \frac{1}{3}\begin{bmatrix} 1 & 1 & 1 \\ 1 & a & a^2 \\ 1 & a^2 & a \end{bmatrix}\begin{bmatrix} 10\angle 0^\circ \\ 20\angle -90^\circ \\ 15\angle 90^\circ \end{bmatrix} = \frac{1}{3}\begin{bmatrix} 10\angle 0^\circ + 20\angle -90^\circ + 15\angle 90^\circ \\ 10\angle 0^\circ + 20\angle 30^\circ + 15\angle 330^\circ \\ 10\angle 0^\circ + 20\angle 150^\circ + 15\angle 210^\circ \end{bmatrix}$$

$$= \begin{bmatrix} 3.333 - j1.667 \\ 13.44 + j0.8333 \\ -6.770 + j0.8333 \end{bmatrix} = \begin{bmatrix} 3.727\angle -26.57^\circ \\ 13.46\angle 3.548^\circ \\ 6.821\angle 173.0^\circ \end{bmatrix} \text{ A}$$

(b)

$$\begin{bmatrix} \bar{I}_a \\ \bar{I}_b \\ \bar{I}_c \end{bmatrix} = \begin{bmatrix} \bar{I}_{ab} - \bar{I}_{ca} \\ \bar{I}_{bc} - \bar{I}_{ab} \\ \bar{I}_{ca} - \bar{I}_{bc} \end{bmatrix} = \begin{bmatrix} 10\angle 0^\circ - 15\angle 90^\circ \\ 20\angle -90^\circ - 10\angle 0^\circ \\ 15\angle 90^\circ - 20\angle -90^\circ \end{bmatrix}$$

$$= \begin{bmatrix} 10 - j15 \\ -10 - j20 \\ 0 + j35 \end{bmatrix} = \begin{bmatrix} 18.03\angle -56.31^\circ \\ 22.36\angle 243.40^\circ \\ 35.\angle 90^\circ \end{bmatrix} \text{ A}$$

(c)

$$\begin{bmatrix} \bar{I}_{L0} \\ \bar{I}_{L1} \\ \bar{I}_{L2} \end{bmatrix} = \frac{1}{3}\begin{bmatrix} 1 & 1 & 1 \\ 1 & a & a^2 \\ 1 & a^2 & a \end{bmatrix}\begin{bmatrix} 18.03\angle -56.31^\circ \\ 22.36\angle 243.4^\circ \\ 35\angle 90^\circ \end{bmatrix}$$

$$= \frac{1}{3}\begin{bmatrix} 18.03\angle -56.31^\circ + 22.36\angle 243.40^\circ + 35\angle 90^\circ \\ 18.03\angle -56.31^\circ + 22.36\angle 3.4^\circ + 35\angle 330^\circ \\ 18.03\angle -56.31^\circ + 22.36\angle 123.4^\circ + 35\angle 210^\circ \end{bmatrix}$$

$$= \begin{bmatrix} 0 + j0 \\ 20.88 - j10.39 \\ -10.87 - j4.612 \end{bmatrix} = \begin{bmatrix} 0 \\ 23.32\angle -26.46^\circ \\ 11.81\angle 203.0^\circ \end{bmatrix} \text{ A} = \begin{bmatrix} 0 \\ \sqrt{3}\,\bar{I}_{\Delta 1}\angle -30^\circ \\ \sqrt{3}\,\bar{I}_{\Delta 2}\angle +30^\circ \end{bmatrix}$$

8.10

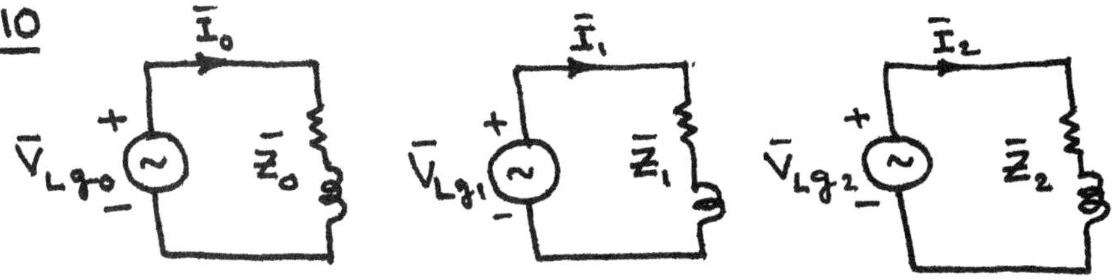

$$\bar{Z}_0 = \bar{Z}_1 = \bar{Z}_2 = 6 + j8 = 10\,\angle 53.13^\circ\ \Omega$$

$$\bar{I}_0 = \bar{V}_{Lg0} / \bar{Z}_0 = 7.551\angle 78.12^\circ / 10\angle 53.13^\circ = 0.7551\angle 24.99^\circ \text{ A}$$

$$\bar{I}_1 = \bar{V}_{Lg1} / \bar{Z}_1 = 275.7\angle -6.631^\circ / 10\angle 53.13^\circ = 27.57\angle -59.76^\circ \text{ A}$$

$$\bar{I}_2 = \bar{V}_{Lg2} / \bar{Z}_2 = 24.87\angle 79.43^\circ / 10\angle 53.13^\circ = 2.487\angle 26.3^\circ \text{ A}$$

$$\begin{bmatrix} \bar{I}_a \\ \bar{I}_b \\ \bar{I}_c \end{bmatrix} = \begin{bmatrix} 1 & 1 & 1 \\ 1 & a^2 & a \\ 1 & a & a^2 \end{bmatrix} \begin{bmatrix} 0.7551\angle 24.99^\circ \\ 27.57\angle -59.76^\circ \\ 2.487\angle 26.3^\circ \end{bmatrix}$$

$$= \begin{bmatrix} 0.7551\angle 24.99^\circ + 27.57\angle -59.76^\circ + 2.487\angle 26.3^\circ \\ 0.7551\angle 24.99^\circ + 27.57\angle 180.24^\circ + 2.487\angle 146.3^\circ \\ 0.7551\angle 24.99^\circ + 27.57\angle 60.24^\circ + 2.487\angle 266.3^\circ \end{bmatrix}$$

$$= \begin{bmatrix} 16.804 - j22.4 \\ 28.96 + j1.584 \\ 14.214 + j21.78 \end{bmatrix} = \begin{bmatrix} 28.00\angle -53.13^\circ \\ 29.00\angle 176.87^\circ \\ 26.00\angle 56.87^\circ \end{bmatrix} \text{ A}$$

NOTE: SINCE THE SOURCE AND LOAD NEUTRALS ARE CONNECTED BY A ZERO-OHM WIRE:

$$\begin{bmatrix} \bar{I}_a \\ \bar{I}_b \\ \bar{I}_c \end{bmatrix} = \begin{bmatrix} \bar{V}_{ag} / \bar{Z}_Y \\ \bar{V}_{bg} / \bar{Z}_Y \\ \bar{V}_{cg} / \bar{Z}_Y \end{bmatrix} = \begin{bmatrix} 280\angle 0^\circ / 10\angle 53.13^\circ \\ 290\angle -130^\circ / 10\angle 53.13^\circ \\ 260\angle 110^\circ / 10\angle 53.13^\circ \end{bmatrix} = \begin{bmatrix} 28.0\angle -53.13^\circ \\ 29.0\angle 176.87^\circ \\ 26.0\angle 56.87^\circ \end{bmatrix} \text{ A}$$

WHICH AGREES WITH THE ABOVE RESULT.

8.11

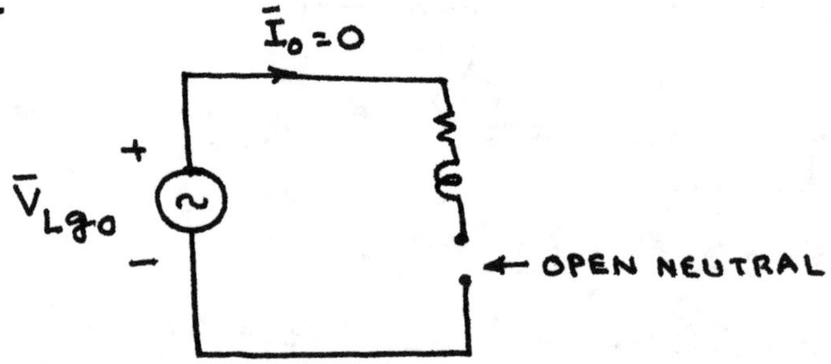

$\bar{I}_0 = 0$; FROM PR. 8.10, $\bar{I}_1 = 27.57\angle{-59.76^\circ}$ A ; $\bar{I}_2 = 2.487\angle{26.3^\circ}$ A

$$\begin{bmatrix} \bar{I}_a \\ \bar{I}_b \\ \bar{I}_c \end{bmatrix} = \begin{bmatrix} 1 & 1 & 1 \\ 1 & a^2 & a \\ 1 & a & a^2 \end{bmatrix} \begin{bmatrix} 0 \\ 27.57\angle{-59.76^\circ} \\ 2.487\angle{26.3^\circ} \end{bmatrix}$$

$$= \begin{bmatrix} 27.57\angle{-59.76^\circ} + 2.487\angle{26.3^\circ} \\ 27.57\angle{180.24^\circ} + 2.487\angle{146.3^\circ} \\ 27.57\angle{60.24^\circ} + 2.487\angle{266.3^\circ} \end{bmatrix}$$

$$= \begin{bmatrix} 16.120 - j22.72 \\ -29.64 + j1.2650 \\ 13.530 + j21.46 \end{bmatrix} = \begin{bmatrix} 27.86\angle{-54.64^\circ} \\ 29.66\angle{177.56^\circ} \\ 25.36\angle{57.77^\circ} \end{bmatrix} \text{A}$$

8.12

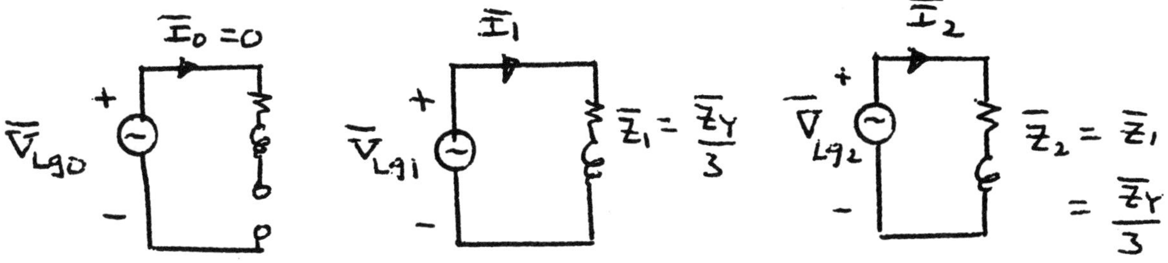

$$\bar{I}_0 = 0 \qquad \bar{I}_1 = \frac{275.7\angle{-6.631^\circ}}{\left(\frac{20}{3}\right)\angle{53.13^\circ}} = 41.36\angle{-59.76^\circ} \text{ A}$$

$$\bar{I}_2 = \frac{24.87\angle{79.43^\circ}}{\left(\frac{20}{3}\right)\angle{53.13^\circ}} = 3.731\angle{26.3^\circ} \text{ A}$$

$$\begin{bmatrix} \bar{I}_a \\ \bar{I}_b \\ \bar{I}_c \end{bmatrix} = \begin{bmatrix} 1 & 1 & 1 \\ 1 & a^2 & a \\ 1 & a & a^2 \end{bmatrix} \begin{bmatrix} 0 \\ 41.36\angle{-59.76^\circ} \\ 3.731\angle{26.3^\circ} \end{bmatrix} = \begin{bmatrix} 41.79\angle{-54.64^\circ} \\ 44.49\angle{177.56^\circ} \\ 38.04\angle{57.77^\circ} \end{bmatrix} \text{ A}$$

8.13

$$\bar{I}_0 = \frac{\bar{V}_{Lg0}}{\bar{Z}_0} = \frac{7.551\angle 78.12^\circ}{3+j10} = 0.7233\angle 4.819^\circ \text{ A}$$

$$\bar{I}_1 = \frac{\bar{V}_{Lg1}}{\bar{Z}_1} = \frac{275.7\angle -6.631^\circ}{7.454\angle 26.57^\circ} = 36.99\angle -33.20^\circ \text{ A}$$

$$\bar{I}_2 = \frac{\bar{V}_{Lg2}}{\bar{Z}_2} = \frac{24.87\angle 79.43^\circ}{7.454\angle 26.57^\circ} = 3.336\angle 52.86^\circ \text{ A}$$

$$\begin{bmatrix} \bar{I}_a \\ \bar{I}_b \\ \bar{I}_c \end{bmatrix} = \begin{bmatrix} 1 & 1 & 1 \\ 1 & a^2 & a \\ 1 & a & a^2 \end{bmatrix} \begin{bmatrix} 0.7233\angle 4.819^\circ \\ 36.99\angle -33.20^\circ \\ 3.336\angle 52.86^\circ \end{bmatrix}$$

$$= \begin{bmatrix} 0.7233\angle 4.819^\circ + 36.99\angle -33.20^\circ + 3.336\angle 52.86^\circ \\ 0.7233\angle 4.819^\circ + 36.99\angle 206.8^\circ + 3.336\angle 172.86^\circ \\ 0.7233\angle 4.819^\circ + 36.99\angle 86.80^\circ + 3.336\angle 292.86^\circ \end{bmatrix}$$

$$= \begin{bmatrix} 33.69 - j17.53 \\ -35.61 - j16.20 \\ 4.082 + j33.92 \end{bmatrix} = \begin{bmatrix} 37.98\angle -27.49^\circ \\ 39.12\angle 204.5^\circ \\ 34.16\angle 83.14^\circ \end{bmatrix} \text{ A}$$

8.14

$$\begin{bmatrix} z_0 & z_{01} & z_{02} \\ z_{10} & z_1 & z_{12} \\ z_{20} & z_{21} & z_2 \end{bmatrix} = \frac{1}{3}\begin{bmatrix} 1 & 1 & 1 \\ 1 & a & a^2 \\ 1 & a^2 & a \end{bmatrix}\begin{bmatrix} (z_{aa}+z_{ab}+z_{ac}) & (z_{aa}+a^2 z_{ab}+a z_{ac}) & (z_{aa}+a z_{ab}+a^2 z_{ac}) \\ (z_{ab}+z_{bb}+z_{bc}) & (z_{ab}+a^2 z_{bb}+a z_{bc}) & (z_{ab}+a z_{bb}+a^2 z_{bc}) \\ (z_{ac}+z_{bc}+z_{cc}) & (z_{ac}+a^2 z_{bc}+a z_{cc}) & (z_{ac}+a z_{bc}+a^2 z_{cc}) \end{bmatrix}$$

$$= \frac{1}{3}\begin{bmatrix} (z_{aa}+z_{bb}+z_{cc})+2(z_{ab}+z_{ac}+z_{bc}) & (z_{aa}+a^2 z_{bb}+a z_{cc})+z_{ab}(a^2+1)+z_{ac}(a+1)+z_{bc}(a+a^2) & (z_{aa}+a z_{bb}+a^2 z_{cc})+z_{ab}(1+a)+z_{ac}(1+a^2)+z_{bc}(a+a^2) \\ (z_{aa}+a z_{bb}+a^2 z_{cc})+z_{ab}(1+a)+z_{ac}(1+a^2)+z_{bc}(a+a^2) & (z_{aa}+a^3 z_{bb}+a^3 z_{cc})+z_{ab}(a^2+a)+z_{ac}(a+a^2)+z_{bc}(a^2+a^4) & (z_{aa}+a^2 z_{bb}+a^4 z_{cc})+z_{ab}(2a)+z_{ac}(2a^2)+z_{bc}(2) \\ (z_{aa}+a^2 z_{bb}+a z_{cc})+z_{ab}(1+a^2)+z_{ac}(1+a)+z_{bc}(a^2+a) & (z_{aa}+a^4 z_{bb}+a^2 z_{cc})+z_{ab}(a^2+a^2)+z_{ac}(2a)+z_{bc}(a^2+a^4) & (z_{aa}+a^3 z_{bb}+a^3 z_{cc})+z_{ab}(a+a^2)+z_{ac}(a+a^2)+z_{bc}(a+a^2) \end{bmatrix}$$

$$= \frac{1}{3}\begin{bmatrix} z_{aa}+z_{bb}+z_{cc}+2z_{ab}+2z_{ac}+2z_{bc} & z_{aa}+a^2 z_{bb}+a z_{cc}-a z_{ab}-a^2 z_{ac}-z_{bc} & z_{aa}+a z_{bb}+a^2 z_{cc}-a^2 z_{ab}-a z_{ac}-z_{bc} \\ z_{aa}+a z_{bb}+a^2 z_{cc}-a^2 z_{ab}-a z_{ac}-z_{bc} & z_{aa}+z_{bb}+z_{cc}-z_{ab}-z_{ac}-z_{bc} & z_{aa}+a^2 z_{bb}+a z_{cc}+2a z_{ab}+2a^2 z_{ac}+2z_{bc} \\ z_{aa}+a^2 z_{bb}+a z_{cc}-a z_{ab}-a^2 z_{ac}-z_{bc} & z_{aa}+a z_{bb}+a^2 z_{cc}+2a^2 z_{ab}+2a z_{ac}+2z_{bc} & z_{aa}+z_{bb}+z_{cc}-z_{ab}-z_{ac}-z_{bc} \end{bmatrix}$$

8.15

(a)

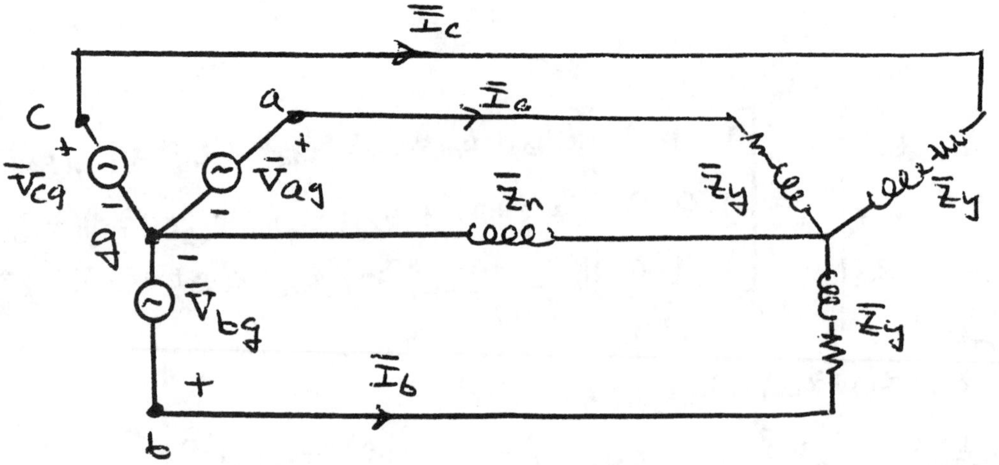

Writing KVL equations [see eqs (8.2.1) – (8.2.3)] :

$$\bar{V}_{ag} = \bar{Z}_y \bar{I}_a + \bar{Z}_n (\bar{I}_a + \bar{I}_b + \bar{I}_c)$$

$$\bar{V}_{bg} = \bar{Z}_y \bar{I}_b + \bar{Z}_n (\bar{I}_a + \bar{I}_b + \bar{I}_c)$$

$$\bar{V}_{cg} = \bar{Z}_y \bar{I}_c + \bar{Z}_n (\bar{I}_a + \bar{I}_b + \bar{I}_c)$$

In matrix format [see eq (8.2.4)]

$$\begin{bmatrix} (\bar{Z}_y+\bar{Z}_n) & \bar{Z}_n & \bar{Z}_n \\ \bar{Z}_n & (\bar{Z}_y+\bar{Z}_n) & \bar{Z}_n \\ \bar{Z}_n & \bar{Z}_n & (\bar{Z}_y+\bar{Z}_n) \end{bmatrix} \begin{bmatrix} \bar{I}_a \\ \bar{I}_b \\ \bar{I}_c \end{bmatrix} = \begin{bmatrix} \bar{V}_{ag} \\ \bar{V}_{bg} \\ \bar{V}_{cg} \end{bmatrix}$$

$$\begin{bmatrix} (3+j5) & j1 & j1 \\ j1 & (3+j5) & j1 \\ j1 & j1 & (3+j5) \end{bmatrix} \begin{bmatrix} \bar{I}_a \\ \bar{I}_b \\ \bar{I}_c \end{bmatrix} = \begin{bmatrix} 100\angle 0^\circ \\ 75\angle 180^\circ \\ 50\angle 90^\circ \end{bmatrix}$$

$$\begin{bmatrix} \bar{I}_a \\ \bar{I}_b \\ \bar{I}_c \end{bmatrix} = \begin{bmatrix} (3+j5) & j1 & j1 \\ j1 & (3+j5) & j1 \\ j1 & j1 & (3+j5) \end{bmatrix}^{-1} \begin{bmatrix} 100\angle 0^\circ \\ 75\angle 180^\circ \\ 50\angle 90^\circ \end{bmatrix}$$

8.15 CONTD. (a) Performing the indicated matrix inverse (a computer solution is suggested):

$$\begin{bmatrix}\bar{I}_a\\ \bar{I}_b\\ \bar{I}_c\end{bmatrix} = \begin{bmatrix} 0.1763\angle{-56.50^\circ} & 0.02618\angle{150.2^\circ} & 0.02618\angle{150.2^\circ}\\ 0.02618\angle{150.2^\circ} & 0.1763\angle{-56.50^\circ} & 0.02618\angle{150.2^\circ}\\ 0.02618\angle{150.2^\circ} & 0.02618\angle{150.2^\circ} & 0.1763\angle{-56.50^\circ}\end{bmatrix}\begin{bmatrix}100\angle{0^\circ}\\ 75\angle{180^\circ}\\ 50\angle{90^\circ}\end{bmatrix}$$

Finally, performing the indicate matrix multiplication:

$$\begin{bmatrix}\bar{I}_a\\ \bar{I}_b\\ \bar{I}_c\end{bmatrix} = \begin{bmatrix} 17.63\angle{-56.50^\circ} + 1.964\angle{330.2^\circ} + 1.309\angle{240.2^\circ}\\ 2.618\angle{150.2^\circ} + 13.22\angle{123.5^\circ} + 1.309\angle{240.2^\circ}\\ 2.618\angle{150.2^\circ} + 1.964\angle{330.2^\circ} + 8.815\angle{33.5^\circ}\end{bmatrix}$$

$$\begin{bmatrix}\bar{I}_a\\ \bar{I}_b\\ \bar{I}_c\end{bmatrix} = \begin{bmatrix} 10.78 - j16.81\\ -10.22 + j11.19\\ 6.783 + j5.191\end{bmatrix} = \begin{bmatrix} 19.97\angle{-57.32^\circ}\\ 15.15\angle{132.4^\circ}\\ 8.541\angle{37.43^\circ}\end{bmatrix} \text{ A}$$

8.15 (b) Step (1) Calculate the sequence components of the applied voltage:

$$\begin{bmatrix}\bar{V}_{g0}\\ \bar{V}_{g1}\\ \bar{V}_{g2}\end{bmatrix} = \frac{1}{3}\begin{bmatrix}1 & 1 & 1\\ 1 & a & a^2\\ 1 & a^2 & a\end{bmatrix}\begin{bmatrix}100\angle{0^\circ}\\ 75\angle{180^\circ}\\ 50\angle{90^\circ}\end{bmatrix}$$

$$= \frac{1}{3}\begin{bmatrix}100\angle{0^\circ} + 75\angle{180^\circ} + 50\angle{90^\circ}\\ 100\angle{0^\circ} + 75\angle{300^\circ} + 50\angle{330^\circ}\\ 100\angle{0^\circ} + 75\angle{60^\circ} + 50\angle{210^\circ}\end{bmatrix}$$

$$= \begin{bmatrix}8.333 + j16.667\\ 60.27 - j29.98\\ 31.40 + j13.32\end{bmatrix} = \begin{bmatrix}18.63\angle{63.43^\circ}\\ 67.32\angle{-26.45^\circ}\\ 34.11\angle{22.99^\circ}\end{bmatrix} \text{ V}$$

8.15 (b) CONTD. Step(2) Draw sequence networks:

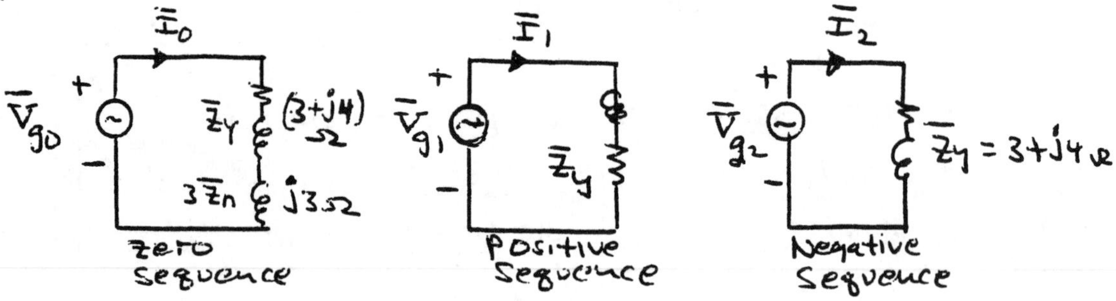

Step(3) solve sequence networks

$$\bar{I}_0 = \frac{\bar{V}_{g0}}{\bar{Z}_0} = \frac{\bar{V}_{g0}}{\bar{Z}_y + 3\bar{Z}_n} = \frac{18.63\angle 63.43^\circ}{3+j7} = \frac{18.63\angle 63.43^\circ}{7.616\angle 66.80^\circ}$$

$$\bar{I}_0 = 2.446\angle -3.37^\circ \text{ A}$$

$$\bar{I}_1 = \frac{\bar{V}_{g1}}{\bar{Z}_1} = \frac{67.32\angle -26.45^\circ}{3+j4} = \frac{67.32\angle -26.45^\circ}{5\angle 53.13^\circ} = 13.46\angle -79.58 \text{ A}$$

$$\bar{I}_2 = \frac{\bar{V}_{g2}}{\bar{Z}_2} = \frac{34.11\angle 22.99^\circ}{5\angle 53.13^\circ} = 6.822\angle -30.14^\circ$$

Step(4) calculate the line currents (phase components):

$$\begin{bmatrix}\bar{I}_a\\ \bar{I}_b\\ \bar{I}_c\end{bmatrix} = \begin{bmatrix}1 & 1 & 1\\ 1 & a^2 & a\\ 1 & a & a^2\end{bmatrix}\begin{bmatrix}2.446\angle -3.37^\circ\\ 13.46\angle -79.58^\circ\\ 6.822\angle -30.14^\circ\end{bmatrix}$$

$$= \begin{bmatrix}2.446\angle -3.37^\circ + 13.46\angle -79.58^\circ + 6.822\angle -30.14^\circ\\ 2.446\angle -3.37^\circ + 13.46\angle 160.42^\circ + 6.822\angle 89.86^\circ\\ 2.446\angle -3.37^\circ + 13.46\angle 40.42^\circ + 6.822\angle 209.86^\circ\end{bmatrix}$$

$$= \begin{bmatrix}10.78 - j16.81\\ -10.22 + j11.19\\ 6.773 + j5.187\end{bmatrix} = \begin{bmatrix}19.97\angle -57.32^\circ\\ 15.15\angle 132.4^\circ\\ 8.531\angle 37.45^\circ\end{bmatrix} \text{ A}$$

8.16

FROM EQ. (8.2.28) AND (8.2.29), THE LOAD IS SYMMETRICAL.

USING EQ. (8.2.31) AND (8.2.32):

$$\bar{Z}_0 = \bar{Z}_{aa} + 2\bar{Z}_{ab} = 6 + j10 \ \Omega$$

$$\bar{Z}_1 = \bar{Z}_2 = \bar{Z}_{aa} - \bar{Z}_{ab} = 6 + j10 \ \Omega$$

$$\underline{\bar{Z}}_S = \begin{bmatrix} 6+j10 & 0 & 0 \\ 0 & 6+j10 & 0 \\ 0 & 0 & 6+j10 \end{bmatrix} \Omega$$

8.17

SINCE $\underline{\bar{Z}}_S$ IS DIAGONAL, THE LOAD IS SYMMETRICAL.

USING EQ. (8.2.31) AND (8.2.32):

$$\bar{Z}_0 = 8 + j12 = \bar{Z}_{aa} + 2\bar{Z}_{ab}$$

$$\bar{Z}_1 = 4 = \bar{Z}_{aa} - \bar{Z}_{ab}$$

SOLVING THE ABOVE TWO EQUATIONS

$$\bar{Z}_{ab} = \frac{1}{3}(8 + j12 - 4) = \frac{1}{3}(4 + j12) = \frac{4}{3} + j4 \ \Omega$$

$$\bar{Z}_{aa} = \bar{Z}_{ab} + 4 = \frac{16}{3} + j4 \ \Omega$$

$$\underline{\bar{Z}}_P = \begin{bmatrix} \frac{16}{3}+j4 & \frac{4}{3}+j4 & \frac{4}{3}+j4 \\ \frac{4}{3}+j4 & \frac{16}{3}+j4 & \frac{4}{3}+j4 \\ \frac{4}{3}+j4 & \frac{4}{3}+j4 & \frac{16}{3}+j4 \end{bmatrix} \Omega$$

8.18

THE LINE-TO-GROUND VOLTAGES ARE

$$\bar{V}_a = \bar{Z}_s \bar{I}_a + \bar{Z}_m \bar{I}_b + \bar{Z}_m \bar{I}_c + \bar{Z}_n \bar{I}_n$$

$$\bar{V}_b = \bar{Z}_m \bar{I}_a + \bar{Z}_s \bar{I}_b + \bar{Z}_m \bar{I}_c + \bar{Z}_n \bar{I}_n$$

$$\bar{V}_c = \bar{Z}_m \bar{I}_a + \bar{Z}_m \bar{I}_b + \bar{Z}_s \bar{I}_c + \bar{Z}_n \bar{I}_n$$

SINCE $\bar{I}_n = \bar{I}_a + \bar{I}_b + \bar{I}_c$, IT FOLLOWS

$$\begin{bmatrix} \bar{V}_a \\ \bar{V}_b \\ \bar{V}_c \end{bmatrix} = \underbrace{\begin{bmatrix} \bar{Z}_s+\bar{Z}_n & \bar{Z}_m+\bar{Z}_n & \bar{Z}_m+\bar{Z}_n \\ \bar{Z}_m+\bar{Z}_n & \bar{Z}_s+\bar{Z}_n & \bar{Z}_m+\bar{Z}_n \\ \bar{Z}_m+\bar{Z}_n & \bar{Z}_m+\bar{Z}_n & \bar{Z}_s+\bar{Z}_n \end{bmatrix}}_{\text{PHASE IMPEDANCE MATRIX } \bar{Z}_p} \begin{bmatrix} \bar{I}_a \\ \bar{I}_b \\ \bar{I}_c \end{bmatrix}$$

OR IN COMPACT FORM $\bar{V}_p = \bar{Z}_p \bar{I}_p$

FROM EQ.(8.2.9) $\bar{Z}_S = A^{-1} \bar{Z}_p A$

$$\therefore \bar{Z}_S = \frac{1}{3}\begin{bmatrix} 1 & 1 & 1 \\ 1 & a & a^2 \\ 1 & a^2 & a \end{bmatrix} \begin{bmatrix} \bar{Z}_s+\bar{Z}_n & \bar{Z}_m+\bar{Z}_n & \bar{Z}_m+\bar{Z}_n \\ \bar{Z}_m+\bar{Z}_n & \bar{Z}_s+\bar{Z}_n & \bar{Z}_m+\bar{Z}_n \\ \bar{Z}_m+\bar{Z}_n & \bar{Z}_m+\bar{Z}_n & \bar{Z}_s+\bar{Z}_n \end{bmatrix} \begin{bmatrix} 1 & 1 & 1 \\ 1 & a^2 & a \\ 1 & a & a^2 \end{bmatrix}$$

$$= \underbrace{\begin{bmatrix} \bar{Z}_s + 3\bar{Z}_n + 2\bar{Z}_m & 0 & 0 \\ 0 & \bar{Z}_s - \bar{Z}_m & 0 \\ 0 & 0 & \bar{Z}_s - \bar{Z}_m \end{bmatrix}}_{\text{SEQUENCE IMPEDANCE MATRIX}}$$

WHEN THERE IS NO MUTUAL COUPLING, $\bar{Z}_m = 0$

$$\therefore \bar{Z}_S = \begin{bmatrix} \bar{Z}_s + 3\bar{Z}_n & 0 & 0 \\ 0 & \bar{Z}_s & 0 \\ 0 & 0 & \bar{Z}_s \end{bmatrix}$$

8.19

(a) THE CIRCUIT IS SHOWN BELOW:

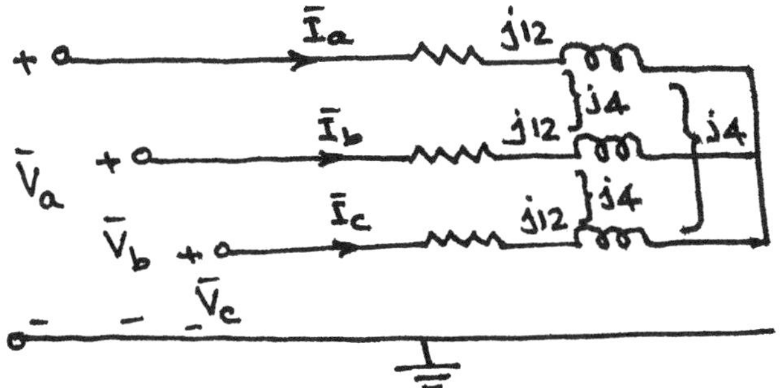

KVL: $(j12)\,\bar{I}_a + (j4)\,\bar{I}_b - (j12)\,\bar{I}_b \underbrace{\;}_{-j4(\bar{I}_a)} = \bar{V}_a - \bar{V}_b = V_{LINE}\,\angle 30^\circ$

$(j12)\,\bar{I}_b + (j4)\,\bar{I}_c - (j12)\,\bar{I}_c - (j4)\,\bar{I}_b = \bar{V}_b - \bar{V}_c = V_{LINE}\,\angle -90^\circ$

KCL: $\bar{I}_a + \bar{I}_b + \bar{I}_c = 0$

IN MATRIX FORM:

$$\begin{bmatrix} j12 - j4 & -(j12 - j4) & 0 \\ 0 & (j12 - j4) & -(j12 - j4) \\ 1 & 1 & 1 \end{bmatrix} \begin{bmatrix} \bar{I}_a \\ \bar{I}_b \\ \bar{I}_c \end{bmatrix} = \begin{bmatrix} V_L\,\angle 30^\circ \\ V_L\,\angle 90^\circ \\ 0 \end{bmatrix}$$

WHERE $V_L = 100\sqrt{3}$.

SOLVING FOR $\bar{I}_a$, $\bar{I}_b$, $\bar{I}_c$, ONE GETS

$\bar{I}_a = 12.5\,\angle -90^\circ$; $\bar{I}_b = 12.5\,\angle 150^\circ$; $\bar{I}_c = 12.5\,\angle 30^\circ$ A

(b) USING SYMMETRICAL COMPONENTS,

$$\bar{V}_s = \begin{bmatrix} 0 \\ 100 \\ 0 \end{bmatrix} ; \quad \bar{Z}_s = \begin{bmatrix} j12 + 2(j4) & 0 & 0 \\ 0 & j12 - j4 & 0 \\ 0 & 0 & j12 - j4 \end{bmatrix}$$

FROM THE SOLUTION OF PROB. 8.18
UPON SUBSTITUTING THE VALUES

$\bar{I}_s = \bar{Z}_s^{-1}\,\bar{V}_s$ AND $\bar{I}_p = A\,\bar{I}_s$ WHERE $A = \begin{bmatrix} 1 & 1 & 1 \\ 1 & a^2 & a \\ 1 & a & a^2 \end{bmatrix}$

WHICH RESULT IN

$\bar{I}_a = 12.5\,\angle -90^\circ$; $\bar{I}_b = 12.5\,\angle 150^\circ$; $\bar{I}_c = 12.5\,\angle 30^\circ$ A

WHICH IS SAME AS IN (a).

8.20

(a) $\bar{Z}_s = A^{-1}\bar{Z}_p A$; $A = \begin{bmatrix} 1 & 1 & 1 \\ 1 & a^2 & a \\ 1 & a & a^2 \end{bmatrix}$; $A^{-1} = \frac{1}{3}\begin{bmatrix} 1 & 1 & 1 \\ 1 & a & a^2 \\ 1 & a^2 & a \end{bmatrix}$

THE LOAD SEQUENCE IMPEDANCE MATRIX COMES OUT AS

$$\bar{Z}_s = \begin{bmatrix} 8+j32 & 0 & 0 \\ 0 & 8+j20 & 0 \\ 0 & 0 & 8+j20 \end{bmatrix} \Omega$$

SEE THE RESULT OF PR. 8.18

(b)

$\bar{V}_p = \begin{bmatrix} 200\angle 25^\circ \\ 100\angle -155^\circ \\ 80\angle 100^\circ \end{bmatrix}$; $\bar{V}_s = A^{-1}\bar{V}_p$; $A^{-1} = \frac{1}{3}\begin{bmatrix} 1 & 1 & 1 \\ 1 & a & a^2 \\ 1 & a^2 & a \end{bmatrix}$

SYMMETRICAL COMPONENTS OF THE LINE-TO-NEUTRAL VOLTAGES ARE GIVEN BY:

$\bar{V}_0 = 47.7739\angle 57.6268^\circ$; $\bar{V}_1 = 112.7841\angle -0.0331^\circ$; $\bar{V}_2 = 61.6231\angle 45.8825^\circ$ V

(c)

$\bar{V}_s = \bar{Z}_s\bar{I}_s$; $\bar{I}_s = \bar{Z}_s^{-1}\bar{V}_s$, WHICH RESULTS IN

$\bar{I}_0 = 1.4484\angle -18.3369^\circ$; $\bar{I}_1 = 5.2359\angle -68.2317^\circ$; $\bar{I}_2 = 2.8608\angle -22.3161^\circ$ A

(d) $\bar{I}_p = A\bar{I}_s$; $A = \begin{bmatrix} 1 & 1 & 1 \\ 1 & a^2 & a \\ 1 & a & a^2 \end{bmatrix}$

THE RESULT IS :

$\bar{I}_a = 8.7507\angle -47.0439^\circ$; $\bar{I}_b = 5.2292\angle 143.2451^\circ$; $\bar{I}_c = 3.0280\angle 39.0675^\circ$ A

8.21

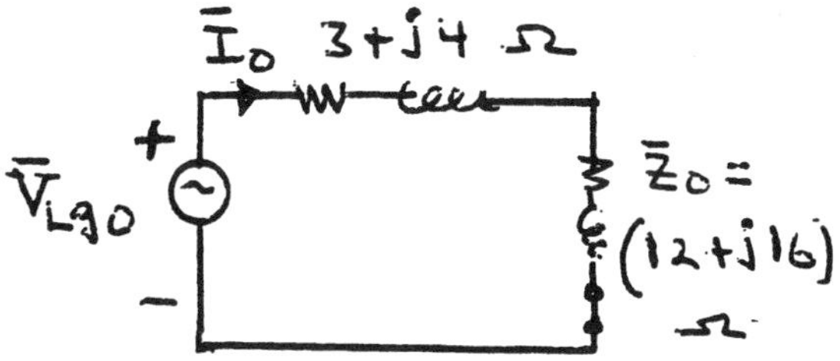

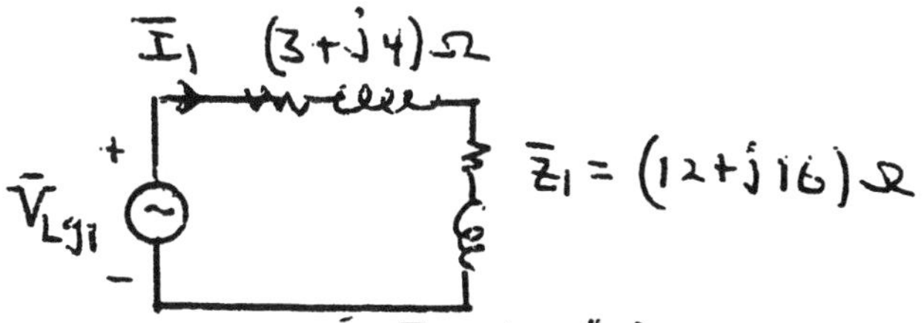

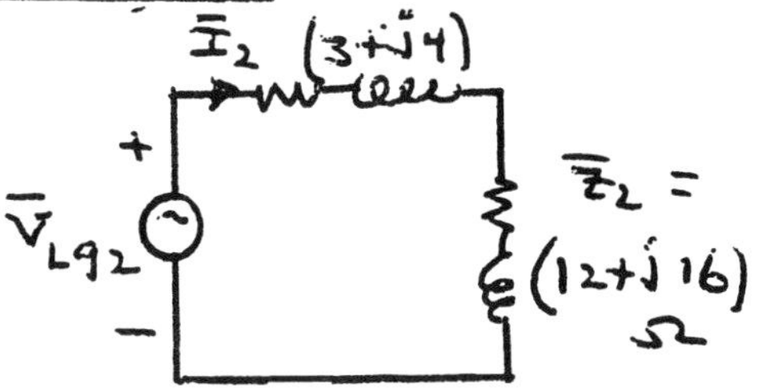

$$\bar{I}_0 = \frac{\bar{V}_{Lg0}}{(3+j4)+\bar{Z}_0} = \frac{7.551\angle 78.12^\circ}{(3+j4)+(12+j16)} = \frac{7.551\angle 78.12^\circ}{25\angle 53.13^\circ} = 0.3020\angle 24.99^\circ \text{ A}$$

$$\bar{I}_1 = \frac{\bar{V}_{Lg1}}{(3+j4)+\bar{Z}_1} = \frac{275.7\angle -6.631^\circ}{25\angle 53.13^\circ} = 11.03\angle -59.76^\circ \text{ A}$$

$$\bar{I}_2 = \frac{\bar{V}_{Lg2}}{(3+j4)+\bar{Z}_2} = \frac{24.87\angle 79.43^\circ}{25\angle 53.13^\circ} = 0.9948\angle 26.30^\circ \text{ A}$$

$$\begin{bmatrix}\bar{I}_a\\ \bar{I}_b\\ \bar{I}_c\end{bmatrix} = \begin{bmatrix}1 & 1 & 1\\ 1 & a^2 & a\\ 1 & a & a^2\end{bmatrix}\begin{bmatrix}0.302\angle 24.99^\circ\\ 11.03\angle -59.76^\circ\\ 0.9948\angle 26.30^\circ\end{bmatrix} = \begin{bmatrix}11.2\angle -53.13^\circ\\ 11.6\angle -176.9^\circ\\ 10.4\angle 56.87^\circ\end{bmatrix} \text{ A}$$

Also, since the source and load neutrals are connected with a zero-ohm neutral wire:

$$\begin{bmatrix}\bar{I}_a\\ \bar{I}_b\\ \bar{I}_c\end{bmatrix} = \begin{bmatrix}\bar{V}_{ag}/(3+j4+\bar{Z}_y)\\ \bar{V}_{bg}/(3+j4+\bar{Z}_y)\\ \bar{V}_{cg}/(3+j4+\bar{Z}_y)\end{bmatrix} = \begin{bmatrix}280\angle 0^\circ/25\angle 53.13^\circ\\ 290\angle -130^\circ/25\angle 53.13^\circ\\ 260\angle 110^\circ/25\angle 53.13^\circ\end{bmatrix} = \begin{bmatrix}11.2\angle -53.13^\circ\\ 11.6\angle -183.13^\circ\\ 10.4\angle 56.87^\circ\end{bmatrix} \text{ A}$$

which checks ✓

8.22

(a) KVL: $\bar{V}_{an} = \bar{Z}_{aa}\bar{I}_a + \bar{Z}_{ab}\bar{I}_b + \bar{Z}_{ab}\bar{I}_c + \bar{Z}_{an}\bar{I}_n + \bar{V}_{a'n'}$

$$- (\bar{Z}_{nn}\bar{I}_n + \bar{Z}_{an}\bar{I}_c + \bar{Z}_{an}\bar{I}_b + \bar{Z}_{an}\bar{I}_a)$$

VOLTAGE DROP ACROSS THE LINE SECTION IS GIVEN BY

$$\bar{V}_{an} - \bar{V}_{a'n'} = (\bar{Z}_{aa} - \bar{Z}_{an})\bar{I}_a + (\bar{Z}_{ab} - \bar{Z}_{an})(\bar{I}_b + \bar{I}_c) + (\bar{Z}_{an} - \bar{Z}_{nn})\bar{I}_n$$

SIMILARLY FOR PHASES b AND C

$$\bar{V}_{bn} - \bar{V}_{b'n'} = (\bar{Z}_{aa} - \bar{Z}_{an})\bar{I}_b + (\bar{Z}_{ab} - \bar{Z}_{an})(\bar{I}_a + \bar{I}_c) + (\bar{Z}_{an} - \bar{Z}_{nn})\bar{I}_n$$

$$\bar{V}_{cn} - \bar{V}_{c'n'} = (\bar{Z}_{aa} - \bar{Z}_{an})\bar{I}_c + (\bar{Z}_{ab} - \bar{Z}_{an})(\bar{I}_a + \bar{I}_b) + (\bar{Z}_{an} - \bar{Z}_{nn})\bar{I}_n$$

KCL: $\bar{I}_n = -(\bar{I}_a + \bar{I}_b + \bar{I}_c)$

UPON SUBSTITUTION

$$\bar{V}_{an} - \bar{V}_{a'n'} = (\bar{Z}_{aa} + \bar{Z}_{nn} - 2\bar{Z}_{an})\bar{I}_a + (\bar{Z}_{ab} + \bar{Z}_{nn} - 2\bar{Z}_{an})\bar{I}_b + (\bar{Z}_{ab} + \bar{Z}_{nn} - 2\bar{Z}_{an})\bar{I}_c$$

$$\bar{V}_{bn} - \bar{V}_{b'n'} = (\bar{Z}_{ab} + \bar{Z}_{nn} - 2\bar{Z}_{an})\bar{I}_a + (\bar{Z}_{aa} + \bar{Z}_{nn} - 2\bar{Z}_{an})\bar{I}_b + (\bar{Z}_{ab} + \bar{Z}_{nn} - 2\bar{Z}_{an})\bar{I}_c$$

$$\bar{V}_{cn} - \bar{V}_{c'n'} = (Z_{ab} + Z_{nn} - 2\bar{Z}_{an})\bar{I}_a + (\bar{Z}_{ab} + \bar{Z}_{nn} - 2\bar{Z}_{an})\bar{I}_b + (\bar{Z}_{aa} + \bar{Z}_{nn} - 2\bar{Z}_{an})\bar{I}_c$$

THE PRESENCE OF THE NEUTRAL CONDUCTOR CHANGES THE SELF- AND MUTUAL IMPEDANCES OF THE PHASE CONDUCTORS TO THE FOLLOWING EFFECTIVE VALUES:

$$\bar{Z}_s \triangleq \bar{Z}_{aa} + \bar{Z}_{nn} - 2\bar{Z}_{an} \quad ; \quad \bar{Z}_m \triangleq \bar{Z}_{ab} + \bar{Z}_{nn} - 2\bar{Z}_{an}$$

USING THE ABOVE DEFINITIONS

$$\begin{bmatrix} \bar{V}_{aa'} \\ \bar{V}_{bb'} \\ \bar{V}_{cc'} \end{bmatrix} = \begin{bmatrix} \bar{V}_{an} - \bar{V}_{a'n'} \\ \bar{V}_{bn} - \bar{V}_{b'n'} \\ \bar{V}_{cn} - \bar{V}_{c'n'} \end{bmatrix} = \begin{bmatrix} \bar{Z}_s & \bar{Z}_m & \bar{Z}_m \\ \bar{Z}_m & \bar{Z}_s & \bar{Z}_m \\ \bar{Z}_m & \bar{Z}_m & \bar{Z}_s \end{bmatrix} \begin{bmatrix} \bar{I}_a \\ \bar{I}_b \\ \bar{I}_c \end{bmatrix}$$

WHERE THE VOLTAGE DROPS ACROSS THE PHASE CONDUCTORS ARE DENOTED BY $\bar{V}_{aa'}$, $\bar{V}_{bb'}$, AND $\bar{V}_{cc'}$.

8.22 CONTD.

(b) THE a-b-c VOLTAGE DROPS AND CURRENTS OF THE LINE SECTION CAN BE WRITTEN IN TERMS OF THEIR SYMMETRICAL COMPONENTS ACCORDING TO EQ. (8.1.9); WITH PHASE a AS THE REFERENCE PHASE, ONE GETS

$$A\begin{bmatrix}\bar V_{aa'0}\\ \bar V_{aa'1}\\ \bar V_{aa'2}\end{bmatrix} = \left\{\begin{bmatrix}\bar Z_s-\bar Z_m & \cdot & \cdot\\ \cdot & \bar Z_s-\bar Z_m & \cdot\\ \cdot & \cdot & \bar Z_s-\bar Z_m\end{bmatrix} + \begin{bmatrix}\bar Z_m & \bar Z_m & \bar Z_m\\ \bar Z_m & \bar Z_m & \bar Z_m\\ \bar Z_m & \bar Z_m & \bar Z_m\end{bmatrix}\right\} A \begin{bmatrix}\bar I_{a0}\\ \bar I_{a1}\\ \bar I_{a2}\end{bmatrix}$$

MULTIPLYING ACROSS BY A^{-1},

$$\begin{bmatrix}\bar V_{aa'0}\\ \bar V_{aa'1}\\ \bar V_{aa'2}\end{bmatrix} = A^{-1}\left\{(\bar Z_s-\bar Z_m)\begin{bmatrix}1 & \cdot & \cdot\\ \cdot & 1 & \cdot\\ \cdot & \cdot & 1\end{bmatrix} + \bar Z_m\begin{bmatrix}1 & 1 & 1\\ 1 & 1 & 1\\ 1 & 1 & 1\end{bmatrix}\right\} A \begin{bmatrix}\bar I_{a0}\\ \bar I_{a1}\\ \bar I_{a2}\end{bmatrix}$$

OR

$$\begin{bmatrix}V_{aa'0}\\ V_{aa'1}\\ V_{aa'2}\end{bmatrix} = \begin{bmatrix}\bar Z_s+2\bar Z_m & \cdot & \cdot\\ \cdot & \bar Z_s-\bar Z_m & \cdot\\ \cdot & \cdot & \bar Z_s-\bar Z_m\end{bmatrix}\begin{bmatrix}\bar I_{a0}\\ \bar I_{a1}\\ \bar I_{a2}\end{bmatrix}$$

NOW DEFINE ZERO-, POSITIVE-, AND NEGATIVE-SEQUENCE IMPEDANCES IN TERMS OF $\bar Z_s$ AND $\bar Z_m$ AS

$$\bar Z_0 = \bar Z_s + 2\bar Z_m = \bar Z_{aa} + 2\bar Z_{ab} + 3\bar Z_{nn} - 6\bar Z_{an}$$

$$\bar Z_1 = \bar Z_s - \bar Z_m = \bar Z_{aa} - \bar Z_{ab}$$

$$\bar Z_2 = \bar Z_s - \bar Z_m = \bar Z_{aa} - \bar Z_{ab}$$

NOW, THE SEQUENCE COMPONENTS OF THE VOLTAGE DROPS BETWEEN THE TWO ENDS OF THE LINE SECTION CAN BE WRITTEN AS THREE UNCOUPLED EQUATIONS:

$$\bar V_{aa'0} = \bar V_{an0} - \bar V_{a'n'0} = \bar Z_0\,\bar I_{a0}$$

$$\bar V_{aa'1} = \bar V_{an1} - \bar V_{a'n'1} = \bar Z_1\,\bar I_{a1}$$

$$\bar V_{aa'2} = \bar V_{an2} - \bar V_{a'n'2} = \bar Z_2\,\bar I_{a2}$$

8.23

(a) THE SEQUENCE IMPEDANCES ARE GIVEN BY

$$\bar{Z}_0 = \bar{Z}_{aa} + 2\bar{Z}_{ab} + 3\bar{Z}_{nn} - 6\bar{Z}_{an} = j60 + j40 + j240 - j180 = j160\ \Omega$$

$$\bar{Z}_1 = \bar{Z}_2 = \bar{Z}_{aa} - \bar{Z}_{ab} = j60 - j20 = j40\ \Omega$$

THE SEQUENCE COMPONENTS OF THE VOLTAGE DROPS IN THE LINE ARE

$$\begin{bmatrix} \bar{V}_{aa'0} \\ \bar{V}_{aa'1} \\ \bar{V}_{aa'2} \end{bmatrix} = A^{-1} \begin{bmatrix} \bar{V}_{an} - \bar{V}_{a'n'} \\ \bar{V}_{bn} - \bar{V}_{b'n'} \\ \bar{V}_{cn} - \bar{V}_{c'n'} \end{bmatrix} = A^{-1} \begin{bmatrix} (182.0 - 154.0) + j(70.0 - 28.0) \\ (72.24 - 44.24) - j(32.62 - 74.62) \\ -(170.24 - 198.24) + j(88.62 - 46.62) \end{bmatrix}$$

$$= A^{-1} \begin{bmatrix} 28.0 + j42.0 \\ 28.0 + j42.0 \\ 28.0 + j42.0 \end{bmatrix} = \begin{bmatrix} 28.0 + j42.0 \\ 0 \\ 0 \end{bmatrix} \text{kV}$$

FROM PR. 8.22 RESULT, IT FOLLOWS THAT

$$\bar{V}_{aa'0} = 28{,}000 + j42{,}000 = j160\,\bar{I}_{a0}\,;\ \bar{V}_{aa'1} = 0 = j40\,\bar{I}_{a1}\,;\ \bar{V}_{aa'2} = 0 = j40\,\bar{I}_{a2}$$

FROM WHICH THE SYMMETRICAL COMPONENTS OF THE CURRENTS IN PHASE a ARE

$$\bar{I}_{a0} = (262.5 - j175)\text{ A}\ ;\quad \bar{I}_{a1} = \bar{I}_{a2} = 0$$

THE LINE CURRENTS ARE THEN GIVEN BY

$$\bar{I}_a = \bar{I}_b = \bar{I}_c = (262.5 - j175)\text{ A}$$

(b) WITHOUT USING SYMMETRICAL COMPONENTS:

THE SELF- AND MUTUAL IMPEDANCES [SEE SOLUTION OF PR. 8.22(a)] ARE

$$\bar{Z}_s = \bar{Z}_{aa} + \bar{Z}_{nn} - 2\bar{Z}_{an} = j60 + j80 - j60 = j80\ \Omega$$

$$\bar{Z}_m = \bar{Z}_{ab} + \bar{Z}_{nn} - 2\bar{Z}_{an} = j20 + j80 - j60 = j40\ \Omega$$

SO, LINE CURRENTS CAN BE CALCULATED AS [SEE SOLUTION OF PR. 8.22(a)]

$$\begin{bmatrix} \bar{V}_{aa'} \\ \bar{V}_{bb'} \\ \bar{V}_{cc'} \end{bmatrix} = \begin{bmatrix} 28 + j42 \\ 28 + j42 \\ 28 + j42 \end{bmatrix} \times 10^3 = \begin{bmatrix} j80 & j40 & j40 \\ j40 & j80 & j40 \\ j40 & j40 & j80 \end{bmatrix} \begin{bmatrix} \bar{I}_a \\ \bar{I}_b \\ \bar{I}_c \end{bmatrix}$$

8.23 CONTD.

$$\begin{bmatrix} \bar{I}_a \\ \bar{I}_b \\ \bar{I}_c \end{bmatrix} = \begin{bmatrix} j80 & j40 & j40 \\ j40 & j80 & j40 \\ j40 & j40 & j80 \end{bmatrix}^{-1} \begin{bmatrix} 28+j42 \\ 28+j42 \\ 28+j42 \end{bmatrix} \times 10^3$$

$$= \begin{bmatrix} 262.5-j175 \\ 262.5-j175 \\ 262.5-j175 \end{bmatrix} \text{A}$$

8.24

(a) $\bar{I}_{AB} = \dfrac{\bar{V}_{AB}}{(18+j10)} = \dfrac{480\angle 0^\circ}{20.59\angle 29.05^\circ} = 23.31\angle -29.05^\circ$ A

$\bar{I}_{BC} = \dfrac{\bar{V}_{BC}}{(18+j10)} = \dfrac{480\angle -120^\circ}{20.59\angle 29.05^\circ} = 23.31\angle -149.06^\circ$ A

(b) $\bar{I}_A = \bar{I}_{AB} = 23.31\angle -29.05^\circ$ A

$\bar{I}_B = \bar{I}_{BC} - \bar{I}_{AB} = 23.31\angle -149.06^\circ - 23.31\angle -29.05^\circ$

$\bar{I}_B = -40.37 - j0.6693 = 40.38\angle 180.95^\circ$ A

$\bar{I}_C = -\bar{I}_{BC} = 23.31\angle 30.95^\circ$ A

(c)
$$\begin{bmatrix} \bar{I}_{L0} \\ \bar{I}_{L1} \\ \bar{I}_{L2} \end{bmatrix} = \frac{1}{3}\begin{bmatrix} 1 & 1 & 1 \\ 1 & a & a^2 \\ 1 & a^2 & a \end{bmatrix}\begin{bmatrix} 23.31\angle -29.05^\circ \\ 40.38\angle 180.95^\circ \\ 23.31\angle 30.95^\circ \end{bmatrix}$$

$$= \frac{1}{3}\begin{bmatrix} 23.31\angle -29.05^\circ + 40.38\angle 180.95^\circ + 23.31\angle 30.95^\circ \\ 23.31\angle -29.05^\circ + 40.38\angle 300.95^\circ + 23.31\angle 270.95^\circ \\ 23.31\angle -29.05^\circ + 40.38\angle 60.95^\circ + 23.31\angle 150.95^\circ \end{bmatrix}$$

$$= \begin{bmatrix} 0 + j0 \\ 13.84 - j23.09 \\ 6.536 + j11.77 \end{bmatrix} = \begin{bmatrix} 0 \\ 26.92\angle -59.06^\circ \\ 13.46\angle 60.96^\circ \end{bmatrix} \text{ A}$$

8.25

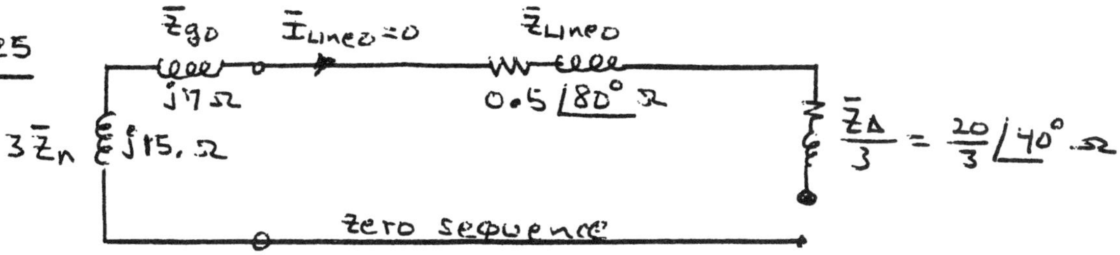

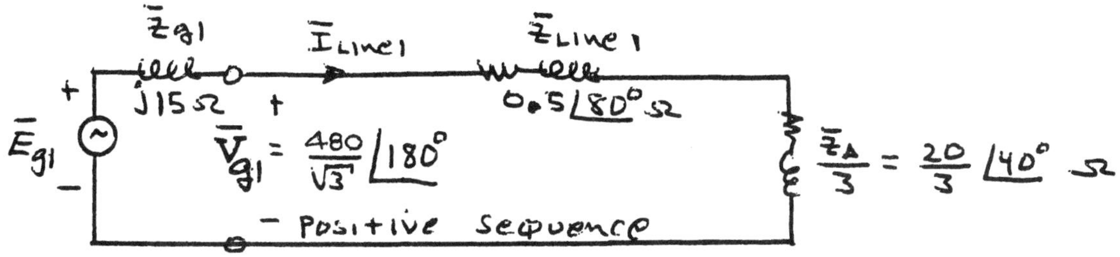

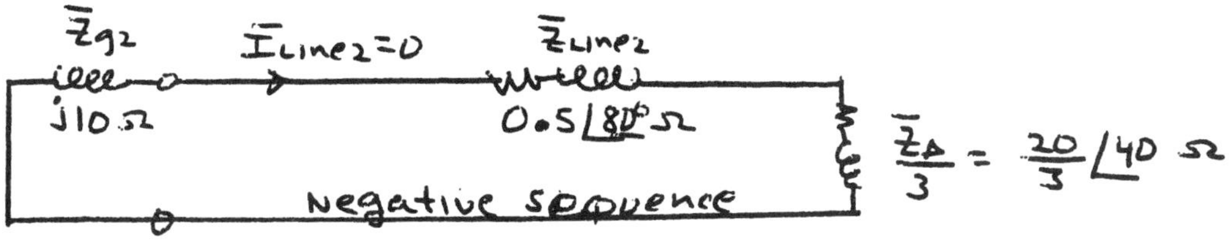

$$\bar{I}_{Line0} = \bar{I}_{Line2} = 0$$

$$\bar{I}_{Line1} = \frac{\bar{V}_{g1}}{\bar{Z}_{Line1} + \frac{\bar{Z}_\Delta}{3}} = \frac{\frac{480}{\sqrt{3}}\angle 180°}{0.5\angle 80° + \frac{20}{3}\angle 40°}$$

$$= \frac{277.14\angle 180°}{5.194 + j4.778} = \frac{277.114\angle 180°}{7.057\angle 42.61°} = 39.27\angle 137.4° \text{ A}$$

8.26

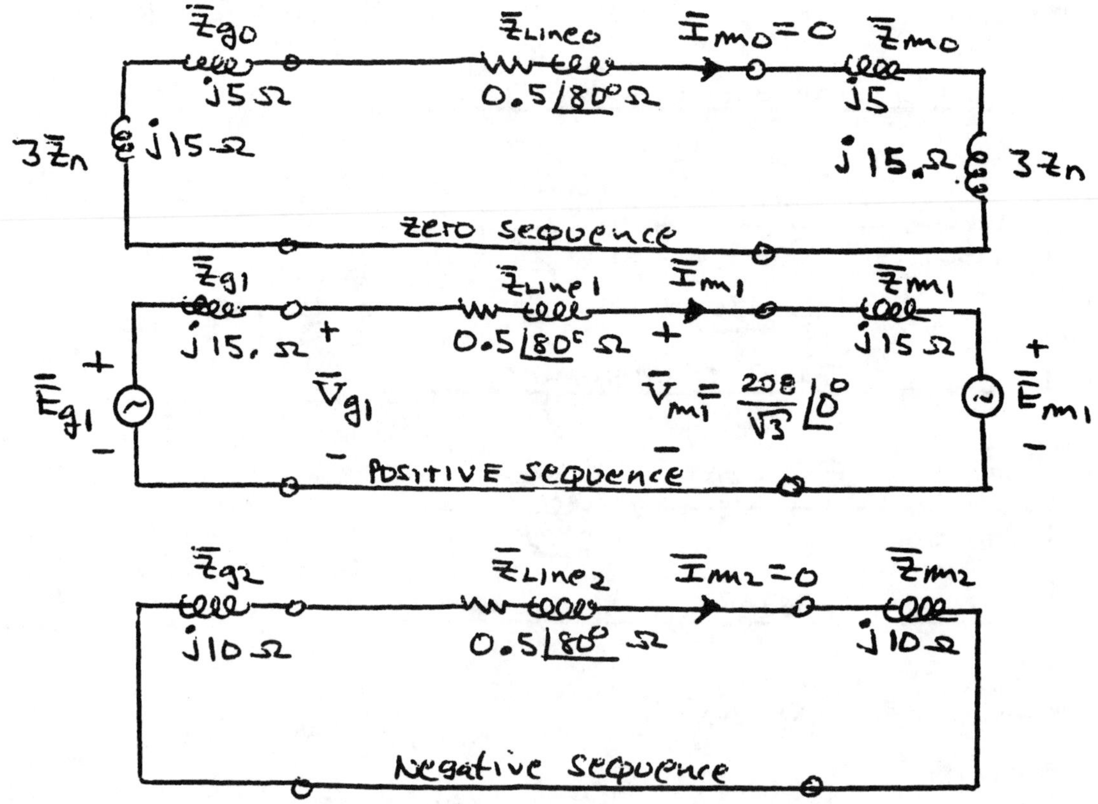

$$\bar{V}_{gan} = \bar{V}_{g1} = \bar{V}_{m1} + \bar{Z}_{Line1}\bar{I}_{m1}$$

$$\bar{I}_{m1} = \frac{10{,}000\,\angle\cos^{-1}0.8}{(208)\sqrt{3}\,(0.8)} = 34.71\angle 36.87°\text{ A}$$

$$\bar{V}_{gan} = \frac{208}{\sqrt{3}}\angle 0° + (0.5\angle 80°)(15.04\angle 36.87°)$$

$$= 120.1\angle 0° + 7.52\angle 116.87°$$

$$= 116.7 + j\,6.708 = 116.9\angle 1.404°\text{ V}$$

$$V_g = \sqrt{3}(116.9) = 202.5\text{ V (LINE-TO-LINE)}$$

8.27 Converting the Δ load to an equivalent Y, and then writing two loop equations:

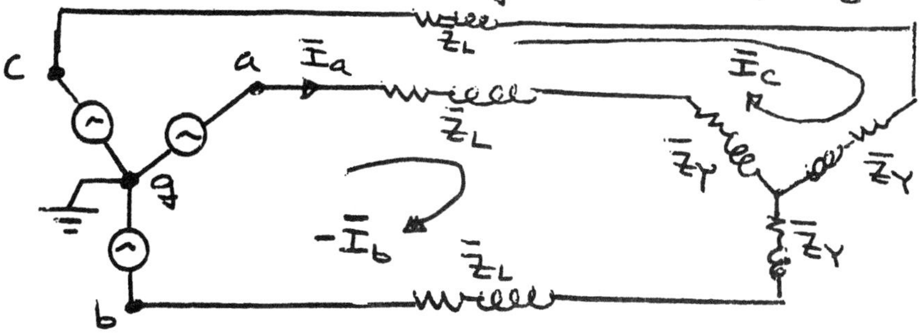

$$\begin{bmatrix} 2(\bar{Z}_L+\bar{Z}_Y) & -(\bar{Z}_L+\bar{Z}_Y) \\ -(\bar{Z}_L+\bar{Z}_Y) & 2(\bar{Z}_L+\bar{Z}_Y) \end{bmatrix} \begin{bmatrix} \bar{I}_c \\ -\bar{I}_b \end{bmatrix} = \begin{bmatrix} \bar{V}_{cg}-\bar{V}_{ag} \\ \bar{V}_{ag}-\bar{V}_{bg} \end{bmatrix}$$

$$\begin{bmatrix} 21.46\underline{/43.78^\circ} & -10.73\underline{/43.78^\circ} \\ -10.73\underline{/43.78^\circ} & 21.46\underline{/43.78^\circ} \end{bmatrix} \begin{bmatrix} \bar{I}_c \\ -\bar{I}_b \end{bmatrix} = \begin{bmatrix} 295\underline{/115^\circ} - 277\underline{/0^\circ} \\ 277\underline{/0^\circ} - 260\underline{/-120^\circ} \end{bmatrix}$$

$$\begin{bmatrix} \bar{I}_c \\ -\bar{I}_b \end{bmatrix} = \begin{bmatrix} 21.46\underline{/43.78^\circ} & -10.73\underline{/43.78^\circ} \\ -10.73\underline{/43.78^\circ} & 21.46\underline{/43.78^\circ} \end{bmatrix}^{-1} \begin{bmatrix} 482.5\underline{/146.35^\circ} \\ 465.1\underline{/28.96^\circ} \end{bmatrix}$$

$$\begin{bmatrix} \bar{I}_c \\ -\bar{I}_b \end{bmatrix} = \begin{bmatrix} 0.06213\underline{/-43.78^\circ} & 0.03107\underline{/-43.78^\circ} \\ 0.03107\underline{/-43.78^\circ} & 0.06213\underline{/-43.78^\circ} \end{bmatrix} \begin{bmatrix} 482.5\underline{/146.35^\circ} \\ 465.1\underline{/28.96^\circ} \end{bmatrix}$$

$$\begin{bmatrix} \bar{I}_c \\ -\bar{I}_b \end{bmatrix} = \begin{bmatrix} 29.98\underline{/102.57^\circ} + 14.45\underline{/-14.82^\circ} \\ 14.99\underline{/102.57^\circ} + 28.90\underline{/-14.82^\circ} \end{bmatrix} = \begin{bmatrix} 7.445 + j25.57 \\ 24.68 + j7.239 \end{bmatrix}$$

$$\begin{bmatrix} \bar{I}_c \\ -\bar{I}_b \end{bmatrix} = \begin{bmatrix} 26.62\underline{/73.77^\circ} \\ 25.71\underline{/16.34^\circ} \end{bmatrix} \text{A}$$

Also, $\bar{I}_a = -\bar{I}_b - \bar{I}_c$

$$\bar{I}_a = (24.68 + j7.239) - (7.445 + j25.57)$$

$$\bar{I}_a = 17.23 - j18.33 = 25.15\underline{/-46.76^\circ}$$

$$\begin{bmatrix} \bar{I}_a \\ \bar{I}_b \\ \bar{I}_c \end{bmatrix} = \begin{bmatrix} 25.15\underline{/-46.76^\circ} \\ 25.71\underline{/196.34^\circ} \\ 26.62\underline{/73.77^\circ} \end{bmatrix} \text{A}$$

which agrees with Ex 8.6. The symmetrical components method is easier because it avoids the need to invert a matrix.

8.28

THE LINE-TO-GROUND FAULT ON PHASE a OF THE MACHINE IS SHOWN BELOW, ALONG WITH THE CORRESPONDING SEQUENCE NETWORKS:

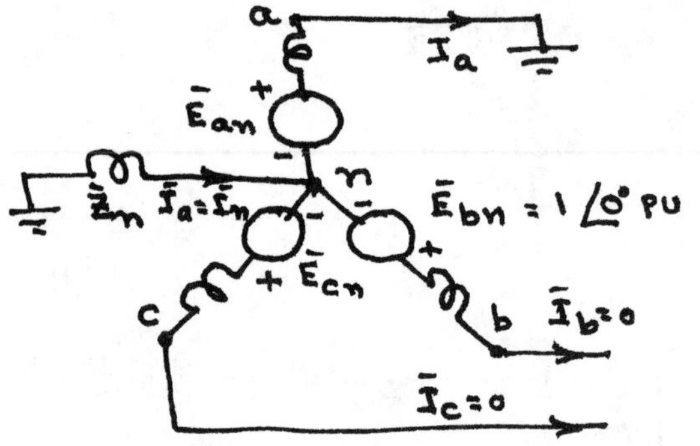

UNLOADED GENERATOR

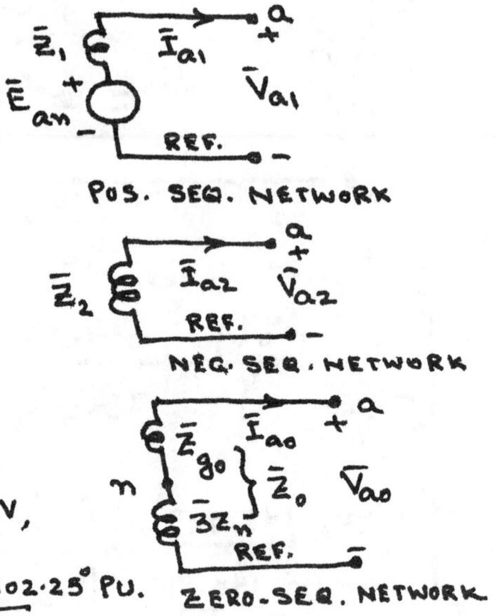

WITH THE BASE VOLTAGE TO NEUTRAL $\frac{13.8}{\sqrt{3}}$ kV,

$\bar{V}_a = 0$; $\bar{V}_b = 1.013\angle -102.25°$; $\bar{V}_c = 1.013\angle 102.25°$ PU.

$= (-0.215 - j0.99)$ PU $\qquad = (-0.215 + j0.99)$ PU

WITH $Z_{base} = \dfrac{(13.8)^2}{20} = 9.52\,\Omega$, $\bar{Z}_1 = \dfrac{j2.38}{9.52} = j0.25$; $\bar{Z}_2 = \dfrac{j3.33}{9.52} = j0.35$;

$\bar{Z}_{g0} = \dfrac{j0.95}{9.52} = j0.1$; $\bar{Z}_n = 0$; $\bar{Z}_0 = j0.1$ PU

THE SYMMETRICAL COMPONENTS OF THE VOLTAGES AT THE FAULT POINT ARE

$$\begin{bmatrix} \bar{V}_{a0} \\ \bar{V}_{a1} \\ \bar{V}_{a2} \end{bmatrix} = \frac{1}{3}\begin{bmatrix} 1 & 1 & 1 \\ 1 & a & a^2 \\ 1 & a^2 & a \end{bmatrix}\begin{bmatrix} 0 \\ -0.215 - j0.99 \\ -0.215 + j0.99 \end{bmatrix} = \begin{bmatrix} -0.143 + j0 \\ 0.643 + j0 \\ -0.500 + j0 \end{bmatrix} \text{PU}$$

$$\bar{I}_{a0} = -\frac{\bar{V}_{a0}}{\bar{Z}_{g0}} = -\frac{(-0.143 + j0)}{j0.1} = -j1.43 \text{ PU}$$

$$\bar{I}_{a1} = \frac{\bar{E}_{an} - \bar{V}_{a1}}{\bar{Z}_1} = \frac{(1 + j0) - (0.643 + j0)}{j0.25} = -j1.43 \text{ PU}$$

$$\bar{I}_{a2} = -\frac{\bar{V}_{a2}}{\bar{Z}_2} = -\frac{(-0.5 + j0)}{j0.35} = -j1.43 \text{ PU}$$

$\therefore$ FAULT CURRENT INTO THE GROUND $\bar{I}_a = \bar{I}_{a0} + \bar{I}_{a1} + \bar{I}_{a2} = 3\bar{I}_{a0} = -j4.29$ PU

8.28 CONTD.

WITH BASE CURRENT $\dfrac{20{,}000}{\sqrt{3} \times 13.8} = 837\text{A}$, THE SUBTRANSIENT CURRENT IN LINE a IS

$$I_a = 4.29 \times 837 = 3590\text{ A}$$

LINE-TO-LINE VOLTAGES DURING THE FAULT ARE: (ON BASE VOLTAGE TO NEUTRAL)

$$\bar{V}_{ab} = \bar{V}_a - \bar{V}_b = 0.215 + j0.99 = 1.01\angle 77.7^\circ \text{ PU} = 8.05\angle 77.7^\circ \text{ kV}$$

$$\bar{V}_{bc} = \bar{V}_b - \bar{V}_c = 0 - j1.98 = 1.98\angle 270^\circ \text{ PU} = 15.78\angle 270^\circ \text{ kV}$$

$$\bar{V}_{ca} = \bar{V}_c - \bar{V}_a = -0.215 + j0.99 = 1.01\angle 102.3^\circ \text{ PU} = 8.05\angle 102.3^\circ \text{ kV}$$

PHASOR DIAGRAMS OF LINE VOLTAGES BEFORE AND AFTER THE FAULT ARE SHOWN BELOW:

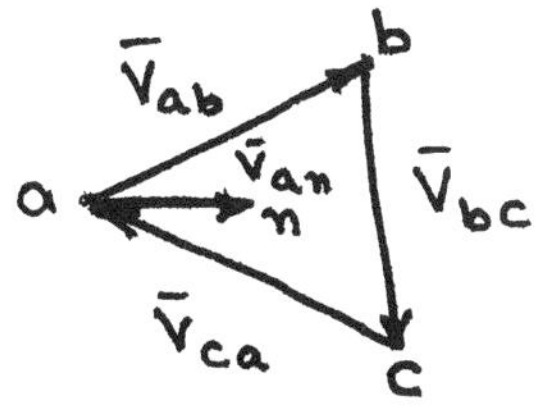

PREFAULT

$\bar{V}_{ab} = 13.8\angle 30^\circ$ kV

$\bar{V}_{bc} = 13.8\angle 270^\circ$ kV

$\bar{V}_{ca} = 13.8\angle 150^\circ$ kV

(BALANCED)

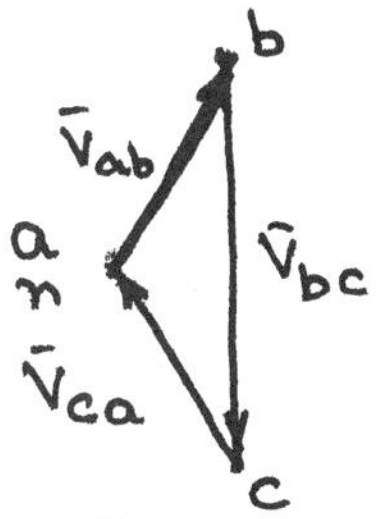

POSTFAULT

$\bar{V}_{ab} = 8.05\angle 77.7^\circ$ kV

$\bar{V}_{bc} = 15.78\angle 270^\circ$ kV

$\bar{V}_{ca} = 8.05\angle 102.3^\circ$ kV

(UNBALANCED)

8.29

(a)

Per unit Zero Sequence

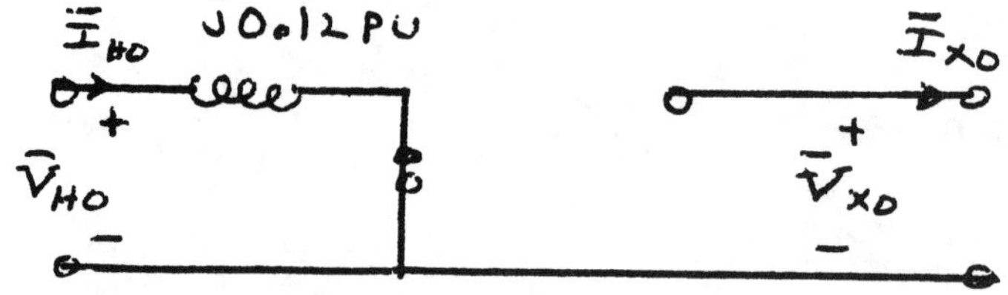

Per unit positive sequence

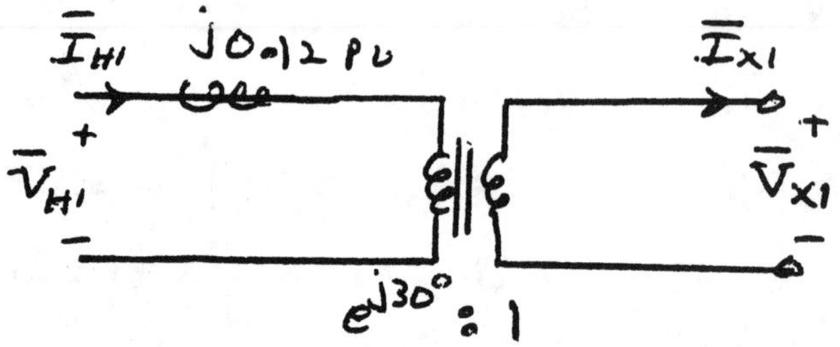

Per unit Negative sequence

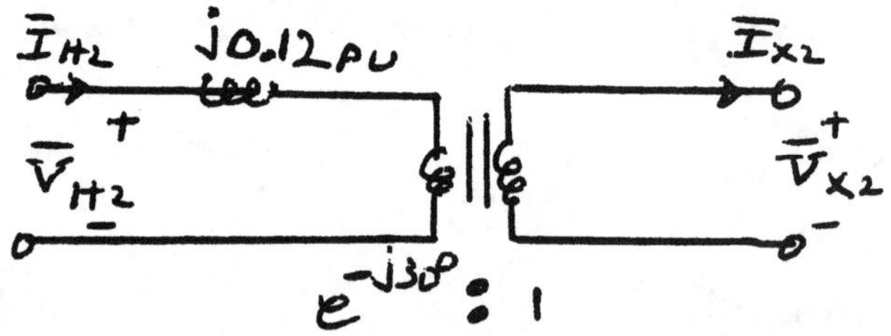

(b)

Per Unit Zero Sequence

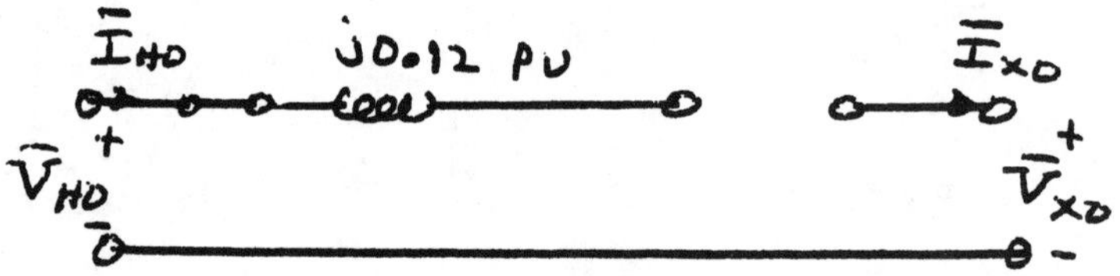

Per unit Positive Sequence

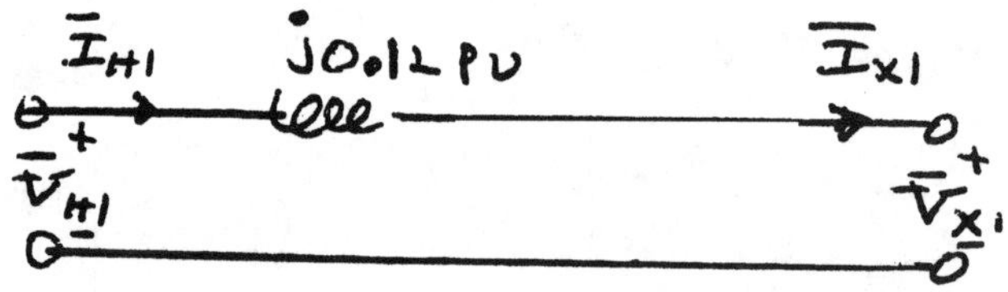

Per unit Negative Sequence

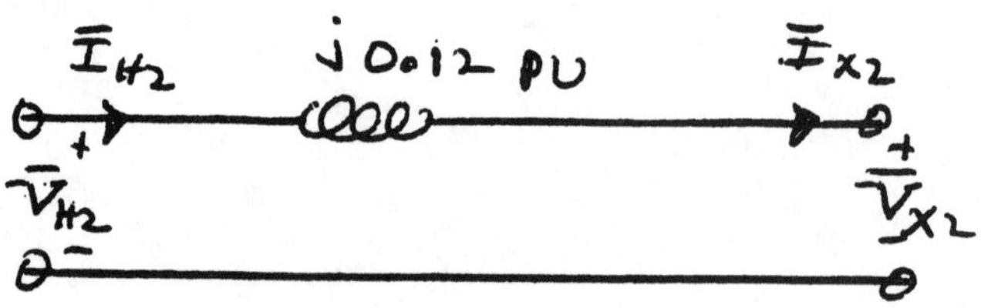

8.30

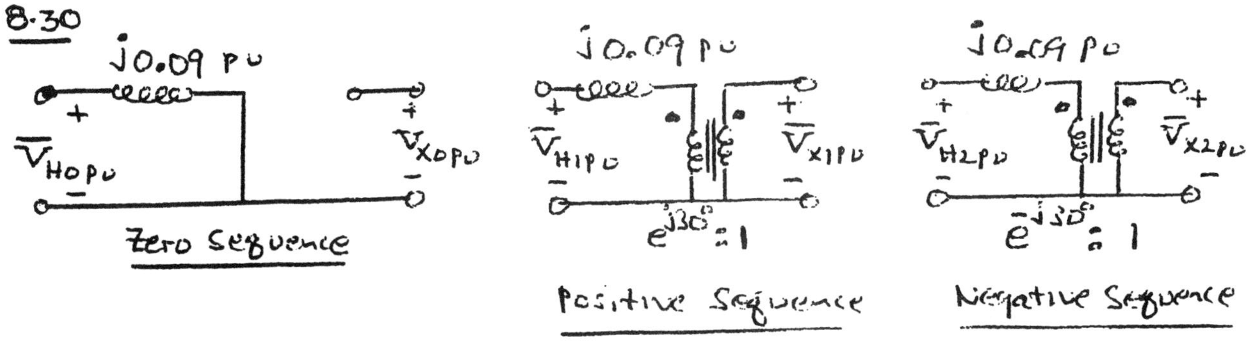

8.31

$$X_{pu\,new} = (0.09)\left(\frac{345}{360}\right)^2\left(\frac{100}{300}\right) = 0.02755 \text{ per unit}$$

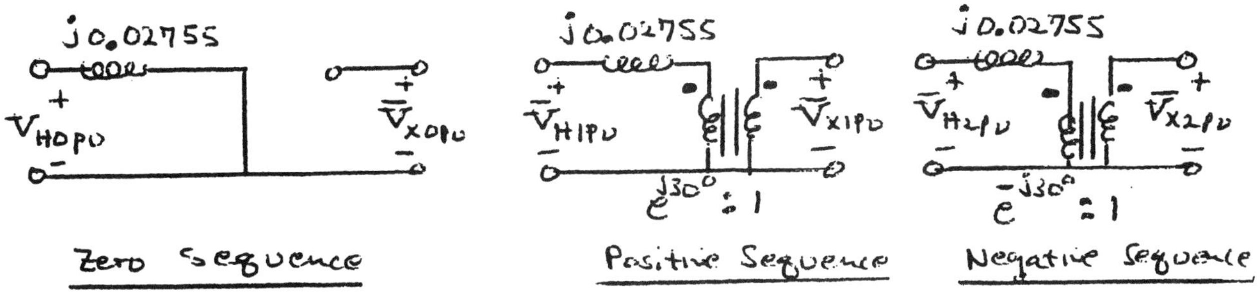

8.32

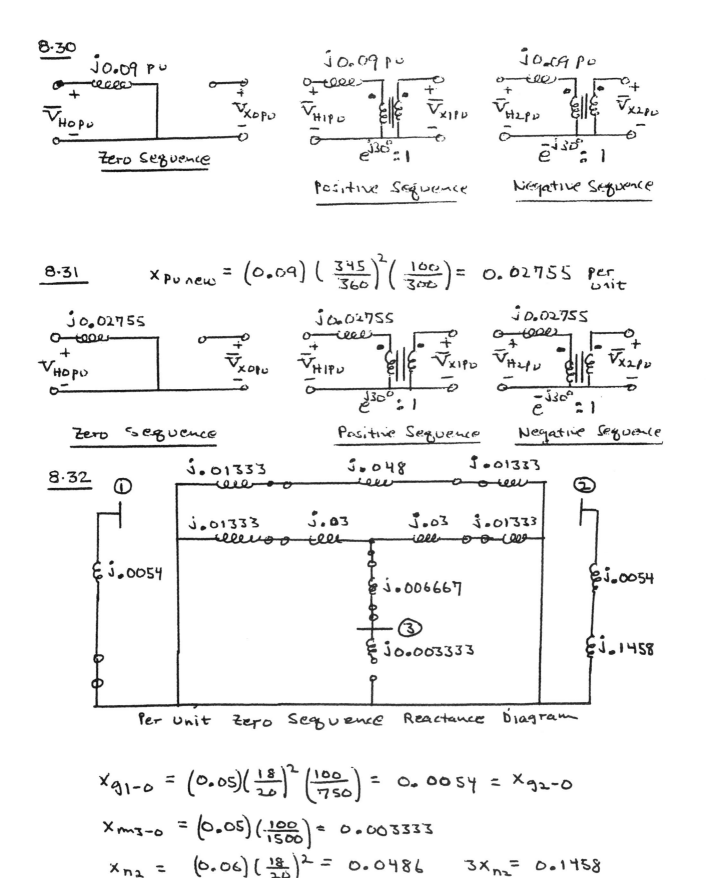

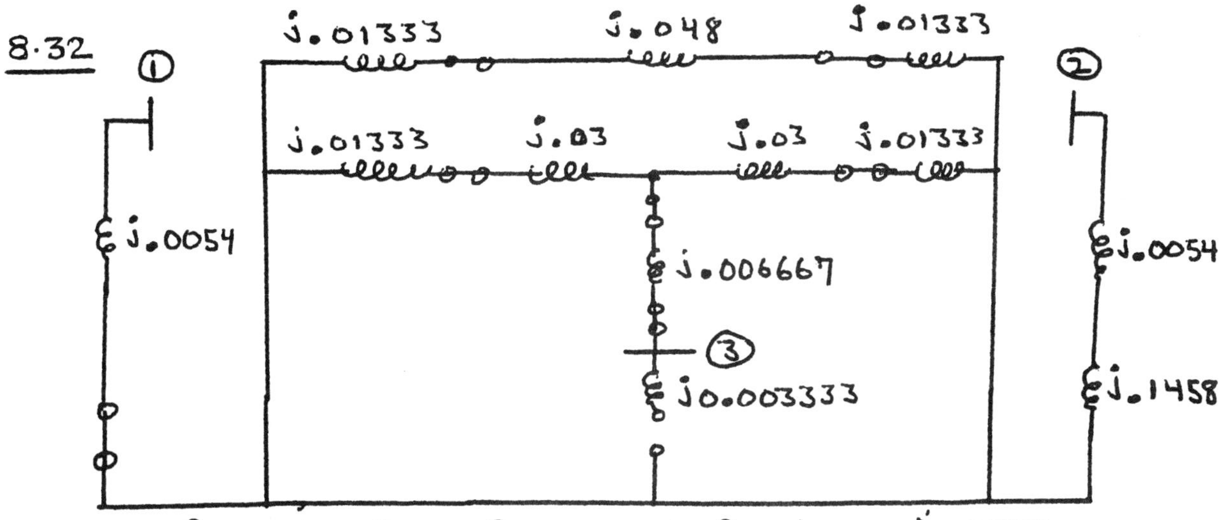

Per Unit Zero Sequence Reactance Diagram

$$X_{g1-0} = (0.05)\left(\frac{18}{20}\right)^2\left(\frac{100}{750}\right) = 0.0054 = X_{g2-0}$$

$$X_{m3-0} = (0.05)\left(\frac{100}{1500}\right) = 0.003333$$

$$X_{n2} = (0.06)\left(\frac{18}{20}\right)^2 = 0.0486 \qquad 3X_{n2} = 0.1458$$

8.33 (a)

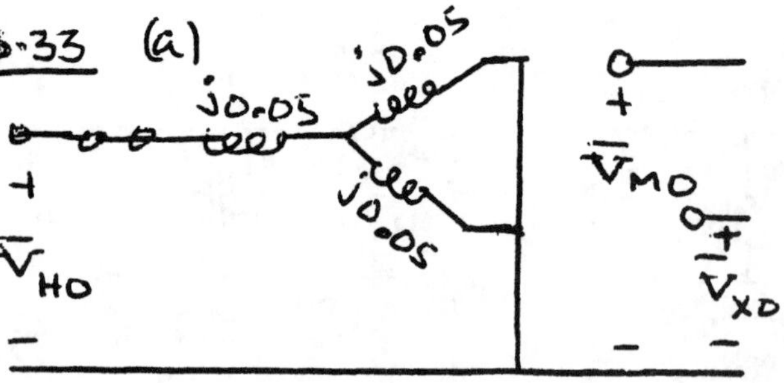

Per Unit Zero Sequence

$X_1 = X_2 = X_3 = \frac{1}{2}(0.1 + 0.1 - 0.1)$

$= 0.05$ per unit

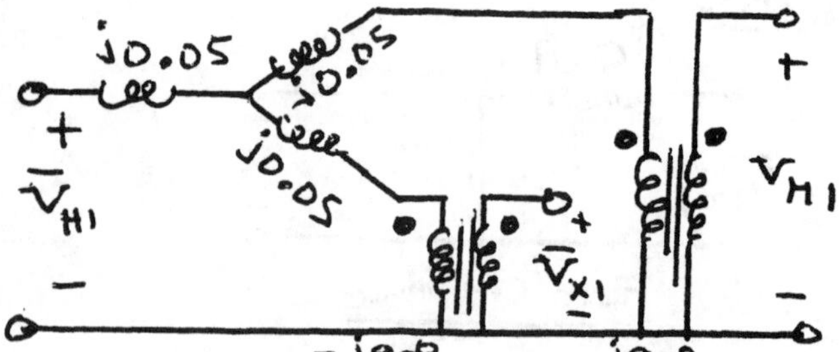

$e^{-j90°}:1$ $e^{j90°}:1$

$(e^{+j90°}:1)$ $(e^{-j90°}:1)$

Per Unit Positive Sequence

(Per unit Negative Sequence)

(b)

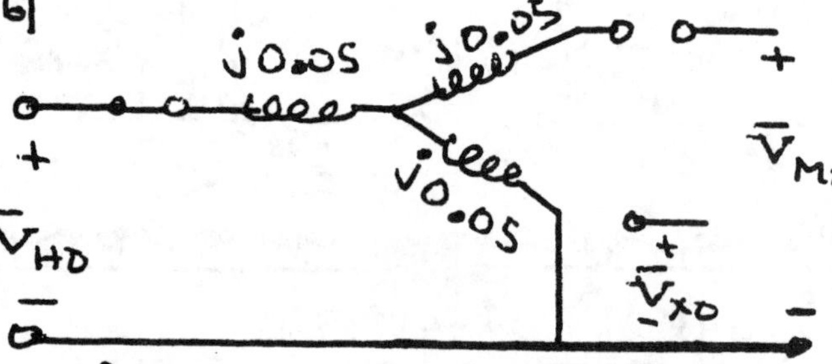

Per Unit Zero Sequence

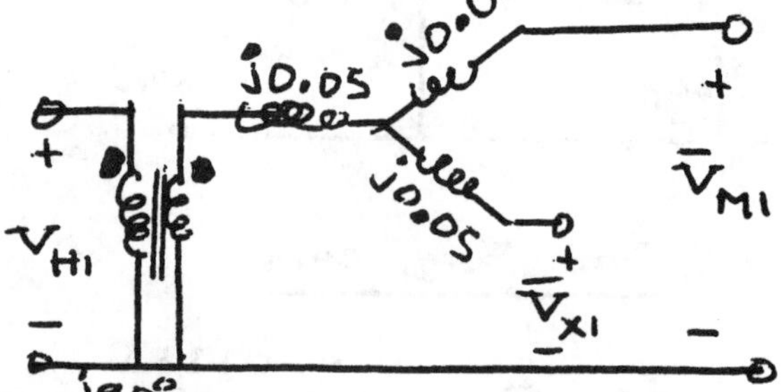

$e^{j90°}:1$

$(e^{-j90°}:1)$

Per Unit Positive Sequence

(Per unit Negative Sequence)

(c)

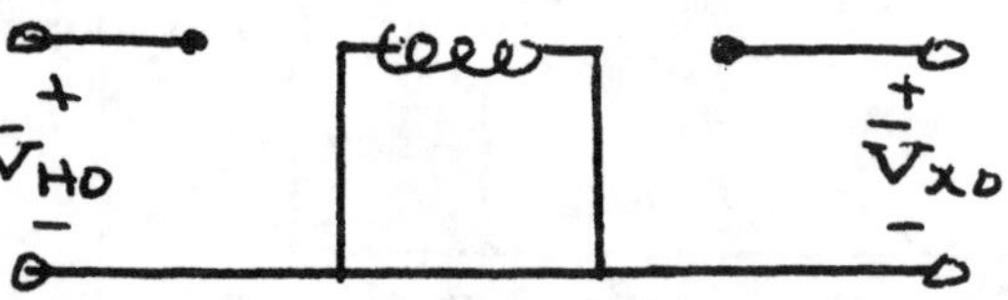

Per Unit Zero Sequence

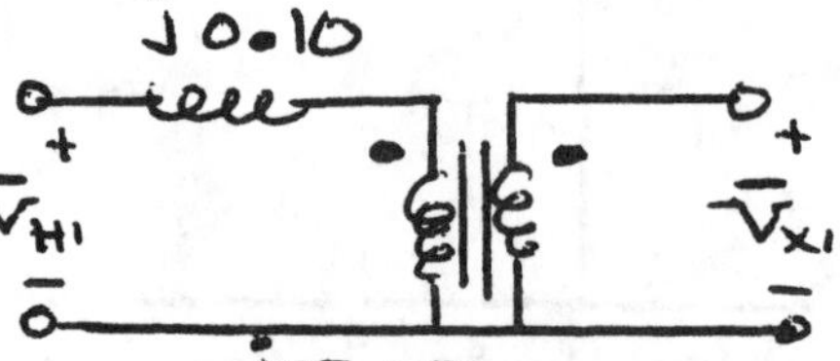

$e^{j23.40°}:1$

$(e^{-j23.40°}:1)$

Per Unit Positive Sequence

(Per unit Negative Sequence)

8.34

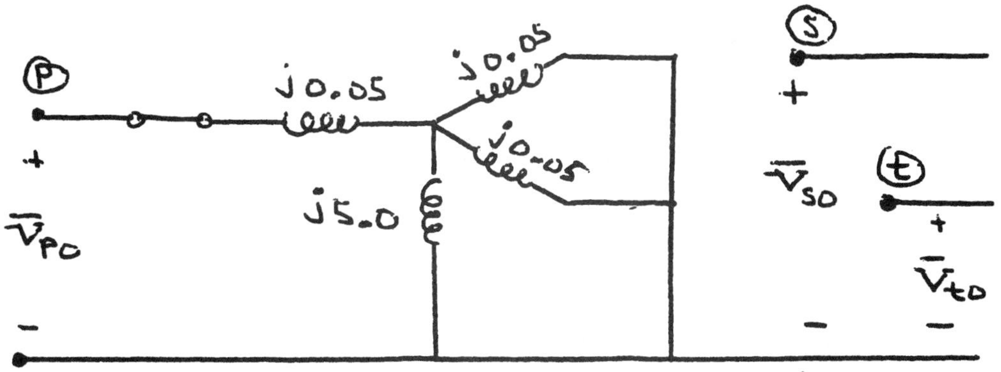

Per unit zero sequence Network

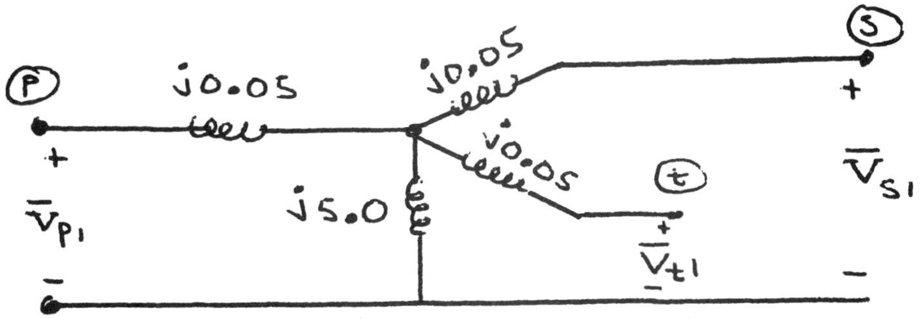

Per unit positive (or negative) sequence network
(Phase shift NOT shown)

p - primary
s - secondary
t - tertiary

8.35

$$\bar{S}_{3\phi} = \bar{V}_{ag}\bar{I}_a^* + \bar{V}_{bg}\bar{I}_b^* + \bar{V}_{cg}\bar{I}_c^*$$

$$= (280\angle 0^\circ)(14.0\angle 53.13^\circ) + (290\angle -130^\circ)(14.5\angle -176.87^\circ)$$

$$+ (260\angle 110^\circ)(13.0\angle -56.87^\circ)$$

$$= 3920\angle 53.13^\circ + 4205\angle 53.13^\circ + 3380\angle 53.13^\circ$$

$$= 11505.\angle 53.13^\circ$$

$$\bar{S}_{3\phi} = 6903 + j9204$$

$$P_{3\phi} = \text{Re}(\bar{S}_{3\phi}) = 6903.\ \text{W}$$
$$Q_{3\phi} = \text{Im}(\bar{S}_{3\phi}) = 9204.\ \text{vars}$$

} delivered to the load.

8.36

(a)

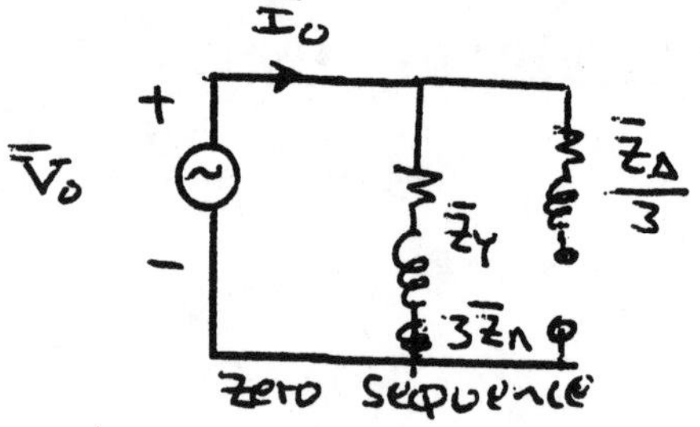

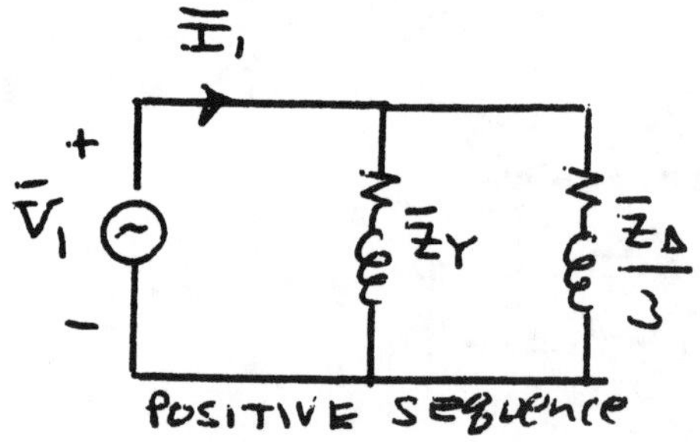

$$\bar{Z}_0 = \bar{Z}_Y + 3\bar{Z}_n$$
$$= 2 + j2 + j3$$
$$= 2 + j5 = 5.385\angle 68.20^\circ$$

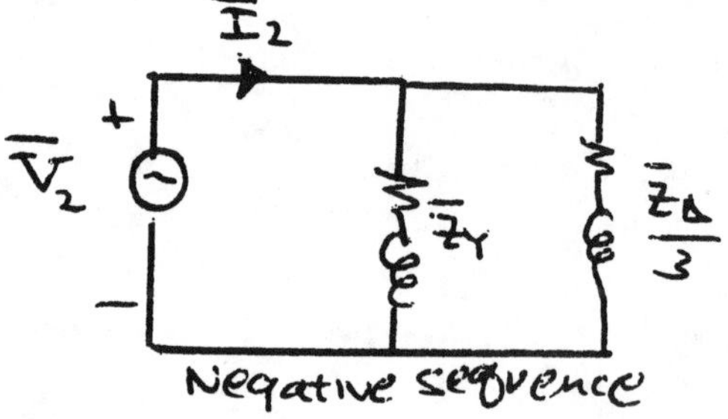

(b) $$\bar{I}_0 = \frac{\bar{V}_0}{\bar{Z}_0} = \frac{10\angle 60^\circ}{5.385\angle 68.20^\circ}$$

$$\bar{I}_0 = 1.857\angle -8.199^\circ\ \text{A}$$

8-36 CONTD.
(b)

$$\bar{Z}_1 = \bar{Z}_Y \,//\, \frac{\bar{Z}_\Delta}{3} = (2+j2)//(2+j2) = 1+j = \sqrt{2}\,\angle 45^\circ\ \Omega$$

$$\bar{I}_1 = \frac{\bar{V}_1}{\bar{Z}_1} = \frac{100\,\angle 0^\circ}{\sqrt{2}\,\angle 45^\circ} = 70.71\,\angle -45^\circ\ \text{A}$$

$$\bar{Z}_2 = \bar{Z}_1 = \sqrt{2}\,\angle 45^\circ\ \Omega$$

$$\bar{I}_2 = \frac{\bar{V}_2}{\bar{Z}_2} = \frac{15\,\angle 200^\circ}{\sqrt{2}\,\angle 45^\circ} = 10.61\,\angle 155^\circ\ \text{A}$$

$$\bar{S}_0 = \bar{V}_0 \bar{I}_0^* = (10\,\angle 60^\circ)(1.857\,\angle 8.199^\circ)$$

$$\bar{S}_0 = 18.57\,\angle 68.199^\circ = 6.897 + j\,17.24$$

$$\bar{S}_1 = \bar{V}_1 \bar{I}_1^* = (100\,\angle 0^\circ)(70.71\,\angle 45^\circ)$$

$$\bar{S}_1 = 7071\,\angle 45^\circ = 5000 + j\,5000$$

$$\bar{S}_2 = \bar{V}_2 \bar{I}_2^* = (15\,\angle 200^\circ)(10.61\,\angle -155^\circ)$$

$$\bar{S}_2 = 159.\,\angle 45^\circ = 112.5 + j\,112.5$$

(c)

$$\bar{S}_{3\phi} = 3\,(\bar{S}_0 + \bar{S}_1 + \bar{S}_2) = 3\,(5119 + j\,5129)$$

$$\bar{S}_{3\phi} = 15{,}358. + j\,15{,}389.$$

$$\bar{S}_{3\phi} = 21.74 \times 10^3\,\angle 45.06^\circ\ \text{VA}$$

8.37

$$\bar{S}_{3\phi} = \bar{V}_{a0}\bar{I}^*_{a0} + \bar{V}_{a1}\bar{I}^*_{a1} + \bar{V}_{a2}\bar{I}^*_{a2}$$

SUBSTITUTING VALUES OF VOLTAGES AND CURRENTS FROM THE SOLUTION OF PR. 8.8,

$$\bar{S}_{3\phi} = 0 + (0.9857\angle 43.6^\circ)(0.9857\angle -43.6^\circ) + (0.2346\angle 250.3^\circ)(0.2346\angle -250.3^\circ)$$

$$= (0.9857)^2 + (0.2346)^2$$

$$= 1.02664 \text{ PU}$$

WITH THE THREE-PHASE 500-kVA BASE,

$$S_{3\phi} = 513.32 \text{ kW}$$

TO COMPUTE DIRECTLY:

THE EQUIVALENT Δ-CONNECTED RESISTORS ARE

$$R_\Delta = 3R_Y = 3\times 10.58 = 31.74\ \Omega$$

FROM THE GIVEN LINE-TO-LINE VOLTAGES

$$S_{3\phi} = \frac{|V_{ab}|^2}{R_\Delta} + \frac{|V_{bc}|^2}{R_\Delta} + \frac{|V_{ca}|^2}{R_\Delta}$$

$$= \frac{(1840)^2 + (2760)^2 + (2300)^2}{31.74}$$

$$= 513.33 \text{ kW}$$

8.38

THE COMPLEX POWER DELIVERED TO THE LOAD IN TERMS OF SYMMETRICAL COMPONENTS: $\bar{S}_{3\phi} = 3(\bar{V}_{a0}\bar{I}^*_{a0} + \bar{V}_{a1}\bar{I}^*_{a1} + \bar{V}_{a2}\bar{I}^*_{a2})$

SUBSTITUTING VALUES FROM THE SOLUTION OF PR. 8.20,

$$\bar{S}_{3\phi} = 3[47.7739\angle 57.6268^\circ(1.4484\angle 18.3369^\circ) + 112.7841\angle -0.0331^\circ(5.2359\angle 68.2317^\circ) + 61.6231\angle 45.8825^\circ(2.8608\angle 22.3161^\circ)]$$

$$= 904.71 + j2337.3 \text{ VA}$$

THE COMPLEX POWER DELIVERED TO THE LOAD BY SUMMING UP THE POWER IN EACH PHASE: $\bar{S}_{3\phi} = \bar{V}_a\bar{I}^*_a + \bar{V}_b\bar{I}^*_b + \bar{V}_c\bar{I}^*_c$; WITH VALUES FROM PR. 8.20 SOLUTION,

$$= 200\angle 25^\circ(8.7507\angle 47.0439^\circ) + 100\angle -155^\circ(5.2292\angle -143.2451^\circ) + 80\angle 100^\circ(3.028\angle -39.0673^\circ)]$$

$$= 904.71 + j2337.3 \text{ VA}$$

CHAPTER 9

9.1 Calculation of per unit reactances

Synchronous generators:

G1 $X_1 = X_d'' = 0.18$ $X_2 = X_d'' = 0.18$ $X_0 = 0.07$

G2 $X_1 = X_d'' = 0.20$ $X_2 = X_d'' = 0.20$ $X_0 = 0.10$

G3 $X_1 = X_d'' = 0.15\left(\frac{13.8}{15}\right)^2\left(\frac{1000}{500}\right) = 0.2539$ $X_0 = 0.05\left(\frac{13.8}{15}\right)^2\left(\frac{1000}{500}\right) = 0.08464$

$X_2 = X_d'' = 0.2539$ $3X_n = 3X_0 = 0.2539$

G4 $X_1 = X_d'' = 0.30\left(\frac{13.8}{15}\right)^2\left(\frac{1000}{750}\right) = 0.3386$

$X_2 = 0.40\left(\frac{13.8}{15}\right)^2\left(\frac{1000}{750}\right) = 0.4514$ $X_0 = 0.10\left(\frac{13.8}{15}\right)^2\left(\frac{1000}{750}\right) = 0.1129$

Transformers:

$X_{T1} = 0.10$ $X_{T2} = 0.10$ $X_{T3} = 0.12\left(\frac{1000}{500}\right) = 0.24$

$X_{T4} = 0.11\left(\frac{1000}{750}\right) = 0.1467$

Transmission Lines:

$$Z_{baseH} = \frac{(765)^2}{1000} = 585.23\ \Omega$$

Positive/Negative Sequence

$X_{12} = \frac{50}{585.23} = 0.08544$

$X_{13} = X_{23} = \frac{40}{585.23} = 0.06835$

Zero Sequence

$X_{12} = \frac{150}{585.23} = 0.2563$

$X_{13} = X_{23} = \frac{100}{585.23} = 0.1709$

9.2 $n = 1$ (Bus 1 = Fault Bus)

Thevenin equivalents as viewed from Bus 1:

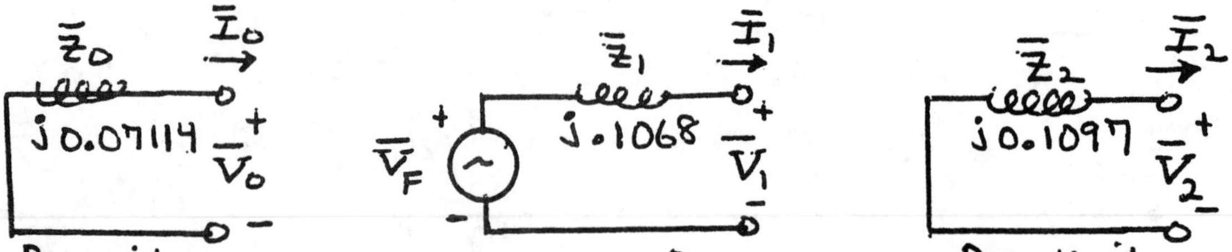

Per unit Zero sequence

$\bar{V}_F = 1.0\angle 0^\circ$ per unit

Per Unit Negative Sequence

Zero Sequence Thevenin Equivalent:

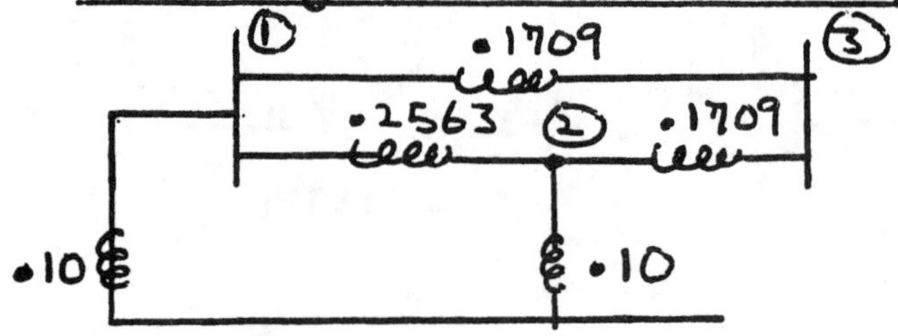

=

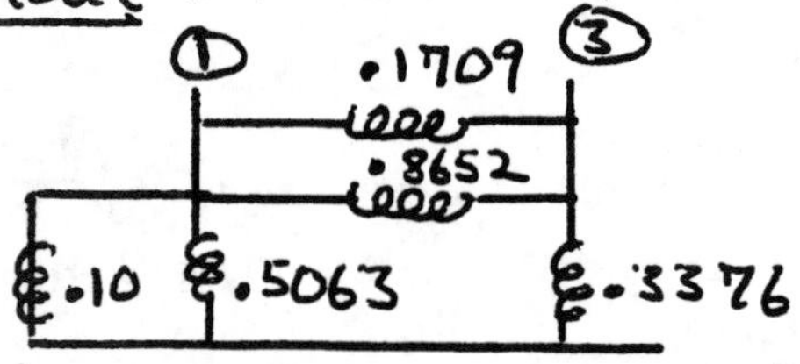

(Using Y-Δ conversion)

=

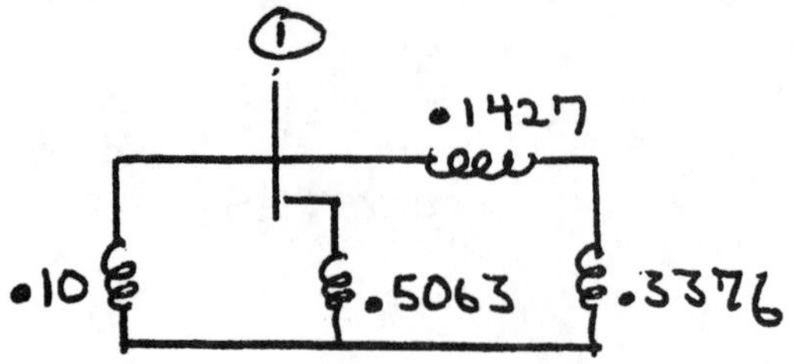

$X_0 = .10 // .5063 // (.1427 + .3376)$

$X_0 = 0.07114$ per unit

Negative Sequence Thevenin Equivalent:

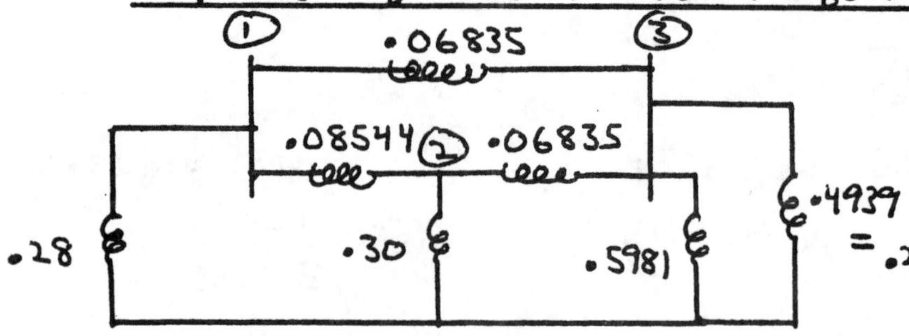

=

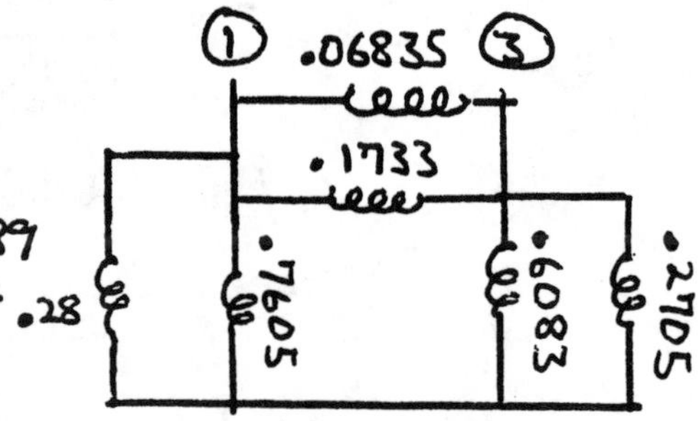

=

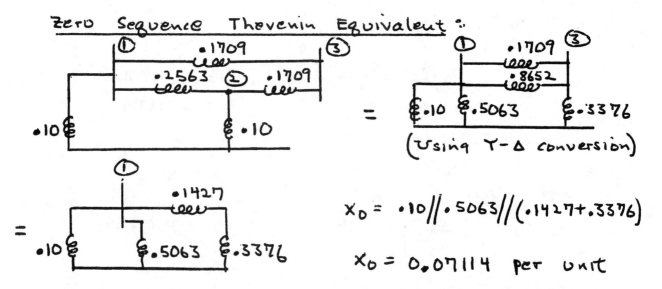

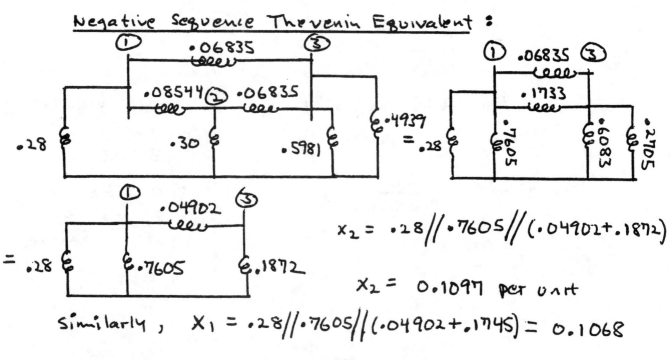

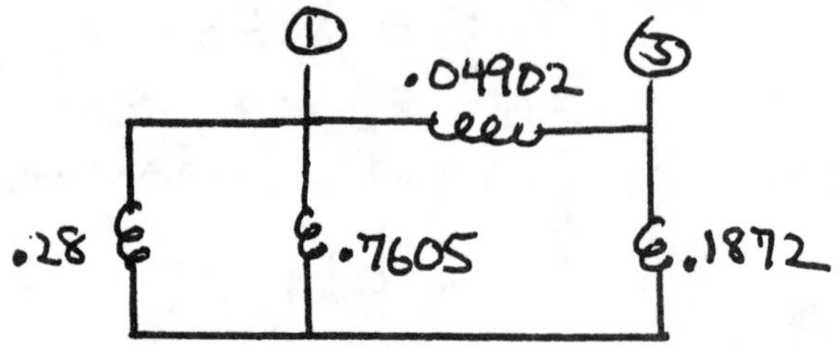

$X_2 = .28 // .7605 // (.04902 + .1872)$

$X_2 = 0.1097$ per unit

Similarly, $X_1 = .28 // .7605 // (.04902 + .1745) = 0.1068$

9.3 Three-phase fault at bus 1.

Using the positive-sequence Thevenin equivalent from Problem 9.2:

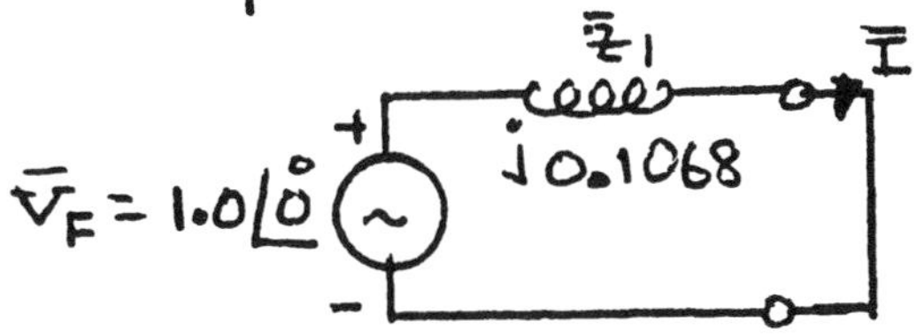

$$I_{baseH} = \frac{S_{base3\phi}}{\sqrt{3}\,V_{baseH}} = \frac{1000}{\sqrt{3}(765)} = 0.7547 \text{ kA}$$

$$\bar{I}_1 = \frac{\bar{V}_F}{\bar{Z}_1} = \frac{1.0\angle 0^\circ}{j0.1068} = -j9.363 \text{ per unit}$$

$$\bar{I}_0 = \bar{I}_2 = 0$$

$$\begin{bmatrix} \bar{I}_A'' \\ \bar{I}_B'' \\ \bar{I}_C'' \end{bmatrix} = \begin{bmatrix} 1 & 1 & 1 \\ 1 & a^2 & a \\ 1 & a & a^2 \end{bmatrix} \begin{bmatrix} 0 \\ -j9.363 \\ 0 \end{bmatrix} = \begin{bmatrix} 9.363\angle -90^\circ \\ 9.363\angle 150^\circ \\ 9.363\angle 30^\circ \end{bmatrix} \text{ per unit}$$

$$\begin{bmatrix} \bar{I}_A'' \\ \bar{I}_B'' \\ \bar{I}_C'' \end{bmatrix} = \begin{bmatrix} 9.363\angle -90^\circ \\ 9.363\angle 150^\circ \\ 9.363\angle 30^\circ \end{bmatrix} \times 0.7547 = \begin{bmatrix} 7.067\angle -90^\circ \\ 7.067\angle 150^\circ \\ 7.067\angle 30^\circ \end{bmatrix} \text{ kA}$$

9.4 Calculation of per unit reactances

Synchronous generators:

G1 $X_1 = X_d'' = (0.2)\left(\frac{1000}{500}\right) = 0.4$ $X_0 = (0.10)\left(\frac{1000}{500}\right)$

$X_2 = X_d'' = 0.4$ $= 0.20$

G2 $X_1 = X_d'' = 0.18\left(\frac{1000}{750}\right) = 0.24$ $X_0 = 0.09\left(\frac{1000}{750}\right)$

$X_2 = X_d'' = 0.24$ $= 0.12$

G3 $X_1 = 0.17$ $X_2 = 0.20$ $X_0 = 0.09$

$X_{base3} = \frac{(20)^2}{1000} = 0.4\,\Omega$ $3X_n = \frac{3\,(0.028)}{0.4} = 0.21$ per unit

Transformers:

$X_{T1} = 0.12\left(\frac{1000}{500}\right) = 0.24$

$X_{T2} = 0.10\left(\frac{1000}{750}\right) = 0.1333$ $X_{T3} = 0.10$

Each Line:

$X_{baseH} = \frac{(500)^2}{1000} = 250\,\Omega$

$X_1 = X_2 = \frac{50}{250} = 0.20$ per unit

$X_0 = \frac{150}{250} = 0.60$ per unit

9.4
CONTD.

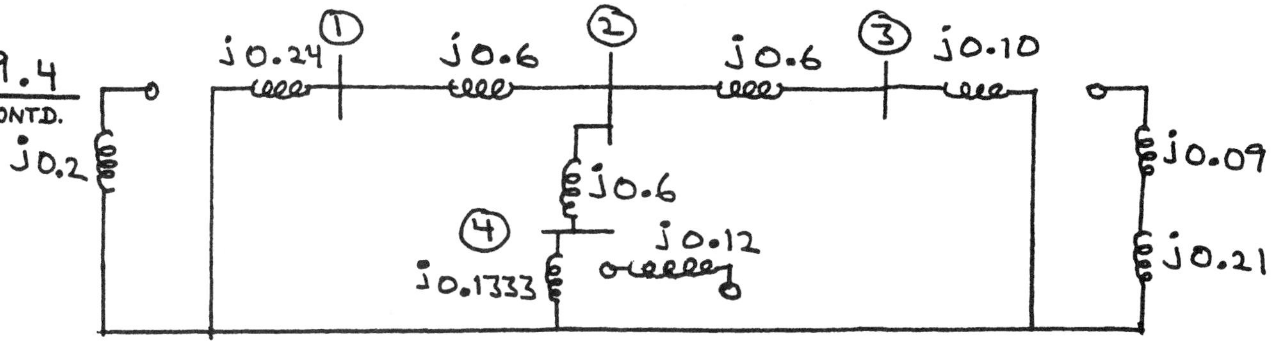

Per unit zero sequence Network

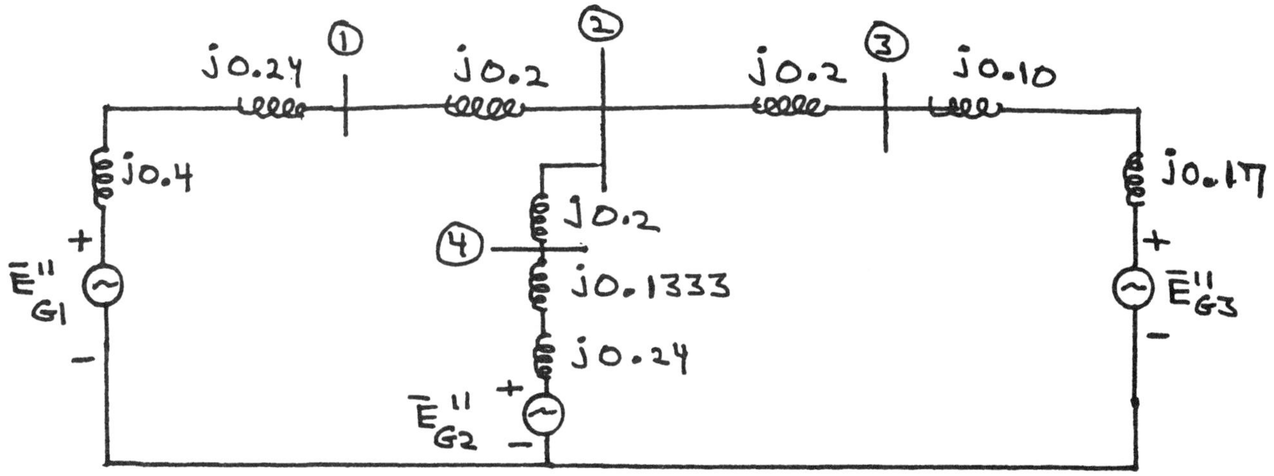

Per unit positive sequence Network

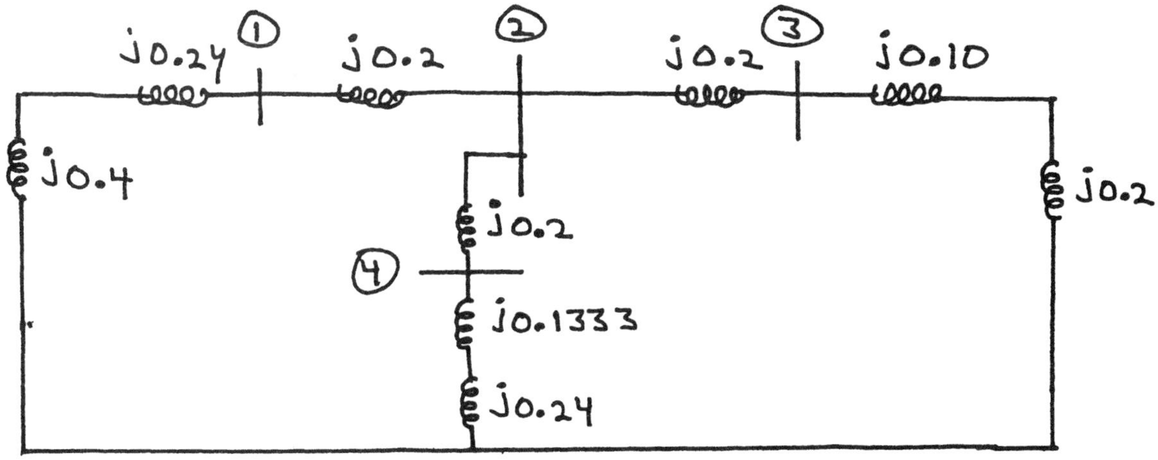

Per unit negative sequence network

9.5 $n = 1$ (Bus 1 = Fault Bus)

Thevenin equivalents as viewed from Bus 1:

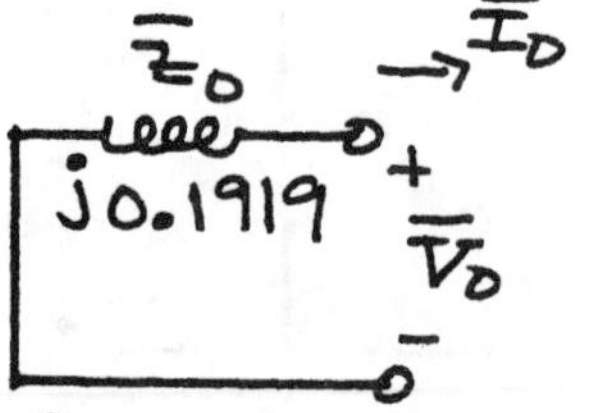

Per unit Zero Sequence

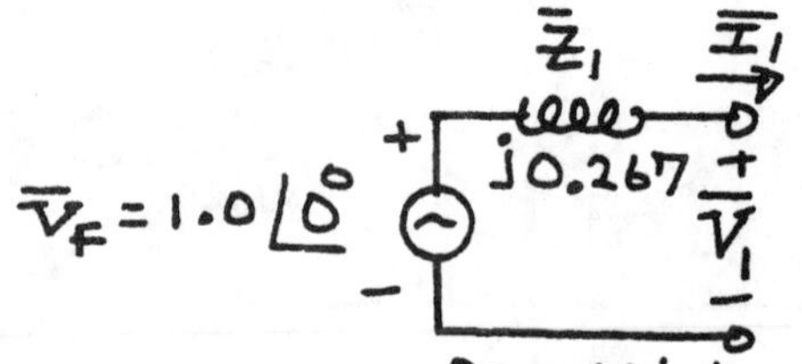

Per Unit Positive Sequence

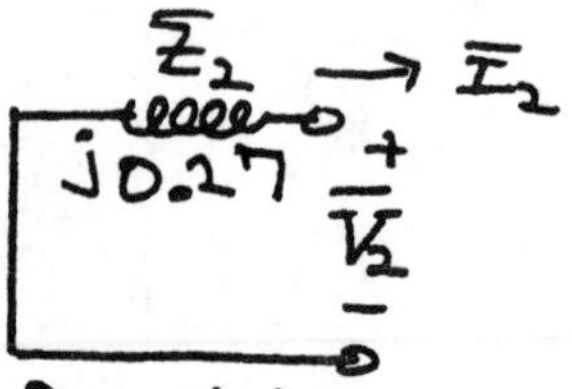

Per Unit Negative Sequence

Zero sequence Thevenin equivalent:

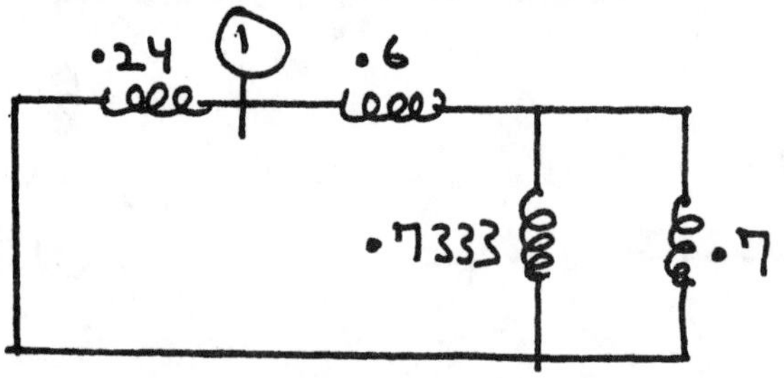

$$X_0 = 0.24 \,//\, [.6 + (.7333 \,//\, .7)]$$

$$X_0 = .24 \,//\, .9581 = 0.1919 \text{ per unit}$$

Positive Sequence Thevenin equivalent:

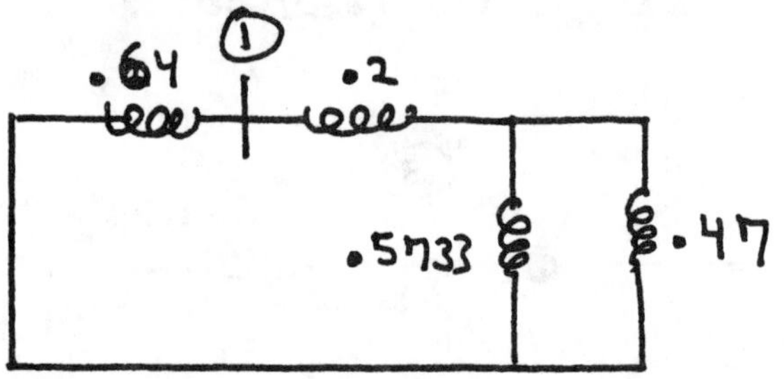

$$X_1 = .64 \,//\, [.2 + (.5733 \,//\, .47)]$$

$$X_1 = .64 \,//\, .4583$$

$$X_1 = 0.2670 \text{ per unit}$$

Negative Sequence Thevenin equivalent:

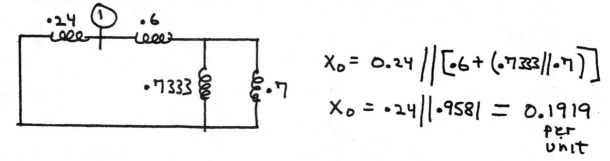

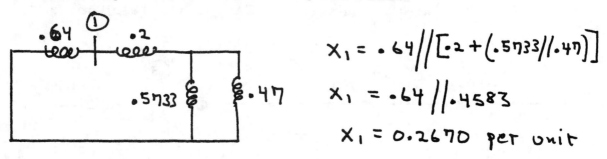

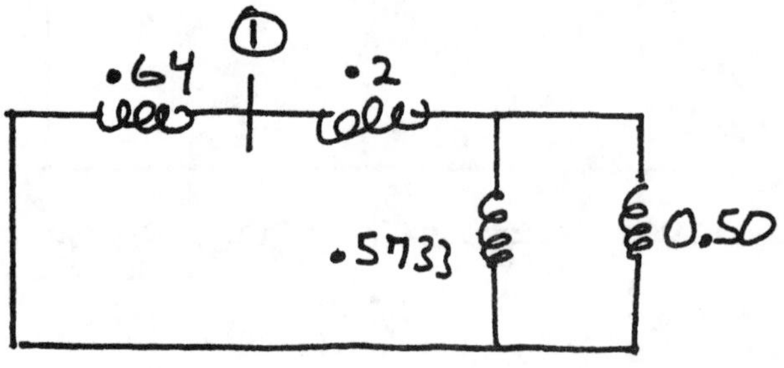

$$X_2 = .64 \,//\, [.2 + (.5733 \,//\, .50)]$$

$$X_2 = .64 \,//\, .4671 = 0.270 \text{ per unit}$$

9.6 Three-phase fault at bus 1.

Using the positive-sequence Thevenin equivalent from Problem 9.5:

$\bar{V}_F = 1.0\angle 0^\circ$

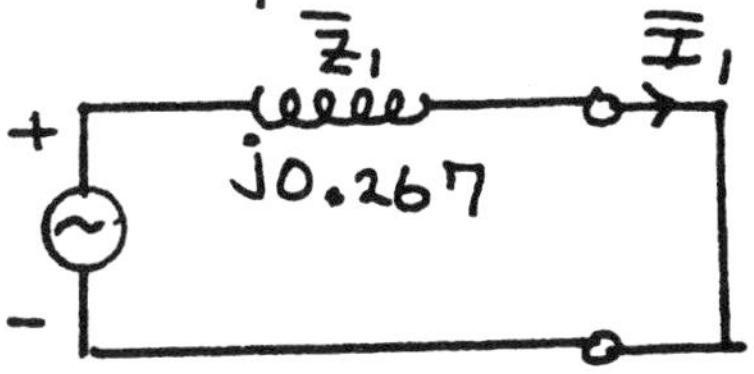

$$I_{\text{base}H} = \frac{1000}{500\sqrt{3}} = 1.155 \text{ kA}$$

$$\bar{I}_1 = \frac{\bar{V}_F}{\bar{Z}_1} = \frac{1.0\angle 0^\circ}{j0.267} = 3.745\angle -90^\circ \text{ per unit}$$

$$\bar{I}_0 = \bar{I}_2 = 0$$

$$\begin{bmatrix} \bar{I}_A'' \\ \bar{I}_B'' \\ \bar{I}_C'' \end{bmatrix} = \begin{bmatrix} 1 & 1 & 1 \\ 1 & a^2 & a \\ 1 & a & a^2 \end{bmatrix} \begin{bmatrix} 0 \\ 3.745\angle -90^\circ \\ 0 \end{bmatrix} = \begin{bmatrix} 3.745\angle -90^\circ \\ 3.745\angle 150^\circ \\ 3.745\angle 30^\circ \end{bmatrix} \text{ per unit}$$

$$\begin{bmatrix} \bar{I}_A'' \\ \bar{I}_B'' \\ \bar{I}_C'' \end{bmatrix} = \begin{bmatrix} 3.745\angle -90^\circ \\ 3.745\angle 150^\circ \\ 3.745\angle 30^\circ \end{bmatrix} \times 1.155 = \begin{bmatrix} 4.325\angle -90^\circ \\ 4.325\angle 150^\circ \\ 4.325\angle 30^\circ \end{bmatrix} \text{ kA}$$

9.7 Calculation of per unit reactances

Synchronous generators:

G1 $X_1 = X_d'' = 0.2\left(\frac{12}{10}\right)^2\left(\frac{100}{50}\right)$

$X_1 = 0.576$ per unit

$X_2 = X_1 = .576$ per unit

$X_0 = (0.1)\left(\frac{12}{10}\right)^2\left(\frac{100}{50}\right)$

$X_0 = 0.288$ per unit

G2 $X_1 = X_d'' = 0.2$

$X_2 = 0.23$

$X_0 = 0.1$

Transformers

$X_{T1} = 0.1\left(\frac{100}{50}\right) = 0.2$ per unit

$X_{T2} = 0.1$ per unit

Each Line:

$Z_{base\,H} = \frac{(138)^2}{100} = 190.44\ \Omega$

$X_1 = X_2 = \frac{40}{190.44} = 0.210$ per unit

$X_0 = \frac{100}{190.44} = 0.5251$ per unit

9.7 CONTD.

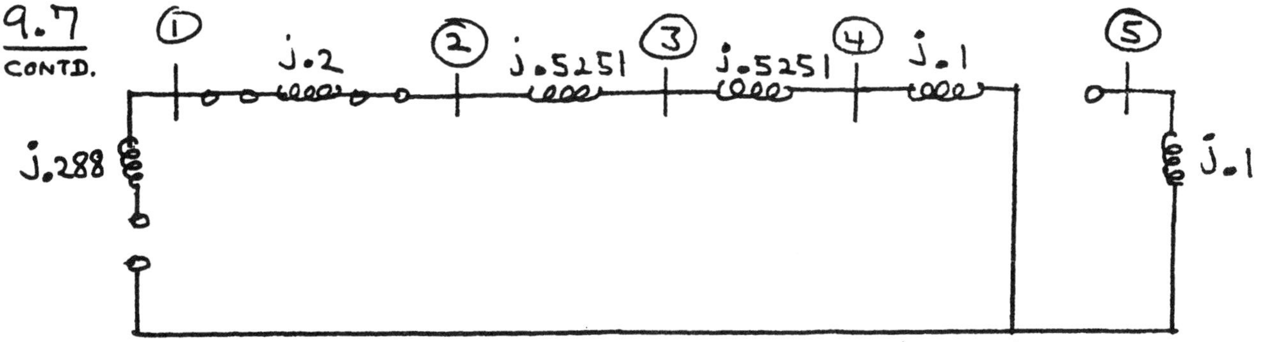

Per unit zero sequence network

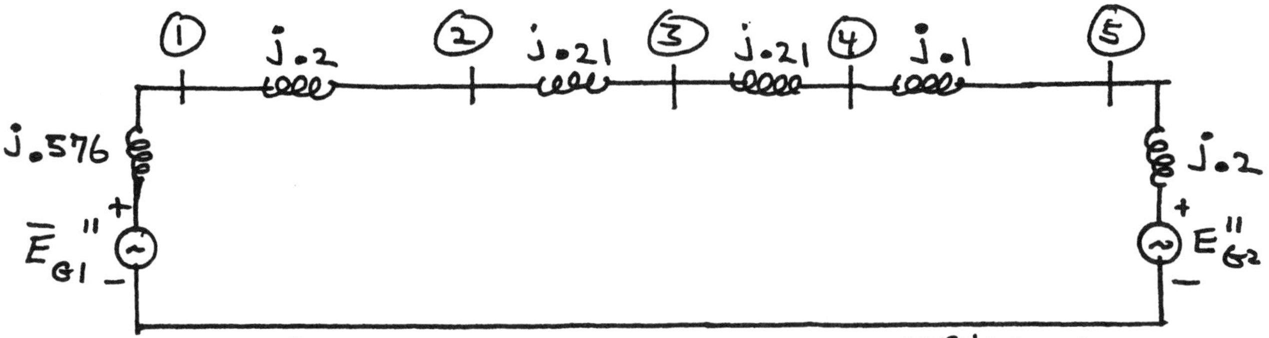

Per unit positive sequence network

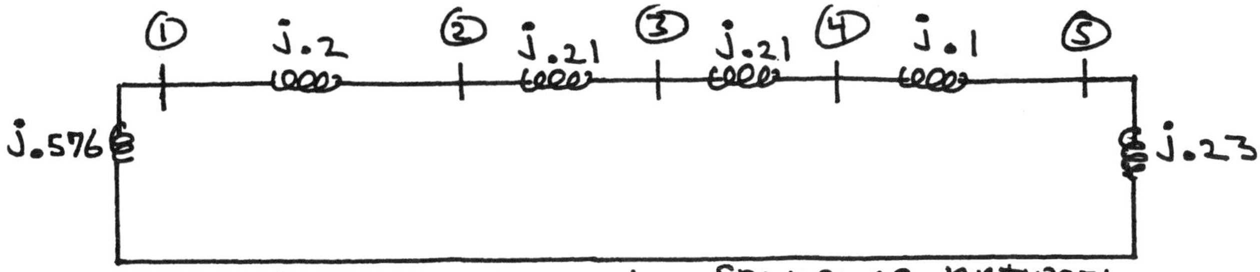

Per unit negative sequence network

9.8 $n = 1$ (Bus 1 = Fault Bus)

Thevenin equivalents as viewed from Bus 1:

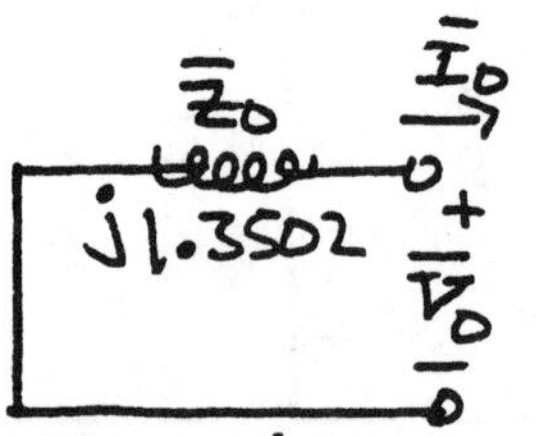

Per Unit Zero Sequence

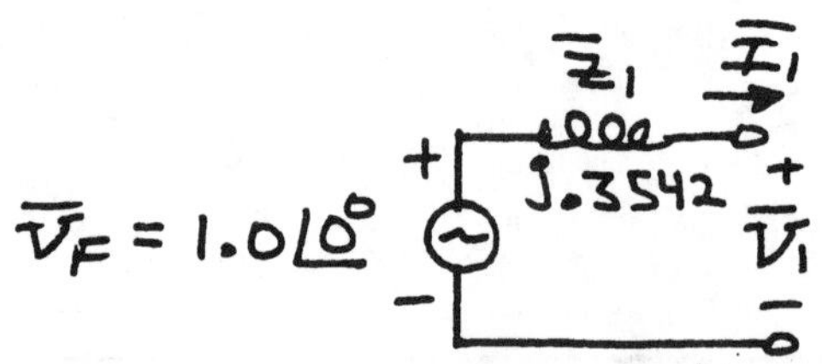

Per Unit Positive sequence

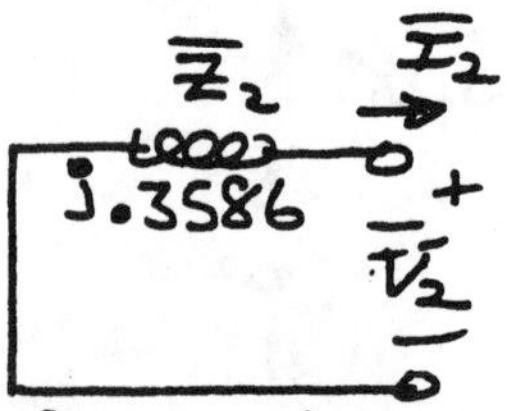

Per unit Negative sequence

<u>Zero Sequence Thevenin equivalent:</u>

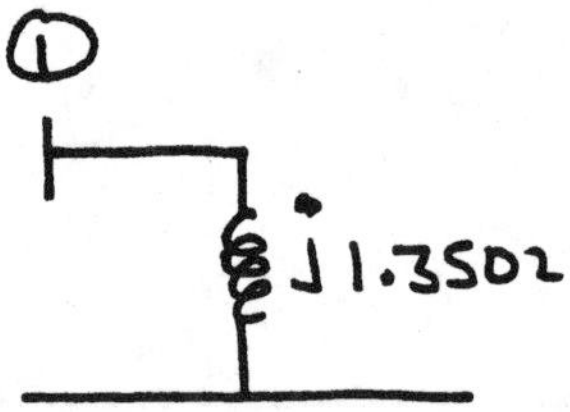

$\bar{Z}_0 = j1.3502$ per unit

<u>Positive Sequence Thevenin equivalent:</u>

$\bar{Z}_1 = j.576 // j.92 = j0.3542$ per unit

<u>Negative sequence Thevenin equivalent:</u>

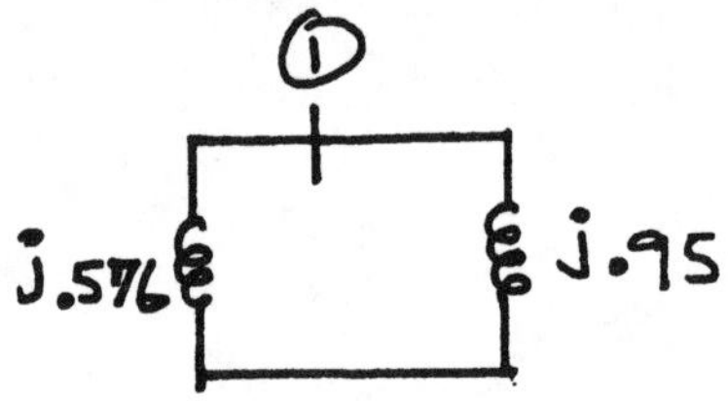

$\bar{Z}_2 = j.576 // j.95 = j0.3586$ per unit

9.9 Three-phase fault at bus 1.

Using the positive-sequence Thevenin equivalent from Problem 9.8:

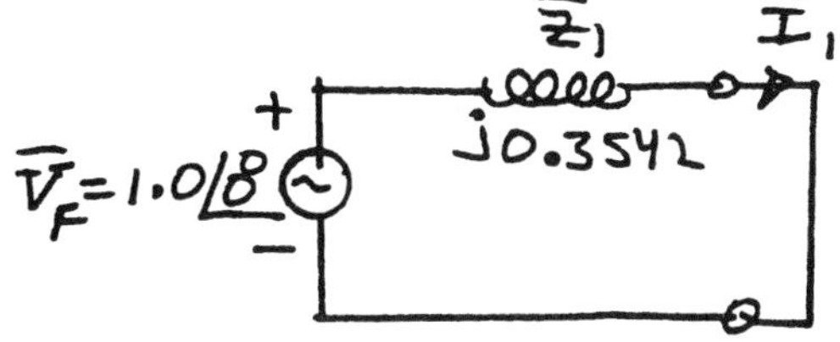

$$I_{base1} = \frac{100}{10\sqrt{3}} = 5.774 \text{ kA}$$

$$\bar{I}_1 = \frac{\bar{V}_F}{\bar{Z}_1} = \frac{1.0\angle 0°}{j.3542} = 2.823\angle -90° \text{ per unit}$$

$$\bar{I}_0 = \bar{I}_2 = 0$$

$$\begin{bmatrix} I_A'' \\ I_B'' \\ I_C'' \end{bmatrix} = \begin{bmatrix} 1 & 1 & 1 \\ 1 & a^2 & a \\ 1 & a & a^2 \end{bmatrix} \begin{bmatrix} 0 \\ 2.823\angle -90° \\ 0 \end{bmatrix} = \begin{bmatrix} 2.823\angle -90° \\ 2.823\angle 150° \\ 2.823\angle 30° \end{bmatrix} \text{ per unit}$$

$$\begin{bmatrix} I_A'' \\ I_B'' \\ I_C'' \end{bmatrix} = \begin{bmatrix} 2.823\angle -90° \\ 2.823\angle 150° \\ 2.823\angle 30° \end{bmatrix} \times 5.774 = \begin{bmatrix} 16.30\angle -90° \\ 16.30\angle 150° \\ 16.30\angle 30° \end{bmatrix} \text{ kA}$$

9.10

(a) THE POSITIVE SEQUENCE NETWORK AND STEPS IN ITS REDUCTION TO ITS THÉVENIN EQUIVALENT ARE SHOWN BELOW:

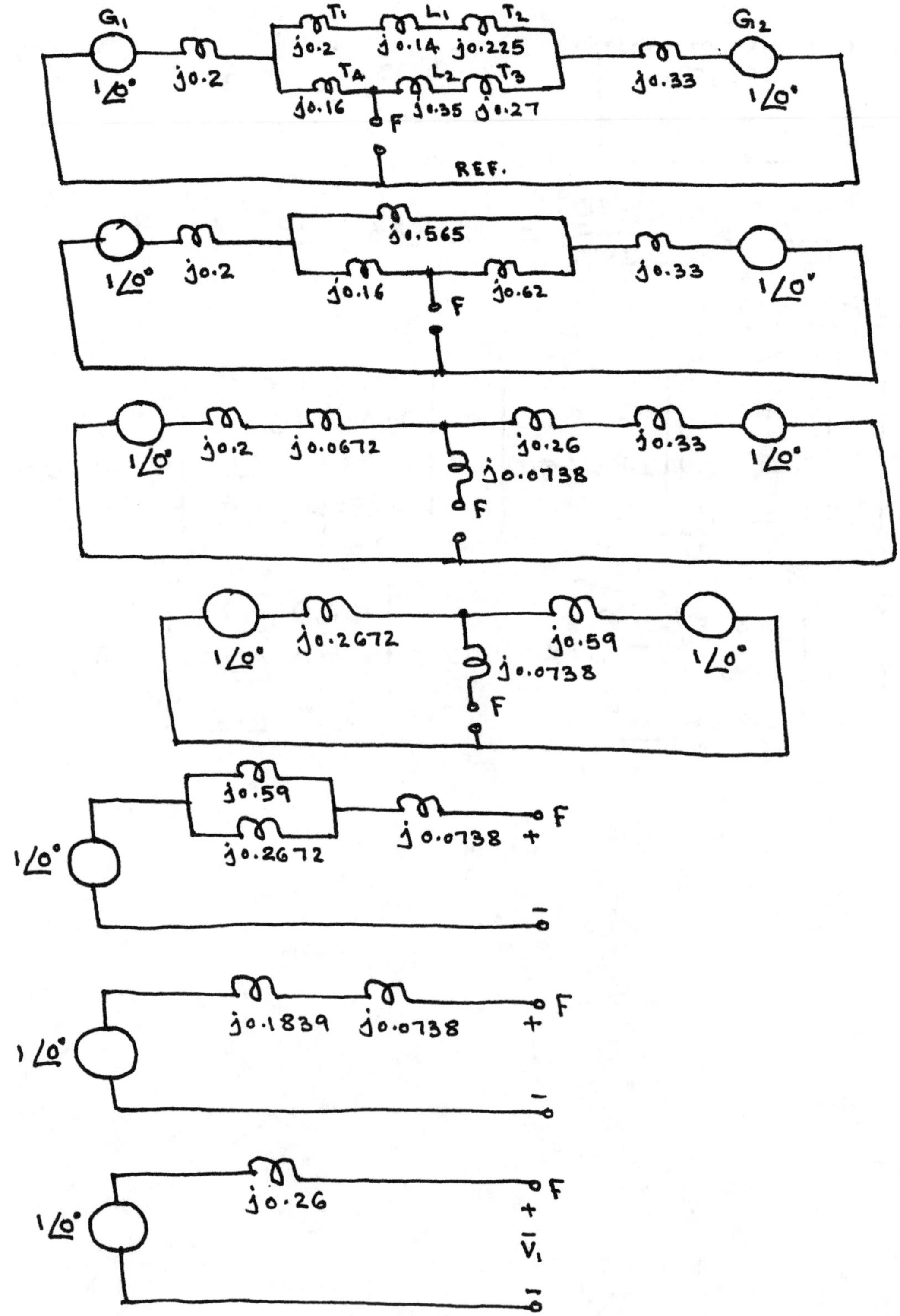

9.10 CONTD.

THE NEGATIVE SEQUENCE NETWORK AND ITS REDUCTION IS SHOWN BELOW:

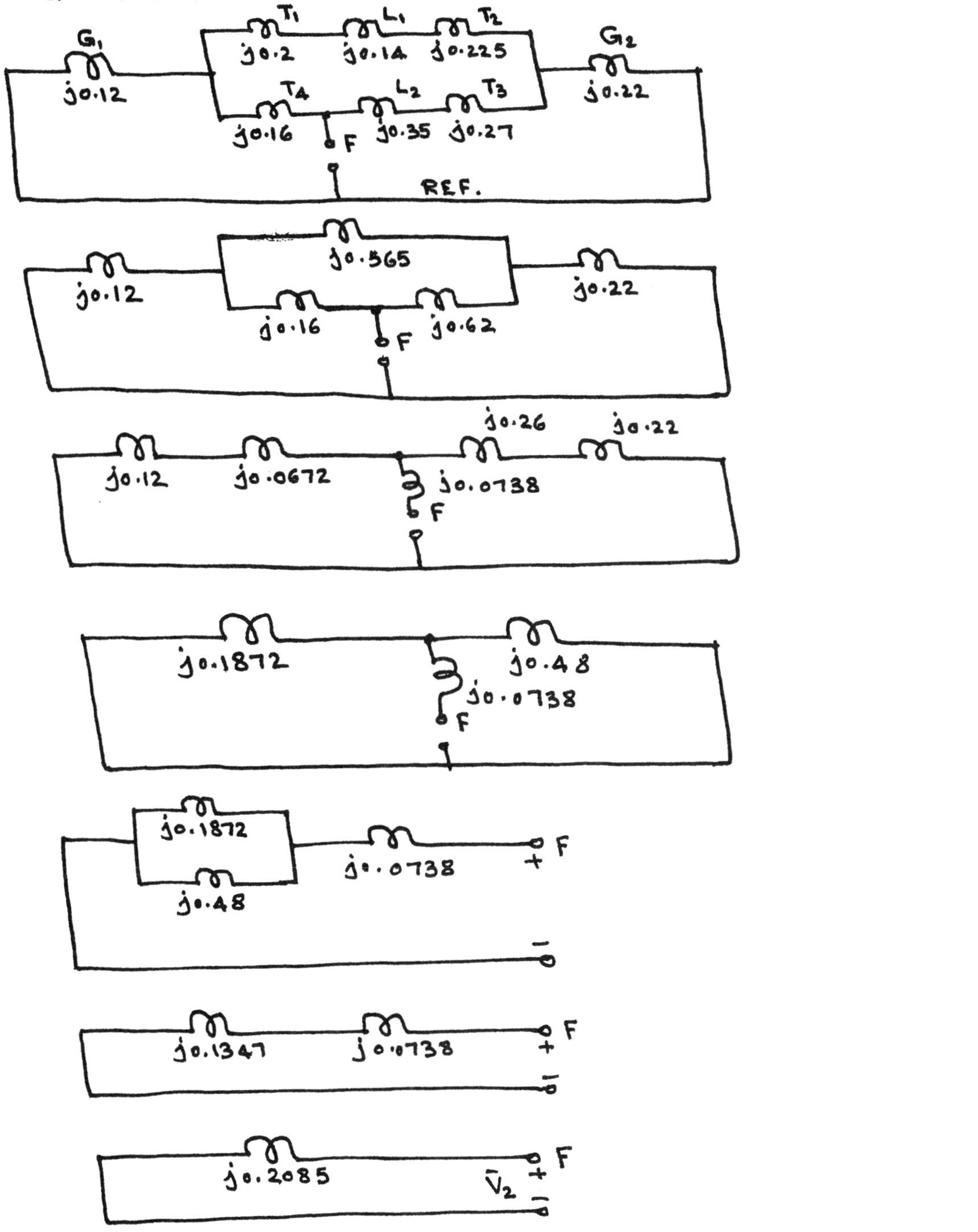

9.10 CONTD.

THE ZERO-SEQUENCE NETWORK AND ITS REDUCTION ARE SHOWN BELOW:

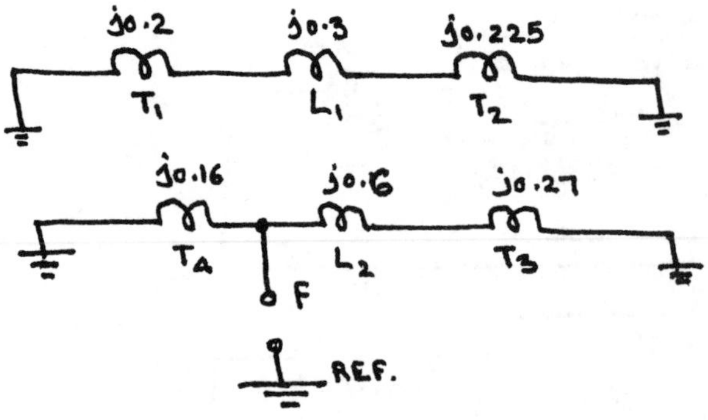

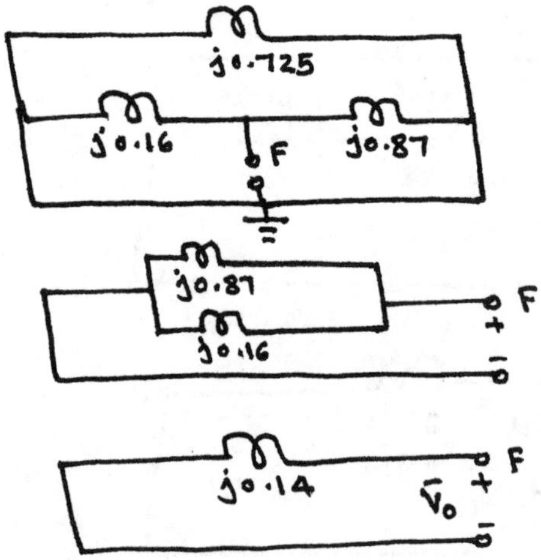

(b)

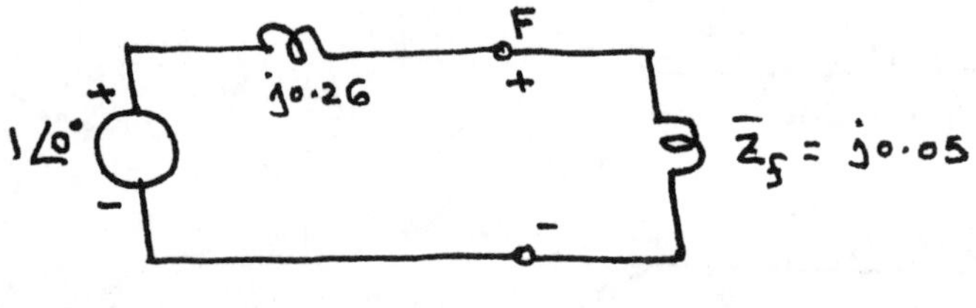

FOR A BALANCED 3-PHASE FAULT, ONLY POSITIVE SEQUENCE NETWORK COMES INTO PICTURE.

$$\bar{I}_{sc} = \bar{I}_a = \bar{I}_{a1} = \frac{1\angle 0^\circ}{j(0.26+0.05)} = 3.23\angle -90^\circ$$

$$I_{sc} = 3.23 \text{ PU}$$

9.11

THE ZERO-, POSITIVE-, AND NEGATIVE SEQUENCE NETWORKS ARE SHOWN BELOW:

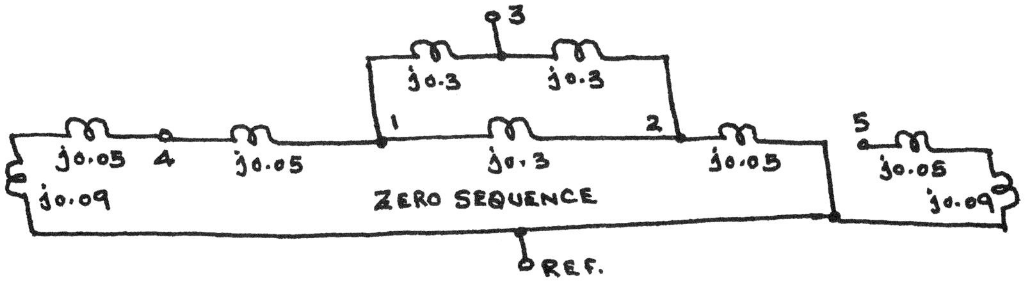

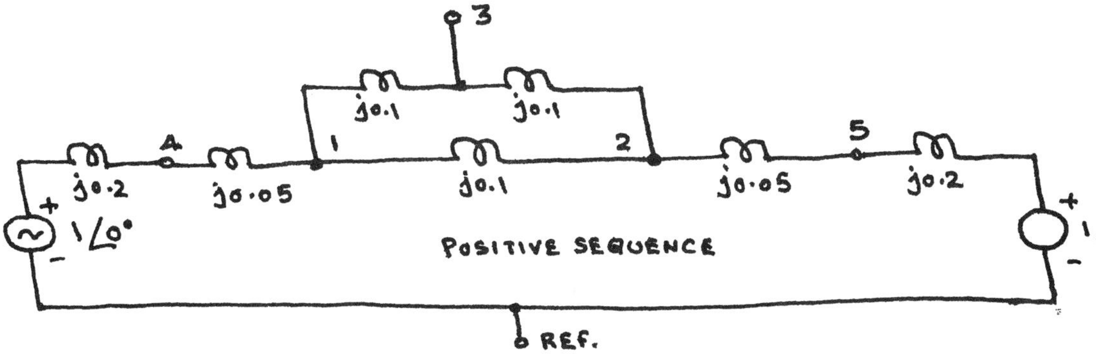

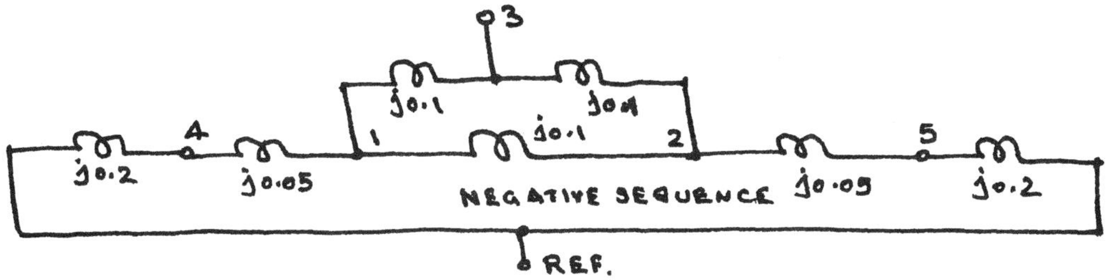

USING DELTA-WYE TRANSFORMATION AND SERIES-PARALLEL COMBINATIONS, THÉVENIN EQUIVALENTS LOOKING INTO BUS 3 ARE SHOWN BELOW:

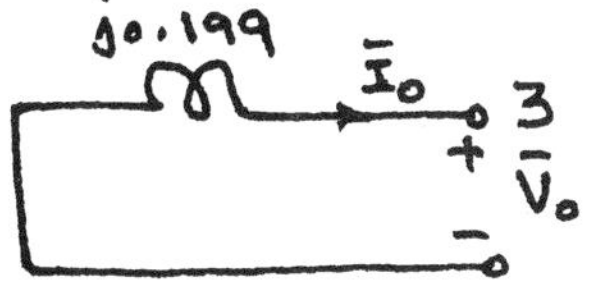

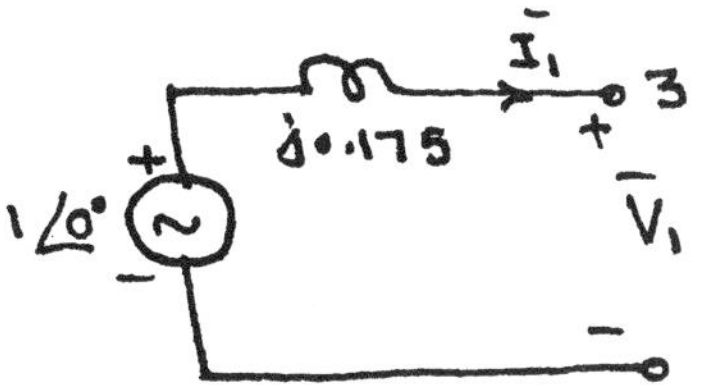

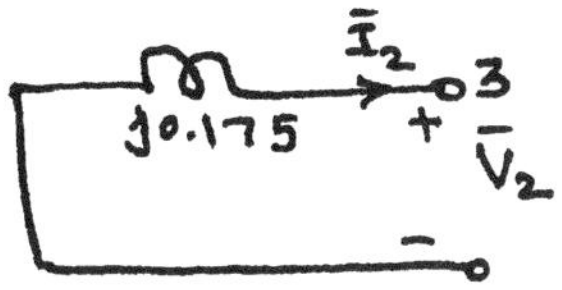

9.11 CONTD.

FOR A BOLTED 3-PHASE FAULT AT BUS 3,

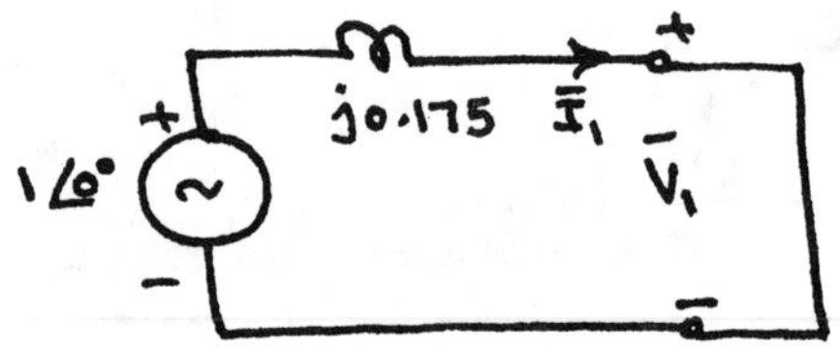

$\bar{V}_1 = 0$; ALSO $\bar{V}_2 = \bar{V}_0 = 0$

$\bar{I}_0 = 0$; $\bar{I}_2 = 0$

$$\bar{I}_1 = \frac{1\angle 0°}{j0.175} = -j5.71$$

THE FAULT CURRENT IS 5.71 PU.

$$\begin{bmatrix}\bar{I}_a\\ \bar{I}_b\\ \bar{I}_c\end{bmatrix} = \begin{bmatrix}1 & 1 & 1\\ 1 & a^2 & a\\ 1 & a & a^2\end{bmatrix}\begin{bmatrix}0\\ -j5.71\\ 0\end{bmatrix} = \begin{bmatrix}5.71\angle -90°\\ 5.71\angle 150°\\ 5.71\angle 30°\end{bmatrix}$$

9.12

FOR A BALANCED 3-PHASE FAULT AT BUS 3, WE NEED THE POSITIVE SEQUENCE IMPEDANCE NETWORK REDUCED TO ITS THÉVENIN'S EQUIVALENT VIEWED FROM BUS 3. THE DEVELOPMENT IS SHOWN BELOW:

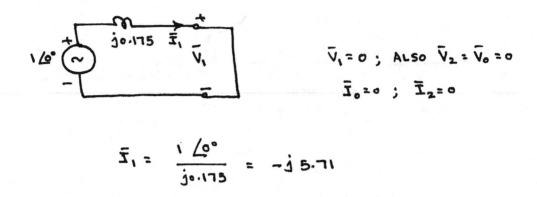

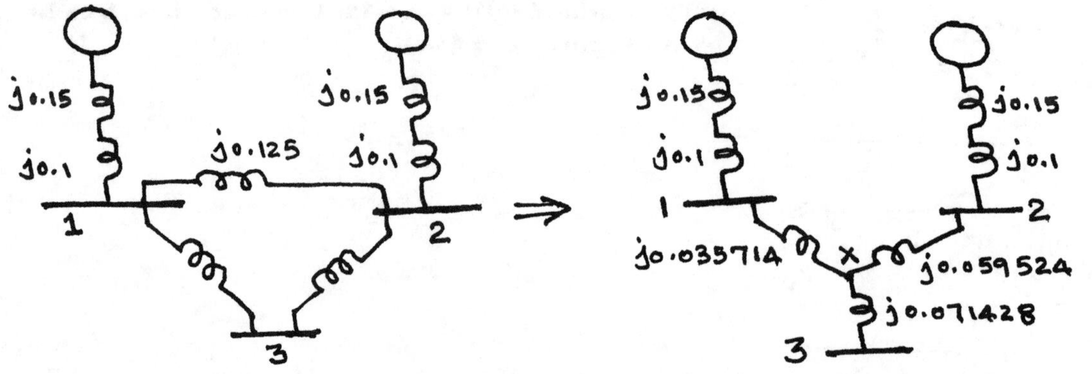

CONVERT THE Δ FORMED BY BUSES 1, 2, AND 3 TO AN EQUIVALENT Y

9.12 CONTD.

$$\bar{Z}_{1x} = \frac{(j0.125)(j0.15)}{j0.525} = j0.0357143$$

$$\bar{Z}_{2x} = \frac{(j0.125)(j0.25)}{j0.525} = j0.0595238$$

$$\bar{Z}_{3x} = \frac{(j0.15)(j0.25)}{j0.525} = j0.0714286$$

USING SERIES - PARALLEL COMBINATIONS, THE POSITIVE SEQUENCE THÉVENIN IMPEDANCE IS GIVEN BY, VIEWED FROM BUS 3:

$$\frac{(j0.2857143)(j0.3095238)}{j0.5952381} + j0.0714286$$

$$= j0.1485714 + j0.0714286 = j0.22$$

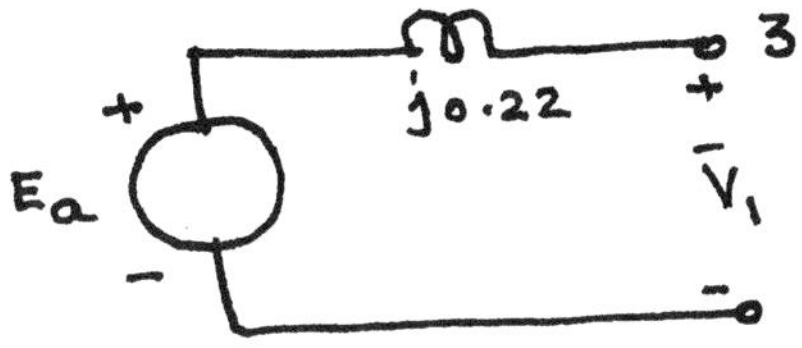

WITH THE NO-LOAD GENERATED EMF TO BE $1\angle 0°$ PU, THE FAULT CURRENT IS GIVEN BY (WITH $\bar{Z}_F = j0.1$)

$$\bar{I}_a = \bar{I}_{a1} = \frac{1.0\angle 0°}{j0.22 + j0.1}$$

$$= -j\,3.125 \text{ PU} = 820.1\angle -90° \text{ A}$$

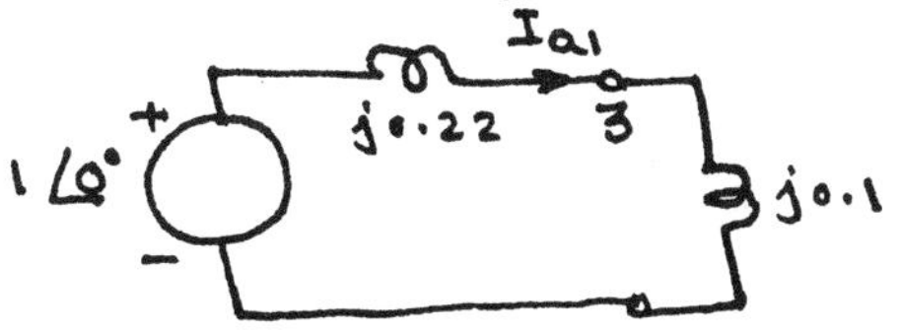

THE FAULT CURRENT IS 820.1 A.

9.13 Bolted single-line-to-ground fault at bus 1.

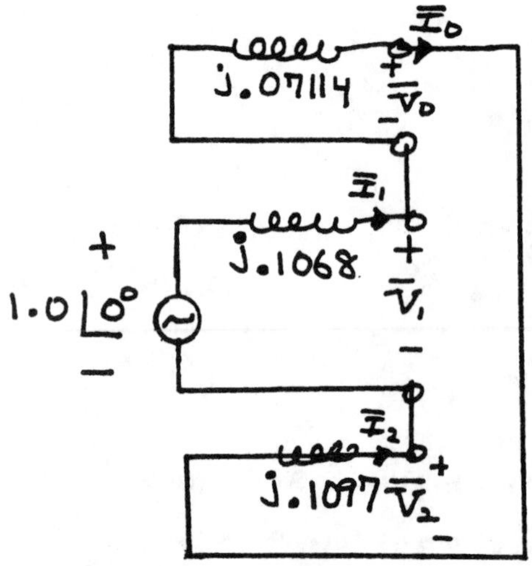

$$\bar{I}_0 = \bar{I}_1 = \bar{I}_2 = \frac{\bar{V}_F}{\bar{Z}_0 + \bar{Z}_1 + \bar{Z}_2}$$

$$= \frac{1.0\angle 0^\circ}{j(0.07114 + 0.1068 + 0.1097)}$$

$$= \frac{1.0\angle 0^\circ}{j0.2876} = -j\,3.4766 \text{ per unit}$$

$$\begin{bmatrix} \bar{I}_A'' \\ \bar{I}_B'' \\ \bar{I}_C'' \end{bmatrix} = \begin{bmatrix} 1 & 1 & 1 \\ 1 & a^2 & a \\ 1 & a & a^2 \end{bmatrix} \begin{bmatrix} -j3.4766 \\ -j3.4766 \\ -j3.4766 \end{bmatrix} = \begin{bmatrix} -j10.43 \\ 0 \\ 0 \end{bmatrix} \text{ per unit} = \begin{bmatrix} -j7.871 \\ 0 \\ 0 \end{bmatrix} \text{kA}$$

Using Eq(9.1):

$$\begin{bmatrix} \bar{V}_0 \\ \bar{V}_1 \\ \bar{V}_2 \end{bmatrix} = \begin{bmatrix} 0 \\ 1.0\angle 0^\circ \\ 0 \end{bmatrix} - \begin{bmatrix} j0.07114 & 0 & 0 \\ 0 & j0.1068 & 0 \\ 0 & 0 & j0.1097 \end{bmatrix} \begin{bmatrix} -j3.4766 \\ -j3.4766 \\ -j3.4766 \end{bmatrix}$$

$$\begin{bmatrix} \bar{V}_0 \\ \bar{V}_1 \\ V_2 \end{bmatrix} = \begin{bmatrix} -0.2473 \\ 0.6287 \\ -0.3814 \end{bmatrix} \text{ per unit}$$

$$\begin{bmatrix} \bar{V}_{Ag} \\ \bar{V}_{Bg} \\ \bar{V}_{Cg} \end{bmatrix} = \begin{bmatrix} 1 & 1 & 1 \\ 1 & a^2 & a \\ 1 & a & a^2 \end{bmatrix} \begin{bmatrix} -0.2473 \\ 0.6287 \\ -0.3814 \end{bmatrix} = \begin{bmatrix} 0 \\ 0.9502\angle 247.0^\circ \\ 0.9502\angle 113.0^\circ \end{bmatrix} \text{ per unit}$$

9.14 Single-Line-to-Ground Arcing Fault at Bus 1.

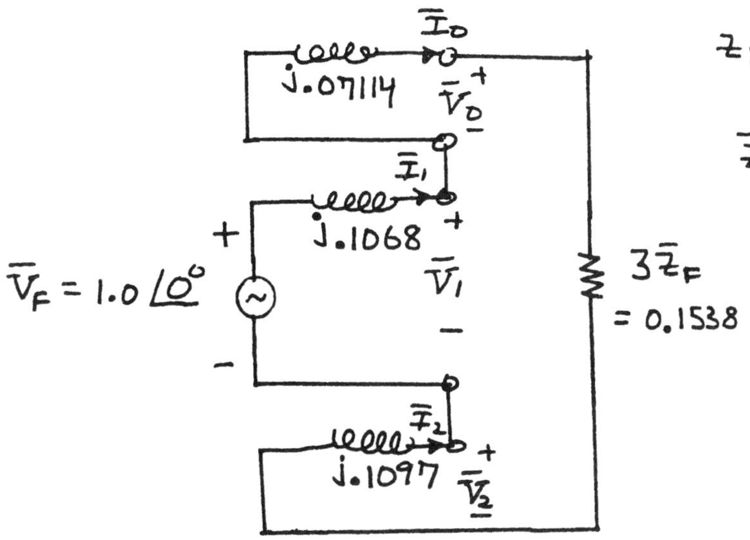

$$Z_{baseH} = \frac{(765)^2}{1000} = 585.2\ \Omega$$

$$\bar{Z}_F = \frac{30\angle 0^\circ}{585.2} = 0.05126\angle 0^\circ \text{ per unit}$$

$$\bar{I}_0 = \bar{I}_1 = \bar{I}_2 = \frac{\bar{V}_F}{\bar{Z}_0 + \bar{Z}_1 + \bar{Z}_2 + 3\bar{Z}_F}$$

$$= \frac{1.0\angle 0^\circ}{0.1538 + j\,0.2876}$$

$$= \frac{1.0\angle 0^\circ}{0.3262\angle 61.86^\circ} = 3.0659\angle -61.86^\circ \text{ per unit}$$

$$\begin{bmatrix} \bar{I}_A'' \\ \bar{I}_B'' \\ \bar{I}_C'' \end{bmatrix} = \begin{bmatrix} 1 & 1 & 1 \\ 1 & a^2 & a \\ 1 & a & a^2 \end{bmatrix} \begin{bmatrix} 3.0659\angle -61.86^\circ \\ 3.0659\angle -61.86^\circ \\ 3.0659\angle -61.86^\circ \end{bmatrix} = \begin{bmatrix} 9.198\angle -61.86^\circ \\ 0 \\ 0 \end{bmatrix} \text{per unit} = \begin{bmatrix} 6.942\angle -61.86^\circ \\ 0 \\ 0 \end{bmatrix} \text{kA}$$

$$\begin{bmatrix} \bar{V}_0 \\ \bar{V}_1 \\ \bar{V}_2 \end{bmatrix} = \begin{bmatrix} 0 \\ 1.0\angle 0^\circ \\ 0 \end{bmatrix} - \begin{bmatrix} j0.07114 & 0 & 0 \\ 0 & j0.1068 & 0 \\ 0 & 0 & j0.1097 \end{bmatrix} \begin{bmatrix} 3.0659\angle -61.86^\circ \\ 3.0659\angle -61.86^\circ \\ 3.0659\angle -61.86^\circ \end{bmatrix}$$

$$\begin{bmatrix} \bar{V}_0 \\ \bar{V}_1 \\ \bar{V}_2 \end{bmatrix} = \begin{bmatrix} 0.2181\angle 208.14^\circ \\ 0.7279\angle -12.25^\circ \\ 0.3363\angle 208.14^\circ \end{bmatrix} \text{ per unit}$$

$$\begin{bmatrix} \bar{V}_{Ag} \\ \bar{V}_{BG} \\ \bar{V}_{CG} \end{bmatrix} = \begin{bmatrix} 1 & 1 & 1 \\ 1 & a^2 & a \\ 1 & a & a^2 \end{bmatrix} \begin{bmatrix} 0.2181\angle 208.14^\circ \\ 0.7279\angle -12.25^\circ \\ 0.3363\angle 208.14^\circ \end{bmatrix} = \begin{bmatrix} 0.4717\angle -61.85^\circ \\ 0.9099\angle 244.2^\circ \\ 1.0105\angle 113.52^\circ \end{bmatrix} \text{ per unit}$$

9.15 Bolted Line-to-Line Fault at Bus 1.

$\bar{V}_F = 1.0\angle 0°$

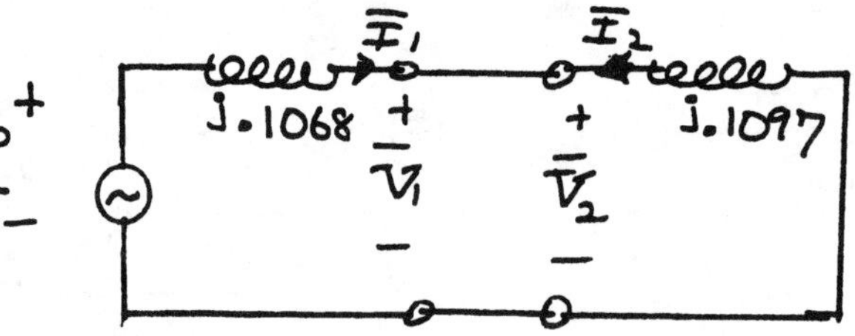

$\bar{I}_0 = 0$

$$\bar{I}_1 = -\bar{I}_2 = \frac{\bar{V}_F}{\bar{Z}_1 + \bar{Z}_2} = \frac{1.0\angle 0°}{j.2165} = -j4.619 \text{ per unit}$$

$$\begin{bmatrix} I_A'' \\ I_B'' \\ I_C'' \end{bmatrix} = \begin{bmatrix} 1 & 1 & 1 \\ 1 & a^2 & a \\ 1 & a & a^2 \end{bmatrix} \begin{bmatrix} 0 \\ -j4.619 \\ +j4.619 \end{bmatrix} = \begin{bmatrix} 0 \\ 8.000\angle 180° \\ 8.000\angle 0° \end{bmatrix} \text{per unit} = \begin{bmatrix} 0 \\ 6.038\angle 180° \\ 6.038\angle 0° \end{bmatrix} \text{kA}$$

$$\begin{bmatrix} \bar{V}_0 \\ \bar{V}_1 \\ \bar{V}_2 \end{bmatrix} = \begin{bmatrix} 0 \\ 1\angle 0° \\ 0 \end{bmatrix} - \begin{bmatrix} j.07114 & 0 & 0 \\ 0 & j0.1068 & 0 \\ 0 & 0 & j0.1097 \end{bmatrix} \begin{bmatrix} 0 \\ -j4.619 \\ -j4.619 \end{bmatrix} = \begin{bmatrix} 0 \\ 0.5067 \\ 0.5067 \end{bmatrix} \text{per unit}$$

$$\begin{bmatrix} \bar{V}_{Ag} \\ \bar{V}_{Bg} \\ \bar{V}_{Cg} \end{bmatrix} = \begin{bmatrix} 1 & 1 & 1 \\ 1 & a^2 & a \\ 1 & a & a^2 \end{bmatrix} \begin{bmatrix} 0 \\ 0.5067 \\ 0.5067 \end{bmatrix} = \begin{bmatrix} 1.013\angle 0° \\ 0.5067\angle 180° \\ 0.5067\angle 180° \end{bmatrix} \text{per unit}$$

9.16 Bolted double-line-to-ground fault at bus 1.

$\bar{V}_F = 1.0\angle 0°$

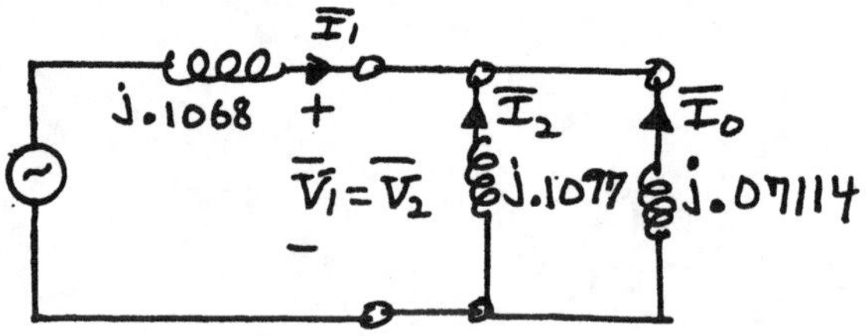

$$\bar{I}_1 = \frac{\bar{V}_F}{\bar{Z}_1 + \bar{Z}_2 // \bar{Z}_0} = \frac{1.0\angle 0°}{j(.1068 + .1097//.0711)} = \frac{1.0\angle 0°}{j0.14995} = 6.669\angle -90° \text{ per unit}$$

$$\bar{I}_2 = -\bar{I}_1\left(\frac{\bar{Z}_0}{\bar{Z}_0 + \bar{Z}_2}\right) = j6.669\left(\frac{.07114}{.18084}\right)$$

$$\bar{I}_2 = j2.623 \text{ per unit}$$

$$\bar{I}_0 = -\bar{I}_1\left(\frac{\bar{Z}_2}{\bar{Z}_0 + \bar{Z}_2}\right) = j6.669\left(\frac{.1097}{.18084}\right) = j4.046 \text{ per unit}$$

9.16 CONTD.

$$\begin{bmatrix} \bar{I}_A'' \\ \bar{I}_B'' \\ \bar{I}_C'' \end{bmatrix} = \begin{bmatrix} 1 & 1 & 1 \\ 1 & a^2 & a \\ 1 & a & a^2 \end{bmatrix} \begin{bmatrix} j4.046 \\ -j6.669 \\ j2.623 \end{bmatrix} = \begin{bmatrix} 0 \\ 10.08\angle 143.0^\circ \\ 10.08\angle 37.02^\circ \end{bmatrix} \text{per unit} = \begin{bmatrix} 0 \\ 7.607\angle 143^\circ \\ 7.607\angle 37^\circ \end{bmatrix} \text{kA}$$

$$\begin{bmatrix} \bar{V}_0 \\ \bar{V}_1 \\ \bar{V}_2 \end{bmatrix} = \begin{bmatrix} 0 \\ 1\angle 0^\circ \\ 0 \end{bmatrix} - \begin{bmatrix} j0.07114 & 0 & 0 \\ 0 & j0.1068 & 0 \\ 0 & 0 & j0.1097 \end{bmatrix} \begin{bmatrix} j4.046 \\ -j6.669 \\ j2.623 \end{bmatrix} = \begin{bmatrix} 0.2878 \\ 0.2878 \\ 0.2878 \end{bmatrix} \text{per unit}$$

$$\begin{bmatrix} V_{Ag} \\ V_{Bg} \\ V_{Cg} \end{bmatrix} = \begin{bmatrix} 1 & 1 & 1 \\ 1 & a^2 & a \\ 1 & a & a^2 \end{bmatrix} \begin{bmatrix} 0.2878 \\ 0.2878 \\ 0.2878 \end{bmatrix} = \begin{bmatrix} 0.8633 \\ 0 \\ 0 \end{bmatrix} \quad \text{per unit}$$

9.17

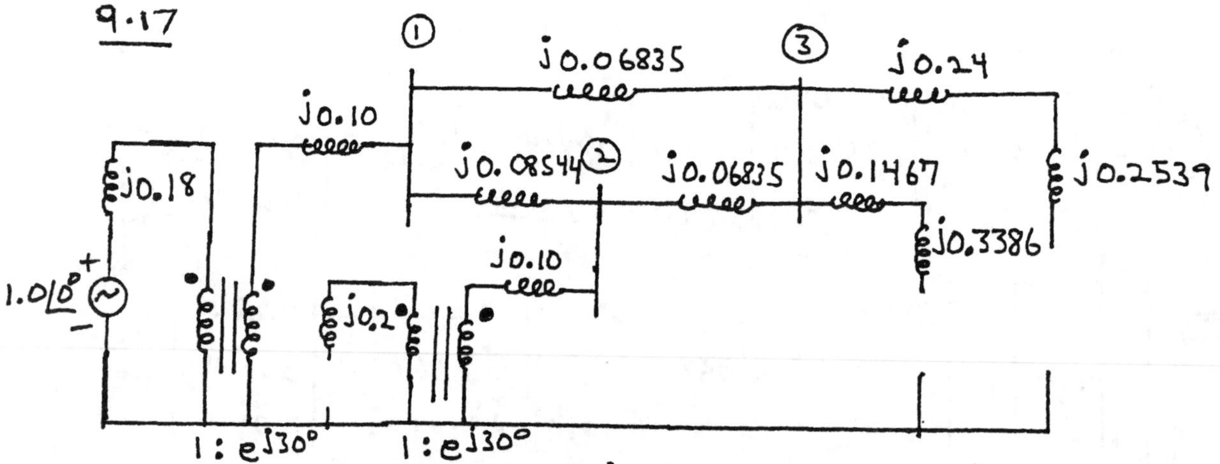

Per Unit Positive Sequence Network

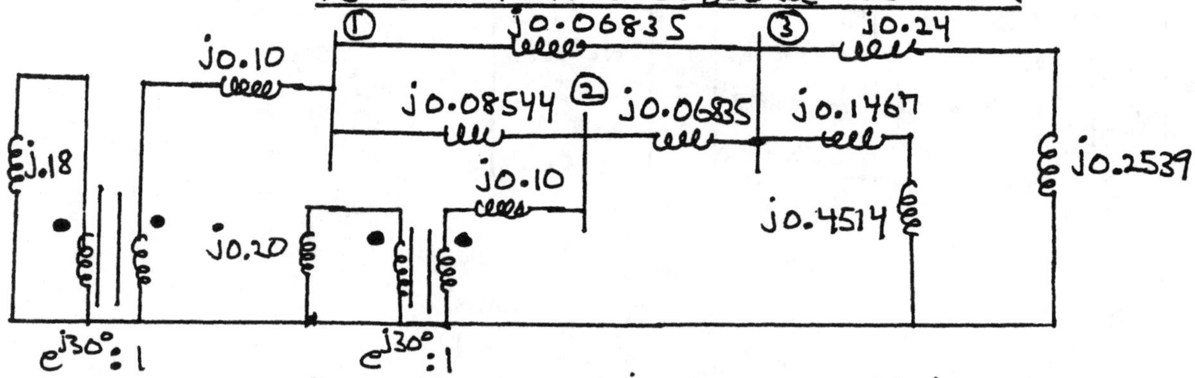

Per unit Negative Sequence Network

The zero sequence network is the same as in Problem 9.1.

The Δ-Y transformer phase shifts have no effect on the fault currents and no effect on the voltages at the fault bus. Therefore, from the results of Problem 9.10 :

$$\begin{bmatrix} I_A'' \\ I_B'' \\ I_C'' \end{bmatrix} = \begin{bmatrix} -j10.43 \\ 0 \\ 0 \end{bmatrix} \text{per unit} = \begin{bmatrix} -j7.871 \\ 0 \\ 0 \end{bmatrix} \text{kA} \qquad \begin{bmatrix} \bar{V}_{Ag} \\ \bar{V}_{Bg} \\ \bar{V}_{Cg} \end{bmatrix} = \begin{bmatrix} 0 \\ 0.9502\angle 247.0^\circ \\ 0.9502\angle 113.0^\circ \end{bmatrix} \text{per unit}$$

9.17 Contributions to the fault from generator 1:
CONTD.

From the zero-sequence network: $\bar{I}_{G1-0} = 0$

From the positive sequence network, using current division:

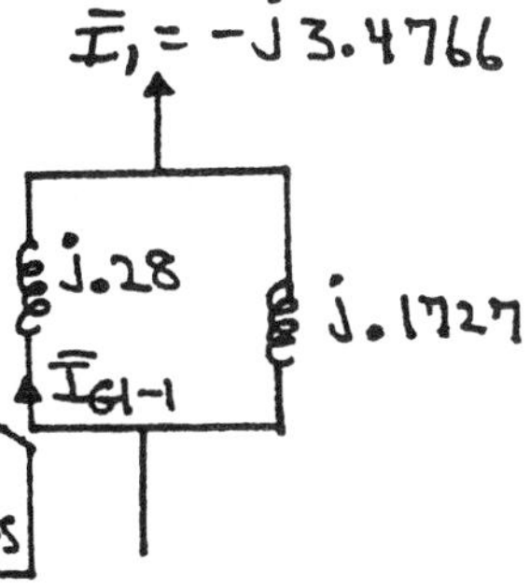

$$\bar{I}_{G1-1} = (-j3.4766)\left(\frac{.1727}{.28+.1727}\right)\underline{/-30^\circ}$$

$$= 1.326\underline{/-120^\circ} \text{ per unit}$$

Transformer Phase Shifts

From the negative sequence network, using current division:

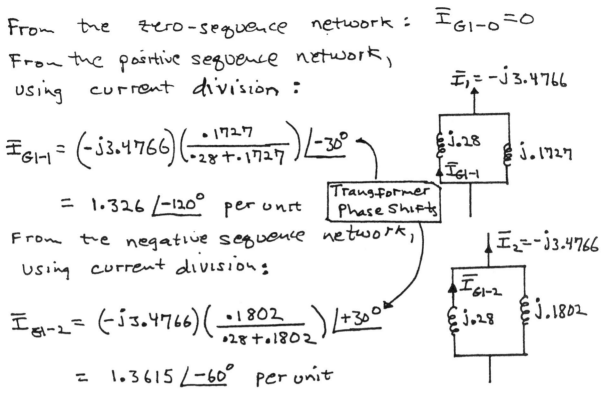

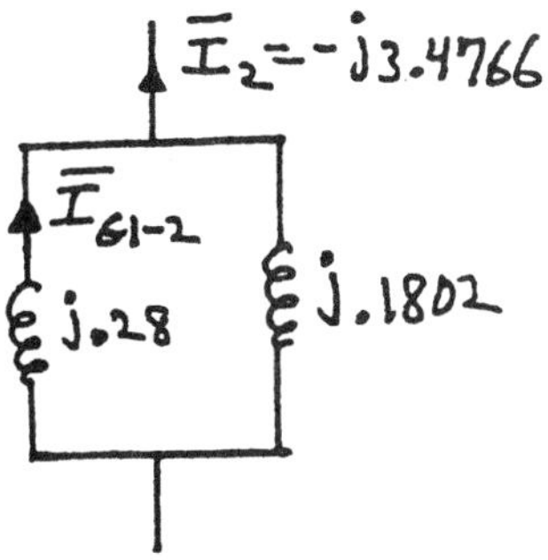

$$\bar{I}_{G1-2} = (-j3.4766)\left(\frac{.1802}{.28+.1802}\right)\underline{/+30^\circ}$$

$$= 1.3615\underline{/-60^\circ} \text{ per unit}$$

Transforming to the phase domain:

$$\begin{bmatrix} \bar{I}''_{G1-A} \\ \bar{I}''_{G1-B} \\ \bar{I}''_{G1-C} \end{bmatrix} = \begin{bmatrix} 1 & 1 & 1 \\ 1 & a^2 & a \\ 1 & a & a^2 \end{bmatrix} \begin{bmatrix} 0 \\ 1.326\underline{/-120^\circ} \\ 1.362\underline{/-60^\circ} \end{bmatrix} = \begin{bmatrix} 2.328\underline{/-89.6^\circ} \\ 2.328\underline{/89.6^\circ} \\ 0.036\underline{/180^\circ} \end{bmatrix} \text{per unit} = \begin{bmatrix} 1.757\underline{/-89.6^\circ} \\ 1.757\underline{/89.6^\circ} \\ 0.027\underline{/180^\circ} \end{bmatrix} \text{kA}$$

9.18

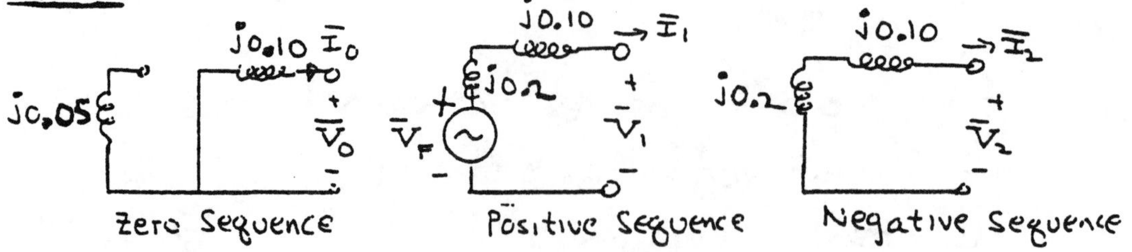

$$I_{base\,H} = \frac{S_{base}}{\sqrt{3}\,V_{base\,H}} = \frac{500}{\sqrt{3}(500)} = 0.5774 \text{ kA}$$

Three-phase fault: $\bar{I}_0 = \bar{I}_2 = 0 \qquad \bar{I}_1 = \dfrac{\bar{V}_F}{Z_1} = \dfrac{1.0\angle 0^\circ}{j0.30} = -j3.333$ per unit

$\bar{I}_a'' = \bar{I}_1 = -j3.333$ per unit $= \underline{\underline{-j1.925}}$ kA

Single line-to-ground fault:

$$\bar{I}_0 = \bar{I}_1 = \bar{I}_2 = \frac{\bar{V}_F}{\bar{Z}_0+\bar{Z}_1+\bar{Z}_2} = \frac{1.0\angle 0^\circ}{j(0.1+0.3+0.3)} = -j1.429 \text{ per unit}$$

$\bar{I}_a'' = 3\bar{I}_0'' = -j4.286$ per unit $= \underline{\underline{-j2.474}}$ kA

Line-to-line fault:

$$\bar{I}_0 = 0 \qquad \bar{I}_1 = -\bar{I}_2 = \frac{\bar{V}_F}{\bar{Z}_1+\bar{Z}_2} = \frac{1.0\angle 0^\circ}{j(0.3+0.3)} = -j1.667 \text{ per unit}$$

$\bar{I}_b'' = (a^2-a)\bar{I}_1 = (a^2-a)(-j1.667) = 2.887\angle 180^\circ$ per unit

$\bar{I}_b'' = \underline{\underline{1.667\angle 180^\circ}}$ kA

Double line-to-ground fault:

$$\bar{I}_1 = \frac{\bar{V}_F}{\bar{Z}_1+\bar{Z}_2//\bar{Z}_0} = \frac{1.0\angle 0^\circ}{j(0.3+0.3//0.1)} = \frac{1.0}{j0.375} = -j2.667 \text{ per unit}$$

$\bar{I}_2 = -\bar{I}_1\left(\dfrac{Z_0}{Z_0+Z_2}\right) = (j2.667)\left(\dfrac{.1}{.4}\right) = j0.667$ per unit

$\bar{I}_0 = -\bar{I}_1\left(\dfrac{Z_2}{Z_0+Z_2}\right) = (j2.667)\left(\dfrac{.3}{.4}\right) = j2.0$ per unit

$\bar{I}_B'' = \bar{I}_0 + a^2\bar{I}_1 + a\bar{I}_2 = 2.0\angle 90^\circ + 2.667\angle 150^\circ + .667\angle 210^\circ = 4.163\angle 134^\circ$ per unit

$= \underline{\underline{2.404\angle 134^\circ}}$ kA

9.19 Bolted single-line-to-ground fault at bus 1.

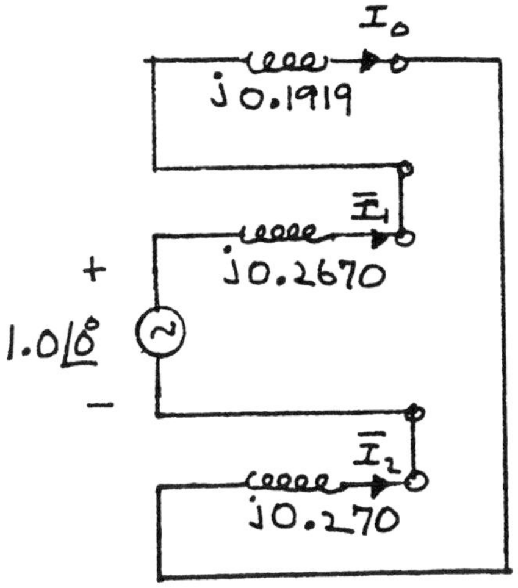

$$\bar{I}_0 = \bar{I}_1 = \bar{I}_2 = \frac{\bar{V}_F}{\bar{Z}_0 + \bar{Z}_1 + \bar{Z}_2}$$

$$= \frac{1.0\underline{/0^\circ}}{j(0.1919 + 0.267 + 0.27)} = -j1.372 \text{ per unit}$$

$$\begin{bmatrix} \bar{I}_A'' \\ \bar{I}_B'' \\ \bar{I}_C'' \end{bmatrix} = \begin{bmatrix} 1 & 1 & 1 \\ 1 & a^2 & a \\ 1 & a & a^2 \end{bmatrix} \begin{bmatrix} -j1.372 \\ -j1.372 \\ -j1.372 \end{bmatrix}$$

$$\begin{bmatrix} \bar{I}_A'' \\ \bar{I}_B'' \\ \bar{I}_C'' \end{bmatrix} = \begin{bmatrix} -j4.116 \\ 0 \\ 0 \end{bmatrix} \text{per unit} = \begin{bmatrix} -j4.753 \\ 0 \\ 0 \end{bmatrix} \text{kA}$$

Contributions to the fault current

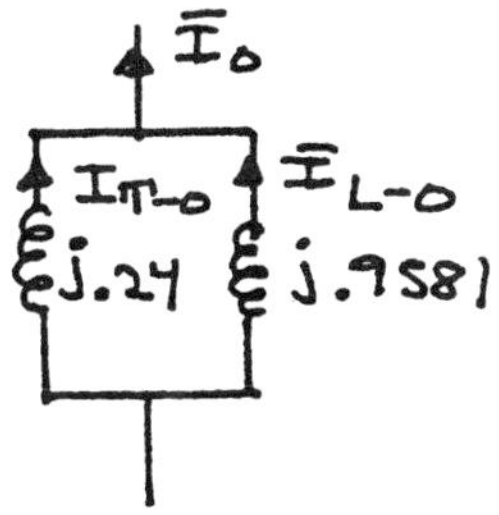

__Zero sequence:__

Transformer: $\bar{I}_{T-0} = -j1.372\left(\frac{.9581}{.24 + .9581}\right)$

$= -j1.097$ per unit

Line: $\bar{I}_{L-0} = -j1.372\left(\frac{.24}{.24 + .9581}\right) = -j0.2748$

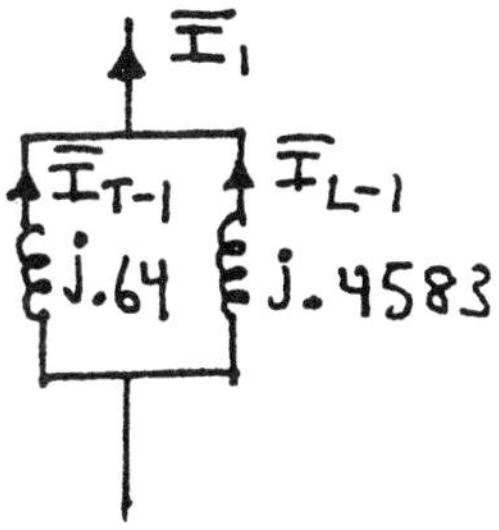

__Positive sequence:__

Transformer: $\bar{I}_{T-1} = -j1.372\left(\frac{.4583}{.64 + .4583}\right)$

$= -j0.5725$

Line: $\bar{I}_{L-1} = -j1.372\left(\frac{.64}{.64 + .4583}\right) = -j0.7994$

9.19 **Negative sequence:**
CONTD.

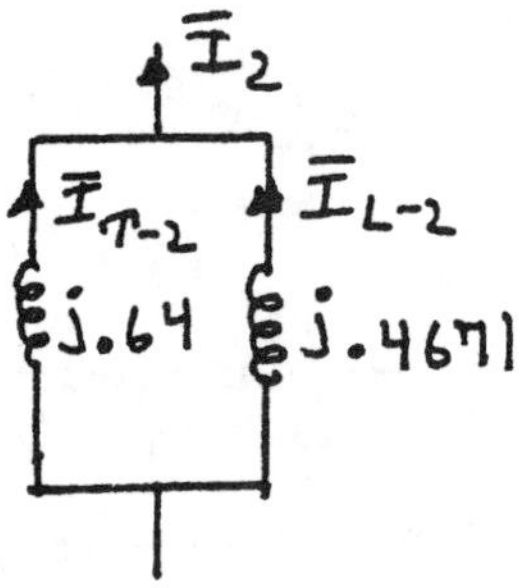

Transformer: $\bar{I}_{T-2} = -j1.372\left(\frac{.4671}{.64+.4671}\right)$

$= -j0.5789$ per unit

Line: $\bar{I}_{L-2} = -j1.372\left(\frac{.64}{.64+.4671}\right) = -j0.7931$ per unit

Transformer:

$$\begin{bmatrix} I''_{T-A} \\ I''_{T-B} \\ I''_{T-C} \end{bmatrix} = \begin{bmatrix} 1 & 1 & 1 \\ 1 & a^2 & a \\ 1 & a & a^2 \end{bmatrix} \begin{bmatrix} -j1.097 \\ -j0.5725 \\ -j0.5789 \end{bmatrix} = \begin{bmatrix} -j2.248 \\ .521\angle -89.4^\circ \\ .521\angle -90.6^\circ \end{bmatrix} \text{per unit} = \begin{bmatrix} -j2.596 \\ .602\angle -89.4^\circ \\ .602\angle -90.6^\circ \end{bmatrix} \text{kA}$$

Line:

$$\begin{bmatrix} \bar{I}''_{L-A} \\ \bar{I}''_{L-B} \\ \bar{I}''_{L-C} \end{bmatrix} = \begin{bmatrix} 1 & 1 & 1 \\ 1 & a^2 & a \\ 1 & a & a^2 \end{bmatrix} \begin{bmatrix} -j0.2748 \\ -j0.7994 \\ -j0.7931 \end{bmatrix} = \begin{bmatrix} -j1.8673 \\ .521\angle 90.6^\circ \\ .521\angle 89.4^\circ \end{bmatrix} \text{per unit} = \begin{bmatrix} -j2.156 \\ .602\angle 90.6^\circ \\ .602\angle 89.4^\circ \end{bmatrix} \text{kA}$$

9.20 Bolted line-to-line fault at bus 1.

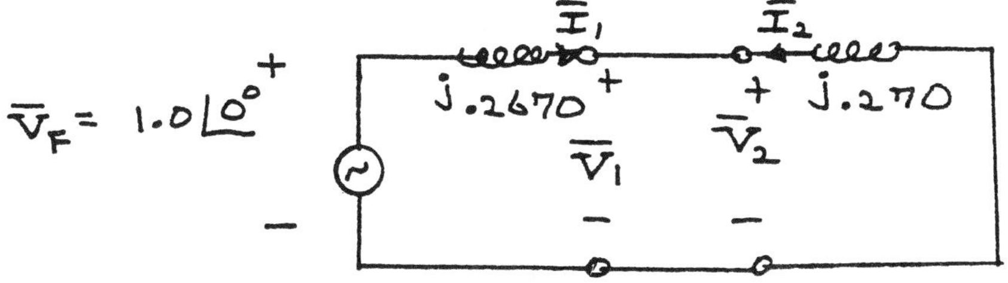

$$\bar{I}_1 = -\bar{I}_2 = \frac{\bar{V}_F}{\bar{Z}_1 + \bar{Z}_2} = \frac{1.0\angle 0^\circ}{j(.2670 + .270)} = -j1.862 \text{ per unit}$$

$\bar{I}_0 = 0$

$$\begin{bmatrix} \bar{I}_A'' \\ \bar{I}_B'' \\ \bar{I}_C'' \end{bmatrix} = \begin{bmatrix} 1 & 1 & 1 \\ 1 & a^2 & a \\ 1 & a & a^2 \end{bmatrix} \begin{bmatrix} 0 \\ -j1.862 \\ +j1.862 \end{bmatrix} = \begin{bmatrix} 0 \\ 3.225\angle 180^\circ \\ 3.225\angle 0^\circ \end{bmatrix} \text{ per unit}$$

$$\begin{bmatrix} \bar{I}_A'' \\ \bar{I}_B'' \\ \bar{I}_C'' \end{bmatrix} = \begin{bmatrix} 0 \\ 3.225\angle 180^\circ \\ 3.225\angle 0^\circ \end{bmatrix} \times 1.155 = \begin{bmatrix} 0 \\ 3.724\angle 180^\circ \\ 3.724\angle 0^\circ \end{bmatrix} \text{ kA}$$

Contributions to the fault current

Zero sequence: $\bar{I}_{T-0} = \bar{I}_{L-0} = 0$

Positive sequence:

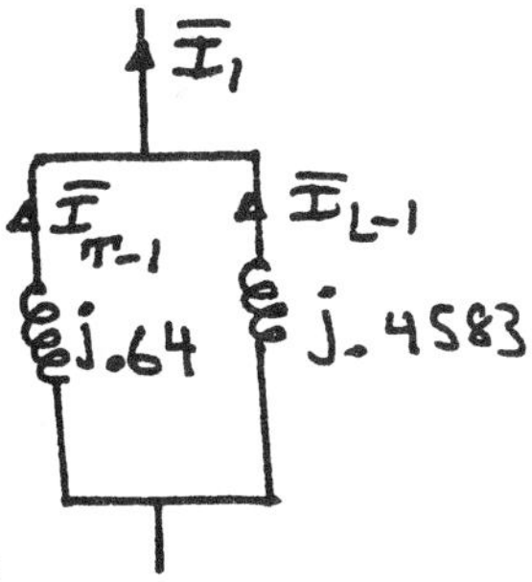

Transformer: $\bar{I}_{T-1} = -j1.862\left(\frac{.4583}{.64 + .4583}\right)$

$= -j0.7770$ per unit

Line: $\bar{I}_{L-1} = -j1.862\left(\frac{.64}{.64 + .4583}\right) = -j1.085$ per unit

Negative sequence:

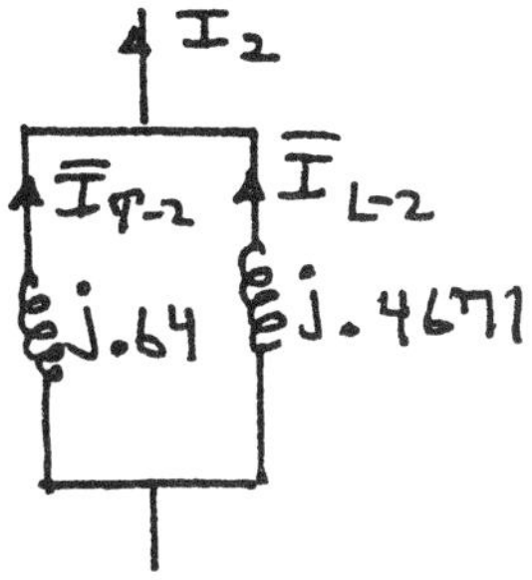

Transformer $\bar{I}_{T-2} = j1.862\left(\frac{.4671}{.64 + .4671}\right)$

$= j0.7856$ per unit

9.20 CONTD.

Line $\quad \bar{I}_{L-2} = j1.862\left(\frac{.64}{.64+.4671}\right) = j1.076$ per unit

Contribution to fault from transformer:

$$\begin{bmatrix} \bar{I}''_{T-A} \\ \bar{I}''_{T-B} \\ \bar{I}''_{T-C} \end{bmatrix} = \begin{bmatrix} 1 & 1 & 1 \\ 1 & a^2 & a \\ 1 & a & a^2 \end{bmatrix} \begin{bmatrix} 0 \\ -j.777 \\ j.7856 \end{bmatrix} = \begin{bmatrix} j.0086 \\ 1.353\angle 180.2^\circ \\ 1.353\angle -0.2^\circ \end{bmatrix} \text{per unit} = \begin{bmatrix} 0.0099\angle 90^\circ \\ 1.562\angle 180.2^\circ \\ 1.562\angle -0.2^\circ \end{bmatrix} \text{kA}$$

Contribution to fault from Line:

$$\begin{bmatrix} \bar{I}''_{L-A} \\ \bar{I}''_{L-B} \\ \bar{I}''_{L-C} \end{bmatrix} = \begin{bmatrix} 1 & 1 & 1 \\ 1 & a^2 & a \\ 1 & a & a^2 \end{bmatrix} \begin{bmatrix} 0 \\ -j1.085 \\ j1.076 \end{bmatrix} = \begin{bmatrix} -j0.0086 \\ 1.871\angle 179.9^\circ \\ 1.871\angle 0.1^\circ \end{bmatrix} \text{per unit} = \begin{bmatrix} 0.0099\angle -90^\circ \\ 2.160\angle 179.9^\circ \\ 2.160\angle 0.1^\circ \end{bmatrix} \text{kA}$$

9.21 Bolted double-line-to-ground fault at bus 1.

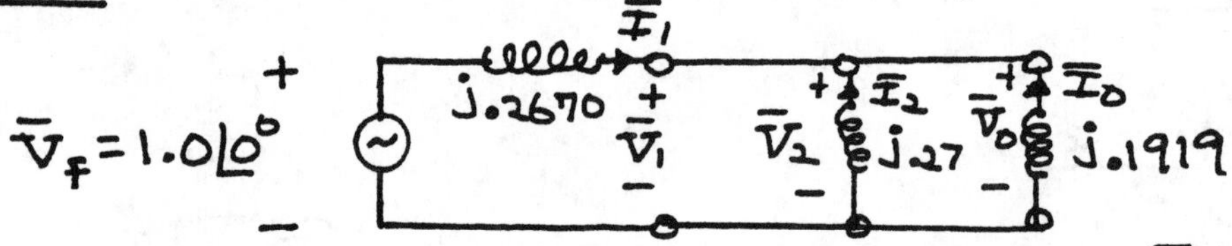

$$\bar{I}_1 = \frac{\bar{V}_F}{\bar{Z}_1 + \bar{Z}_2 \| \bar{Z}_0}$$

$$\bar{I}_1 = \frac{1.0\angle 0^\circ}{j(.267 + .27\|.1919)} = \frac{1.0\angle 0^\circ}{j0.3792} = -j2.637 \text{ per unit}$$

$$\bar{I}_2 = -\bar{I}_1\left(\frac{\bar{Z}_0}{\bar{Z}_0+\bar{Z}_2}\right) = j2.637\left(\frac{.1919}{.27+.1919}\right)$$

$\bar{I}_2 = j1.096$ per unit

$$\bar{I}_0 = -\bar{I}_1\left(\frac{\bar{Z}_2}{\bar{Z}_0+\bar{Z}_2}\right) = j2.637\left(\frac{.27}{.27+.1919}\right)$$

$\bar{I}_0 = j1.541$ per unit

9.21 CONTD.

$$\begin{bmatrix} \bar{I}''_A \\ \bar{I}''_B \\ \bar{I}''_C \end{bmatrix} = \begin{bmatrix} 1 & 1 & 1 \\ 1 & a^2 & a \\ 1 & a & a^2 \end{bmatrix} \begin{bmatrix} j1.541 \\ -j2.637 \\ j1.096 \end{bmatrix} = \begin{bmatrix} 0 \\ 3.975\angle 144.3^\circ \\ 3.975\angle 35.57^\circ \end{bmatrix} \text{per unit} \times 1.155 = \begin{bmatrix} 0 \\ 4.590\angle 144.3^\circ \\ 4.590\angle 35.57^\circ \end{bmatrix} \text{kA}$$

Contributions to the fault current

<u>Zero sequence:</u>

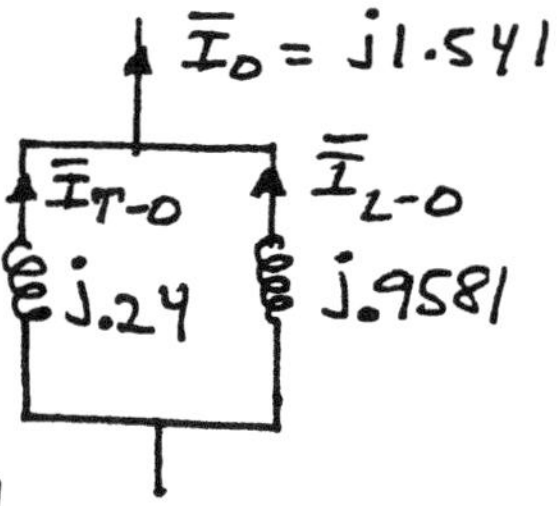

Transformer: $\bar{I}_{T-0} = j1.541\left(\dfrac{.9581}{.24+.9581}\right) = j1.232$ per unit

Line: $\bar{I}_{L-0} = j1.541\left(\dfrac{.24}{.24+.9581}\right) = j0.3087$ per unit

<u>Positive sequence:</u>

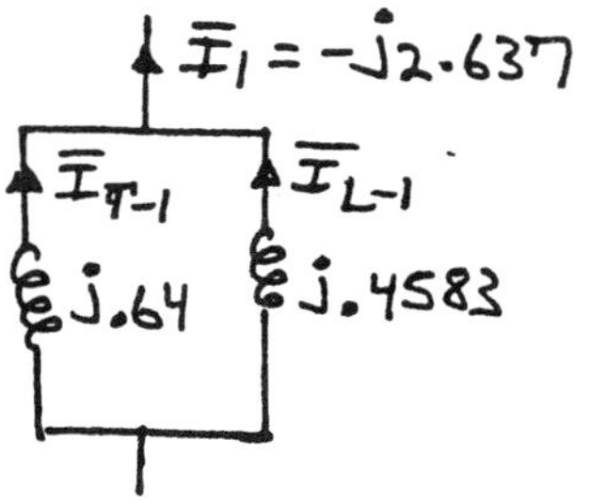

$\bar{I}_{T-1} = (-j2.637)\left(\dfrac{.4583}{.64+.4583}\right) = -j1.100$

$I_{L-1} = (-j2.637)\left(\dfrac{.64}{.64+.4583}\right) = -j1.537$ per unit

<u>Negative sequence:</u>

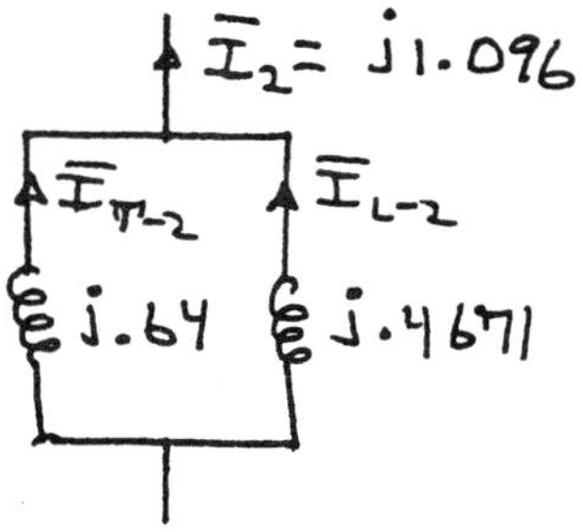

$\bar{I}_{T-2} = (j1.096)\left(\dfrac{.4671}{.64+.4671}\right) = j0.4624$

$\bar{I}_{L-2} = (j1.096)\left(\dfrac{.64}{.64+.4671}\right) = j0.6336$

Contribution to fault from transformer:

$$\begin{bmatrix} \bar{I}''_{T-A} \\ \bar{I}''_{T-B} \\ \bar{I}''_{T-C} \end{bmatrix} = \begin{bmatrix} 1 & 1 & 1 \\ 1 & a^2 & a \\ 1 & a & a^2 \end{bmatrix} \begin{bmatrix} j1.232 \\ -j1.10 \\ j0.4624 \end{bmatrix} = \begin{bmatrix} j0.5944 \\ 2.058\angle 131.1^\circ \\ 2.058\angle 48.90^\circ \end{bmatrix} \text{per unit} \times 1.155 = \begin{bmatrix} 0.6864\angle 90^\circ \\ 2.376\angle 131.1^\circ \\ 2.376\angle 48.90^\circ \end{bmatrix} \text{kA}$$

Contributions to fault from Line:

$$\begin{bmatrix} \bar{I}''_{L-A} \\ \bar{I}''_{L-B} \\ \bar{I}''_{L-C} \end{bmatrix} = \begin{bmatrix} 1 & 1 & 1 \\ 1 & a^2 & a \\ 1 & a & a^2 \end{bmatrix} \begin{bmatrix} j.3087 \\ -j1.537 \\ j[\text{illegible}] \end{bmatrix} = \begin{bmatrix} -j.594 \\ 2.028\angle 158.0^\circ \\ 2.028\angle 22.0^\circ \end{bmatrix} \text{per unit} \times 1.155 = \begin{bmatrix} 0.686\angle -90^\circ \\ 2.342\angle 158^\circ \\ [\text{illegible}] \end{bmatrix} \text{kA}$$

9.22 Bolted single-line-to-ground fault at bus 1.

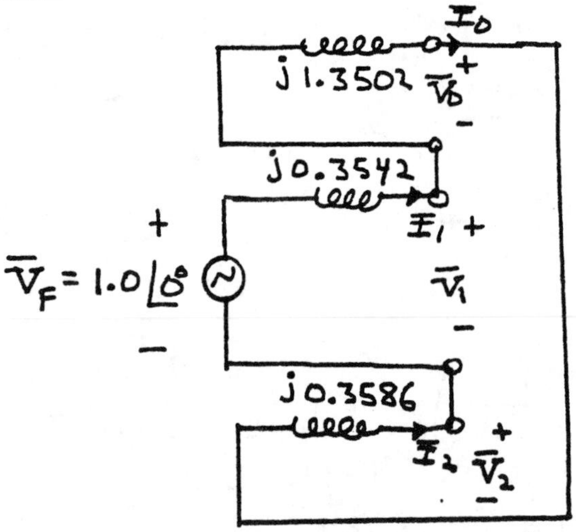

$$\bar{I}_0 = \bar{I}_1 = \bar{I}_2 = \frac{\bar{V}_F}{\bar{Z}_0 + \bar{Z}_1 + \bar{Z}_2}$$

$$= \frac{1.0\angle 0°}{j(1.3502 + 0.3542 + 0.3586)}$$

$$= -j0.4847 \text{ per unit}$$

$$I_{base1} = \frac{100}{10\sqrt{3}} = 5.774 \text{ kA}$$

$$\begin{bmatrix} \bar{I}_A'' \\ \bar{I}_B'' \\ \bar{I}_C'' \end{bmatrix} = \begin{bmatrix} 1 & 1 & 1 \\ 1 & a^2 & a \\ 1 & a & a^2 \end{bmatrix} \begin{bmatrix} -j.4847 \\ -j.4847 \\ -j.4847 \end{bmatrix} = \begin{bmatrix} -j1.454 \\ 0 \\ 0 \end{bmatrix} \text{per unit} \times 5.774 = \begin{bmatrix} -j8.396 \\ 0 \\ 0 \end{bmatrix} \text{kA}$$

Contributions to fault current

Zero sequence:

Generator G1 $\quad \bar{I}_{G1-0} = 0$

Transformer T1 $\quad \bar{I}_{T1-0} = -j0.4847$ per unit

Positive sequence:

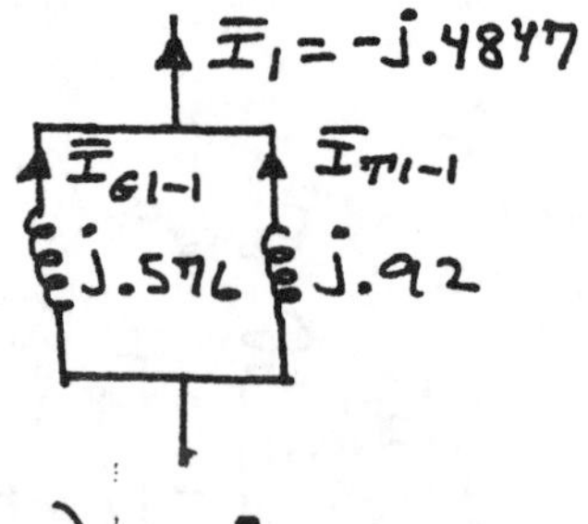

Generator G1 $\quad \bar{I}_{G1-1} = -j.4847\left(\frac{.92}{.92+.576}\right)$

$= -j0.2981$ per unit

Transformer T1 $\quad \bar{I}_{T1-1} = -j.4847\left(\frac{.576}{.92+.576}\right) = -j0.1866$ per unit

Negative sequence:

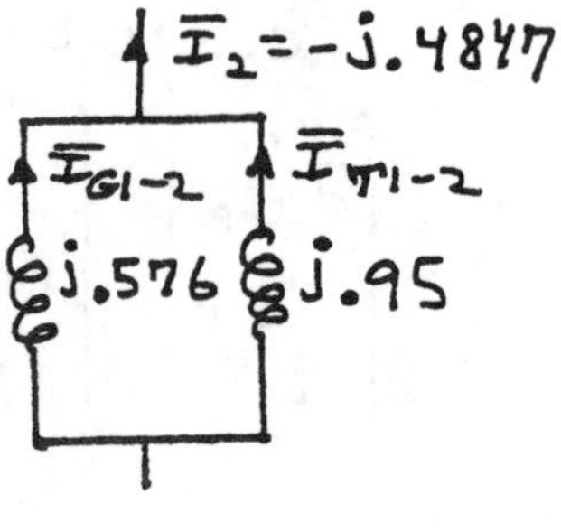

Generator G1 $\quad \bar{I}_{G1-2} = -j.4847\left(\frac{.95}{.95+.576}\right)$

$= -j0.3017$ per unit

Transformer T1 $\quad \bar{I}_{T1-2} = -j.4847\left(\frac{.576}{.576+.95}\right)$

$= -j.1830$

9.22 CONTD. Contribution to fault from generator G1:

$$\begin{bmatrix} \bar{I}''_{G1-A} \\ \bar{I}''_{G1-B} \\ \bar{I}''_{G1-C} \end{bmatrix} = \begin{bmatrix} 1 & 1 & 1 \\ 1 & a^2 & a \\ 1 & a & a^2 \end{bmatrix} \begin{bmatrix} 0 \\ -j.2981 \\ -j.3017 \end{bmatrix} = \begin{bmatrix} -j0.5998 \\ 0.2999\,\angle 89.4^\circ \\ 0.2999\,\angle 90.6^\circ \end{bmatrix} \text{per unit} \times 5.774 = \begin{bmatrix} 3.463\,\angle -90^\circ \\ 1.731\,\angle 89.4^\circ \\ 1.731\,\angle 90.6^\circ \end{bmatrix} \text{kA}$$

Contribution to fault from transformer T1:

$$\begin{bmatrix} \bar{I}''_{T1-A} \\ \bar{I}''_{T1-B} \\ \bar{I}''_{T1-C} \end{bmatrix} = \begin{bmatrix} 1 & 1 & 1 \\ 1 & a^2 & a \\ 1 & a & a^2 \end{bmatrix} \begin{bmatrix} -j.4847 \\ -j.1866 \\ -j.1830 \end{bmatrix} = \begin{bmatrix} -j.8543 \\ 0.2999\,\angle -90.6^\circ \\ 0.2999\,\angle -89.4^\circ \end{bmatrix} \text{per unit} \times 5.774 = \begin{bmatrix} 4.932\,\angle -90^\circ \\ 1.731\,\angle -90.6^\circ \\ 1.731\,\angle -89.4^\circ \end{bmatrix} \text{kA}$$

9.23 Arcing single-line-to-ground fault at bus 1.

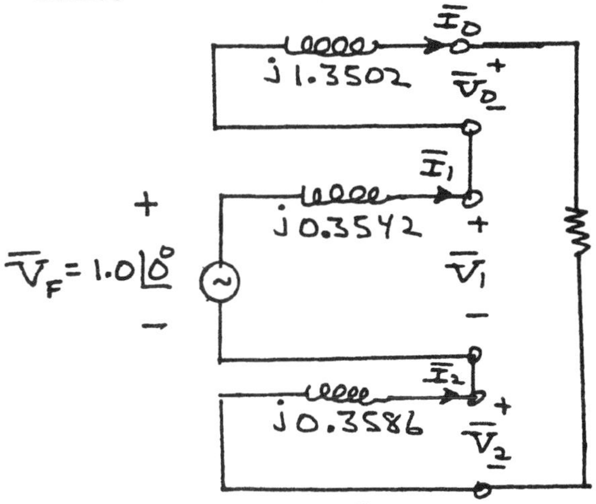

$$\bar{I}_0 = \bar{I}_1 = \bar{I}_2 = \frac{\bar{V}_F}{\bar{Z}_0 + \bar{Z}_1 + \bar{Z}_2 + 3\bar{Z}_F}$$

$$= \frac{1.0\,\angle 0^\circ}{0.15 + j(1.3502 + .3542 + .3586)}$$

$$= \frac{1.0\,\angle 0^\circ}{2.068\,\angle 85.84^\circ}$$

$$= 0.4834\,\angle -85.84^\circ \text{ per unit}$$

$$\begin{bmatrix} \bar{I}''_A \\ \bar{I}''_B \\ \bar{I}''_C \end{bmatrix} = \begin{bmatrix} 1 & 1 & 1 \\ 1 & a^2 & a \\ 1 & a & a^2 \end{bmatrix} \begin{bmatrix} .4834\,\angle 85.84^\circ \\ .4834\,\angle 85.84^\circ \\ .4834\,\angle 85.84^\circ \end{bmatrix} = \begin{bmatrix} 1.450\,\angle 85.84^\circ \\ 0 \\ 0 \end{bmatrix} \text{per unit} \times 5.774 = \begin{bmatrix} 8.374\,\angle 85.84^\circ \\ 0 \\ 0 \end{bmatrix} \text{kA}$$

9.23 Contributions to Fault current

zero sequence:

Generator G1: $\bar{I}_{G1-0} = 0$

Transformer T1: $\bar{I}_{T1-0} = 0.4834\angle{-85.84^\circ}$ per unit

Positive sequence:

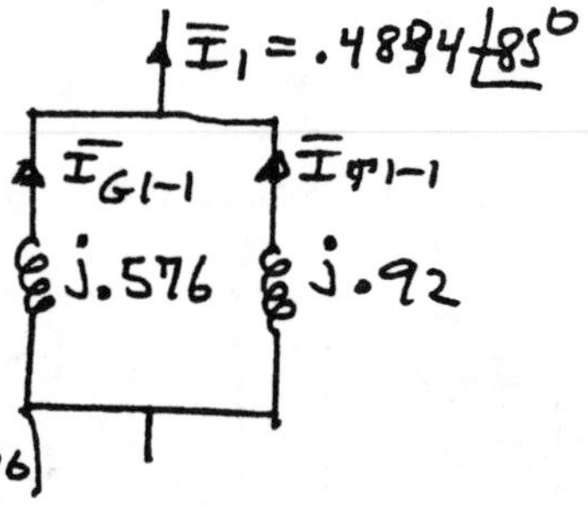

Generator G1: $\bar{I}_{G1-1} = .4834\angle{-85.84^\circ}\left(\frac{.92}{.92+.576}\right)$

$= 0.2973\angle{-85.84^\circ}$

Transformer T1: $\bar{I}_{T1-1} = .4834\angle{-85.84^\circ}\left(\frac{.576}{.92+.576}\right)$

$= 0.1861\angle{-85.84^\circ}$ per unit

Negative Sequence

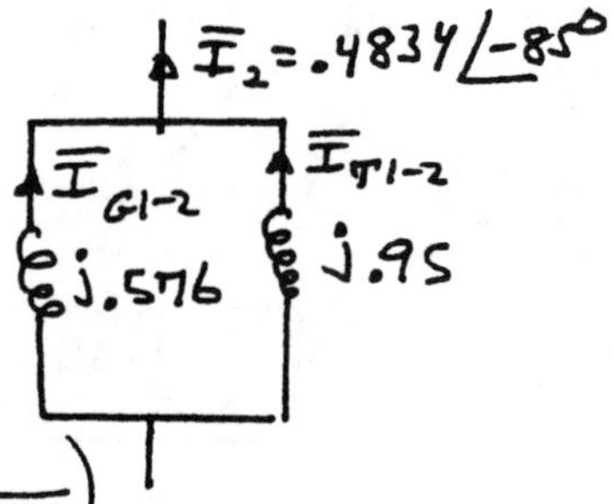

Generator G1: $\bar{I}_{G1-2} = .4834\angle{-85.84^\circ}\left(\frac{.95}{.576+.95}\right)$

$= 0.3009\angle{-85.84^\circ}$

Transformer T1: $\bar{I}_{T1-2} = .4834\angle{-85.84^\circ}\left(\frac{.576}{.576+.95}\right)$

$= 0.1825\angle{-85.84^\circ}$ per unit

Contribution to fault from generator G1:

$$\begin{bmatrix} \bar{I}''_{G1-A} \\ \bar{I}''_{G1-B} \\ \bar{I}''_{G1-C} \end{bmatrix} = \begin{bmatrix} 1 & 1 & 1 \\ 1 & a^2 & a \\ 1 & a & a^2 \end{bmatrix} \begin{bmatrix} 0 \\ 0.2973\angle{-85.84^\circ} \\ 0.3009\angle{-85.84^\circ} \end{bmatrix} = \begin{bmatrix} .5982\angle{-85.84^\circ} \\ .2991\angle{93.56^\circ} \\ .2991\angle{94.76^\circ} \end{bmatrix} \text{per unit} \times 5.774 = \begin{bmatrix} 3.454\angle{-85.84^\circ} \\ 1.727\angle{93.56^\circ} \\ 1.727\angle{94.76^\circ} \end{bmatrix} \text{kA}$$

contribution to fault from transformer T1:

$$\begin{bmatrix} \bar{I}''_{T1-A} \\ \bar{I}''_{T1-B} \\ \bar{I}''_{T1-C} \end{bmatrix} = \begin{bmatrix} 1 & 1 & 1 \\ 1 & a^2 & a \\ 1 & a & a^2 \end{bmatrix} \begin{bmatrix} .4834\angle{-85.84^\circ} \\ .1861\angle{-85.84^\circ} \\ .1825\angle{-85.84^\circ} \end{bmatrix} = \begin{bmatrix} 0.852\angle{-85.84^\circ} \\ 0.2991\angle{-86.44^\circ} \\ 0.2991\angle{-85.24^\circ} \end{bmatrix} \text{per unit} \times 5.774 = \begin{bmatrix} 4.919\angle{-85.84^\circ} \\ 1.727\angle{-86.44^\circ} \\ 1.727\angle{-85.24^\circ} \end{bmatrix} \text{kA}$$

9.24 Bolted Line-to-Line fault at bus 1.

$\bar{V}_F = 1.0\angle 0^\circ$

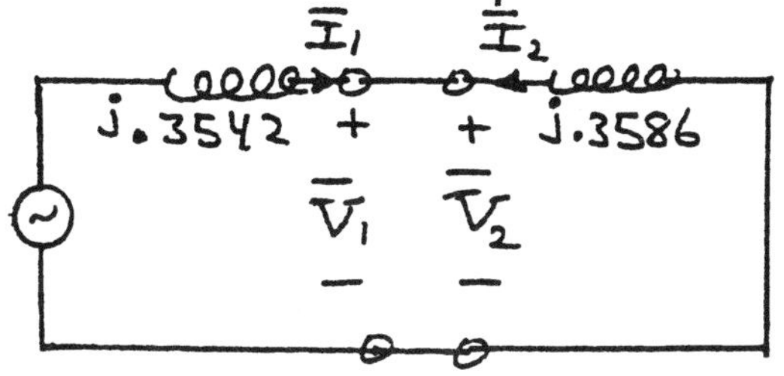

$$\bar{I}_1 = -\bar{I}_2 = \frac{\bar{V}_F}{\bar{Z}_1 + \bar{Z}_2} = \frac{1.0\angle 0^\circ}{j(.3542 + .3586)} = -j1.403 \text{ per unit}$$

$$\bar{I}_0 = 0$$

$$\begin{bmatrix} \bar{I}_A'' \\ \bar{I}_B'' \\ \bar{I}_C'' \end{bmatrix} = \begin{bmatrix} 1 & 1 & 1 \\ 1 & a^2 & a \\ 1 & a & a^2 \end{bmatrix} \begin{bmatrix} 0 \\ -j1.403 \\ +j1.403 \end{bmatrix} = \begin{bmatrix} 0 \\ 2.430\angle 180^\circ \\ 2.430\angle 0^\circ \end{bmatrix} \text{per unit} \times 5.774 = \begin{bmatrix} 0 \\ 14.03\angle 180^\circ \\ 14.03\angle 0^\circ \end{bmatrix} \text{kA}$$

Contributions to Fault current.

Zero sequence:

Generator G1 : $\bar{I}_{G1-0} = 0$

Transformer T1 : $\bar{I}_{T1-0} = 0$

Positive sequence:

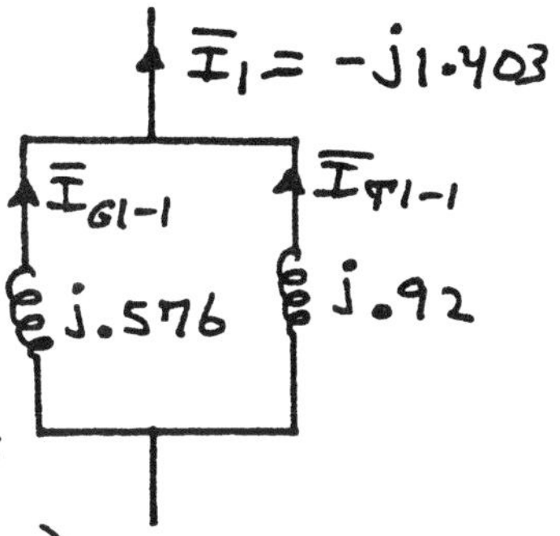

Generator G1 : $\bar{I}_{G1-1} = -j1.403\left(\frac{.92}{.92 + .576}\right)$

$= -j0.8628$ per unit

Transformer T1 : $\bar{I}_{T1-1} = -j1.403\left(\frac{.576}{.576 + .92}\right) = -j0.5402$

Negative sequence:

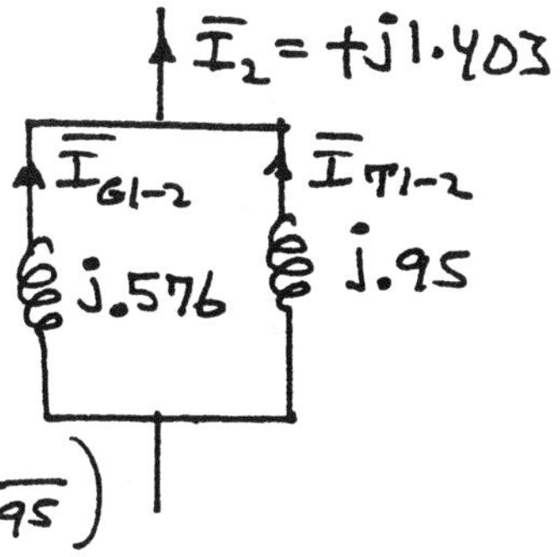

Generator G1 : $\bar{I}_{G1-2} = (j1.403)\left(\frac{.95}{.95 + .576}\right)$

$= j0.8734$ per unit

Transformer T1 : $\bar{I}_{T1-2} = (j1.403)\left(\frac{.576}{.576 + .95}\right)$

$= j0.5296$ per unit

9.24 CONTD. Contribution to fault from generator G1:

$$\begin{bmatrix} \bar{I}''_{G1-A} \\ \bar{I}''_{G1-B} \\ \bar{I}''_{G1-C} \end{bmatrix} = \begin{bmatrix} 1 & 1 & 1 \\ 1 & a^2 & a \\ 1 & a & a^2 \end{bmatrix} \begin{bmatrix} 0 \\ -j.8628 \\ j.8734 \end{bmatrix} = \begin{bmatrix} j0.0106 \\ 1.504\angle{-179.8^\circ} \\ 1.504\angle{-0.2^\circ} \end{bmatrix} \text{per unit} \times 5.774 = \begin{bmatrix} 0.0612\angle{90^\circ} \\ 8.683\angle{-179.8^\circ} \\ 8.683\angle{-0.2^\circ} \end{bmatrix} \text{kA}$$

Contribution to fault from transformer T1:

$$\begin{bmatrix} \bar{I}''_{T1-A} \\ \bar{I}''_{T1-B} \\ \bar{I}''_{T1-C} \end{bmatrix} = \begin{bmatrix} 1 & 1 & 1 \\ 1 & a^2 & a \\ 1 & a & a^2 \end{bmatrix} \begin{bmatrix} 0 \\ -j.5402 \\ j.5296 \end{bmatrix} = \begin{bmatrix} -j0.0106 \\ 0.9265\angle{179.7^\circ} \\ 0.9265\angle{0.33^\circ} \end{bmatrix} \text{per unit} \times 5.774 = \begin{bmatrix} 0.0612\angle{-90^\circ} \\ 5.349\angle{179.7^\circ} \\ 5.349\angle{0.33^\circ} \end{bmatrix} \text{kA}$$

9.25 Bolted double-line-to-ground fault at bus 1.

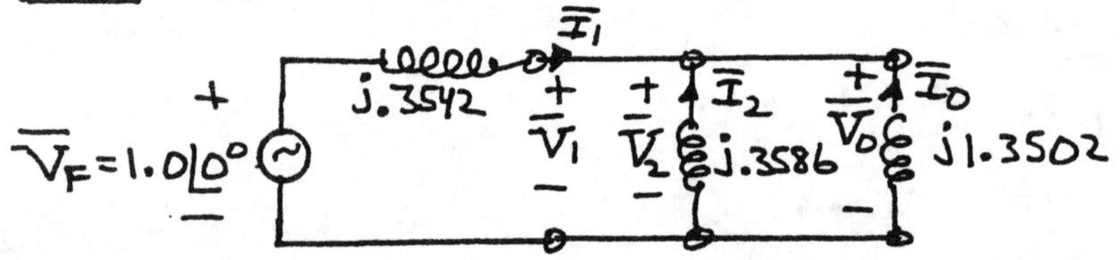

$$\bar{I}_1 = \frac{\bar{V}_F}{\bar{Z}_1 + \bar{Z}_2 // \bar{Z}_0} = \frac{1.0\angle{0^\circ}}{j(.3542 + .3586 \| 1.3502)} = \frac{1.0\angle{0^\circ}}{j0.6375} = -j1.569 \text{ per unit}$$

$$\bar{I}_0 = -\bar{I}_1\left(\frac{\bar{Z}_2}{\bar{Z}_2 + \bar{Z}_0}\right) = j1.569\left(\frac{.3586}{.3586 + 1.3502}\right) = j0.3292 \text{ per unit}$$

$$\bar{I}_2 = -\bar{I}_1\left(\frac{\bar{Z}_0}{\bar{Z}_0 + \bar{Z}_2}\right) = j1.569\left(\frac{1.3502}{1.3502 + .3586}\right) = j1.2394 \text{ per unit}$$

$$\begin{bmatrix} \bar{I}''_A \\ \bar{I}''_B \\ \bar{I}''_C \end{bmatrix} = \begin{bmatrix} 1 & 1 & 1 \\ 1 & a^2 & a \\ 1 & a & a^2 \end{bmatrix} \begin{bmatrix} j0.3292 \\ -j1.569 \\ j1.2394 \end{bmatrix} = \begin{bmatrix} 0 \\ 2.482\angle{168.5^\circ} \\ 2.482\angle{11.48^\circ} \end{bmatrix} \text{per unit} \times 5.774 = \begin{bmatrix} 0 \\ 14.33\angle{168.5^\circ} \\ 14.33\angle{11.48^\circ} \end{bmatrix} \text{kA}$$

9.25 Contributions to Fault current:

Zero sequence:

Generator G1: $\bar{I}_{G1-0} = 0$

Transformer T1: $\bar{I}_{T1-0} = j0.3292$ per unit

Positive sequence:

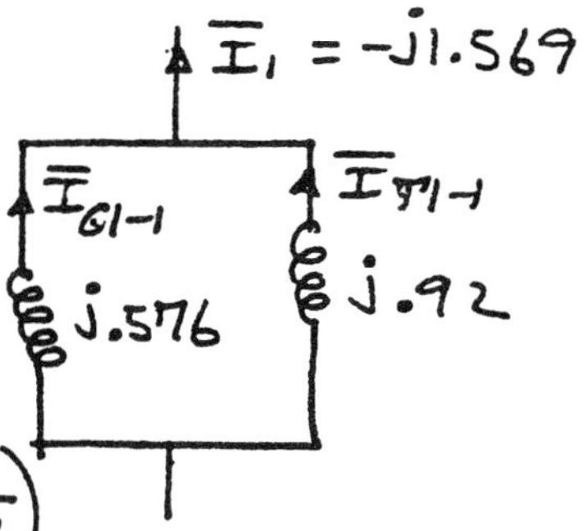

Generator G1: $\bar{I}_{G1-1} = -j1.569\left(\frac{.92}{.92+.576}\right)$

$= -j0.9646$ per unit

Transformer T1: $\bar{I}_{T1-1} = -j1.569\left(\frac{.576}{.576+.92}\right)$

$= -j0.6039$ per unit

Negative sequence:

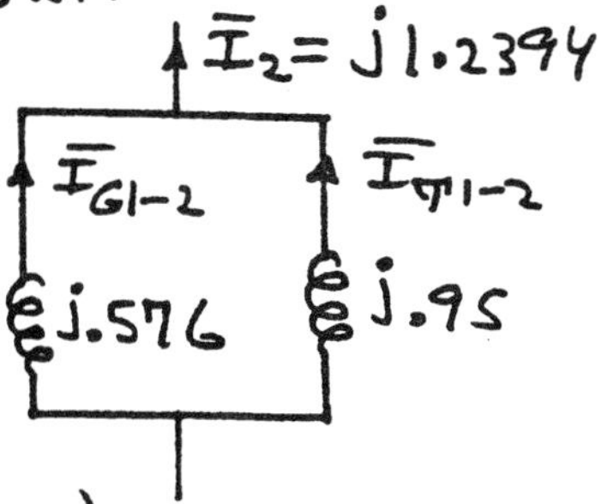

Generator G1: $\bar{I}_{G1-2} = j1.2394\left(\frac{.95}{.95+.576}\right)$

$= j0.7716$ per unit

Transformer T1: $\bar{I}_{T1-2} = j1.2394\left(\frac{.576}{.576+.95}\right) = j0.4678$ per unit

Contribution to fault from generator G1:

$$\begin{bmatrix} \bar{I}''_{G1-A} \\ \bar{I}''_{G1-B} \\ \bar{I}''_{G1-C} \end{bmatrix} = \begin{bmatrix} 1 & 1 & 1 \\ 1 & a^2 & a \\ 1 & a & a^2 \end{bmatrix} \begin{bmatrix} 0 \\ -j.9646 \\ j.7716 \end{bmatrix} = \begin{bmatrix} -j0.193 \\ 1.507\angle 176.3^\circ \\ 1.507\angle 3.67^\circ \end{bmatrix} \text{per unit} \times 5.774 = \begin{bmatrix} 1.114\angle -90^\circ \\ 8.701\angle 176.3^\circ \\ 8.701\angle 3.67^\circ \end{bmatrix}$$

kA

Contribution to fault from transformer T1:

$$\begin{bmatrix} \bar{I}''_{T1-A} \\ \bar{I}''_{T1-B} \\ \bar{I}''_{T1-C} \end{bmatrix} = \begin{bmatrix} 1 & 1 & 1 \\ 1 & a^2 & a \\ 1 & a & a^2 \end{bmatrix} \begin{bmatrix} j0.3292 \\ -j0.6039 \\ j0.4678 \end{bmatrix} = \begin{bmatrix} j0.1931 \\ 1.010\angle 156.8^\circ \\ 1.010\angle 23.17^\circ \end{bmatrix} \text{per unit} \times 5.774 = \begin{bmatrix} 1.114\angle 90^\circ \\ 5.831\angle 156.8^\circ \\ 5.831\angle 23.17^\circ \end{bmatrix}$$

kA

9.26

$\bar{I}_a = (\bar{I}_0 + \bar{I}_1 + \bar{I}_2) = 0 \qquad \bar{I}_{a'} = (I_{0'} + I_{1'} + I_{2'}) = 0$

Also $\bar{V}_{bb'} = \bar{V}_{cc'} = 0$, or

$$\begin{bmatrix} V_{00'} \\ V_{11'} \\ V_{22'} \end{bmatrix} = \frac{1}{3}\begin{bmatrix} 1 & 1 & 1 \\ 1 & a & a^2 \\ 1 & a^2 & a \end{bmatrix}\begin{bmatrix} \bar{V}_{aa'} \\ 0 \\ 0 \end{bmatrix} = \begin{bmatrix} \bar{V}_{aa'}/3 \\ \bar{V}_{aa'}/3 \\ \bar{V}_{aa'}/3 \end{bmatrix}$$

which gives $\bar{V}_{00'} = \bar{V}_{11'} = \bar{V}_{22'} = 0$

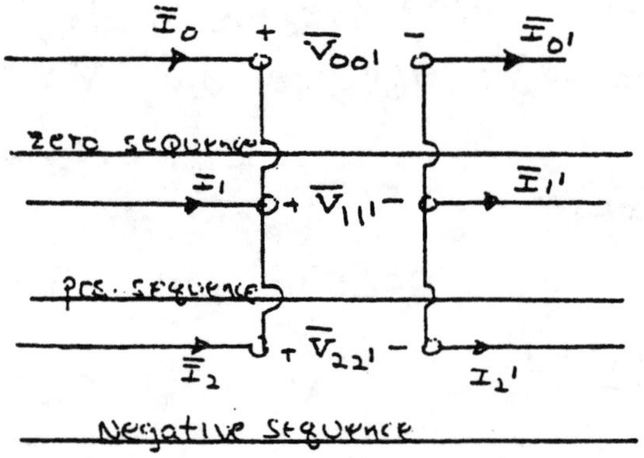

9.27

$I_b = I_c = 0$, or

$$\begin{bmatrix} I_0 \\ I_1 \\ I_2 \end{bmatrix} = \frac{1}{3}\begin{bmatrix} 1 & 1 & 1 \\ 1 & a & a^2 \\ 1 & a^2 & a \end{bmatrix}\begin{bmatrix} I_a \\ 0 \\ 0 \end{bmatrix} = \begin{bmatrix} I_a/3 \\ I_a/3 \\ I_a/3 \end{bmatrix} \Rightarrow I_0 = I_1 = I_2$$

similarly $I_{0'} = I_{1'} = I_{2'}$ Also $\bar{V}_{aa'} = (\bar{V}_{00'} + \bar{V}_{11'} + \bar{V}_{22'}) = 0$

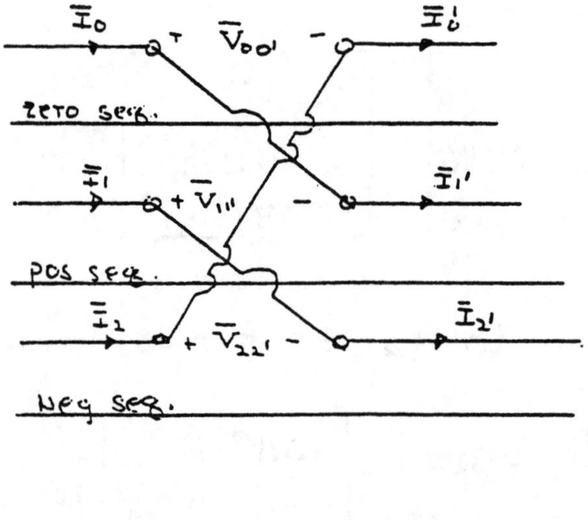

9.28

(a) FOR A SINGLE LINE-TO-GROUND FAULT, THE SEQUENCE NETWORKS FROM THE SOLUTION OF PR. 9.10 ARE TO BE CONNECTED IN SERIES.

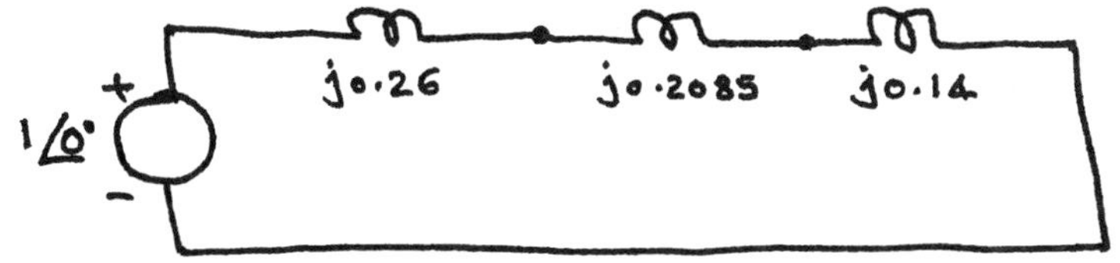

THE SEQUENCE CURRENTS ARE GIVEN BY

$$\bar{I}_0 = \bar{I}_1 = \bar{I}_2 = \frac{1}{j(0.26+0.2085+0.14)} = 1.65\angle{-90^\circ}\ \text{PU}$$

THE SUBTRANSIENT FAULT CURRENT IS

$$\bar{I}_a = 3(1.65\angle{-90^\circ}) = 4.95\angle{-90^\circ}\ \text{PU}$$

$$\bar{I}_b = \bar{I}_c = 0$$

THE SEQUENCE VOLTAGES ARE GIVEN BY EQ. (9.1.1):

$$\bar{V}_1 = 1\angle 0^\circ - \bar{I}_1\bar{Z}_1 = 1\angle 0^\circ - (1.65\angle{-90^\circ})(0.26\angle 90^\circ) = 0.57\ \text{PU}$$

$$\bar{V}_2 = -\bar{I}_2\bar{Z}_2 = -(1.65\angle{-90^\circ})(0.2085\angle 90^\circ) = -0.34\ \text{PU}$$

$$\bar{V}_0 = -\bar{I}_0\bar{Z}_0 = -(1.65\angle{-90^\circ})(0.14\angle 90^\circ) = -0.23\ \text{PU}$$

THE LINE-TO-GROUND (PHASE) VOLTAGES AT THE FAULTED BUS ARE

$$\begin{bmatrix}\bar{V}_{ag}\\ \bar{V}_{bg}\\ \bar{V}_{cg}\end{bmatrix} = \begin{bmatrix}1 & 1 & 1\\ 1 & a^2 & a\\ 1 & a & a^2\end{bmatrix}\begin{bmatrix}-0.23\\ 0.57\\ -0.34\end{bmatrix} = \begin{bmatrix}0\\ 0.86\angle{-113.64^\circ}\\ 0.86\angle 113.64^\circ\end{bmatrix}\ \text{PU}$$

(b)

FOR A LINE-TO-LINE FAULT THROUGH A FAULT IMPEDANCE $\bar{Z}_F = j0.05$, THE SEQUENCE NETWORK CONNECTION IS SHOWN BELOW:

9.28 CONTD.

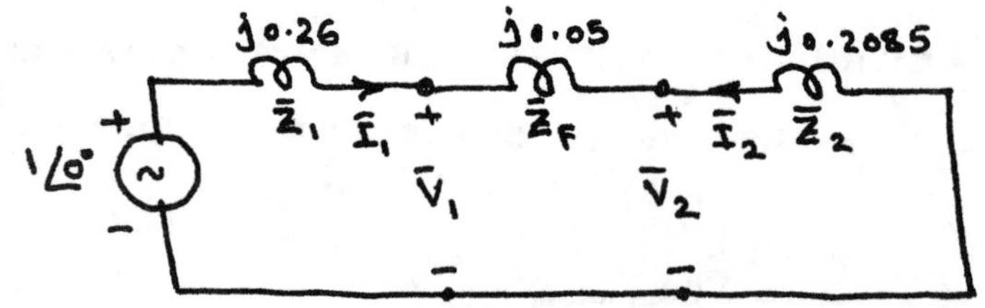

$$\bar{I}_1 = -\bar{I}_2 = \frac{1\angle 0°}{0.5185\angle 90°} = 1.93\angle -90° \text{ PU}$$

$$\bar{I}_0 = 0$$

THE PHASE CURRENTS ARE GIVEN BY (EQ. 8.1.20 ~ 8.1.22)

$$\bar{I}_a = 0 \quad ; \quad \bar{I}_b = -\bar{I}_c = (a^2 - a)\bar{I}_1 = 3.34\angle -180° \text{ PU}$$

THE SEQUENCE VOLTAGES ARE

$$\bar{V}_1 = 1\angle 0° - \bar{I}_1\bar{Z}_1 = 1\angle 0° - (1.93\angle -90°)(0.26\angle 90°)$$
$$= 0.5 \text{ PU}$$

$$\bar{V}_2 = -\bar{I}_2\bar{Z}_2 = -(-1.93\angle -90°)(0.2085\angle 90°)$$
$$= 0.4 \text{ PU}$$

$$\bar{V}_0 = -\bar{I}_0\bar{Z}_0 = 0$$

THE PHASE VOLTAGES ARE THEN GIVEN BY

$$\bar{V}_a = \bar{V}_1 + \bar{V}_2 + \bar{V}_0 = 0.9 \text{ PU}$$

$$\bar{V}_b = a^2\bar{V}_1 + a\bar{V}_2 + \bar{V}_0 = 0.46\angle -169.11° \text{ PU}$$

$$\bar{V}_c = a\bar{V}_1 + a^2\bar{V}_2 + \bar{V}_0 = 0.46\angle 169.11° \text{ PU}$$

CHECK: $\bar{V}_b - \bar{V}_c = \bar{I}_b\bar{Z}_F = 0.17\angle -90°$

(C) FOR A DOUBLE LINE-TO-GROUND FAULT WITH GIVEN CONDITIONS, THE SEQUENCE NETWORK CONNECTION IS SHOWN BELOW:

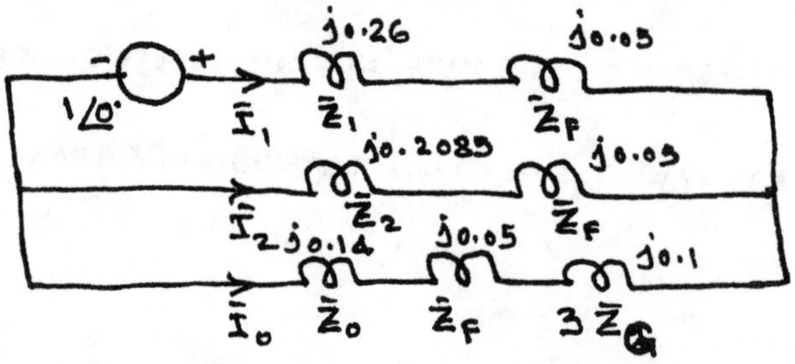

9.28 CONTD.

THE REDUCTIONS ARE SHOWN BELOW:

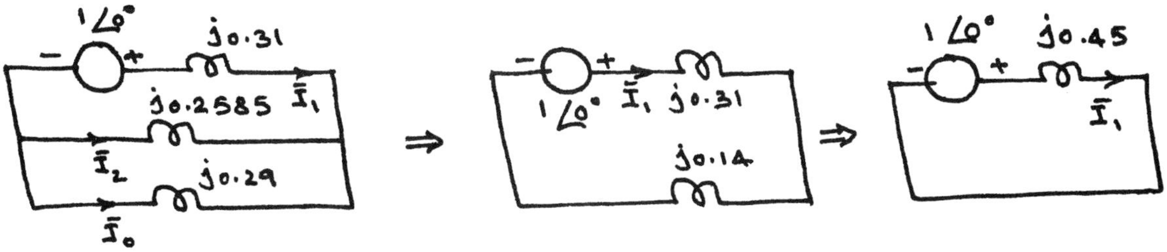

$$\therefore\ \bar{I}_1 = 1\angle 0° / 0.45\angle 90° = 2.24\angle -90°$$

$$\bar{I}_2 = -\bar{I}_1\left(\frac{0.29}{0.29 + 0.2585}\right) = -1.18\angle -90°$$

$$\bar{I}_0 = -1.06\angle -90°$$

THE SEQUENCE VOLTAGES ARE GIVEN BY

$$\bar{V}_1 = 1\angle 0° - \bar{I}_1\bar{Z}_1 = 1\angle 0° - (2.24\angle -90°)(0.26\angle 90°) = 0.42$$

$$\bar{V}_2 = -\bar{I}_2\bar{Z}_2 = -(-1.18\angle -90°)(0.2085\angle 90°) = 0.25$$

$$\bar{V}_0 = -\bar{I}_0\bar{Z}_0 = -(-1.06\angle -90°)(0.14\angle 90°) = 0.15$$

THE PHASE CURRENTS ARE CALCULATED AS

$$\bar{I}_a = 0\ ; \quad \bar{I}_b = a^2\bar{I}_1 + a\bar{I}_2 + \bar{I}_0 = 3.36\angle 151.77°\ ;$$

$$\bar{I}_c = a\bar{I}_1 + a^2 I_2 + \bar{I}_0 = 3.36\angle 28.23°.$$

THE NEUTRAL FAULT CURRENT IS $\bar{I}_b + \bar{I}_c = 3\bar{I}_0 = -3.18\angle -90°$.

THE PHASE VOLTAGES ARE OBTAINED AS

$$\bar{V}_a = \bar{V}_1 + \bar{V}_2 + \bar{V}_0 = 0.82$$

$$\bar{V}_b = a^2 V_1 + a\bar{V}_2 + \bar{V}_0 = 0.24\angle -141.49°$$

$$\bar{V}_c = a\bar{V}_1 + a^2\bar{V}_2 + \bar{V}_0 = 0.24\angle 141.49°$$

9.29

(a) FOR A SINGLE LINE-TO-GROUND FAULT AT BUS 3, THE INTERCONNECTION OF THE SEQUENCE NETWORKS IS SHOWN BELOW:

(SEE SOLUTION OF PR. 9.11)

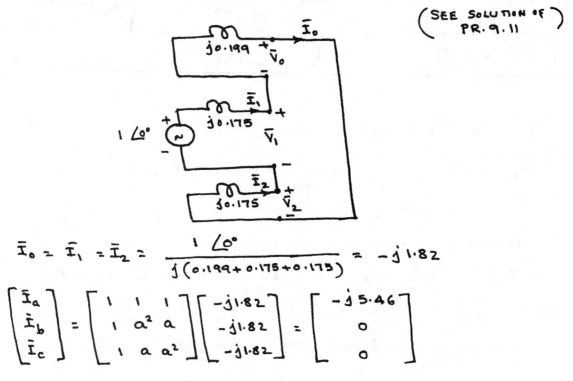

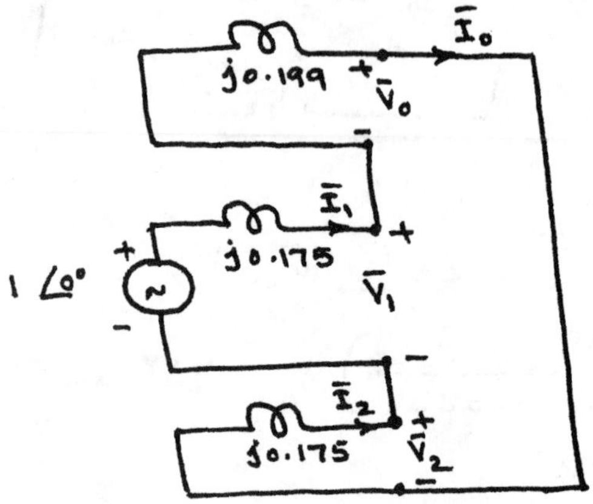

$$\bar{I}_0 = \bar{I}_1 = \bar{I}_2 = \frac{1\angle 0^\circ}{j(0.199+0.175+0.175)} = -j1.82$$

$$\begin{bmatrix}\bar{I}_a\\ \bar{I}_b\\ \bar{I}_c\end{bmatrix} = \begin{bmatrix}1 & 1 & 1\\ 1 & a^2 & a\\ 1 & a & a^2\end{bmatrix}\begin{bmatrix}-j1.82\\ -j1.82\\ -j1.82\end{bmatrix} = \begin{bmatrix}-j5.46\\ 0\\ 0\end{bmatrix}$$

SEQUENCE VOLTAGES ARE GIVEN BY

$$\bar{V}_0 = -j0.199(-j1.82) = -0.362;\quad \bar{V}_1 = 1 - j0.175(-j1.82) = 0.681;$$
$$\bar{V}_2 = -j0.175(-j1.82) = -0.319$$

THE PHASE VOLTAGES ARE CALCULATED AS

$$\begin{bmatrix}\bar{V}_a\\ \bar{V}_b\\ \bar{V}_c\end{bmatrix} = \begin{bmatrix}1 & 1 & 1\\ 1 & a^2 & a\\ 1 & a & a^2\end{bmatrix}\begin{bmatrix}-0.362\\ 0.681\\ -0.319\end{bmatrix} = \begin{bmatrix}0\\ 1.022\angle 238^\circ\\ 1.022\angle 122^\circ\end{bmatrix}$$

(b) FOR A LINE-TO-LINE FAULT AT BUS 3, THE SEQUENCE NETWORKS ARE INTERCONNECTED AS SHOWN BELOW:

9.29 CONTD.

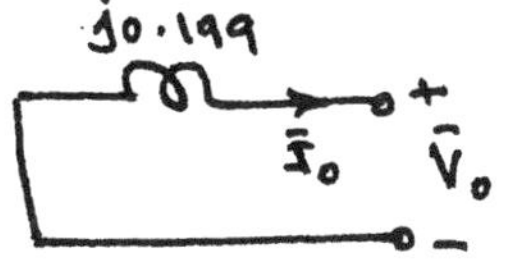

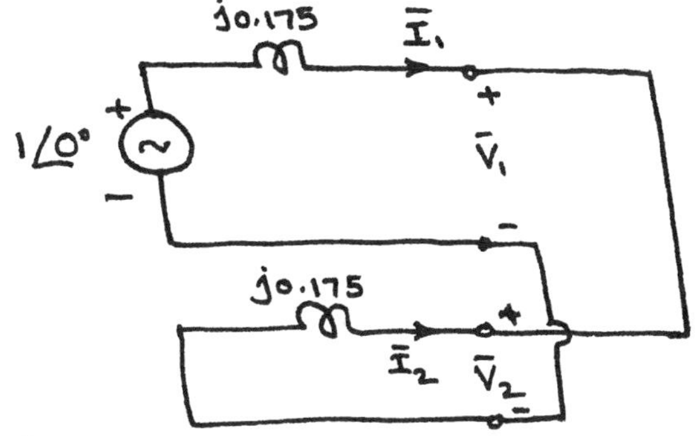

$\bar{I}_0 = 0$

$$\bar{I}_1 = -\bar{I}_2 = \frac{1\angle 0°}{j0.175 + j0.175} = -j2.86$$

PHASE CURRENTS ARE THEN

$$\begin{bmatrix} \bar{I}_a \\ \bar{I}_b \\ \bar{I}_c \end{bmatrix} = \begin{bmatrix} 1 & 1 & 1 \\ 1 & a^2 & a \\ 1 & a & a^2 \end{bmatrix} \begin{bmatrix} 0 \\ -j2.86 \\ j2.86 \end{bmatrix} = \begin{bmatrix} 0 \\ -4.95 \\ 4.95 \end{bmatrix}$$

THE SEQUENCE VOLTAGES ARE

$$\bar{V}_0 = 0 \quad ; \quad \bar{V}_1 = \bar{V}_2 = \bar{I}_1 (j0.175) = 0.5$$

PHASE VOLTAGES ARE CALCULATED AS

$$\begin{bmatrix} \bar{V}_a \\ \bar{V}_b \\ \bar{V}_c \end{bmatrix} = \begin{bmatrix} 1 & 1 & 1 \\ 1 & a^2 & a \\ 1 & a & a^2 \end{bmatrix} \begin{bmatrix} 0 \\ 0.5 \\ 0.5 \end{bmatrix} = \begin{bmatrix} 1.0 \\ -0.5 \\ -0.5 \end{bmatrix}$$

(C) FOR A DOUBLE LINE-TO-GROUND FAULT AT BUS 3, THE SEQUENCE NETWORK INTERCONNECTION IS SHOWN BELOW:

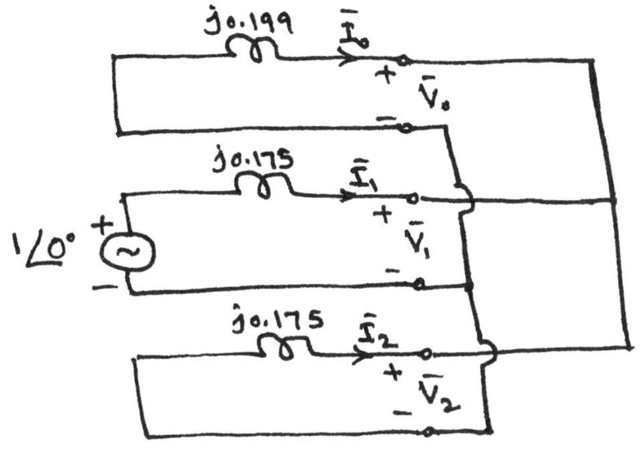

9.29 CONTD.

SEQUENCE CURRENTS ARE CALCULATED AS

$$\bar{I}_1 = \frac{1\angle 0°}{j0.175 + [j0.175(j0.199)/(j0.175 + j0.199)]} = -j3.73$$

$$\bar{I}_2 = \frac{0.199}{0.175 + 0.199}(j3.73) = j1.99$$

$$\bar{I}_0 = \frac{0.175}{0.175 + 0.199}(j3.73) = j1.75$$

PHASE CURRENTS ARE GIVEN BY

$$\begin{bmatrix} \bar{I}_a \\ \bar{I}_b \\ \bar{I}_c \end{bmatrix} = \begin{bmatrix} 1 & 1 & 1 \\ 1 & a^2 & a \\ 1 & a & a^2 \end{bmatrix} \begin{bmatrix} j1.75 \\ -j3.73 \\ j1.99 \end{bmatrix} = \begin{bmatrix} 0 \\ 5.6\angle 152.1° \\ 5.6\angle 27.9° \end{bmatrix}$$

THE NEUTRAL FAULT CURRENT IS $\bar{I}_b + \bar{I}_c = 3\bar{I}_0 = j5.25$

SEQUENCE VOLTAGES ARE OBTAINED AS

$$\bar{V}_0 = \bar{V}_1 = \bar{V}_2 = -(j1.75)(j0.199) = 0.348$$

PHASE VOLTAGES ARE THEN

$$\begin{bmatrix} \bar{V}_a \\ \bar{V}_b \\ \bar{V}_c \end{bmatrix} = \begin{bmatrix} 1 & 1 & 1 \\ 1 & a^2 & a \\ 1 & a & a^2 \end{bmatrix} \begin{bmatrix} 0.348 \\ 0.348 \\ 0.348 \end{bmatrix} = \begin{bmatrix} 1.044 \\ 0 \\ 0 \end{bmatrix}$$

(d) IN ORDER TO COMPUTE CURRENTS AND VOLTAGES AT THE TERMINALS OF GENERATORS G1 AND G2, WE NEED TO RETURN TO THE ORIGINAL SEQUENCE CIRCUITS IN THE SOLUTION OF PROB. 9.11.

GENERATOR G1 (BUS 4):

FOR A SINGLE LINE-TO-GROUND FAULT, SEQUENCE NETWORK INTERCONNECTION IS SHOWN BELOW:

9.29 CONTD.

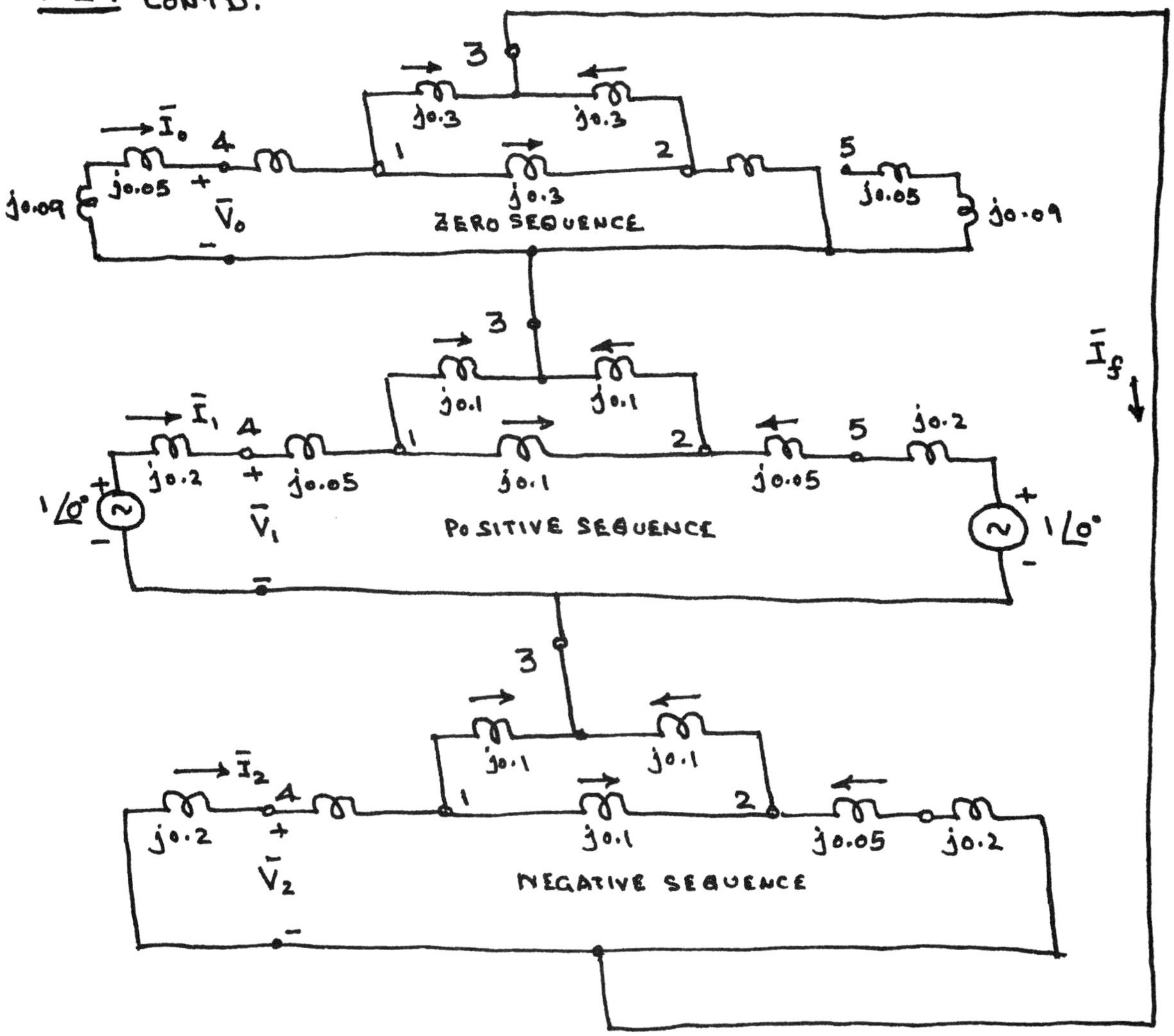

FROM THE SOLUTON OF PROB. 9.29, $\bar{I}_f = -j1.82$

FROM THE CIRCUIT ABOVE, $\bar{I}_1 = \bar{I}_2 = \frac{1}{2}\bar{I}_f = -j0.91$

TRANSFORMING THE Δ OF (j0.3) IN THE ZERO-SEQUENCE NETWORK INTO AN EQUIVALENT Y OF (j0.1), AND USING THE CURRENT DIVIDER,

$$\bar{I}_0 = \frac{0.15}{0.29+0.15}(-j1.82) = -j0.62$$

PHASE CURRENTS ARE THEN

$$\begin{bmatrix}\bar{I}_a\\ \bar{I}_b\\ \bar{I}_c\end{bmatrix} = \begin{bmatrix}1 & 1 & 1\\ 1 & a^2 & a\\ 1 & a & a^2\end{bmatrix}\begin{bmatrix}-j0.62\\ -j0.91\\ -j0.91\end{bmatrix} = \begin{bmatrix}2.44\angle -90^\circ\\ 0.29\angle 90^\circ\\ 0.29\angle 90^\circ\end{bmatrix}$$

9.29 CONTD.

SEQUENCE VOLTAGES ARE CALCULATED AS

$\bar{V}_0 = -(-j0.62)(j0.14) = -0.087$; $\bar{V}_1 = 1 - j0.2(-j0.91) = 0.818$;

$\bar{V}_2 = -j0.2(-j0.91) = -0.182$

PHASE VOLTAGES ARE THEN

$$\begin{bmatrix} \bar{V}_a \\ \bar{V}_b \\ \bar{V}_c \end{bmatrix} = \begin{bmatrix} 1 & 1 & 1 \\ 1 & a^2 & a \\ 1 & a & a^2 \end{bmatrix} \begin{bmatrix} -0.087 \\ 0.818 \\ -0.182 \end{bmatrix} = \begin{bmatrix} 0.549\angle 0^\circ \\ 0.956\angle 245^\circ \\ 0.956\angle 115^\circ \end{bmatrix}$$

GENERATOR G2 (BUS 5):

FROM THE INTERCONNECTED SEQUENCE NETWORKS AND SOLUTION OF PROB. 9.29,

$\bar{I}_f = -j1.82$; $\bar{I}_1 = \bar{I}_2 = \frac{1}{2}\bar{I}_f = -j0.91$; $\bar{I}_0 = 0$

RECALL THAT Y-Δ TRANSFORMER CONNECTIONS PRODUCE 30° PHASE SHIFTS IN SEQUENCE QUANTITIES. THE HV QUANTITIES ARE TO BE SHIFTED 30° AHEAD OF THE CORRESPONDING LV QUANTITIES FOR POSITIVE SEQUENCE, AND VICE VERSA FOR NEGATIVE SEQUENCE. ONE MAY HOWEVER NEGLECT PHASE SHIFTS.

SINCE BUS 5 IS THE LV SIDE, CONSIDERING PHASE SHIFTS,

$\bar{I}_1 = 0.91\angle -90^\circ - 30^\circ = 0.91\angle -120^\circ$; $\bar{I}_2 = 0.91\angle -90^\circ + 30^\circ = 0.91\angle -60^\circ$

PHASE CURRENTS ARE THEN GIVEN BY

$$\begin{bmatrix} \bar{I}_a \\ \bar{I}_b \\ \bar{I}_c \end{bmatrix} = \begin{bmatrix} 1 & 1 & 1 \\ 1 & a^2 & a \\ 1 & a & a^2 \end{bmatrix} \begin{bmatrix} 0 \\ 0.91\angle -120^\circ \\ 0.91\angle -60^\circ \end{bmatrix} = \begin{bmatrix} 1.58\angle -90^\circ \\ 1.58\angle +90^\circ \\ 0 \end{bmatrix}$$

POSITIVE AND NEGATIVE SEQUENCE VOLTAGES ARE THE SAME AS ON THE G1 SIDE:

$\bar{V}_1 = 0.818$; $\bar{V}_2 = -0.182$; $\bar{V}_0 = 0$; WITH PHASE SHIFT $\bar{V}_1 = 0.818\angle -30^\circ$, $\bar{V}_2 = 0.182\angle 210^\circ$

PHASE VOLTAGES ARE CALCULATED AS

$$\begin{bmatrix} \bar{V}_a \\ \bar{V}_b \\ \bar{V}_c \end{bmatrix} = \begin{bmatrix} 1 & 1 & 1 \\ 1 & a^2 & a \\ 1 & a & a^2 \end{bmatrix} \begin{bmatrix} 0 \\ 0.818\angle -30^\circ \\ 0.182\angle 210^\circ \end{bmatrix} = \begin{bmatrix} 0.744\angle -42.2^\circ \\ 0.744\angle 222.2^\circ \\ 1.00\angle 90^\circ \end{bmatrix}$$

9.30

REFER TO THE SOLUTION OF PROB. 9.12.

(a) THE NEGATIVE SEQUENCE NETWORK IS THE SAME AS THE POSITIVE SEQUENCE NETWORK WITHOUT THE SOURCE.

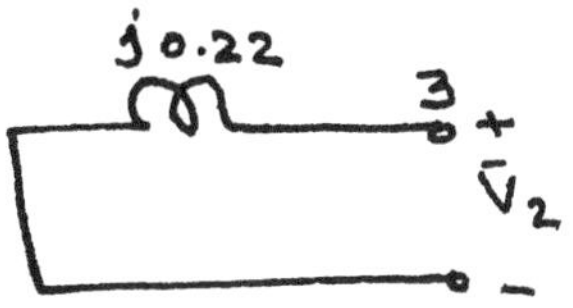

THE ZERO-SEQUENCE NETWORK IS SHOWN BELOW CONSIDERING THE TRANSFORMER WINDING CONNECTIONS:

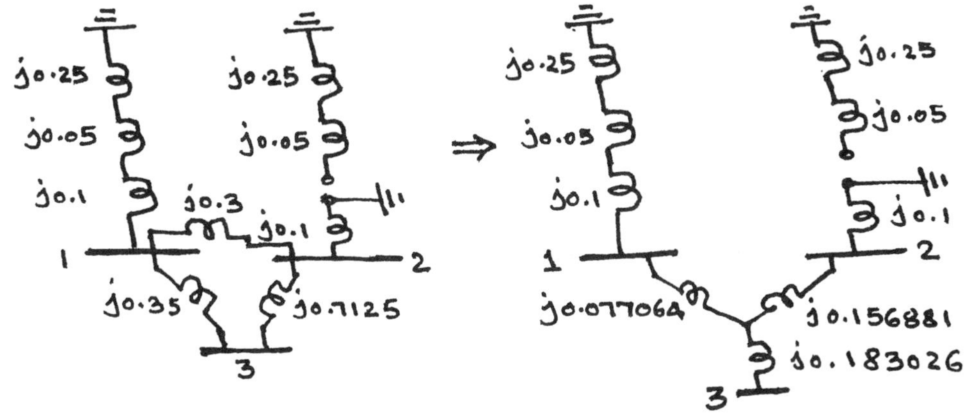

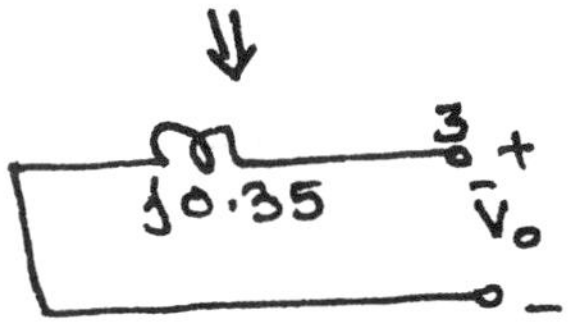

FOR THE SINGLE LINE-TO-GROUND FAULT AT BUS 3 THROUGH A FAULT IMPEDANCE $\bar{Z}_F = j0.1$,

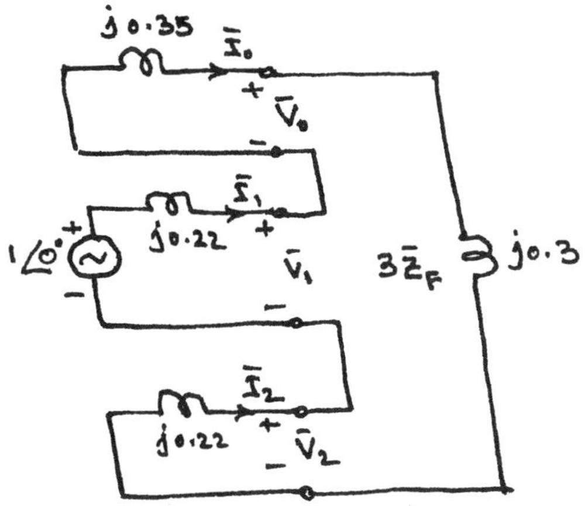

$$\bar{I}_0 = \bar{I}_1 = \bar{I}_2 = \frac{1\angle 0^\circ}{j(0.22+0.22+0.35+0.3)}$$

$$= -j0.9174$$

FAULT CURRENTS ARE

$$\begin{bmatrix} \bar{I}_a \\ \bar{I}_b \\ \bar{I}_c \end{bmatrix} = \begin{bmatrix} 1 & 1 & 1 \\ 1 & a^2 & a \\ 1 & a & a^2 \end{bmatrix} \begin{bmatrix} \bar{I}_0 \\ \bar{I}_1 \\ \bar{I}_2 \end{bmatrix} = \begin{bmatrix} -j2.7523 \\ 0 \\ 0 \end{bmatrix}$$

9.30 CONTD.

(b) FOR A LINE-TO-FAULT AT BUS 3 THROUGH A FAULT IMPEDANCE OF $j0.1$,

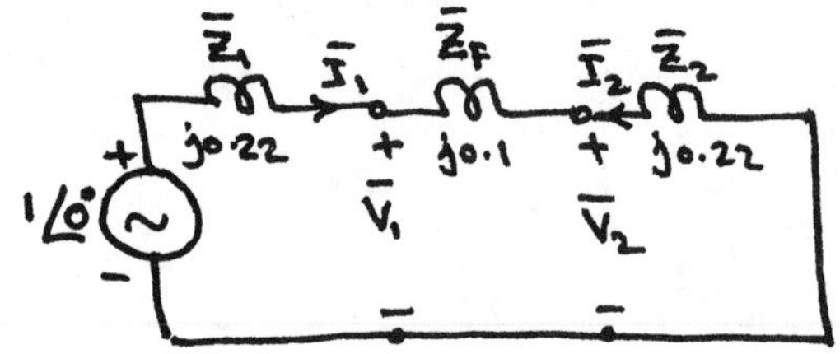

$$\bar{I}_0 = 0$$

$$\bar{I}_1 = -\bar{I}_2 = \frac{1}{j(0.22+0.22+0.1)} = -j1.8519$$

FAULT CURRENTS ARE THEN

$$\begin{bmatrix} \bar{I}_a \\ \bar{I}_b \\ \bar{I}_c \end{bmatrix} = \begin{bmatrix} 1 & 1 & 1 \\ 1 & a^2 & a \\ 1 & a & a^2 \end{bmatrix} \begin{bmatrix} 0 \\ -j1.8519 \\ j1.8519 \end{bmatrix} = \begin{bmatrix} 0 \\ -3.2075 \\ 3.2075 \end{bmatrix}$$

(c) FOR A DOUBLE LINE-TO-GROUND FAULT AT BUS 3 THROUGH A COMMON FAULT IMPEDANCE TO GROUND $\bar{Z}_F = j0.1$,

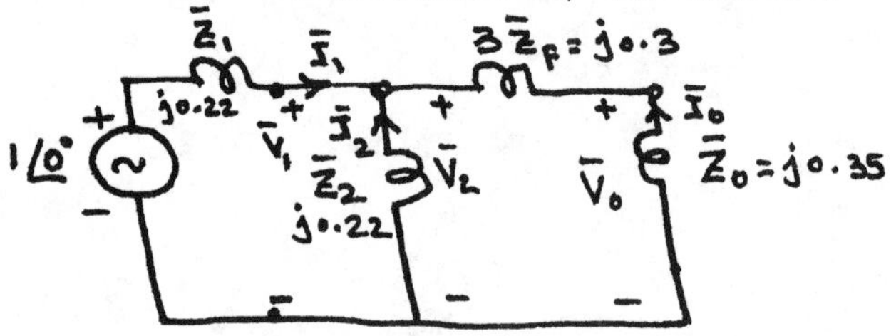

$$\bar{I}_1 = \frac{1\angle 0^\circ}{j0.22 + \frac{j0.22(j0.35 + j0.3)}{j0.22 + j0.35 + j0.3}} = -j2.6017$$

$$\bar{I}_2 = \frac{1-(j0.22)(-j2.6017)}{j0.22} = j1.9438$$

$$\bar{I}_0 = -\frac{1-(j0.22)(-j2.6017)}{j0.35 + j0.3} = j0.6579$$

FAULT PHASE CURRENTS ARE THEN

$$\begin{bmatrix} \bar{I}_a \\ \bar{I}_b \\ \bar{I}_c \end{bmatrix} = \begin{bmatrix} 1 & 1 & 1 \\ 1 & a^2 & a \\ 1 & a & a^2 \end{bmatrix} \begin{bmatrix} j0.6579 \\ -j2.6017 \\ j1.9438 \end{bmatrix} = \begin{bmatrix} 0 \\ 4.058\angle 165.93^\circ \\ 4.058\angle 14.07^\circ \end{bmatrix}$$

NEUTRAL FAULT CURRENT AT BUS 3 $= \bar{I}_b + \bar{I}_c = 3\bar{I}_0 = 1.9732\angle 90^\circ$

9.31

POSITIVE SEQUENCE NETWORK OF THE SYSTEM IS SHOWN BELOW:

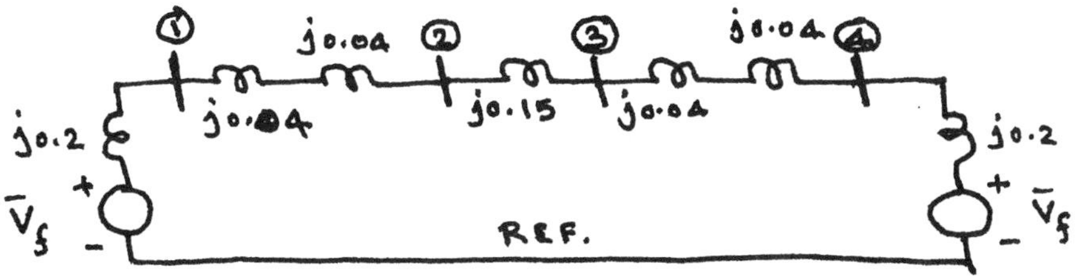

NEGATIVE SEQUENCE NETWORK IS SAME AS ABOVE WITHOUT SOURCES.

THE ZERO SEQUENCE NETWORK IS SHOWN BELOW:

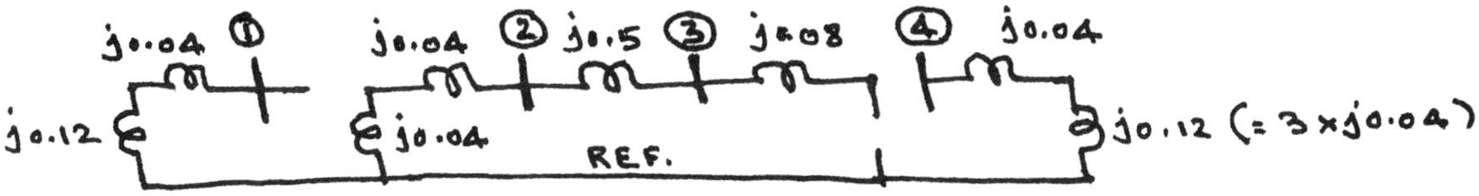

USING ANY ONE OF THE METHODS/ALGORITHMS, SEQUENCE $\bar{Z}_{BUS}$ CAN BE OBTAINED.

$$
\bar{Z}_{BUS1} = \bar{Z}_{BUS2} =
\begin{array}{c}
① \\ ② \\ ③ \\ ④
\end{array}
\begin{bmatrix}
\overset{①}{j0.1437} & \overset{②}{j0.1211} & \overset{③}{j0.0789} & \overset{④}{j0.0563} \\
j0.1211 & j0.1696 & j0.1104 & j0789 \\
j0.0789 & j0.1104 & j0.1696 & j0.1211 \\
j0.0563 & j0.0789 & j0.1211 & j0.1437
\end{bmatrix}
$$

$$
\bar{Z}_{BUS0} =
\begin{array}{c}
① \\ ② \\ ③ \\ ④
\end{array}
\begin{bmatrix}
\overset{①}{j0.16} & \overset{②}{0} & \overset{③}{0} & \overset{④}{0} \\
0 & j0.08 & j0.08 & 0 \\
0 & j0.08 & j0.58 & 0 \\
0 & 0 & 0 & j0.16
\end{bmatrix}
$$

CHOOSING THE VOLTAGE AT BUS 3 AS $1\angle 0°$, THE PREFAULT CURRENT IN LINE ②-③ IS

$$
\bar{I}_{23} = \frac{P - jQ}{\bar{V}_3^*} = \frac{0.5(0.8 - j0.6)}{1\angle 0°} = 0.4 - j0.3 \quad PU
$$

LINE ②-③ HAS PARAMETERS GIVEN BY

$$
\bar{Z}_1 = \bar{Z}_2 = j0.15 \ ; \quad \bar{Z}_0 = j0.5
$$

9.31 CONTD.

DENOTING THE OPEN-CIRCUIT POINTS OF THE LINE AS p AND p', TO SIMULATE OPENING, WE NEED TO DEVELOP THÉVENIN-EQUIVALENT SEQUENCE NETWORKS LOOKING INTO THE SYSTEM BETWEEN POINTS p AND p'.

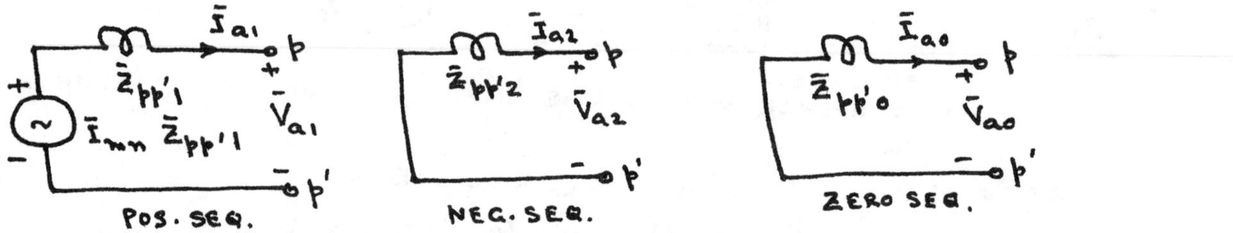

BEFORE ANY CONDUCTOR OPENS, THE CURRENT $\bar{I}_{mn}$ IN PHASE a OF THE LINE (m) – (n) IS POSITIVE SEQUENCE, GIVEN BY

$$\bar{I}_{mn} = \frac{\bar{V}_m - \bar{V}_n}{\bar{Z}_1}$$

$$\bar{Z}_{pp'1} = -\frac{\bar{Z}_1^2}{\bar{Z}_{Th,mn,1} - \bar{Z}_1} \; ; \; \bar{Z}_{pp'2} = \frac{-\bar{Z}_2^2}{\bar{Z}_{Th,mn,2} - \bar{Z}_2} \; ; \; \bar{Z}_{pp'0} = \frac{-\bar{Z}_0^2}{\bar{Z}_{Th,mn,0} - \bar{Z}_0}$$

TO SIMULATE OPEING PHASE a BETWEEN POINTS p AND p', THE SEQUENCE NETWORK CONNECTION IS SHOWN BELOW:

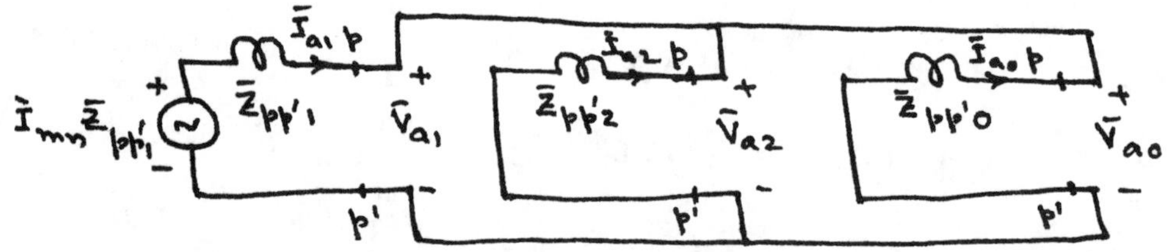

TO SIMULATE OPENING PHASES b AND c BETWEEN POINTS p AND p', THE SEQUENCE NETWORK CONNECTION IS SHOWN BELOW:

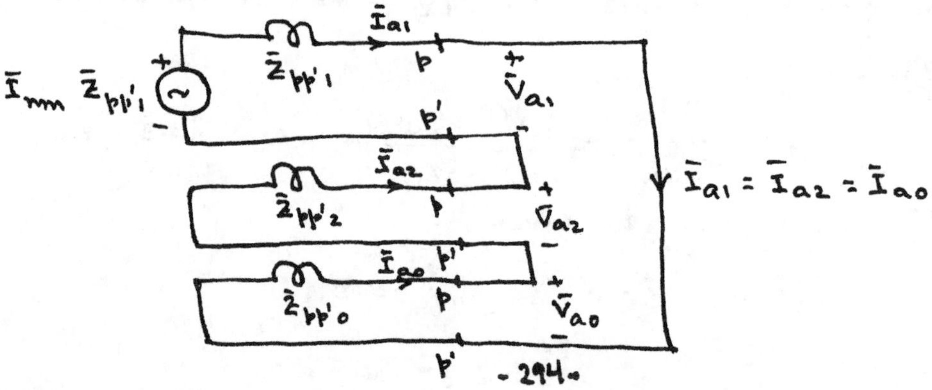

9.31 CONTD.

IN THIS PROBLEM

$$\bar{Z}_{pp'1} = \bar{Z}_{pp'2} = \frac{-\bar{Z}_1^2}{\bar{Z}_{22\,1} + \bar{Z}_{33\,1} - 2\bar{Z}_{23\,1} - \bar{Z}_1} = \frac{-j(0.15)^2}{j0.1696 + j0.1696 - 2(j0.1104) - j0.15}$$

$$= j\,0.7120$$

$$\bar{Z}_{pp'0} = \frac{-\bar{Z}_0^2}{\bar{Z}_{22\,0} + \bar{Z}_{33\,0} - 2\bar{Z}_{23\,0} - \bar{Z}_0} = \frac{-(j0.5)^2}{j0.08 + j0.58 - 2(j0.08) - j0.5}$$

$$= \infty$$

NOTE THAT AN INFINITE IMPEDANCE IS SEEN LOOKING INTO THE ZERO SEQUENCE NETWORK BETWEEN POINTS p AND p' OF THE OPENING, IF THE LINE FROM BUS ② TO BUS ③ IS OPENED. ALSO BUS ③ WOULD BE ISOLATED FROM THE REFERENCE BY OPENING THE CONNECTION BETWEEN BUS ② AND BUS ③.

(a) ONE OPEN CONDUCTOR:

$$\bar{V}_{a0} = \bar{V}_{a1} = \bar{V}_{a2} = \bar{I}_{23}\,\frac{\bar{Z}_{pp'1}\,\bar{Z}_{pp'2}}{\bar{Z}_{pp'1} + \bar{Z}_{pp'2}} = (0.4 - j0.3)\frac{(j0.712)(j0.712)}{j(0.712 + 0.712)}$$

$$= 0.1068 + j\,0.1424$$

$$\Delta\bar{V}_{3\,1} = \Delta\bar{V}_{3\,2} = \frac{\bar{Z}_{32\,1} - \bar{Z}_{33\,1}}{\bar{Z}_1}\bar{V}_{a1} = \frac{j0.1104 - j0.1696}{j0.15}(0.1068 + j0.1424)$$

$$= -0.0422 - j0.0562$$

$$\Delta\bar{V}_{3\,0} = \frac{\bar{Z}_{32\,0} - \bar{Z}_{33\,0}}{\bar{Z}_0}\bar{V}_{a0} = \frac{j0.08 - j0.58}{j0.5}(0.1068 + j0.1424)$$

$$= -0.1068 - j\,0.1424$$

$$\Delta\bar{V}_3 = \Delta\bar{V}_{3\,0} + \Delta\bar{V}_{3\,1} + \Delta\bar{V}_{3\,2} = -0.1068 - j0.1424 - 2(0.0422 + j0.0562)$$

$$= -0.1912 - j0.2548$$

SINCE THE PREFAULT VOLTAGE AT BUS ③ IS $1\angle 0^\circ$, THE NEW VOLTAGE AT BUS ③ IS

$$\bar{V}_3 + \Delta\bar{V}_3 = (1 + j0) + (-0.1912 - j0.2548)$$

$$= 0.8088 - j0.2548 = 0.848\angle -17.5^\circ \text{ PU}$$

9.31 CONTD.

(b) TWO OPEN CONDUCTORS:

INSERTING AN INFINITE IMPEDANCE OF THE ZERO SEQUENCE NETWORK IN SERIES BETWEEN POINTS p AND p' OF THE POSITIVE-SEQUENCE NETWORK CAUSES AN OPEN CIRCUIT IN THE LATTER. NO POWER TRANSFER CAN OCCUR IN THE SYSTEM. OBVIOUSLY, POWER CAN NOT BE TRANSFERRED BY ONLY ONE PHASE CONDUCTOR OF THE TRANSMISSION LINE, SINCE THE ZERO SEQUENCE NETWORK OFFERS NO RETURN PATH FOR CURRENT.

9.32 $\bar{I}_{1-1} = \dfrac{\bar{V}_F}{\bar{Z}_{11-1}} = \dfrac{1.0\angle 0^\circ}{j0.12} = -j8.333$ per unit

$$\begin{bmatrix} \bar{I}''_{1a} \\ \bar{I}''_{1b} \\ \bar{I}''_{1c} \end{bmatrix} = \begin{bmatrix} 1 & 1 & 1 \\ 1 & a^2 & a \\ 1 & a & a^2 \end{bmatrix} \begin{bmatrix} 0 \\ 8.333\angle -90^\circ \\ 0 \end{bmatrix} = \begin{bmatrix} 8.333\angle -90^\circ \\ 8.333\angle 150^\circ \\ 8.333\angle 30^\circ \end{bmatrix} \text{ per unit}$$

using Eq (9.5.9) with $k=2$ and $n=1$:

$$\begin{bmatrix} \bar{V}_{2-0} \\ \bar{V}_{2-1} \\ \bar{V}_{2-2} \end{bmatrix} = \begin{bmatrix} 0 \\ 1\angle 0^\circ \\ 0 \end{bmatrix} - \begin{bmatrix} 0 & 0 & 0 \\ 0 & j0.08 & 0 \\ 0 & 0 & j0.08 \end{bmatrix} \begin{bmatrix} 0 \\ -j8.333 \\ 0 \end{bmatrix} = \begin{bmatrix} 0 \\ 0.3333 \\ 0 \end{bmatrix} \text{ per unit}$$

$$\begin{bmatrix} \bar{V}_{2ag} \\ \bar{V}_{2bg} \\ \bar{V}_{2cg} \end{bmatrix} = \begin{bmatrix} 1 & 1 & 1 \\ 1 & a^2 & a \\ 1 & a & a^2 \end{bmatrix} \begin{bmatrix} 0 \\ 0.3333 \\ 0 \end{bmatrix} = \begin{bmatrix} 0.3333\angle 0^\circ \\ 0.3333\angle 240^\circ \\ 0.3333\angle 120^\circ \end{bmatrix} \text{ per unit}$$

9.33 $\bar{I}_{1-0} = \bar{I}_{1-1} = \bar{I}_{1-2} = \dfrac{\bar{V}_F}{\bar{Z}_{11-0} + \bar{Z}_{11-1} + \bar{Z}_{11-2}} = \dfrac{1.0\angle 0^\circ}{j(0.10 + 0.12 + 0.12)}$

$= -j2.941$ per unit

$$\begin{bmatrix} \bar{I}''_{1a} \\ \bar{I}''_{1b} \\ \bar{I}''_{1c} \end{bmatrix} = \begin{bmatrix} 1 & 1 & 1 \\ 1 & a^2 & a \\ 1 & a & a^2 \end{bmatrix} \begin{bmatrix} -j2.941 \\ -j2.941 \\ -j2.941 \end{bmatrix} = \begin{bmatrix} -j8.824 \\ 0 \\ 0 \end{bmatrix} \text{ per unit}$$

using Eq (9.5.9) with $k=2$ and $n=1$:

$$\begin{bmatrix} \bar{V}_{2-0} \\ \bar{V}_{2-1} \\ \bar{V}_{2-2} \end{bmatrix} = \begin{bmatrix} 0 \\ 1\angle 0^\circ \\ 0 \end{bmatrix} - \begin{bmatrix} 0 & 0 & 0 \\ 0 & j.08 & 0 \\ 0 & 0 & j.08 \end{bmatrix} \begin{bmatrix} -j2.941 \\ -j2.941 \\ -j2.941 \end{bmatrix} = \begin{bmatrix} 0 \\ 0.7647 \\ -0.2353 \end{bmatrix} \text{ per unit}$$

$$\begin{bmatrix} \bar{V}_{2ag} \\ \bar{V}_{2bg} \\ \bar{V}_{2cg} \end{bmatrix} = \begin{bmatrix} 1 & 1 & 1 \\ 1 & a^2 & a \\ 1 & a & a^2 \end{bmatrix} \begin{bmatrix} 0 \\ .7647 \\ -.2353 \end{bmatrix} = \begin{bmatrix} 0.5294\angle 0^\circ \\ 0.9056\angle 253.0^\circ \\ 0.9056\angle 107.0^\circ \end{bmatrix} \text{ per unit}$$

9.34 $\bar{I}_{1-1} = -\bar{I}_{1-2} = \dfrac{\bar{V}_F}{\bar{Z}_{11-1} + \bar{Z}_{11-2}} = \dfrac{1.0\angle 0°}{j(.12 + .12)}$

$= -j4.167$ per unit

$$\begin{bmatrix} \bar{I}''_{1a} \\ \bar{I}''_{1b} \\ \bar{I}''_{1c} \end{bmatrix} = \begin{bmatrix} 1 & 1 & 1 \\ 1 & a^2 & a \\ 1 & a & a^2 \end{bmatrix} \begin{bmatrix} 0 \\ -j4.167 \\ +j4.167 \end{bmatrix} = \begin{bmatrix} 0 \\ 7.217\angle 180° \\ 7.217\angle 0° \end{bmatrix} \text{ per unit}$$

Using Eq (9.5.9) with $k = 2$ and $n = 1$:

$$\begin{bmatrix} \bar{V}_{2-0} \\ \bar{V}_{2-1} \\ \bar{V}_{2-2} \end{bmatrix} = \begin{bmatrix} 0 \\ 1\angle 0° \\ 0 \end{bmatrix} - \begin{bmatrix} 0 & 0 & 0 \\ 0 & j0.08 & 0 \\ 0 & 0 & j0.08 \end{bmatrix} \begin{bmatrix} 0 \\ -j4.167 \\ j4.167 \end{bmatrix} = \begin{bmatrix} 0 \\ 0.6667 \\ 0.3333 \end{bmatrix} \text{ per unit}$$

$$\begin{bmatrix} \bar{V}_{2ag} \\ \bar{V}_{2bg} \\ \bar{V}_{2cg} \end{bmatrix} = \begin{bmatrix} 1 & 1 & 1 \\ 1 & a^2 & a \\ 1 & a & a^2 \end{bmatrix} \begin{bmatrix} 0 \\ .6667 \\ .3333 \end{bmatrix} = \begin{bmatrix} 1.0 \\ 0.5774\angle 210° \\ 0.5774\angle 150° \end{bmatrix} \text{ per unit}$$

9.35 $\bar{I}_{1-1} = \dfrac{\bar{V}_F}{\bar{Z}_{11-1} + \bar{Z}_{11-2} // \bar{Z}_{11-0}} = \dfrac{1.0\angle 0°}{j(0.12 + 0.12 // 0.10)}$

$= -j5.729$ per unit

$\bar{I}_{1-2} = (+j5.729)\left(\dfrac{0.10}{0.22}\right) = j2.604$ per unit

$\bar{I}_{1-0} = (+j5.729)\left(\dfrac{0.12}{0.22}\right) = j3.125$ per unit

$$\begin{bmatrix} \bar{I}''_{1a} \\ \bar{I}''_{1b} \\ \bar{I}''_{1c} \end{bmatrix} = \begin{bmatrix} 1 & 1 & 1 \\ 1 & a^2 & a \\ 1 & a & a^2 \end{bmatrix} \begin{bmatrix} j3.125 \\ -j5.729 \\ +j2.604 \end{bmatrix} = \begin{bmatrix} 0 \\ 8.605\angle 147.0° \\ 8.605\angle 33.0° \end{bmatrix} \text{ per unit}$$

Using Eq (9.5.9) with $k = 2$ and $n = 1$:

$$\begin{bmatrix} \bar{V}_{2-0} \\ \bar{V}_{2-1} \\ \bar{V}_{2-2} \end{bmatrix} = \begin{bmatrix} 0 \\ 1.0\angle 0° \\ 0 \end{bmatrix} - \begin{bmatrix} 0 & 0 & 0 \\ 0 & j.08 & 0 \\ 0 & 0 & j.08 \end{bmatrix} \begin{bmatrix} j3.125 \\ -j5.729 \\ j2.604 \end{bmatrix} = \begin{bmatrix} 0 \\ 0.5417 \\ 0.2083 \end{bmatrix} \text{ per unit}$$

9.35 CONTD.

$$\begin{bmatrix} \bar{V}_{2ag} \\ \bar{V}_{2bg} \\ \bar{V}_{2cg} \end{bmatrix} = \begin{bmatrix} 1 & 1 & 1 \\ 1 & a^2 & a \\ 1 & a & a^2 \end{bmatrix} \begin{bmatrix} 0 \\ .5417 \\ .2083 \end{bmatrix} = \begin{bmatrix} 0.750 \\ 0.4733\angle 217.6^\circ \\ 0.4733\angle 142.4^\circ \end{bmatrix} \text{ per unit}$$

9.36 Zero sequence bus impedance matrix:

Step (1) Add $\bar{Z}_b = j0.10$ from the reference to bus 1 (type 1)

$$\bar{Z}_{bus\text{-}0} = j\,0.10 \text{ per unit}$$

Step (2) Add $\bar{Z}_b = j\,0.2563$ from bus 1 to bus 2 (type 2)

$$\bar{Z}_{bus\text{-}0} = j\begin{bmatrix} 0.10 & 0.10 \\ 0.10 & 0.3563 \end{bmatrix} \text{ per unit}$$

Step (3) Add $\bar{Z}_b = j0.10$ from the reference to bus 2 (type 3)

$$\bar{Z}_{bus\text{-}0} = j\begin{bmatrix} 0.1 & 0.1 \\ 0.1 & 0.3563 \end{bmatrix} - \frac{j}{.4563}\begin{bmatrix} .10 \\ .3563 \end{bmatrix}\begin{bmatrix} .10 & .3563 \end{bmatrix} = j\begin{bmatrix} .07808 & .02192 \\ .02192 & .07808 \end{bmatrix}$$

Step (4) Add $\bar{Z}_b = j0.1709$ from bus 2 to bus 3 (type 2)

$$\bar{Z}_{bus\text{-}0} = j\begin{bmatrix} 0.07808 & 0.02192 & 0.02192 \\ 0.02192 & 0.07808 & 0.07808 \\ 0.02192 & 0.07808 & 0.24898 \end{bmatrix} \text{ per unit}$$

Step (5) Add $\bar{Z}_b = j0.1709$ from bus 1 to bus 3 (type 4)

$$\bar{Z}_{bus\text{-}0} = j\begin{bmatrix} .07808 & .02192 & .02192 \\ .02192 & .07808 & .07808 \\ .02192 & .07808 & .24898 \end{bmatrix} - \frac{j}{.45412}\begin{bmatrix} .05616 \\ -.05616 \\ -.22706 \end{bmatrix}\begin{bmatrix} .05616 & -.05616 & -.22706 \end{bmatrix}$$

$$\bar{Z}_{bus\text{-}0} = j\begin{bmatrix} 0.07114 & 0.02887 & 0.05 \\ 0.02887 & 0.07114 & 0.05 \\ 0.05 & 0.05 & 0.13545 \end{bmatrix} \text{ per unit}$$

9.36 CONTD. Positive Sequence bus impedance matrix:

Step (1) Add $\bar{Z}_b = j0.28$ from the reference to bus 1 (type 1)

$$\bar{Z}_{bus-1} = j\begin{bmatrix} 0.28 \end{bmatrix} \text{ per unit}$$

Step (2) Add $\bar{Z}_b = j\,0.08544$ from bus 1 to bus 2 (type 2)

$$\bar{Z}_{bus-1} = j\begin{bmatrix} .28 & .28 \\ .28 & .36544 \end{bmatrix} \text{ per unit}$$

Step (3) Add $\bar{Z}_b = j0.3$ from the reference to bus 2 (type 3)

$$\bar{Z}_{bus-1} = j\begin{bmatrix} .28 & .28 \\ .28 & .36544 \end{bmatrix} - \frac{j}{.66544}\begin{bmatrix} .28 \\ .36544 \end{bmatrix}\begin{bmatrix} .28 & .36544 \end{bmatrix} = j\begin{bmatrix} .16218 & .12623 \\ .12623 & .16475 \end{bmatrix}$$

Step (4) Add $\bar{Z}_b = j.06835$ from bus 2 to bus 3 (type 2)

$$\bar{Z}_{bus-1} = j\begin{bmatrix} 0.16218 & 0.12623 & 0.12623 \\ 0.12623 & 0.16475 & 0.16475 \\ 0.12623 & 0.16475 & 0.2331 \end{bmatrix} \text{ per unit}$$

Step (5) Add $\bar{Z}_b = j.06835$ from bus 1 to bus 3 (type 4)

$$\bar{Z}_{bus-1} = j\begin{bmatrix} .16218 & .12623 & .12623 \\ .12623 & .16475 & .16475 \\ .12623 & .16475 & .2331 \end{bmatrix} - \frac{j}{.21117}\begin{bmatrix} .03595 \\ -.03852 \\ -.10687 \end{bmatrix}\begin{bmatrix} .03595 & -.03852 & -.10687 \end{bmatrix}$$

$$\bar{Z}_{bus-1} = j\begin{bmatrix} .15606 & .13279 & .14442 \\ .13279 & .15772 & .14526 \\ .14442 & .14526 & .17901 \end{bmatrix} \text{ per unit}$$

Step (6) Add $\bar{Z}_b = j(.4853 // .4939) = j0.2448$ from the reference to bus 3 (type 3)

$$\bar{Z}_{bus-1} = j\begin{bmatrix} .15606 & .13279 & .14442 \\ .13279 & .15772 & .14526 \\ .14442 & .14526 & .17901 \end{bmatrix} - \frac{j}{.42379}\begin{bmatrix} .14442 \\ .14526 \\ .17901 \end{bmatrix}\begin{bmatrix} .14442 & .14526 & .17901 \end{bmatrix}$$

$$\bar{Z}_{bus-1} = j\begin{bmatrix} 0.1068 & 0.08329 & 0.08342 \\ 0.08329 & 0.1079 & 0.08390 \\ 0.08342 & 0.08390 & 0.10340 \end{bmatrix} \text{ per unit}$$

9.36 CONTD. Negative sequence bus impedance matrix:

Steps (1)–(5) are the same as for $\bar{Z}_{bus-1}$.

Step (6) Add $\bar{Z}_b = j(.5981 // .4939) = j0.2705$ from the reference bus to bus 3 (type 3)

$$\bar{Z}_{bus-2} = j\begin{bmatrix} .15606 & .13279 & .14442 \\ .13279 & .15772 & .14526 \\ .14442 & .14526 & .17901 \end{bmatrix} - \frac{j}{.44951}\begin{bmatrix} .14442 \\ .14526 \\ .17901 \end{bmatrix}\begin{bmatrix} .14442 & .14526 & .17901 \end{bmatrix}$$

$$\bar{Z}_{bus-2} = j\begin{bmatrix} 0.1097 & 0.08612 & 0.08691 \\ 0.08612 & 0.11078 & 0.08741 \\ 0.08691 & 0.08741 & 0.10772 \end{bmatrix} \text{ per unit}$$

9.37 From the results of problem 9.29, $\bar{Z}_{11-0} = j0.07114$, $\bar{Z}_{11-1} = j0.1068$, and $\bar{Z}_{11-2} = j0.1097$ per unit are the same as the Thevenin equivalent sequence impedances at bus 1, as calculated in Problem 9.2. Therefore, the fault currents calculated from the sequence impedance matrices will be the same as those calculated in Problems 9.3 and 9.10 – 9.13.

9.38 Zero sequence bus impedance matrix:

Step (1) Add $\bar{Z}_b = j\,0.24$ from the reference to bus 1 (type 1)

$$\bar{Z}_{bus-0} = j\,[\,0.24\,] \quad \text{per unit}$$

Step (2) Add $\bar{Z}_b = j\,0.6$ from bus 1 to bus 2 (type 2)

$$\bar{Z}_{bus-0} = j\begin{bmatrix} 0.24 & 0.24 \\ 0.24 & 0.84 \end{bmatrix} \quad \text{per unit}$$

Step (3) Add $\bar{Z}_b = j\,0.6$ from bus 2 to bus 3 (type 2)

$$\bar{Z}_{bus-0} = j\begin{bmatrix} 0.24 & 0.24 & 0.24 \\ 0.24 & 0.84 & 0.84 \\ 0.24 & 0.84 & 1.44 \end{bmatrix} \quad \text{per unit}$$

Step (4) Add $\bar{Z}_b = j\,0.10$ from the reference to bus 3 (type 3)

$$\bar{Z}_{bus-0} = j\begin{bmatrix} .24 & .24 & .24 \\ .24 & .84 & .84 \\ .24 & .84 & 1.44 \end{bmatrix} - \frac{j}{1.54}\begin{bmatrix} .24 \\ .84 \\ 1.44 \end{bmatrix}\begin{bmatrix} .24 & .84 & 1.44 \end{bmatrix}$$

$$\bar{Z}_{bus-0} = j\begin{bmatrix} 0.2026 & 0.1091 & 0.01558 \\ 0.1091 & 0.3818 & 0.05455 \\ 0.01558 & 0.05455 & 0.09351 \end{bmatrix} \quad \text{per unit}$$

Step (5) Add $\bar{Z}_b = j\,0.6$ from bus 2 to bus 4 (type 2)

$$\bar{Z}_{bus-0} = j\begin{bmatrix} 0.2026 & 0.1091 & 0.01558 & 0.1091 \\ 0.1091 & 0.3818 & 0.05455 & 0.3818 \\ 0.01558 & 0.05455 & 0.09351 & 0.05455 \\ 0.1091 & 0.3818 & 0.05455 & 0.9818 \end{bmatrix} \quad \text{per unit}$$

9.38 CONTD. step(6) Add $\bar{Z}_b = j\,0.1333$ from the reference bus to bus 4 (type 3)

$$\bar{Z}_{bus-0} = j\begin{bmatrix} .2026 & .1091 & .01558 & .1091 \\ .1091 & .3818 & .05455 & .3818 \\ .01558 & .05455 & .09351 & .05455 \\ .1091 & .3818 & .05455 & .9818 \end{bmatrix} - \frac{j}{1.1151}\begin{bmatrix} .1091 \\ .3818 \\ .05455 \\ .9818 \end{bmatrix}\begin{bmatrix} .1091 & .3818 & .05455 & .9818 \end{bmatrix}$$

$$\bar{Z}_{bus-0} = j\begin{bmatrix} 0.1919 & 0.07175 & 0.01024 & 0.01304 \\ 0.07175 & 0.2511 & 0.03587 & 0.04564 \\ 0.01024 & 0.03587 & 0.09084 & 0.006521 \\ 0.01304 & 0.04564 & 0.006521 & 0.1174 \end{bmatrix} \text{ per unit}$$

Positive sequence bus impedance matrix:
(see Problem 8.18)

$$\bar{Z}_{bus-1} = j\begin{bmatrix} 0.2671 & 0.1505 & 0.0865 & 0.0980 \\ 0.1505 & 0.1975 & 0.1135 & 0.1286 \\ 0.0865 & 0.1135 & 0.1801 & 0.0739 \\ 0.0980 & 0.1286 & 0.0739 & 0.2140 \end{bmatrix} \text{ per unit}$$

Negative sequence bus impedance matrix:
Steps (1)–(4) are the same as for $\bar{Z}_{bus-1}$ (see Problem 8.18).
Step (5) Add $\bar{Z}_b = j\,0.3$ from the reference bus to bus 3 (type 3)

$$\bar{Z}_{bus-2} = j\begin{bmatrix} .64 & .64 & .64 & .64 \\ .64 & .84 & .84 & .84 \\ .64 & .84 & 1.04 & .84 \\ .64 & .84 & .84 & 1.04 \end{bmatrix} - \frac{j}{1.34}\begin{bmatrix} .64 \\ .84 \\ 1.04 \\ .84 \end{bmatrix}\begin{bmatrix} .64 & .84 & 1.04 & .84 \end{bmatrix}$$

9.38 CONTD.

$$\bar{Z}_{bus-2} = j\begin{bmatrix} .3343 & .2388 & .1433 & .2388 \\ .2388 & .3134 & .1881 & .3134 \\ .1433 & .1881 & .2328 & .1881 \\ .2388 & .3134 & .1881 & .5134 \end{bmatrix} \text{ per unit}$$

step (6) Add $\bar{Z}_b = j0.3733$ from the reference to bus 4 (type 3)

$$\bar{Z}_{bus-2} = j\begin{bmatrix} .3343 & .2388 & .1433 & .2388 \\ .2388 & .3134 & .1881 & .3134 \\ .1433 & .1881 & .2328 & .1881 \\ .2388 & .3134 & .1881 & .5134 \end{bmatrix} - \frac{j}{.8867}\begin{bmatrix} .2388 \\ .3134 \\ .1881 \\ .5134 \end{bmatrix}\begin{bmatrix} .2388 & .3134 & .1881 & .5134 \end{bmatrix}$$

$$\bar{Z}_{bus-2} = j\begin{bmatrix} 0.2700 & 0.1544 & 0.09264 & 0.1005 \\ 0.1544 & 0.2026 & 0.1216 & 0.1319 \\ 0.09264 & 0.1216 & 0.1929 & 0.07919 \\ 0.1005 & 0.1319 & 0.07919 & 0.2161 \end{bmatrix} \text{ per unit}$$

9.39 From the results of Problem 9.31, $\bar{Z}_{11-0} = j0.1919$, $\bar{Z}_{11-1} = j0.2671$, and $\bar{Z}_{11-2} = j0.2700$ per unit are the same as the Thevenin equivalent sequence impedances at bus 1, as calculated in Problem 9.5. Therefore, the fault currents calculated from the sequence impedance matrices are the same as those calculated in Problems 9.6, 9.16–9.18.

9.40 Zero sequence bus impedance matrix:

Working backwards from bus 4:

step (1) Add $z_b = j0.1$ from the reference bus to bus 4 (type 1)

$$\overline{Z}_{bus-0} = \begin{matrix} 4 \\ \left[j\,0.1 \right] \end{matrix} 4 \quad \text{per unit}$$

step (2) Add $\overline{Z}_b = j0.5251$ from bus 4 to bus 3 (type 2)

$$\overline{Z}_{bus-0} = j\begin{matrix} & 3 & 4 \\ \begin{bmatrix} 0.6251 & 0.1 \\ 0.1 & 0.1 \end{bmatrix} & \begin{matrix} 3 \\ 4 \end{matrix} \end{matrix} \quad \text{per unit}$$

step (3) Add $\overline{Z}_b = j0.5251$ from bus 3 to bus 2 (type 2)

$$\overline{Z}_{bus-0} = j\begin{matrix} & 2 & 3 & 4 \\ \begin{bmatrix} 1.1502 & 0.6251 & 0.1 \\ 0.6251 & 0.6251 & 0.1 \\ 0.1 & 0.1 & 0.1 \end{bmatrix} & \begin{matrix} 2 \\ 3 \\ 4 \end{matrix} \end{matrix} \quad \text{per unit}$$

step (4) Add $\overline{Z}_b = j0.2$ from bus 2 to bus 1 (type 2)

$$\overline{Z}_{bus-0} = j\begin{matrix} & 1 & 2 & 3 & 4 \\ \begin{bmatrix} 1.3502 & 1.1502 & 0.6251 & 0.1 \\ 1.1502 & 1.1502 & 0.6251 & 0.1 \\ 0.6251 & 0.6251 & 0.6251 & 0.1 \\ 0.1 & 0.1 & 0.1 & 0.1 \end{bmatrix} & \begin{matrix} 1 \\ 2 \\ 3 \\ 4 \end{matrix} \end{matrix} \quad \begin{matrix} \text{per} \\ \text{unit} \end{matrix}$$

step (5) Add $\overline{Z}_b = j0.1$ from the reference to bus 5 (type 1)

$$\overline{Z}_{bus-0} = j\begin{bmatrix} 1.3502 & 1.1502 & 0.6251 & 0.1 & 0 \\ 1.1502 & 1.1502 & 0.6251 & 0.1 & 0 \\ 0.6251 & 0.6251 & 0.6251 & 0.1 & 0 \\ 0.1 & 0.1 & 0.1 & 0.1 & 0 \\ 0 & 0 & 0 & 0 & 0.1 \end{bmatrix} \quad \begin{matrix} \text{per} \\ \text{unit} \end{matrix}$$

9.40 CONTD. Positive sequence bus impedance matrix:

See Problem 8.19

$$\bar{Z}_{bus-1} = j\begin{bmatrix} 0.3542 & 0.2772 & 0.1964 & 0.1155 & 0.0770 \\ 0.2772 & 0.3735 & 0.2645 & 0.1556 & 0.1037 \\ 0.1964 & 0.2645 & 0.3361 & 0.1977 & 0.1318 \\ 0.1155 & 0.1556 & 0.1977 & 0.2398 & 0.1599 \\ 0.0770 & 0.1037 & 0.1318 & 0.1599 & 0.1733 \end{bmatrix}$$

per unit

Negative sequence bus impedance matrix:

Steps (1) – (5) are the same as for $\bar{Z}_{bus-1}$ (see Problem 8.19)

Step (6) Add $\bar{Z}_b = j0.23$ from the reference bus to bus 5 (type 3)

$$\bar{Z}_{bus-2} = j\begin{bmatrix} .576 & .576 & .576 & .576 & .576 \\ .576 & .776 & .776 & .776 & .776 \\ .576 & .776 & .986 & .986 & .986 \\ .576 & .776 & .986 & 1.196 & 1.196 \\ .576 & .776 & .986 & 1.196 & 1.296 \end{bmatrix} - \frac{j}{1.526}\begin{bmatrix} .576 \\ .776 \\ .986 \\ 1.196 \\ 1.296 \end{bmatrix}\begin{bmatrix} .576 & .776 & .986 & 1.196 & 1.296 \end{bmatrix}$$

$$\bar{Z}_{bus-2} = j\begin{bmatrix} 0.3586 & 0.2831 & 0.2038 & 0.1246 & 0.08682 \\ 0.2831 & 0.3814 & 0.2746 & 0.1678 & 0.1170 \\ 0.2038 & 0.2746 & 0.3489 & 0.2132 & 0.1486 \\ 0.1246 & 0.1678 & 0.2132 & 0.2586 & 0.1803 \\ 0.08682 & 0.1170 & 0.1486 & 0.1803 & 0.1953 \end{bmatrix}$$

per unit

9.41 From the results of Problem 9.33,

$\bar{Z}_{11-0} = j1.3502$, $\bar{Z}_{11-1} = j0.3542$, and $\bar{Z}_{11-2} = j0.3586$ per unit are the same as the Thevenin equivalent sequence impedances at bus 1, as calculated in Problem 9.8. Therefore, the fault currents calculated from the sequence impedance matrices are the same as those calculated in Problems 9.9, 9.19 – 9.22.

9.42

(a) & (b) EITHER BY INVERTING $\bar{Y}_{BUS}$ OR BY THE BUILDING ALGORITHM $\bar{Z}_{BUS}$ CAN BE OBTAINED AS

$\bar{Z}_{BUS}$ =

	①	②	③	④	⑤
①	j 0.0793	j 0.0558	j 0.0382	j 0.0511	j 0.0608
②	j 0.0558	j 0.1338	j 0.0664	j 0.0630	j 0.0605
③	j 0.0382	j 0.0664	j 0.0875	j 0.0720	j 0.0603
④	j 0.0511	j 0.0630	j 0.0720	j 0.2321	j 0.1002
⑤	j 0.0608	j 0.0605	j 0.0603	j 0.1002	j 0.1301

(c)

THÉVENIN EQUIVALENT CIRCUITS TO CALCULATE VOLTAGES AT BUS ③ AND BUS ⑤ DUE TO FAULT AT BUS ④ ARE SHOWN BELOW:

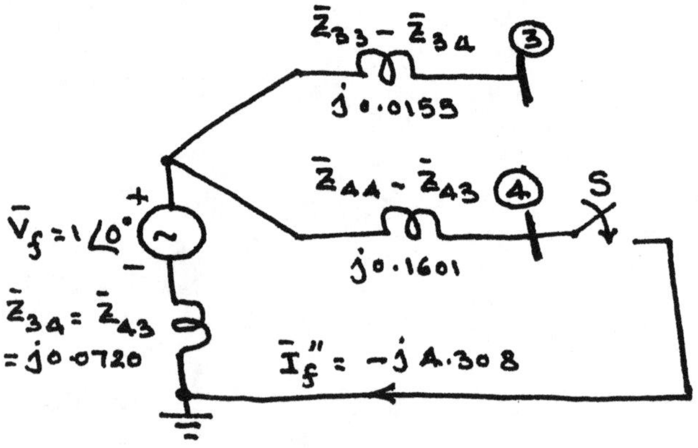

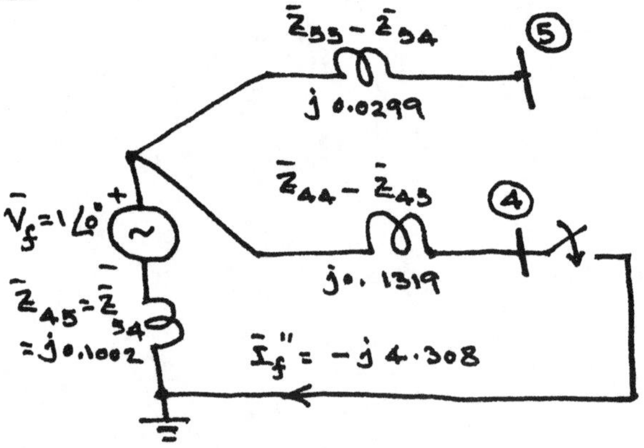

SIMPLY BY CLOSING S, THE SUBTRANSIENT CURRENT IN THE 3-PHASE FAULT AT BUS ④ IS GIVEN BY

$$\bar{I}_f'' = \frac{1.0}{j0.2321} = -j\,4.308$$

THE VOLTAGE AT BUS ③ DURING THE FAULT IS

$$\bar{V}_3 = \bar{V}_f - \bar{I}_f'' \bar{Z}_{34} = 1 - (-j4.308)(j0.0720) = 0.6898$$

THE VOLTAGE AT BUS ⑤ DURING THE FAULT IS

$$\bar{V}_5 = \bar{V}_f - \bar{I}_f'' \bar{Z}_{54} = 1 - (-j4.308)(j0.1002) = 0.5683$$

CURRENTS INTO THE FAULT AT BUS ④ OVER THE LINE IMPEDANCES ARE

9.42 CONTD.

FROM BUS ③ : $\dfrac{0.6898}{j0.336} = -j2.053$

FROM BUS ⑤ : $\dfrac{0.5683}{j0.252} = -j2.255$

HENCE, TOTAL FAULT CURRENT AT BUS ④ $= -j\,4.308$ PU

9.43

THE IMPEDANCE OF LINE ①-② IS $\bar{Z}_b = j0.168$.

$\bar{Z}_{BUS}$ IS GIVEN IN THE SOLUTION OF PROB. 9.42.

THE THÉVENIN EQUIVALENT CIRCUIT LOOKING INTO THE SYSTEM BETWEEN BUSES ① AND ② IS SHOWN BELOW:

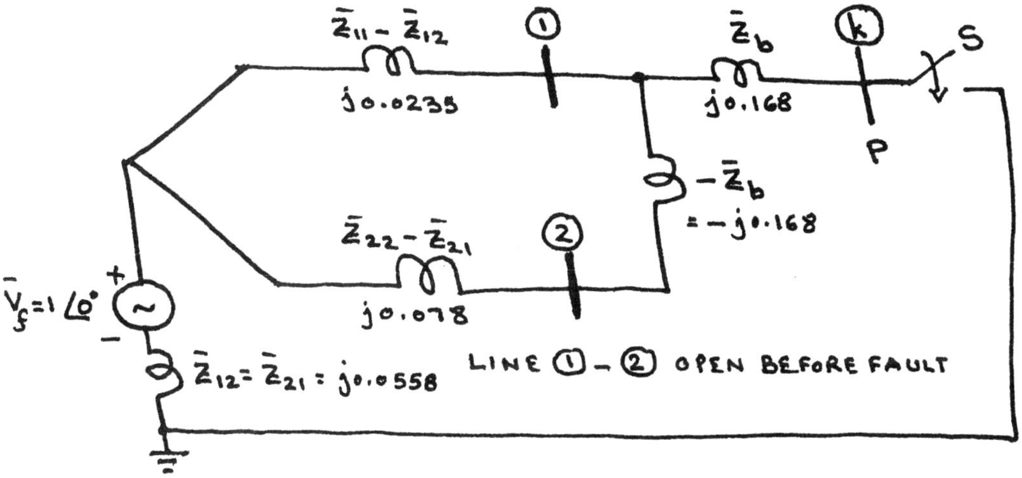

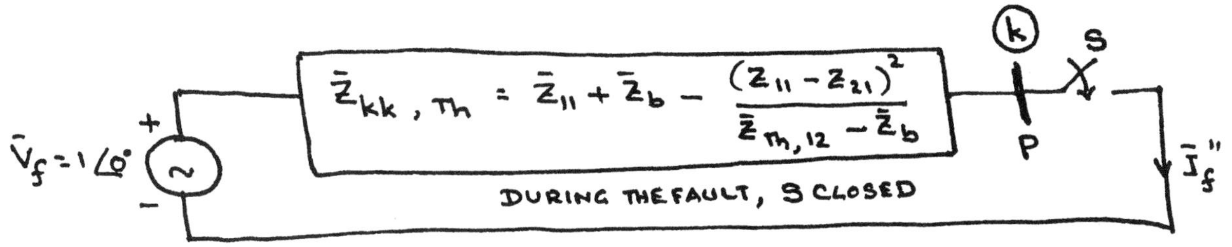

$$\bar{Z}_{kk,Th} = j0.168 + \frac{(j0.0235)(-j0.09)}{j(0.0235 - 0.09)} + j0.0558 = j0.2556$$

∴ SUBTRANSIENT CURRENT INTO LINE-END FAULT $\bar{I}_f'' = 1/j0.2556 = -j3.912$ PU

9.44

(a)

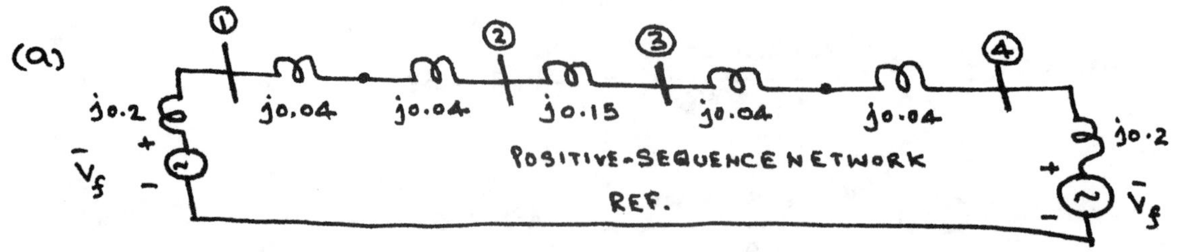

NEGATIVE-SEQUENCE NETWORK IS SAME AS ABOVE WITHOUT SOURCES.

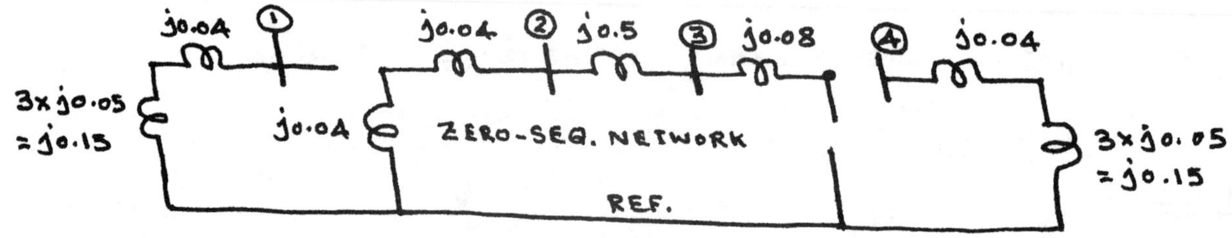

$$\bar{Z}_{BUS\,1}=\bar{Z}_{BUS\,2}=\begin{array}{c}\\ ①\\ ②\\ ③\\ ④\end{array}\begin{array}{c}\begin{array}{cccc}① & ② & ③ & ④\end{array}\\ \left[\begin{array}{cccc} j0.1437 & j0.1211 & j0.0789 & j0.0563\\ j0.1211 & j0.1696 & j0.1104 & j0.0789\\ j0.0789 & j0.1104 & j0.1696 & j0.1211\\ j0.0563 & j0.0789 & j0.1211 & j0.1437 \end{array}\right]\end{array}$$

$$\bar{Z}_{BUS\,0}=\begin{array}{c}\\ ①\\ ②\\ ③\\ ④\end{array}\begin{array}{c}\begin{array}{cccc}① & ② & ③ & ④\end{array}\\ \left[\begin{array}{cccc} j0.19 & 0 & 0 & 0\\ 0 & j0.08 & j0.08 & 0\\ 0 & j0.08 & j0.58 & 0\\ 0 & 0 & 0 & j0.19 \end{array}\right]\end{array}$$

(b) FOR THE LINE-TO-LINE FAULT, THÉVENIN EQUIVALENT CIRCUIT:

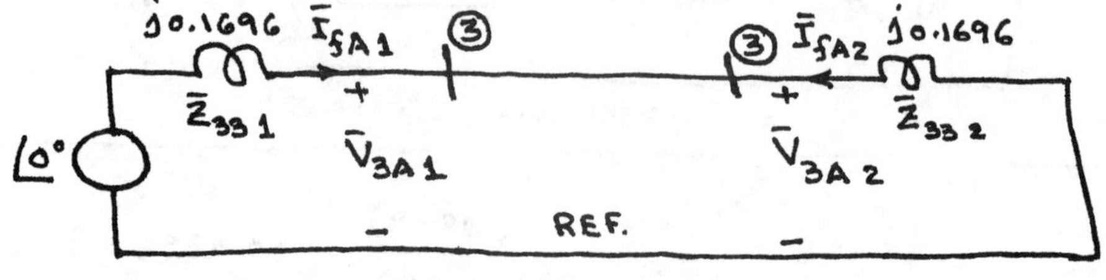

UPPER CASE A IS USED BECAUSE FAULT IS IN THE HV-TRANSMISSION LINE CIRCUIT.

9.44 CONTD.

$$\bar{I}_{fA1} = -\bar{I}_{fA2} = \frac{1\angle 0°}{j0.1696 + j0.1696} = -j2.9481$$

$$\bar{I}_{fA} = \bar{I}_{fA1} + \bar{I}_{fA2} = 0$$

$$\bar{I}_{fB} = a^2\,\bar{I}_{fA1} + a\,\bar{I}_{fA2} = -5.1061 + j0 = 855\angle 180°\ \text{A}$$

$$\bar{I}_{fC} = -\bar{I}_{fB} = 5.1061 + j0 = 855\angle 0°\ \text{A}$$

∵ BASE CURRENT IN HV TRANSMISSION LINE IS $\frac{100{,}000}{\sqrt{3}\times 345} = 167.35\text{A}$

SYMMETRICAL COMPONENTS OF PHASE-A VOLTAGE TO GROUND AT BUS ③ ARE

$$\bar{V}_{3A0} = 0;\quad \bar{V}_{3A1} = \bar{V}_{3A2} = 1-(j0.1696)(-j2.9481) = 0.5 + j0$$

LINE-TO-GROUND VOLTAGES AT FAULT BUS ③ ARE

$$\bar{V}_{3A} = \bar{V}_{3A0} + \bar{V}_{3A1} + \bar{V}_{3A2} = 0 + 0.5 + 0.5 = 1\angle 0°$$

$$\bar{V}_{3B} = \bar{V}_{3A0} + a^2\,\bar{V}_{3A1} + a\,\bar{V}_{3A2} = 0.5\angle 180°$$

$$\bar{V}_{3C} = \bar{V}_{3B} = 0.5\angle 180°$$

LINE-TO-LINE VOLTAGES AT FAULT BUS ③ ARE

$$\bar{V}_{3,AB} = \bar{V}_{3A} - \bar{V}_{3B} = 1.5\angle 0° = 1.5\times\frac{345}{\sqrt{3}} = 299\angle 0°\ \text{kV}$$

$$\bar{V}_{3,BC} = \bar{V}_{3B} - \bar{V}_{3C} = 0$$

$$\bar{V}_{3,CA} = \bar{V}_{3C} - \bar{V}_{3A} = 1.5\angle 180° = 299\angle 180°\ \text{kV}$$

AVOIDING, FOR THE MOMENT, PHASE SHIFTS DUE TO Δ-Y TRANSFORMER CONNECTED TO MACHINE 2, SEQUENCE VOLTAGES OF PHASE A AT BUS ④ USING THE BUS-IMPEDANCE MATRIX ARE CALCULATED AS

$$\bar{V}_{4A0} = -\bar{Z}_{430}\,\bar{I}_{fA0} = 0$$

$$\bar{V}_{4A1} = \bar{V}_f - \bar{Z}_{431}\,\bar{I}_{fA1} = 1-(j0.1211)(-j2.9481) = 0.643$$

$$\bar{V}_{4A2} = -\bar{Z}_{432}\,\bar{I}_{fA2} = -(j0.1211)(j2.9481) = 0.357$$

9.44 CONTD.

ACCOUNTING FOR PHASE SHIFTS

$\bar{V}_{4a1} = \bar{V}_{4A1} \angle -30^\circ = 0.643 \angle -30^\circ = 0.5569 - j0.3215$

$\bar{V}_{4a2} = \bar{V}_{4A2} \angle 30^\circ = 0.357 \angle 30^\circ = 0.3092 + j0.1785$

$\bar{V}_{4a} = \bar{V}_{4a0} + \bar{V}_{4a1} + \bar{V}_{4a2} = 0.8661 - j0.143 = 0.8778 \angle -9.4^\circ$

PHASE – b VOLTAGES AT TERMINALS OF MACHINE 2 ARE

$\bar{V}_{4b0} = \bar{V}_{4a0} = 0$

$\bar{V}_{4b1} = a^2 \bar{V}_{4a1} = 0.643 \angle 240^\circ - 30^\circ = -0.5569 - j0.3215$

$\bar{V}_{4b2} = a \bar{V}_{4a2} = 0.357 \angle 120^\circ + 30^\circ = -0.3092 + j0.1785$

$\bar{V}_{4b} = \bar{V}_{4b0} + \bar{V}_{4b1} + \bar{V}_{4b2} = -0.8661 - j0.143 = 0.8778 \angle -170.6^\circ$

FOR PHASE c OF MACHINE 2

$\bar{V}_{4c0} = \bar{V}_{4a0} = 0$

$\bar{V}_{4c1} = a \bar{V}_{4a1} = 0.643 \angle 90^\circ \; ; \; \bar{V}_{4c2} = a^2 \bar{V}_{4a2} = 0.357 \angle -90^\circ$

$\bar{V}_{4c} = \bar{V}_{4c0} + \bar{V}_{4c1} + \bar{V}_{4c2} = j0.286$

LINE-TO-LINE VOLTAGES AT TERMINALS OF MACHINE 2 ARE GIVEN BY

$\bar{V}_{4,ab} = \bar{V}_{4a} - \bar{V}_{4b} = 1.7322 + j0 = 1.7322 \times \frac{20}{\sqrt{3}} = 20 \angle 0^\circ$ kV

$\bar{V}_{4,bc} = \bar{V}_{4b} - \bar{V}_{4c} = -0.8661 - j0.429 = 0.9665 \angle -153.65^\circ = 11.2 \angle -153.65^\circ$ kV

$\bar{V}_{4,ca} = \bar{V}_{4c} - \bar{V}_{4a} = -0.8661 + j0.429 = 0.9665 \angle 153.65^\circ = 11.2 \angle 153.65^\circ$ kV

(c) FOR THE DOUBLE LINE-TO-LINE FAULT, CONNECTION OF THÉVENIN EQUIVALENTS OF SEQUENCE NETWORKS IS SHOWN BELOW:

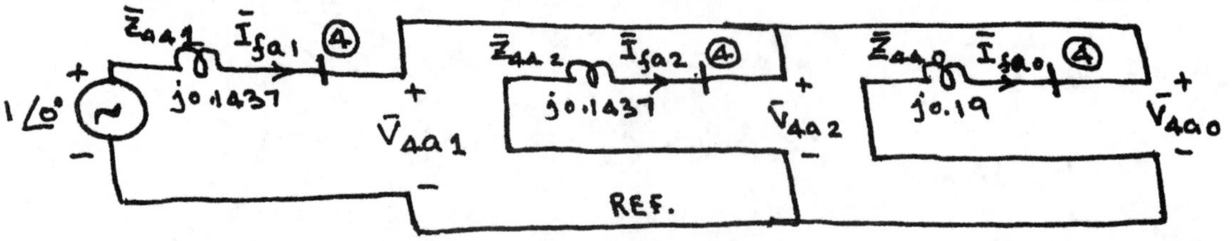

9.44 CONTD.

$$\bar{I}_{fa1} = \frac{1\angle 0^\circ}{j0.1437 + \frac{j0.1437(j0.19)}{j(0.1437+0.19)}} = -j4.4342$$

SEQUENCE VOLTAGES AT THE FAULT ARE

$$\bar{V}_{4a1} = \bar{V}_{4a2} = \bar{V}_{4a0} = 1 - (-j4.4342)(j0.1437) = 0.3628$$

$$\bar{I}_{fa2} = j4.4342 \frac{j0.19}{j(0.1437+0.19)} = j2.5247$$

$$\bar{I}_{fa0} = j4.4342 \frac{j0.1437}{j(0.1437+0.19)} = j1.9095$$

CURRENTS OUT OF THE SYSTEM AT THE FAULT POINT ARE

$$\bar{I}_{fa} = \bar{I}_{fa0} + \bar{I}_{fa1} + \bar{I}_{fa2} = 0$$

$$\bar{I}_{fb} = \bar{I}_{fa0} + a^2\bar{I}_{fa1} + a\bar{I}_{fa2} = -6.0266 + j2.8642 = 6.6726\angle 154.6^\circ$$

$$\bar{I}_{fc} = \bar{I}_{fa0} + a\bar{I}_{fa1} + a^2\bar{I}_{fa2} = 6.0266 + j2.8642 = 6.6726\angle 25.4^\circ$$

CURRENT I_f INTO THE GROUND IS

$$\bar{I}_f = \bar{I}_{fb} + \bar{I}_{fc} = 3\bar{I}_{fa0} = j5.7285$$

a-b-c VOLTAGES AT THE FAULT BUS ARE

$$\bar{V}_{4a} = \bar{V}_{4a0} + \bar{V}_{4a1} + \bar{V}_{4a2} = 3\bar{V}_{4a1} = 3(0.3628) = 1.0884$$

$$\bar{V}_{4b} = \bar{V}_{4c} = 0$$

$$\bar{V}_{4,ab} = \bar{V}_{4a} - \bar{V}_{4b} = 1.0884 \;;\; \bar{V}_{4,bc} = \bar{V}_{4b} - \bar{V}_{4c} = 0 \;;$$

$$\bar{V}_{4,ca} = \bar{V}_{4c} - \bar{V}_{4a} = -1.0884$$

$$\text{BASE CURRENT} = \frac{100\times 10^3}{\sqrt{3}\times 20} = 2887\text{A}$$

$$\therefore \bar{I}_{fa} = 0 \;;\; \bar{I}_{fb} = 19.262\angle 154.6^\circ \text{ kA} \;;\; \bar{I}_{fc} = 19.262\angle 25.4^\circ \text{ kA}$$

$$\bar{I}_f = 16.538\angle 90^\circ \text{kA}$$

BASE LINE-TO-NEUTRAL VOLTAGE IN MACHINE 2 IS $20/\sqrt{3}$ kV

$$\therefore \bar{V}_{4,ab} = 12.568\angle 0^\circ \text{kV} \;;\; \bar{V}_{4,bc} = 0 \;;\; \bar{V}_{4,ca} = 12.568\angle 180^\circ \text{kV}$$

9.45

(a) $\bar{Z}_{BUS\,1}$ AND $\bar{Z}_{BUS\,2}$ ARE SAME AS IN THE SOLUTION OF PROB. 9.44.

HOWEVER, BECAUSE THE TRANSFORMERS ARE SOLIDLY GROUNDED ON BOTH SIDES, THE ZERO-SEQUENCE NETWORK IS CHANGED AS SHOWN BELOW:

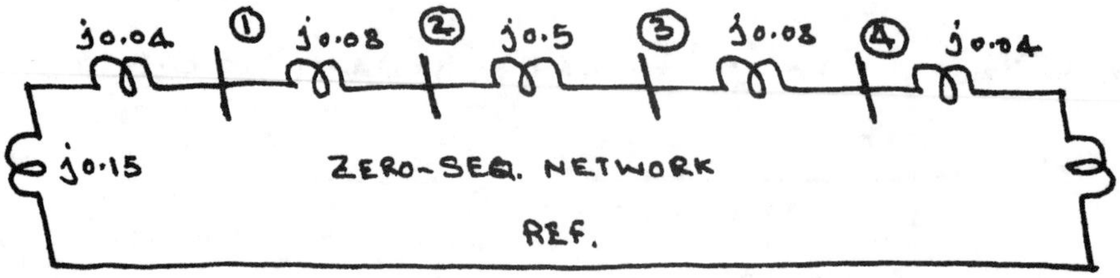

FOR THE SINGLE LINE-TO-GROUND FAULT, SERIES CONNECTION OF THE THÉVENIN EQUIVALENTS OF THE SEQUENCE NETWORKS IS SHOWN BELOW:

$$\bar{Z}_{BUS\,0} = \begin{array}{c} \\ ① \\ ② \\ ③ \\ ④ \end{array} \begin{bmatrix} ① & ② & ③ & ④ \\ j0.1553 & j0.1407 & j0.0493 & j0.0347 \\ j0.1407 & j0.1999 & j0.0701 & j0.0493 \\ j0.0493 & j0.0701 & j0.1999 & j0.1407 \\ j0.0347 & j0.0493 & j0.1407 & j0.1553 \end{bmatrix}$$

(b)

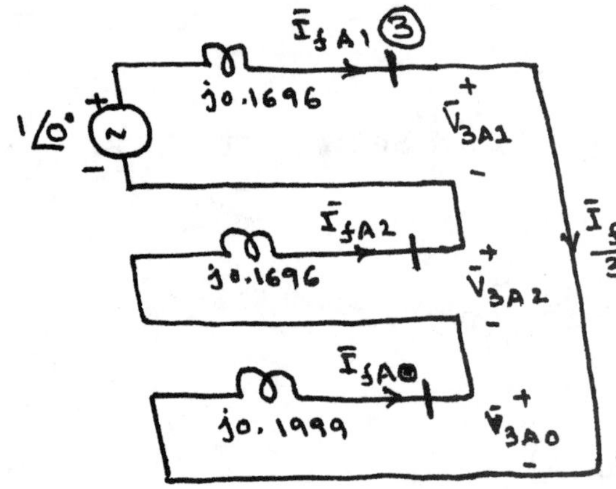

$$\bar{I}_{fA0} = \bar{I}_{fA1} = \bar{I}_{fA2} = \frac{1\angle 0°}{j(0.1696+0.1696+0.1999)} = -j\,1.8549$$

$$\bar{I}_{fA} = 3\,\bar{I}_{fA0} = -j\,5.5648 = 931\angle 270° \text{ A}$$

∵ BASE CURRENT IN HV TRANS. LINE IS

$$\frac{100{,}000}{\sqrt{3}\times 345} = 167.35\text{A}$$

PHASE-a SEQUENCE VOLTAGES AT BUS ④, TERMINALS OF MACHINE 2, ARE

$\bar{V}_{4a0} = -\bar{Z}_{430}\,\bar{I}_{fA0} = -(j0.1407)(-j1.8549) = -0.2610$

$\bar{V}_{4a1} = 1-(j0.1211)(-j1.8549) = 0.7754 \quad [= \bar{V}_f - \bar{Z}_{431}\,\bar{I}_{fA1}]$

$\bar{V}_{4a2} = -(j0.1211)(-j1.8549) = -0.2246 \quad [= -\bar{Z}_{432}\,\bar{I}_{fA2}]$

9.45 CONTD.

NOTE: SUBSCRIPTS A AND a DENOTE HV AND LV CIRCUITS, RESPECTIVELY, OF THE Y-Y CONNECTED TRANSFORMER. NO PHASE SHIFT IS INVOLVED.

$$\begin{bmatrix} \bar{V}_{4a} \\ \bar{V}_{4b} \\ \bar{V}_{4c} \end{bmatrix} = \begin{bmatrix} 1 & 1 & 1 \\ 1 & a^2 & a \\ 1 & a & a^2 \end{bmatrix} \begin{bmatrix} -0.2610 \\ +0.7754 \\ -0.2246 \end{bmatrix} = \begin{bmatrix} 0.2898 + j0 \\ -0.5364 - j0.866 \\ -0.5364 + j0.866 \end{bmatrix} = \begin{bmatrix} 0.2898 \angle 0^\circ \\ 1.0187 \angle -121.8^\circ \\ 1.0187 \angle 121.8^\circ \end{bmatrix}$$

LINE-TO-GROUND VOLTAGES OF MACHINE 2 IN kV ARE: (MULTIPLY BY $20/\sqrt{3}$)

$$\bar{V}_{4a} = 3.346 \angle 0^\circ \text{ kV}; \quad \bar{V}_{4b} = 11.763 \angle -121.8^\circ \text{ kV}; \quad \bar{V}_{4c} = 11.763 \angle 121.8^\circ \text{ kV}$$

SYMMETRICAL COMPONENTS OF PHASE-a CURRENT ARE

$$\bar{I}_{a0} = -\frac{\bar{V}_{4a0}}{jX_0} = \frac{0.2610}{j0.04} = -j\,6.525$$

$$\bar{I}_{a1} = \frac{\bar{V}_f - \bar{V}_{4a1}}{jX''} = \frac{1.0 - 0.7754}{j0.2} = -j\,1.123$$

$$\bar{I}_{a2} = -\frac{\bar{V}_{4a2}}{jX_2} = \frac{0.2246}{j0.2} = -j\,1.123$$

THE PHASE-C CURRENTS IN MACHINE 2 ARE CALCULATED AS

$$\bar{I}_c = \bar{I}_{a0} + a\bar{I}_{a1} + a^2\bar{I}_{a2}$$

$$= -j6.525 + a(-j1.123) + a^2(-j1.123)$$

$$= -j\,5.402$$

BASE CURRENT IN THE MACHINE CIRCUITS IS $\dfrac{100 \times 10^3}{\sqrt{3}(20)} = 2886.751$ A

$$\therefore I_c = 15{,}594 \text{ A}$$

9.46 Using equations (9.5.9) in (8.1.3), the phase "a" voltage at bus k for a fault at bus n is:

$$V_{ka} = V_{k\text{-}0} + V_{k\text{-}1} + V_{k\text{-}2}$$

$$= V_F - (Z_{kn\text{-}0} I_{n\text{-}0} + Z_{kn\text{-}1} I_{n\text{-}1} + Z_{kn\text{-}2} I_{n2})$$

For a single line-to-ground fault, (9.5.3),

$$I_{n\text{-}0} = I_{n\text{-}1} = I_{n\text{-}2} = \frac{V_F}{Z_{nn\text{-}0} + Z_{nn\text{-}1} + Z_{nn\text{-}2} + 3Z_F}$$

Therefore,

$$V_{ka} = V_F\left[1 - \frac{Z_{kn\text{-}0} + Z_{kn\text{-}1} + Z_{kn\text{-}2}}{Z_{nn\text{-}0} + Z_{nn\text{-}1} + Z_{nn\text{-}2} + 3Z_F}\right]$$

The results in Table 9.5 for Example 9.8 neglect resistances of all components (machines, transformers, transmission lines). Also the fault impedance Z_F is zero. As such, the impedances in the above equation all have the same phase angle (90°), and the phase "a"voltage V_{ka} therefore has the same angle as the prefault voltage V_F, which is zero degrees.

Note also that pre-fault load currents are neglected.

Chapter 9

Note, the PowerWorld problems in Chapter 9 were solved ignoring the effect of the Δ-Y transformer phase shift [see Example 9.6]. An upgraded version of PowerWorld Simulator is available from www.powerworld.com/gloversarma that (optionally) allows inclusion of this phase shift.

Problem 9.47

Single line-to-ground

Problem 9.48

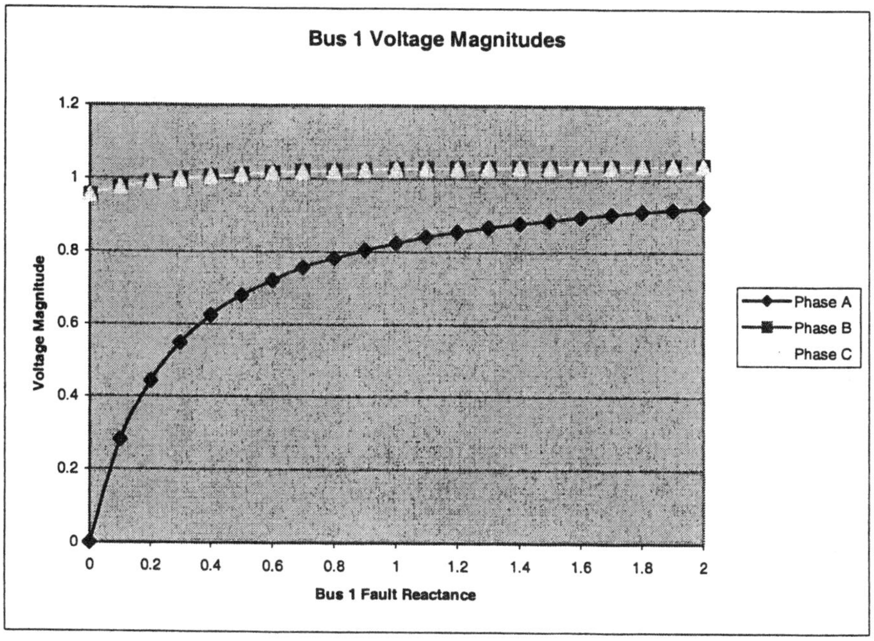

Problem 9.49 (Line-to-line fault)

Contributions to Fault Current

Fault Bus	Gen, Line or XF.	Bus to Bus	Current Phase A	Phase B	Phase C
1	G1	G1 to 1	0	5.052	5.052
	T1	5 to 1	0	3.075	3.075
2	L1	4 to 2	0	1.486	1.486
	L2	5 to 2	0	2.505	2.505
3	G2	G2 to 3	0	10.104	10.104
	T2	4 to 3	0	2.358	2.358
4	L1	2 to 4	0	0.376	0.376
	L3	5 to 4	0	2.255	2.255

	T2	3 to 4	0	6.995	6.995
5	L2	2 to 5	0	0.602	0.602
	L3	4 to 5	0	3.613	3.613
	T1	1 to 5	0	3.497	3.497

Problem 9.50 (Double line-to-ground fault)

Contributions to Fault Current

			Current		
Fault Bus	Gen, Line or XF	Bus to Bus	Phase A	Phase B	Phase C
1	G1	G1 to 1	1.875	8.223	8.223
	T1	5 to 1	1.875	3.215	3.215
2	L1	4 to 2	0.023	1.572	1.572
	L2	5 to 2	0.023	2.670	2.670
3	G2	G2 to 3	1.148	13.224	13.224
	T2	4 to 3	1.148	2.426	2.426
4	L1	2 to 4	0.151	0.435	0.435
	L3	5 to 4	0.907	2.610	2.610
	T2	3 to 4	4.597	7.363	7.363
5	L2	2 to 5	0.206	0.672	0.672
	L3	4 to 5	1.234	4.033	4.033
	T2	1 to 5	1.952	3.631	3.631

Problem 9.51

Fault Current 12.049 pu at –90 deg

Contributions to Fault Current

			Current		
Fault Bus	Gen, Line or XF	Bus to Bus	Phase A	Phase B	Phase C
1	G1	G1 to 1	8.734	1.658	1.658
	T1	5 to 1	3.315	3.315	3.315
2	L1	4 to 2	1.258	0.014	0.014
	L2	5 to 2	2.311	0.014	0.014
3	G2	G2 to 3	14.068	1.123	1.123
	T2	4 to 3	2.247	1.123	1.123
4	L1	2 to 4	0.278	0.056	0.056
	L3	5 to 4	1.670	0.336	0.336
	T2	3 to 4	6.824	3.412	3.412
5	L2	2 to 5	0.455	0.092	0.092
	L3	4 to 5	2.841	0.440	0.440

T2	1 to 5	3.217	1.606	1.606

Problem 9.52

Fault Current 11.233 pu at –90 deg

Contributions to Fault Current

Fault Bus	Gen, Line or Trsfr.	Bus to Bus	Current Phase A	Phase B	Phase C
1	G1	G1 to 1	0.128	0.105	0.105
	T1	5 to 1	2.99	1.514	1.514
2	L1	4 to 2	1.295	0.058	0.058
	L2	5 to 2	2.169	0.058	0.058
3	G2	G2 to 3	14.298	0.936	0.936
	T2	4 to 3	1.824	0.936	0.936
4	L1	2 to 4	0.405	0.101	0.101
	L3	5 to 4	2.431	0.608	0.608
	T2	3 to 4	6.965	3.489	3.489
5	L2	2 to 5	0.670	0.181	0.181
	L3	4 to 5	4.022	1.085	1.085
	T2	1 to 5	2.937	1.483	1.483

Problem 9.53

Fault Current = 23.774 p.u. at -102.04 degrees

54% of buses have voltage magnitude below 0.75 p.u.

Generator	Phase Cur A	Phase Cur B	Phase Cur C	Phase Ang A	Phase Ang B	Phase Ang C
LAUF69	8.327	1.006	0.758	-109.4	-119.8	-82.7
SLACK345	4.450	2.079	2.162	-78.6	-145.2	86.8
BLT69	3.704	0.817	1.030	-85.4	-132.5	75.4
BLT138	3.122	1.244	1.562	-77.6	-156.5	73.9
JO345	2.945	1.296	1.513	-78.7	-131.0	101.4
RODGER69	1.522	0.292	0.474	-88.3	-143.1	84.0

Problem 9.54

Fault Current = 7.642 p.u. at –93.39 degrees

11% of buses have voltage magnitude below 0.75 p.u.

Generator	Phase Cur A	Phase Cur B	Phase Cur C	Phase Ang A	Phase Ang B	Phase Ang C
SLACK345	3.254	2.389	1.851	-62.6	-141.3	91.1
BLT138	2.019	1.394	1.474	-59.6	-156.6	78.5
BLT69	1.834	0.973	0.977	-65.6	-140.2	86.2
LAUF69	1.808	0.286	0.325	-97.4	-175.2	17.3

JO345	1.729	1.368	1.497	-44.4	-132.4	104.4
RODGER69	0.614	0.358	0.445	-57.2	-145.7	91.6

CHAPTER 10

10.1 Using Eq (10.2.1):

$$V' = \frac{1}{n} V = \frac{345 \times 10^3}{3000} = \underline{\underline{115.\,V}} \text{ (line-to-line)}$$

$$I = \frac{S_{3\phi}}{\sqrt{3}\, V_{LL}} = \frac{600. \times 10^6}{(\sqrt{3})(345 \times 10^3)} = 1004.\ A$$

From Eq (10.2.2), $I_e = 0$ for zero CT error.
Then, from Figure 10.7:

$$I' + I_e = I' + 0 = \frac{1}{n} I = \left(\frac{5}{1200}\right)(1004.) = 4.184$$

$$\underline{\underline{I' = 4.184\ A}}$$

10.2 (a) Step (1) – $I' = 10.\ A$

Step (2) – From Figure 10.7,

$$E' = (Z' + Z_B) I' = (0.082 + 1)(10) = 10.82\ V$$

Step (3) – From Figure 10.8, $I_e = 0.6\ A$

Step (4) – From Figure 10.7,

$$I = \left(\frac{100}{5}\right)(10. + 0.6) = \underline{\underline{212.}}\ A$$

(b) Step (1) – $I' = 13.\ A$

Step (2) – From Figure 10.7,

$$E' = (Z' + Z_B) I' = (0.082 + 1.3)(13)$$

$$= 18.0\ V$$

Step (3) – From Figure 10.8, $I_e = 1.8\ A$

Step (4) – From Figure 10.7,

$$I = \left(\frac{100}{5}\right)(13. + 1.8) = \underline{\underline{296.}}\ A$$

10.2 CONTD.

(c)

I'	5.	8.	10.	13.	15.
I	105.	168.	212.	296.	700.

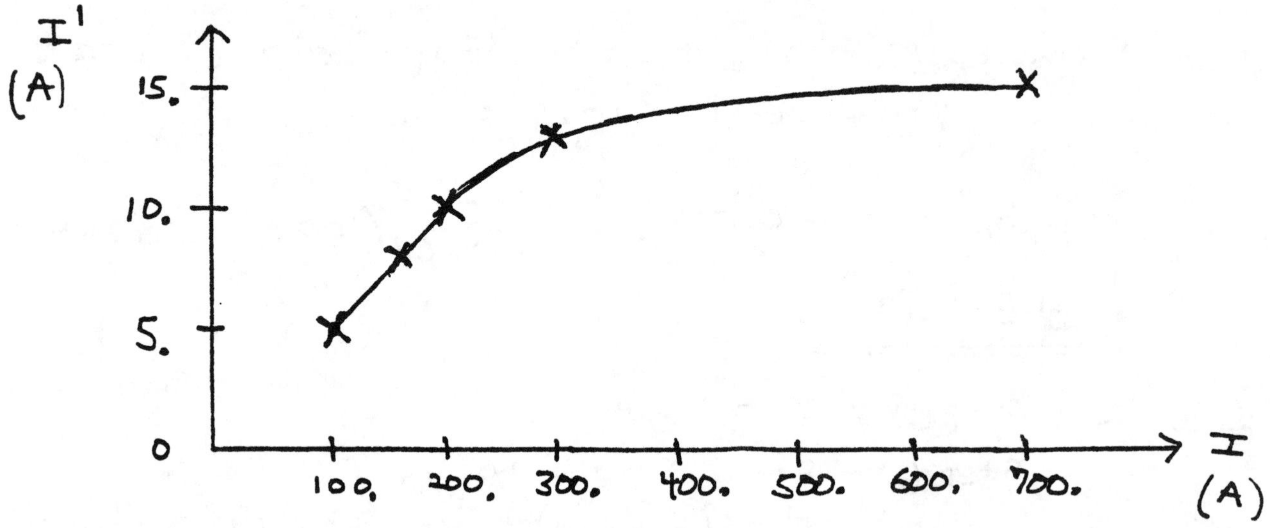

(d) With a 5-A tap setting and a minimum fault-to-pickup ratio of 2, the minimum relay trip current for reliable operation is $I'_{min} = 2 \times 5 = 10$ A. From (a) above with $I'_{min} = 10$ A, $I_{min} = \underline{212.\text{ A}}$

That is, the relay will trip reliably for fault currents exceeding 212. A

10.3

From Figure 10.8, the secondary resistance $Z' = 0.125\ \Omega$ for the 200:5 CT.

(a) Step(1) − $I' = 10.\ A$

Step(2) − $E = (Z' + Z_B)I' = (0.125 + 1)(10) = 11.25\ V$

Step(3) − From Figure 10.8, $I_e = 0.18\ A$

Step(4) − $I = \left(\frac{200}{5}\right)(10. + 0.18) = \underline{\underline{407.2\ A}}$

(b) Step(1) − $I' = 10.\ A$

Step(2) − $E = (Z' + Z_B)I' = (0.125 + 4)(10) = 41.25\ V$

Step(3) − From Figure 10.8, $I_e = 1.5\ A$

Step(4) − $I = \left(\frac{200}{5}\right)(10. + 1.5) = \underline{\underline{460.\ A}}$

(c) Step(1) − $I' = 10.\ A$

Step(2) − $E = (Z' + Z_B)I' = (0.125 + 5)(10) = 51.25\ V$

Step(3) − From Figure 10.8, $I_e = 30.\ A$

Step(4) − $I = \left(\frac{200}{5}\right)(10. + 30.) = \underline{\underline{1600.\ A}}$

10.4

NOTE ERROR IN PRINTING: VT SHOULD BE PT.

(a) $N_1/N_2 = 240{,}000/120 = 2000/1$

$\therefore \bar{V}_{ab} = 230{,}000\angle 0^\circ / 2000 = 115\angle 0^\circ$

$\bar{V}_{bc} = 230{,}000\angle 120^\circ / 2000 = 115\angle -120^\circ$

$\bar{V}_{ca} = -(\bar{V}_{ab} + \bar{V}_{bc}) = -(115\angle -60^\circ) = 115\angle +120^\circ$

(b) $\bar{V}_{ab} = 115\angle 0^\circ$; BUT NOW $\bar{V}_{bc} = -115\angle -120^\circ = 115\angle 60^\circ$

$\therefore \bar{V}_{ca} = -(\bar{V}_{ab} + \bar{V}_{bc}) = 199\angle -150^\circ$

THE OUTPUT OF THE PT BANK IS NOT BALANCED THREE PHASE.

10.5

DESIGNATING SECONDARY VOLTAGE AS E_2, READ TWO POINTS ON THE MAGNETIZATION CURVE (I_e, E_2) : (1, 63) AND (10, 100)

THE NON LINEAR CHARACTERISTIC CAN BE REPRESENTED BY THE SO-CALLED FROHLICH EQUATION $E_2 = (A I_e)/(B + I_e)$. USING THAT

$$63 = \frac{A}{B+1} \quad \text{AND} \quad 100 = \frac{10A}{B+10}$$

SOLVE FOR A AND B : $A = 107$ AND $B = 0.698$

FOR PARTS (a) AND (b), $\bar{Z}_T = (4.9 + 0.1) + j(0.5 + 0.5) = 5 + j1$
$= 5.099\angle 11.3^\circ\ \Omega$

(a) THE CT ERROR IS THE PERCENTAGE OF MISMATCH BETWEEN THE INPUT CURRENT (IN SECONDARY TERMS) DENOTED BY $\bar{I}_2'$ AND THE OUTPUT CURRENT $\bar{I}_2$ IN TERMS OF THEIR MAGNITUDES:

$$\text{CT ERROR} = \frac{|\bar{I}_2' - \bar{I}_2|}{I_2'} \times 100$$

$E_T = I_2' Z_T = 4(5.099) = 20.4$

$I_e = 20.4/\sqrt{25 + [1 + 107/(0.698 + I_e)]^2} = 0.163$ (BY ITERATION)

10.5 CONTD.

FROM FROHLICH'S EQUATION

$$E_2 = \frac{0.163\,(107)}{0.698 + 0.163} = 20.3$$

$$I_2 = \frac{E_2}{Z_T} = \frac{20.3}{5.099} = 3.97$$

$$\text{CT ERROR} = \frac{0.03}{4} = 0.7\%$$

(b) FOR THE FAULTED CASE

$E_T = 12\,(5.099) = 61.2\text{ V}$; $I_e = 0.894\text{ A}$ (BY ITERATION)

$E_2 = 60.1\text{ V}$; $I_2 = 60.1/5.099 = 11.78\text{A}$

$$\text{CT ERROR} = \frac{0.22}{12} \times 100 = 1.8\%$$

(c) FOR THE HIGHER BURDEN, $\bar{Z}_T = 15 + j2 = 15.13\angle 7.6°\ \Omega$

FOR THE GIVEN LOAD CONDITION, $E_T = 4\,(15.13) = 60.5\text{V}$

$I_e = 0.814\text{ A}$; $E_2 = 57.6\text{ V}$; $I_2 = \frac{57.6}{15.13} = 3.81\text{ A}$

$$\therefore \text{CT ERROR} = \frac{0.19}{4} \times 100 = 4.8\%$$

(d) FOR THE FAULT CONDITION, $E_T = 181.6\text{V}$; $I_e = 9.21\text{A}$;

$E_2 = 99.5\text{V}$; $I_2 = \frac{99.5}{15.13} = 6.58\text{A}$

$$\therefore \text{CT ERROR} = \frac{5.42}{12} \times 100 = 45.2\%$$

THUS, CT ERROR INCREASES WITH INCREASING CT CURRENT AND IS FURTHER INCREASED BY THE HIGH TERMINATING IMPEDANCE.

10.6

ASSUMING THE CT TO BE IDEAL, I_2 WOULD BE 12 A; THE DEVICE WOULD DETECT THE 1200-A PRIMARY CURRENT (OR ANY FAULT CURRENT DOWN TO 800 A) INDEPENDENT OF $\bar{Z}_L$.

(a) IN THE SOLUTION OF PROB. 10.5,(b) $I_2 = 11.78$ A

THEREFORE, THE FAULT IS DETECTED

(b) IN PROB. 10.5(d), $I_2 = 6.58$ A

THE FAULT IS THEN NOT DETECTED. THE ASSUMPTION THAT THE CT WAS IDEAL IN THIS CASE WOULD HAVE RESULTED IN FAILING TO DETECT A FAULTED SYSTEM.

10.7

(a) The current tap setting (pickup current) is $I_p = 1.0$ A

$\frac{I'}{I_p} = \frac{10}{1} = 10.$ From curve 1/2 in Figure 10.12

$t_{operating} = \underline{\underline{0.08 \text{ seconds}}}$

(b) $\frac{I'}{I_p} = \frac{10}{2} = 5.$ Interpolating between curve 1

and curve 2 in Figure 10.12, $t_{operating} = \underline{\underline{0.55 \text{ sec}}}$

(c) $\frac{I'}{I_p} = \frac{10}{2} = 5.$ From curve 7, $t_{operating} = \underline{\underline{3. \text{ sec}}}$

(d) $\frac{I'}{I_p} = \frac{10}{3} = 3.33$ From curve 7, $t_{operating} = \underline{\underline{5.2 \text{ sec}}}$

(e) $\frac{I'}{I_p} = \frac{10}{12} < 1$ The relay does not

operate. It remains in the blocking position.

10.8

From the plot of I' vs I in Problem 10.2 (c),
$I' \approx 14.5$ A. $\frac{I'}{I_p} = \frac{14.5}{5} = 2.9$

From curve 4 in Figure 10.12, $t_{operating} = \underline{\underline{3.7 \text{ sec}}}$

10.9

(a) $\tau = RC = 1S$

$v_o = 2(1 - e^{-t})$; AT $t = T_{delay}$, $v_o = 1$

$\therefore \quad 1 - e^{-T_{delay}} = 0.5 \quad$ OR $\quad e^{T_{delay}} = 2$

THUS $\quad T_{delay} = \ln 2 = 0.693\,S$

(b) $\tau = RC = 10\,S$

$v_o = 2(1 - e^{-t/10})$; AT $t = T_{delay}$, $v_o = 1$

$\therefore \quad e^{T_{delay}/10} = 2 \quad$ OR $\quad T_{delay}/10 = \ln 2$

THUS $\quad T_{delay} = 6.93\,S$

THE CIRCUIT TIME RESPONSE IS SKETCHED BELOW:

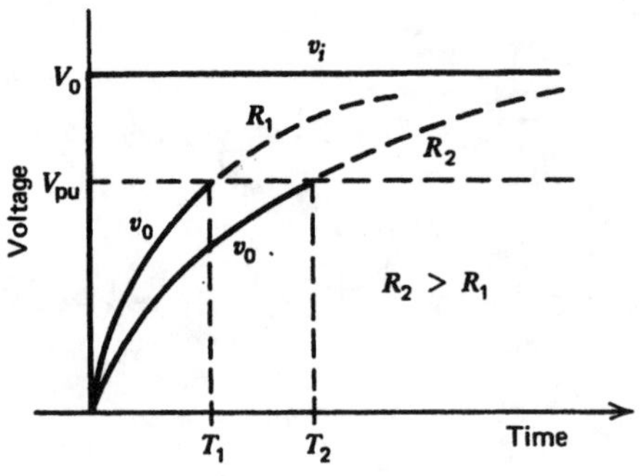

10.10

FROM THE SOLUTION OF PROB. 10.5 (b), $I_2 = I_{relay} = 11.78\,A$

$\frac{I_{relay}}{I_{pickup}} = \frac{11.78}{5} = 2.36$ CORRESPONDING TO WHICH, FROM CURVE 2,

$T_{operating} = 1.2\,S$

10.11

(a) For the 700. A fault current at bus 3, fault-to-pickup current ratios and relay operating times are:

B3 $\frac{I'_{3fault}}{TS3} = \frac{700/(200/5)}{3} = \frac{17.5}{3} = 5.83$

From curve 1/2 of Figure 10.12, $t_{operating3} = 0.10$ seconds. Adding the breaker operating time, primary protection clears this fault in $(0.10 + 0.083) = 0.183$ seconds.

B2 $\frac{I'_{2fault}}{TS2} = \frac{700/(200/5)}{5} = \frac{17.5}{5} = 3.5$

From curve 2 in Figure 10.12, $t_{operating2} = 1.3$ seconds. The coordination time interval between B3 and B2 is $(1.3 - 0.183) = 1.12$ seconds.

(b) For the 1500. A fault current at bus 2:

B2 $\frac{I'_{2fault}}{TS2} = \frac{1500/(200/5)}{5} = \frac{37.5}{5} = 7.5$

From curve 2 of Figure 10.12, $t_{operating2} = 0.55$ seconds. Adding the breaker operating time, primary

10.11 CONTD. protection clears this fault in $(0.55 + 0.083) = 0.633$ seconds,

B1
$$\frac{I'_{1\,fault}}{TS1} = \frac{1500/(400/5)}{5} = \frac{18.75}{5} = 3.75$$

From curve 3 of Figure 10.12, $t_{operating\,1} = 1.8$ seconds. The coordination time interval between B2 and B1 is $(1.8 - 0.633) = 1.17$ seconds.

Fault-to-Pickup ratios are all > 2.0
Coordination time intervals are all > 0.3 seconds

10.12 First select current Tap Settings (TSs). Starting at B3, the primary and secondary CT currents for maximum load L3 are:

$$I_{L3} = \frac{S_{L3}}{V_3\sqrt{3}} = \frac{9 \times 10^6}{34.5 \times 10^3 \sqrt{3}} = 150.6 \text{ A}$$

$$I'_{L3} = \frac{150.6}{(200/5)} = 3.77 \text{ A}$$

From Figure 10.12, select 4 A TS3, which is the lowest TS above 3.77 A.

$$I_{L2} = \frac{(S_{L2} + S_{L3})}{V_2\sqrt{3}} = \frac{(9.0 + 9.0) \times 10^6}{34.5 \times 10^3 \sqrt{3}} = 301.2 \text{ A}$$

$$I'_{L2} = \frac{301.2}{(400/5)} = 3.77 \text{ A}$$

Again, select 4A TS2 for B2.

10-12 CONTD.

$$I_{L1} = \frac{S_{L1}+S_{L2}+S_{L3}}{V_1\sqrt{3}} = \frac{(9+9+9)\times 10^6}{34.5\times 10^3\sqrt{3}} = 451.8 \text{ A}$$

$$I'_{L1} = \frac{451.8}{(600/5)} = 3.77$$

Again select a 4 A TSI for B1.

Next select Time Dial Settings (TDSs). Starting at B3, the largest fault current through B3 is 3000. A, for the maximum fault at bus 2 (just to the right of B3). The fault to pickup ratio at B3 for this fault is

$$\frac{I'_{3\,\text{fault}}}{TS3} = \frac{3000/(200/5)}{4} = 18.75$$

Select TDS = 1/2 at B3, in order to clear this fault as rapidly as possible. Then from curve 1/2 in Fig 10.12, $t_{operating3}$ = 0.05 sec. Adding the breaker operating time (5 cycles = 0.083 sec), primary protection clears this fault in 0.05 + 0.083 = 0.133 sec.

For this same fault, the fault-to-pickup ratio at B2 is

$$\frac{I'_{2\,\text{Fault}}}{TS2} = \frac{3000/(400/5)}{4} = \frac{37.5}{4} = 9.4$$

Adding B3 relay operating time, breaker operating time, and 0.3 sec coordination interval,

10.12 CONTD.

$(0.05 + 0.083 + 0.3) = 0.433$ sec, which is the desired B2 relay operating time. From Figure 10.12, select TDS2 = 2.

Next select the TDS at B1. The largest fault current through B2 is 5000. A, for the maximum fault at bus 1 (just to the right of B2). The fault-to-pickup ratio at B2 for this fault is

$$\frac{I'_{2\,Fault}}{TS2} = \frac{5000/(400/5)}{4} = \frac{62.5}{4} = 15.6$$

From curve 2 in Fig 10.12, the relay operating time is 0.38 sec. Adding the 0.083 sec breaker operating time and 0.3 sec coordination time interval, we want a B1 relay operating time of $(0.38 + 0.083 + 0.3) = 0.763$ sec. Also, for this same fault,

$$\frac{I'_{1\,Fault}}{TS1} = \frac{5000/(600/5)}{4} = \frac{41.66}{4} = 10.4$$

From Fig 10.12, select TDS1 = 3.5.

Breaker	Relay	TS	TDS
B1	CO-8	4	3.5
B2	CO-8	4	2
B3	CO-8	4	1/2

SOLUTION Problem 10.7

10.13 For the 1500. A fault current at bus 3, fault-to-pickup current ratios and relay operating times are:

B3 $\frac{I'_{3Fault}}{TS3} = \frac{1500/(200/5)}{4} = \frac{37.5}{4} = 9.4$

From curve 1/2 of Figure 10.12, $t_{operating3} = 0.08$ sec
Adding breaker operating time, primary relaying clears this fault in $0.08 + 0.083 = 0.163$ sec

B2 $\frac{I'_{2Fault}}{TS2} = \frac{1500/(400/5)}{4} = \frac{18.75}{4} = 4.7$

From curve 2 in Fig 10.12, $t_{operating2} = 0.85$ sec
The coordination time interval between B3 and B2 is $(0.85 - 0.163) = 0.69$ sec

B1 $\frac{I'_{1Fault}}{TS1} = \frac{1500/(600/5)}{4} = \frac{12.5}{4} = 3.1$

From curve 3.5 in Figure 10.12, $t_{operating1} = 2.8$ s
The coordination time interval between B3 and B1 is $(2.8 - 0.163) = 2.6$ sec.

For the 2250. A fault current at bus 2, fault-to-pickup current ratios and relay operating times are:

B2 $\frac{I'_{2Fault}}{TS2} = \frac{2250/(400/5)}{4} = \frac{28.13}{4} = 7.0$

From curve 2 in Fig. 10.12, $t_{operating2} = 0.6$ sec

Adding breaker operating time, primary protection clears this fault in $(0.6 + 0.083)$ $= 0.683$ sec.

B1 $\frac{I'_{1fault}}{TS1} = \frac{2250/(600/5)}{4} = \frac{18.75}{4} = 4.7$

From curve 3.5 in Figure 10.12, $t_{operating1} = 1.5$ sec
The coordination time interval between B2 and B1 is $(1.5 - 0.683) = 0.82$ sec

Fault-to-pickup ratios are all > 2.0
Coordination time intervals are all > 0.3 sec

10.14

THE LOAD CURRENTS ARE CALCULATED AS

$$I_1 = \frac{4\times10^6}{\sqrt{3}(11\times10^3)} = 209.95A; \quad I_2 = \frac{2.5\times10^6}{\sqrt{3}(11\times10^3)} = 131.22A; \quad I_3 = \frac{6.75\times10^6}{\sqrt{3}(11\times10^3)} = 354.28A$$

THE NORMAL CURRENTS THROUGH THE SECTIONS ARE THEN GIVEN BY

$$I_{21} = I_1 = 209.95A; \quad I_{32} = I_{21} + I_2 = 341.16A; \quad I_s = I_{32} + I_3 = 695.44A$$

WITH THE GIVEN CT RATIOS, THE NORMAL RELAY CURRENTS ARE

$$i_{21} = \frac{209.95}{(200/5)} = 5.25A; \quad i_{32} = \frac{341.16}{(200/5)} = 8.53A; \quad i_s = \frac{695.44}{(400/5)} = 8.69A$$

NOW OBTAIN C.T.S (CURRENT TAP SETTINGS) OR PICKUP CURRENT IN SUCH A WAY THAT THE RELAY DOES NOT TRIP UNDER NORMAL CURRENTS.

FOR THIS TYPE OF RELAY, CTS AVAILABLE ARE 4, 5, 6, 7, 8, 10, AND 12 A.

FOR POSITION 1, THE NORMAL CURRENT IN THE RELAY IS 5.25A; SO CHOOSE $(CTS)_1 = 6A$

CHOOSING THE NEAREST SETTING HIGHER THAN THE NORMAL CURRENT.

FOR POSITION 2, NORMAL CURRENT BEING 8.53A, CHOOSE $(CTS)_2 = 10A$.

FOR POSITION 3, NORMAL CURRENT BEING 8.69A, CHOOSE $(CTS)_3 = 10A$.

NEXT, SELECT THE INTENTIONAL DELAY INDICATED BY TDS, TIME DIAL SETTING.

UTILIZE THE SHORT-CIRCUIT CURRENTS TO COORDINATE THE RELAYS.

THE CURRENT IN THE RELAY AT 1 ON SHORT CIRCUIT IS $i_{sc1} = \frac{2500}{(200/5)} = 62.5A$

EXPRESSED AS A MULTIPLE OF THE CTS OR PICKUP VALUE,

$$\frac{i_{sc1}}{(CTS)_1} = \frac{62.5}{6} = 10.42$$

CHOOSE THE LOWEST TDS FOR THIS RELAY FOR FASTEST ACTION.

THUS $(TDS)_1 = \frac{1}{2}$

10.14 CONTD.

REFERING TO THE RELAY CHARACTERISTIC, THE OPERATING TIME FOR RELAY 1 FOR A FAULT AT 1 IS OBTAINED AS $T_{11} = 0.15\,S$.

TO SET THE RELAY AT 2 RESPONDING TO A FAULT AT 1, ALLOW 0.1S FOR BREAKER OPERATION AND AN ERROR MARGIN OF 0.3S IN ADDITION TO T_{11}.

$$\text{THUS} \quad T_{21} = T_{11} + 0.1 + 0.3 = 0.55\,S$$

SHORT CIRCUIT FOR A FAULT AT 1 AS A MULTIPLE OF THE CTS AT 2 IS

$$\frac{i_{sc1}}{(CTS)_2} = \frac{62.5}{10} = 6.25$$

FROM THE CHARACTERISTICS FOR 0.55S OPERATING TIME AND 6.25 RATIO,

$$(TDS)_2 = 2$$

NOW, SETTING THE RELAY AT 3:

FOR A FAULT AT BUS 2, THE SHORT-CIRCUIT CURRENT IS 3000 A, FOR WHICH RELAY 2 RESPONDS IN A TIME T_{22} CALCULATED AS

$$\frac{i_{sc2}}{(CTS)_2} = \frac{3000}{(200/5)\,10} = 7.5$$

FOR $(TDS)_2 = 2$, FROM THE RELAY CHARACTERISTIC, $T_{22} = 0.5\,S$

ALLOWING THE SAME MARGIN FOR RELAY 3 TO RESPOND FOR A FAULT AT 2, AS FOR RELAY 2 RESPONDING TO A FAULT AT 1,

$$T_{32} = T_{22} + 0.1 + 0.3 = 0.9\,S$$

THE CURRENT IN THE RELAY EXPRESSED AS A MULTIPLE OF PICKUP IS

$$\frac{i_{sc2}}{(CTS)_3} = \frac{3000}{(400/5)\,10} = 3.75$$

THUS, FOR $T_3 = 0.9S$, AND THE ABOVE RATIO, FROM THE RELAY CHARACTERISTIC

$$(TDS)_3 = 2.5$$

NOTE: CALCULATIONS HERE DID NOT ACCOUNT FOR HIGHER LOAD STARTING CURRENTS THAT CAN BE AS HIGH AS 5 TO 7 TIMES RATED VALUES.

10.15

(a) Three-phase permanent fault on the load side of bus 3.

From Table 10.7, the three-phase fault current at bus 3 is 2000 A. From Figure 10.19, the 560 A fast recloser opens 0.04 s after the 2000 A fault occurs, then recloses 1/2 s later into the permanent fault, opens again after 0.04 s, and recloses into the fault a second time after a 2 s delay. Then the 560 A delayed recloser opens 1.5 s later. During this time interval, the 100T fuse clears the fault. The delayed recloser then recloses 5 to 10 s later, restoring service to loads 1 and 2

10.15 (b) Single Line-to-Ground permanent fault
CONTD. at bus 4 on the load side of the recloser.
From Table 10.7, the 1L-G fault current at bus 4 is 2600 A. From Figure 10.19, the 280 A fast recloser (ground unit) opens after 0.034 s, recloses 1/2 s later into the permanent fault, opens again after 0.034 s, and recloses a second time after a 2 s delay. Then the 280 A delayed recloser (ground unit) opens 0.7 s later, recloses 5 to 10. s later, then opens again after 0.7 s and permanently locks out.

(c) Three-phase permanent fault at bus 4 on the source side of the recloser.
From Table 10.7, the three-phase fault at bus 4 is 3000. A. From Figure 10.19, the phase overcurrent relay trips after 0.95 s, thereby energizing the circuit breaker trip coil, causing the breaker to open.

10.16

LOAD CURRENT $= \frac{4000}{\sqrt{3}(34.5)} = 66.9$ A; MAX. FAULT CURRENT = 1000A; MIN. FAULT CURRENT = 500A

(a) FOR THIS CONDITION, THE RECLOSER MUST OPEN BEFORE THE FUSE MELTS.

THE MAXIMUM CLEARING TIME FOR THE RECLOSER SHOULD BE LESS THAN THE MINIMUM MELTING TIME FOR THE FUSE AT A CURRENT OF 500A.

REFERRING TO FIG. 10.43, THE MAXIMUM CLEARING TIME FOR THE RECLOSER IS ABOUT 0.135 S.

(b) FOR THIS CONDITION, THE MINIMUM CLEARING TIME FOR THE RECLOSER SHOULD BE GREATER THAN THE MAXIMUM CLEARING TIME FOR THE FUSE AT A CURRENT OF 1000 A.

REFERRING TO FIG. 10.43, THE MINIMUM CLEARING TIME IS ABOUT 0.056 S.

10.17 (a) For a fault at P1, only breakers B34 and B43 operate; the other breakers do not operate. B23 should coordinate with B34 so that B34 operates before B23 (and before B12, and before B1). Also, B4 should coordinate with B43 so that B43 operates before B4.

(b) For a fault at P2, only breakers B23 and B32 operate; the other breakers do not operate. B12 should coordinate with B23 so that B23 operates before B12 (and before B1). Also B43 should coordinate with B32 so that B32 operates before B43 (and before B4).

(c) For a fault at P3, only breakers B12 and B21 operate; the other breakers do not operate. B32 should coordinate with B21 so that B21 operates before B32 (and before B43, and before B4). Also, B1 should coordinate with B12 so that B12 operates before B1.

(d)

Fault Bus	Operating Breakers
1	B1 and B21
2	B12 and B32
3	B23 and B43
4	B4 and B34

10.18

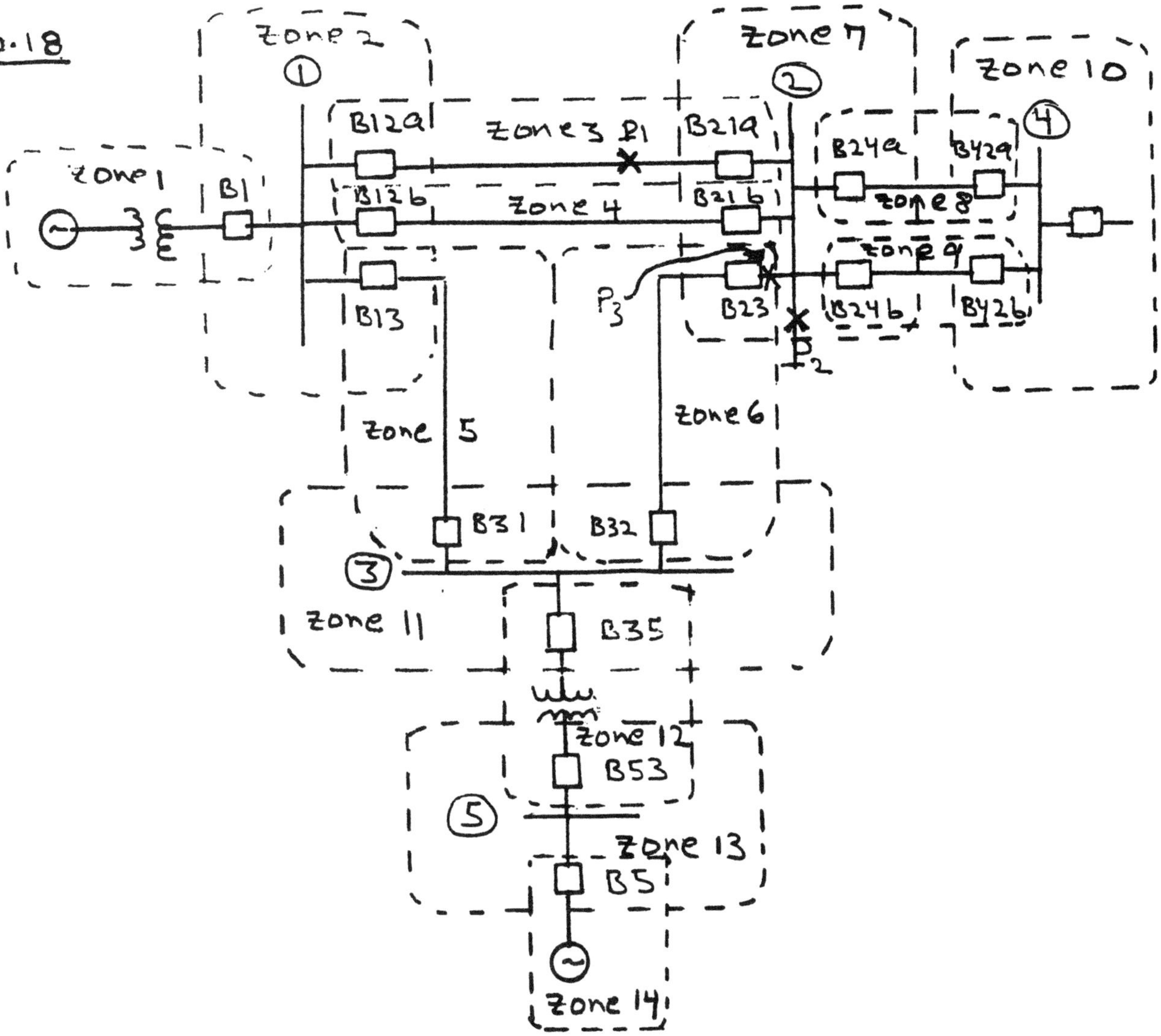

(a) For a fault at P_1, breakers in zone 3 operate (B12a and B21a).

(b) For a fault at P_2, breakers in zone 7 operate (B21a, B21b, B23, B24a, B24b).

(c) For a fault at P_3, breakers in zone 6 and zone 7 operate (B23, B32, B21a, B21b, B24a, and B24b).

10.19

(a)

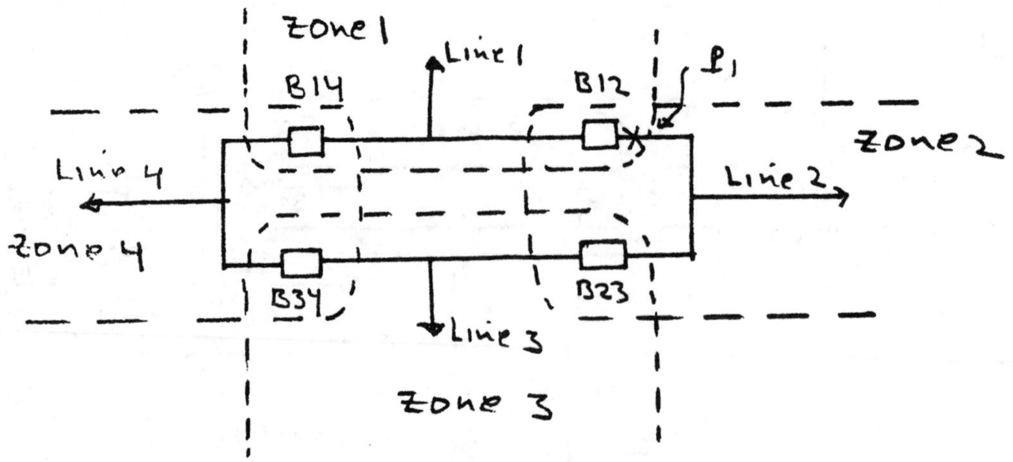

Ring Bus

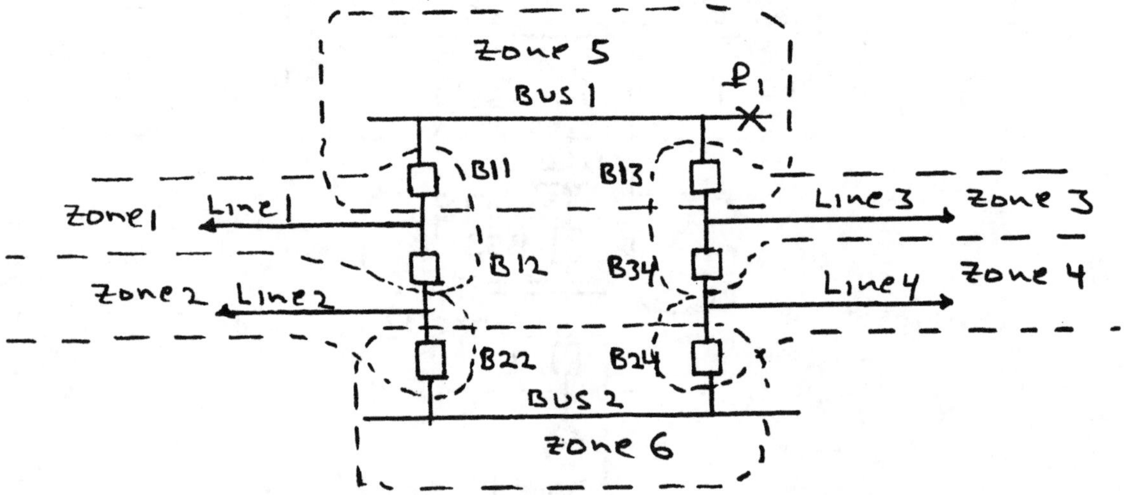

Breaker-and-a-Half Double-Bus

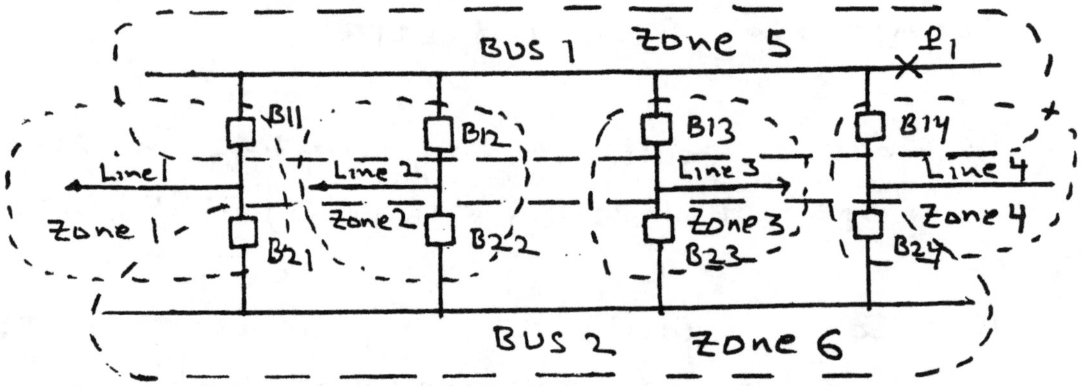

Double-Breaker Double-Bus

10.19 CONTD.

(b)

Scheme	Breakers That Open For Fault on Line 1
Ring Bus	B12 and B14
Breaker-and ½, Double Bus	B11 and B12
Double Breaker, Double Bus	B11 and B21

(c)

Scheme	Lines Removed For a Fault at P1
Ring Bus	Line 1 and Line 2
Breaker-and ½, Double Bus	None
Double Breaker, Double Bus	None

(d)

Scheme	Breakers That Open For a Fault on Line 1 with Stuck Breaker
Ring Bus	B12, B14 and either B23 or B34
Breaker-and ½, Double Bus	B11, B12 and either B13 or B22
Double Breaker, Double Bus	B11, B21 and all other breakers on bus 1 or bus 2.

10.20 (a)
$$Z' = \frac{V'_{LN}}{I'_L} = \frac{V_{LN}/(4500/1)}{I_L/(1500/5)} = \left(\frac{V_{LN}}{I_L}\right)\frac{1}{15}$$

$$Z' = \frac{Z}{15}$$

Set the B12 Zone 1 relay for 80% reach of Line 1-2:

$$Z_{r1} = 0.8(6+j60)/15 = \underline{\underline{0.32+j3.2}}\ \Omega \text{ secondary}$$

Set the B12 Zone 2 relay for 120% reach of Line 1-2:

$$Z_{r2} = 1.2(6+j60)/15 = \underline{\underline{0.48+j4.8}}\ \Omega \text{ secondary}$$

Set the B12 Zone 3 relay for 100% reach of line 1-2 and 120% reach of Line 2-3.

$$Z_{r3} = 1.0(6+j60)/15 + 1.2(5+j50)/15 = \underline{\underline{0.8+j8.0\ \Omega \text{ secondary}}}$$

10.20 CONTD. (b) The secondary impedance viewed by B12 during emergency loading is:

$$\bar{Z}' = \left(\frac{\bar{V}_{LN}}{\bar{I}_L}\right)\left(\frac{1}{15}\right) = \left(\frac{\frac{500}{\sqrt{3}}\angle 0^\circ}{1.4\angle -\cos^{-1}0.9}\right)\frac{1}{15} = 13.7\angle 25.8^\circ \ \Omega$$

$\bar{Z}'$ exceeds the zone 3 setting of $(0.8 + j8.0) = 8.04\angle 84.3^\circ \ \Omega$ for B12. Hence, the impedance during emergency loading lies outside the trip region of this 3-zone mho relay (See Figure 10.29 b).

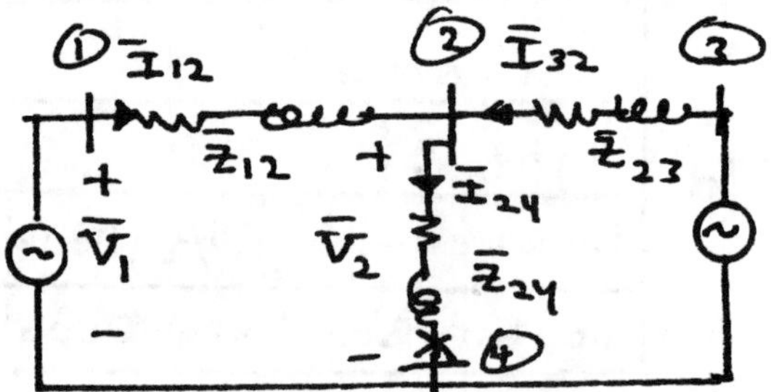

Three-phase bolted Fault at bus 4.

10.21 (a) For the bolted three-phase fault at bus 4, the apparent primary impedance seen by the B12 relay is:

$$\bar{Z}_{apparent} = \frac{\bar{V}_1}{\bar{I}_{12}} = \frac{\bar{V}_1 - \bar{V}_2 + \bar{V}_2}{\bar{I}_{12}} = \underbrace{\frac{(\bar{V}_1 - \bar{V}_2)}{\bar{I}_{12}}}_{\bar{Z}_{12}} + \frac{\bar{V}_2}{\bar{I}_{12}}$$

$$\bar{Z}_{apparent} = \bar{Z}_{12} + \frac{\bar{V}_2}{\bar{I}_{12}}$$

Using $\bar{V}_2 = \bar{Z}_{24}\bar{I}_{24}$ and $\bar{I}_{24} = \bar{I}_{12} + \bar{I}_{32}$:

$$\bar{Z}_{apparent} = \bar{Z}_{12} + \frac{\bar{Z}_{24}(\bar{I}_{12} + \bar{I}_{32})}{\bar{I}_{12}} = \bar{Z}_{12} + \bar{Z}_{24} + \left(\frac{\bar{I}_{32}}{\bar{I}_{12}}\right)\bar{Z}_{24}$$

which is the desired result.

10.21 CONTD.

(b)

The apparent secondary impedance seen by the B12 relay for the bolted three-phase fault at bus 4 is:

$$Z'_{apparent} = \frac{\bar{Z}_{apparent}}{(n_v/n_I)} = \frac{(3+j40) + (6+j80) + \left(\frac{\bar{I}_{32}}{\bar{I}_{12}}\right)(6+j80)}{(n_v/n_I)}$$

$$\bar{Z}'_{apparent} = \frac{\left[9 + 6\left(\frac{\bar{I}_{32}}{\bar{I}_{12}}\right)\right] + j\left[120 + 80\left(\frac{\bar{I}_{32}}{\bar{I}_{12}}\right)\right]}{(n_v/n_I)} \quad \Omega$$

where n_v is the VT ratio and n_I is the CT ratio.

Also, the B12 Zone 3 relay is set with a secondary impedance:

$$\bar{Z}_{r3} = \frac{(3+j40) + 1.2(6+j80)}{(n_v/n_I)} = \frac{10.2 + j136}{(n_v/n_I)} \quad \Omega \text{ secondary}$$

Comparing $\bar{Z}_{r3}$ with $\bar{Z}'_{apparent}$, $\bar{Z}'_{apparent}$ exceeds $\bar{Z}_{r3}$ when $(\bar{I}_{32}/\bar{I}_{12}) > 0.2$. Hence $\bar{Z}'_{apparent}$ lies outside the trip region for the three-phase fault at bus 4 when $(\bar{I}_{32}/\bar{I}_{12}) > 0.2$; remote backup of line 2-4 at B12 is then ineffective.

10.22

$$R_r = \frac{(1)^2\, 2}{(2^2+0.8^2)} = 0.431 \text{ pu} \quad ; \quad X_r = \frac{(1)^2\, 0.8}{(2^2+0.8^2)} = 0.1724 \text{ pu}$$

THE X-R DIAGRAM IS GIVEN BELOW:

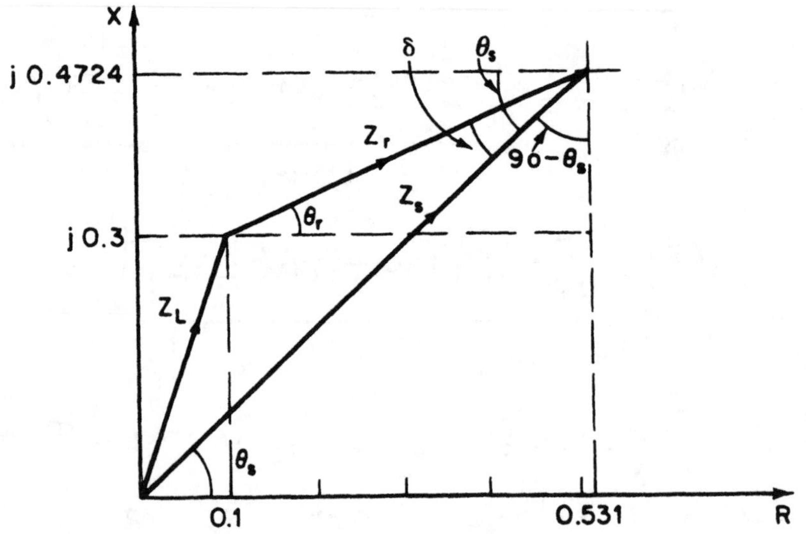

BASED ON THE DIAGRAM, $\bar{Z}_s$ CAN BE OBTAINED ANALYTICALLY OR GRAPHICALLY:

$$\bar{Z}_s = \bar{Z}_L + \bar{Z}_r = (0.1+0.431)+j(0.3+0.1724)$$

$$= 0.7107 \angle 41.66^\circ$$

$$\delta = \theta_s - \theta_r = 41.66^\circ - \tan^{-1}\left(\frac{0.1724}{0.431}\right)$$

$$= 41.66^\circ - 22^\circ$$

$$= 19.66^\circ$$

10.23

(a) GIVEN THE REACHES,

ZONE 1 : $Z_r = 0.1 \times 80\% = 0.08$; ZONE 2: $0.1 \times 120\% = 0.12$; ZONE 3: $0.1 \times 250\% = 0.25$

IN VIEW OF THE SYSTEM SYMMETRY, ALL SIX SETS OF RELAYS HAVE IDENTICAL SETTINGS.

(b) IT SHOULD BE GIVEN IN THE PROBLEM STATEMENT THAT

THE SYSTEM IS THE SAME AS PROB. 9.11.

$V_{LN\,base} = \frac{230}{\sqrt{3}} = 133\text{ kV}$; $I_{L\,base} = \frac{100}{0.23\sqrt{3}} = 251\text{ A}$

THE EQUIVALENT INSTRUMENT TRANSFORMER'S SECONDARY QUANTITIES ARE

$V_{base} = 133\left(\frac{115}{133}\right) = 115\text{ V}$; $I_{base} = 251\left(\frac{5}{400}\right) = 3.14\text{ A}$

$\therefore Z_{base} = 115/3.14 = 36.7\,\Omega$

$\therefore$ THE SETTINGS ARE (BY MULTIPLYING BY 36.7)

ZONE 1: $2.93\,\Omega$; ZONE 2: $4.40\,\Omega$; ZONE 3: $9.16\,\Omega$

(c) THE OPERATING REGION FOR THREE ZONE DISTANCE RELAY WITH DIRECTIONAL RESTRAINT AS PER THE ARRANGEMENT OF FIG. 10.50 IS SHOWN BELOW:

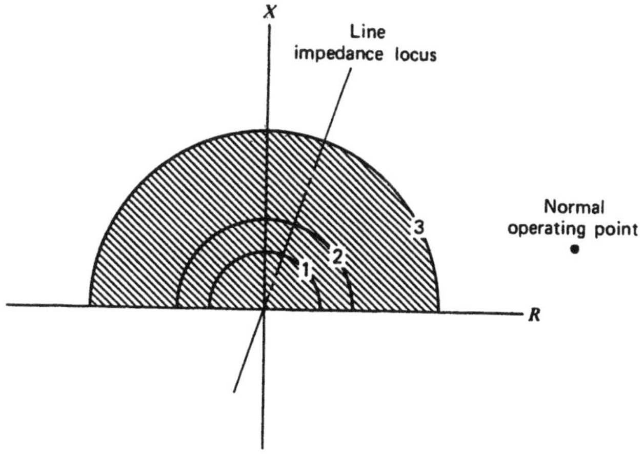

LOCATE POINT X ON THE DIAGRAM

10.23 CONTD.

COMMENT ON LINE BREAKER OPERATIONS:

B31: FAULT IN ZONE 1; INSTANTANEOUS OPERATION

B32: DIRECTIONAL UNIT SHOULD BLOCK OPERATION

B23: FAULT IN ZONE 2; DELAYED OPERATION

B31 SHOULD TRIP FIRST, PREVENTING B23 FROM TRIPPING.

B21: FAULT DUTY IS LIGHT. FAULT IN ZONE 3, IF DETECTED AT ALL.

B12: DIRECTIONAL UNIT SHOULD BLOCK OPERATION.

B13: FAULT IN ZONE 2; JUST OUTSIDE OF ZONE 1; DELAYED OPERATION

LINE BREAKERS B13 AND B31 CLEAR THE FAULT AS DESIRED. IN ADDITION, BREAKERS B1 AND B4 MUST BE COORDINATED WITH B13 SO THAT THE TRIP SEQUENCE IS B13, B1, AND B4 FROM FASTEST TO SLOWEST. LIKEWISE, B13, B31, AND B23 SHOULD BE FASTER THAN B2 AND B5.

10.24

For a 20% mismatch between I_1' and I_2', select a 1.20 upper slope in Figure 10.34. That is:

$$\frac{2+k}{2-k} = 1.20 \qquad \text{solving, } k = 0.1818$$

10.25

(a) OUTPUT VOLTAGES ARE GIVEN BY

$$\bar{V}_1 = jX_m\bar{I}_1 = j5(-j16) = 80\text{V}$$

$$\bar{V}_2 = jX_m\bar{I}_2 = j5(-j7) = 35\text{V}$$

$$\bar{V}_3 = jX_m\bar{I}_3 = j5(j36) = -180\text{V}$$

$$\bar{V}_4 = jX_m\bar{I}_4 = j5(-j13) = 65\text{V}$$

$$\therefore\ \bar{V}_0 = \bar{V}_1 + \bar{V}_2 + \bar{V}_3 + \bar{V}_4 = 80+35-180+65 = 0$$

THUS THERE IS NO VOLTAGE TO OPERATE THE VOLTAGE RELAY VR.

FOR THE EXTERNAL FAULT ON LINE 3, VOLTAGES AND CURRENTS ARE SHOWN BELOW:

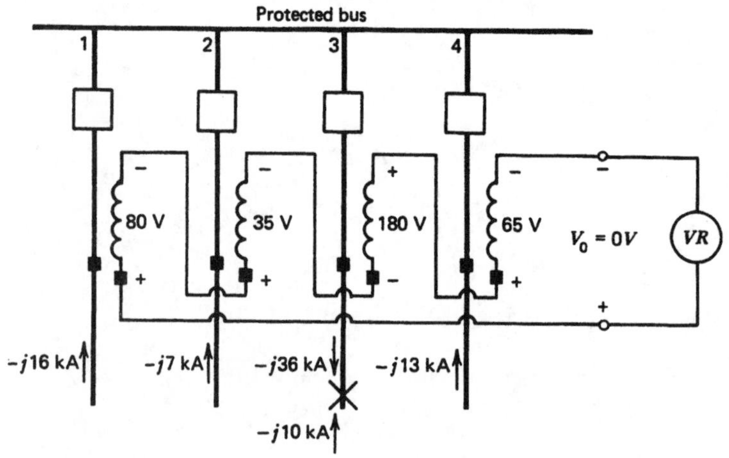

(b) MOVING THE FAULT LOCATION TO THE BUS, AS SHOWN BELOW, THE FAULT CURRENTS AND CORRESPONDING VOLTAGES ARE INDICATED. NOW

$V_0 = 80+35+50+65 = 230\text{V}$ AND THE VOLTAGE RELAY VR WILL TRIP ALL FOUR LINE BREAKERS TO CLEAR THE FAULT.

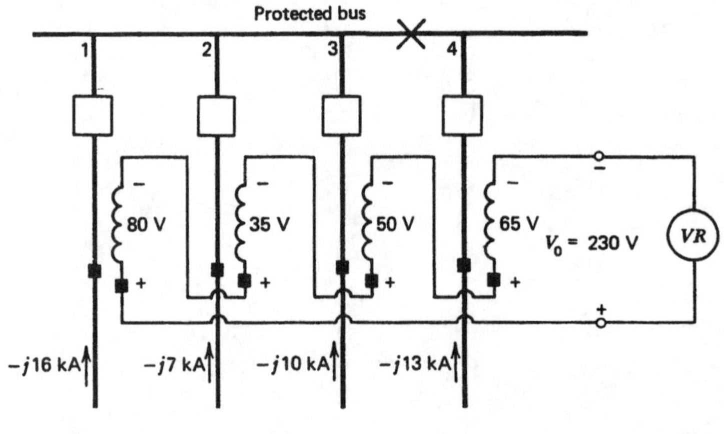

10.25 CONTD.

(C) BY MOVING THE EXTERNAL FAULT FROM LINE 3 TO A CORRESPONDING POINT

(i) ON LINE 2

THE CASE IS DISPLAYED BELOW:

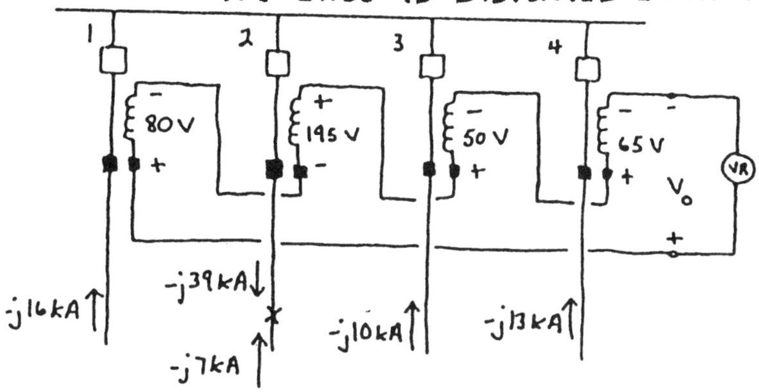

HERE $V_o = 80 - 195 + 50 + 65 = 0$

VR WOULD NOT OPERATE.

(ii) ON LINE 4

THIS CASE IS DISPLAYED BELOW:

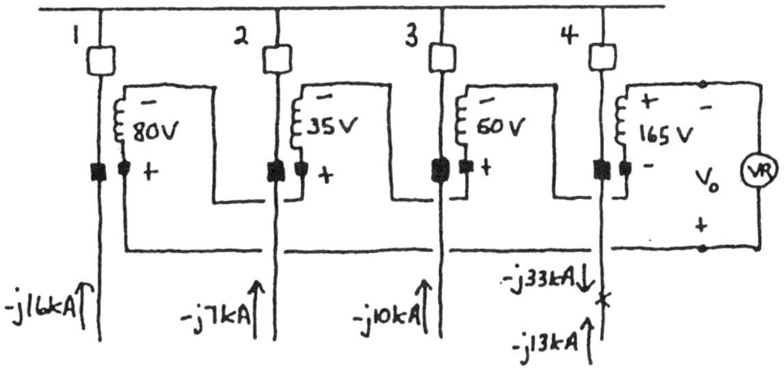

HERE $V_o = 80 + 35 + 50 - 165 = 0$

VR WOULD NOT OPERATE.

10.26 First select CT ratios. The transformer rated primary current is:

$$I_{1\,rated} = \frac{5\times10^6}{20\times10^3} = 250.\ A$$

From Table 10.2, select a $\underline{\underline{300:5}}$ CT ratio on the 20 kV (primary) side to give $I_1' = (250)(5/300) = 4.167$ A at rated conditions. Similarly:

$$I_{2\,rated} = \frac{5\times10^6}{8.66\times10^3} = 577.4\ A$$

select a $\underline{\underline{600:5}}$ secondary CT ratio so that $I_2' = (577.4)(5/600) = 4.811$ A at rated conditions.

Next, select relay taps to balance currents in the restraining windings. The ratio of currents in the restraining windings is:

$$\frac{I_2'}{I_1'} = \frac{4.811}{4.167} = 1.155.$$

The closest relay tap ratio is $T_2'/T_1' = \underline{\underline{1.10}}$. The percentage mismatch for this tap setting is:

$$\%\text{Mismatch} = \left|\frac{(I_1'/T_1') - (I_2'/T_2')}{(I_2'/T_2')}\right| \times 100 = \left|\frac{\left(\frac{4.167}{5}\right) - \left(\frac{4.811}{5.5}\right)}{\left(\frac{4.811}{5}\right)}\right| \times 100$$

$$= \underline{\underline{4.7\%}}$$

10.27

Connect CTs in Δ on the 500 kV Y side, and in Y on the 345. kV Δ side of the transformer.

Rated current on the 345. kV Δ side is

$$I_{a\,rated} = \frac{500.\times 10^6}{345.\times 10^3\sqrt{3}} = 836.7 \text{ A}$$

Select a 900:5 CT ratio on the 345 kV Δ side to give $I_a' = (836.7)(5/900) = 4.649$ A at rated conditions, in the CT secondaries and in the restraining windings.

Similarly, rated current on the 500. kV Y side is

$$I_{A\,rated} = \frac{500\times 10^6}{500\times 10^3\sqrt{3}} = 577.4 \text{ A}$$

Select a 600:5 CT ratio on the 500 kV Y side to give $I_A' = (577.4)(5/600) = 4.811$ A in the 500 kV CT secondaries and $I_{AB}' = 4.811\sqrt{3} = 8.333$ A in the restraining windings.

Next, select relay taps to balance currents in the restraining windings.

$$\frac{I_{AB}'}{I_a'} = \frac{8.333}{4.649} = 1.79$$

The closest tap ratio is $T_{AB}'/T_a' = 1.8$ for a tap setting of 5:9. The percentage mismatch for this relay tap setting is:

$$\%\text{ Mismatch} = \left|\frac{(I_{AB}'/T_{AB}') - (I_a'/T_a')}{(I_a'/T_a')}\right| \times 100 = \left|\frac{(8.333/9) - (4.649/5)}{(4.649/5)}\right| \times 100$$

$$= 0.4\%$$

10.28

THE PRIMARY LINE CURRENT IS $\dfrac{15\times10^6}{\sqrt{3}(33\times10^3)} = 262.43\text{A}$ (say I_p)

THE SECONDARY LINE CURRENT IS $262.43\times3 = 787.3\text{A}$ (say I_s)

THE CT CURRENT ON THE PRIMARY SIDE IS $i_p = 262.43\left(\frac{5}{300}\right) = 4.37\text{A}$

THE CT CURRENT ON THE SECONDARY SIDE IS $i_s = 787.3\left(\frac{5}{2000}\right)\sqrt{3} = 3.41\text{A}$

[NOTE: $\sqrt{3}$ IS APPLIED TO GET THE VALUE ON THE LINE SIDE OF Δ - CONNECTED CT'S.]

THE RELAY CURRENT UNDER NORMAL LOAD IS

$$i_r = i_p - i_s = 4.37 - 3.41 = 0.96\text{ A}$$

WITH 1.25 OVERLOAD RATIO, THE RELAY SETTING SHOULD BE

$$I_r = 1.25(0.96) = 1.2\text{A}$$

10.29

THE PRIMARY LINE CURRENT IS $I_p = \dfrac{30\times10^6}{\sqrt{3}(33\times10^3)} = 524.88\text{A}$

SECONDARY LINE CURRENT IS $I_s = 3I_p = 1574.64\text{ A}$

THE CT CURRENT ON THE PRIMARY SIDE IS $I_1 = 524.88\left(\frac{5}{500}\right) = 5.25\text{A}$

AND THAT ON THE SECONDARY SIDE IS $I_2 = 1574.64\left(\frac{5}{2000}\right)\sqrt{3} = 6.82\text{A}$

RELAY CURRENT AT 200% OF THE RATED CURRENT IS THEN

$$2(I_2 - I_1) = 2(6.82 - 5.25) = 3.14\text{ A}$$

10.30

LINE CURRENTS ARE: $I_\Delta = \dfrac{15\times10^6}{\sqrt{3}(33\times10^3)} = 262.44\text{ A}$

$$I_Y = \dfrac{15\times10^6}{\sqrt{3}(11\times10^3)} = 787.3\text{ A}$$

IF THE CT'S ON HV-SIDE ARE CONNECTED IN Y, THEN THE CT RATIO ON THE HV-SIDE IS $787.3/5 = 157.46$

SIMILARLY, THE CT RATIO ON THE LV-SIDE IS $262.44(5/\sqrt{3}) = 757.6$

CHAPTER 11

11.1

(a)

THE OPEN-LOOP TRANSFER FUNCTION G(S) IS GIVEN BY

$$G(s) = \frac{k_a k_e k_f}{(1+T_a s)(1+T_e s)(1+T_f s)}$$

(b)

$$\frac{\Delta e}{\Delta V_{ref}} = \frac{1}{1+G(s)} = \frac{(1+T_a s)(1+T_e s)(1+T_f s)}{(1+T_a s)(1+T_e s)(1+T_f s)+k_a k_e k_f}$$

FOR STEADY STATE, SETTING $s=0$

$$\Delta e_{ss} = \frac{(\Delta V_{ref})_{ss}}{1+k}, \quad \text{WHERE } k = k_a k_e k_f$$

OR $\quad 1+k = (\Delta V_{ref})_{ss} / \Delta e_{ss}$

FOR THE CONDITION STIPULATED, $\quad 1+k \geq 100$

OR $\quad k \geq 99$

(c)

$$\Delta V_t(t) = \mathcal{L}^{-1}\left[\frac{G(s)}{1+G(s)} \Delta V_{ref}(s)\right]$$

THE RESPONSE OF THE SYSTEM WILL DEPEND ON THE CHARACTERISTIC ROOTS OF THE EQUATION $\quad 1+G(s)=0$

(i) IF THE ROOTS S_1, S_2, AND S_3 ARE REAL AND DISTINCT, THE RESPONSE WILL THEN INCLUDE THE TRANSIENT COMPONENTS

$A_1 e^{s_1 t}$, $A_2 e^{s_2 t}$, AND $A_3 e^{s_3 t}$.

(ii) IF THERE ARE A PAIR OF COMPLEX CONJUGATE ROOTS S_1, S_2 $(=\alpha \pm j\omega)$, THEN THE DYNAMIC RESPONSE WILL BE OF THE FORM $\quad A e^{\alpha t} \sin(\omega t + \phi)$.

11.2

(a) THE OPEN-LOOP TRANSFER FUNCTION OF THE AVR SYSTEM IS

$$KG(s)H(s) = \frac{K_A}{(1+0.1s)(1+0.4s)(1+s)(1+0.05s)}$$

$$= \frac{500K_A}{s^4+33.5s^3+307.5s^2+775s+500}$$

THE CLOSED-LOOP TRANSFER FUNCTION OF THE SYSTEM IS

$$\frac{V_t(s)}{V_{ref}(s)} = \frac{25K_A(s+20)}{s^4+33.5s^3+307.5s^2+775s+500+500K_A}$$

(b) THE CHARACTERISTIC EQUATION IS GIVEN BY

$$1+KG(s)H(s) = 1+\frac{500K_A}{s^4+33.5s^3+307.5s^2+775s+500} = 0$$

WHICH RESULTS IN THE CHARACTERISTIC POLYNOMIAL EQUATION

$$s^4+33.5s^3+307.5s^2+775s+500+500K_A = 0$$

THE ROUTH-HURWITZ ARRAY FOR THIS POLYNOMIAL IS SHOWN BELOW:

s^4	1	307.5	$500+500K_A$
s^3	33.5	775	0
s^2	284.365	$500+500K_A$	0
s^1	$58.9K_A-716.1$	0	0
s^0	$500+500K_A$		

FROM THE s^1 ROW, IT IS SEEN THAT K_A MUST BE LESS THAN 12.16 FOR CONTROL SYSTEM STABILITY, ALSO FROM THE s^0 ROW, K_A MUST BE GREATER THAN −1. THUS, WITH POSITIVE VALUES OF K_A, FOR CONTROL SYSTEM STABILITY, THE AMPLIFIER GAIN MUST BE

$$K_A < 12.16$$

11.2 CONTD.

FOR K = 12.16, THE AUXILIARY EQUATION FROM THE S^2 ROW IS

$$284.365 S^2 + 6580 = 0 \quad \text{OR} \quad S = \pm j4.81$$

THAT IS, FOR K = 12.16, THERE ARE A PAIR OF CONJUGATE POLES ON THE $j\omega$ AXIS, AND THE CONTROL SYSTEM IS MARGINALLY STABLE.

(c) FROM THE CLOSED-LOOP TRANSFER FUNCTION OF THE SYSTEM, THE STEADY-STATE RESPONSE IS

$$(V_t)_{ss} = \lim_{S \to 0} S V_t(s) = \frac{K_A}{1+K_A}$$

FOR THE AMPLIFIER GAIN OF $K_A = 10$, THE STEADY-STATE RESPONSE IS

$$(V_t)_{ss} = \frac{10}{1+10} = 0.909$$

AND THE STEADY-STATE ERROR IS

$$(V_e)_{ss} = 1.0 - 0.909 = 0.091$$

11.3

(a)

AFTER SUBSTITUTING THE PARAMETERS IN THE BLOCK DIAGRAM AND APPLYING THE MASON'S GAIN FORMULA, THE CLOSED-LOOP TRANSFER FUNCTION IS OBTAINED AS

$$\frac{V_t(s)}{V_{ref}(s)} = \frac{250(S^2 + 45S + 500)}{S^5 + 58.5S^4 + 13{,}645 S^3 + 270{,}962.5S^2 + 274{,}875S + 137{,}500}$$

(b) THE STEADY-STATE RESPONSE IS

$$(V_t)_{ss} = \lim_{S \to 0} S V_t(s) = \frac{(250)(500)}{137{,}500} = 0.909$$

11.3 CONTD.

THE TERMINAL VOLTAGE STEP RESPONSE IS DEPICTED BELOW:

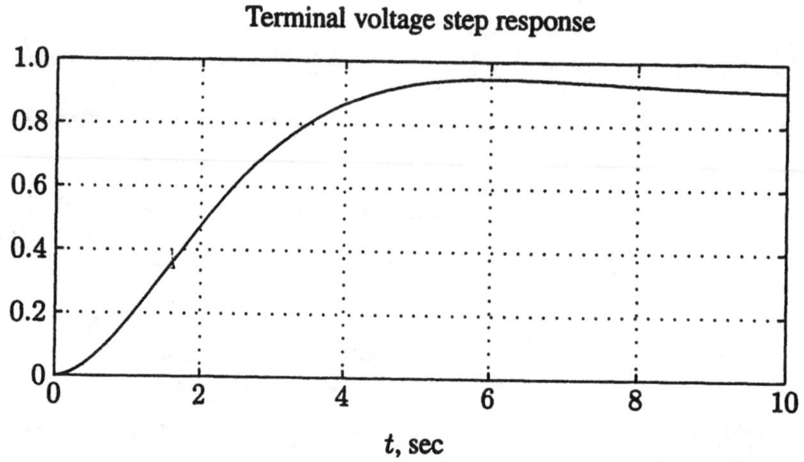

11.4

THE BLOCK DIAGRAM OF AN AVR COMPENSATED WITH A PID CONTROLLER IS SHOWN BELOW:

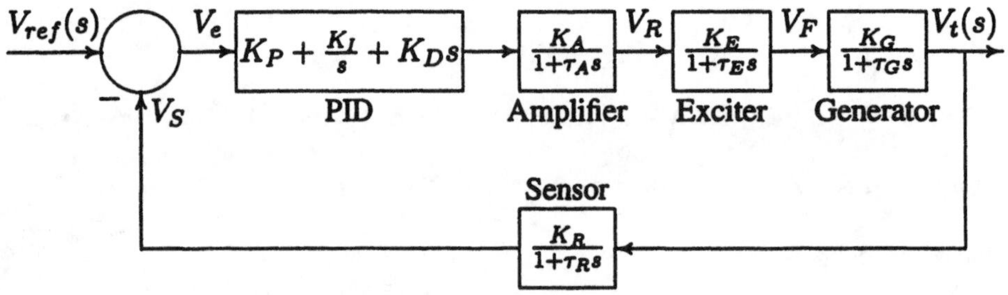

THE DERIVATIVE CONTROLLER ADDS A FINITE ZERO TO THE OPEN-LOOP PLANT TRANSFER FUNCTION AND IMPROVES THE TRANSIENT RESPONSE. THE INTEGRAL CONTROLLER ADDS A POLE AT ORIGIN AND INCREASES THE SYSTEM TYPE BY ONE AND REDUCES THE STEADY-STATE ERROR DUE TO A STEP FUNCTION TO ZERO.

11.5 (a) Converting the regulation constants to a 100-MVA system base:

$R_{1\,newpu} = 0.04$

$R_{2\,new\,pu} = 0.05\left(\frac{100}{200}\right) = 0.025$

$R_{3\,newpu} = 0.06\left(\frac{100}{600}\right) = 0.01$

Using (11.2.3):

$$\beta = \left(\frac{1}{.04} + \frac{1}{.025} + \frac{1}{.01}\right) = \underline{\underline{165.}} \text{ per unit}$$

(b) Using (11.2.4) with $\Delta P_{ref} = 0$ and $\Delta P_m = \frac{-100}{100}$ P.U.

$$-1.0 = -165\,\Delta f$$

$$\Delta f = 6.0606 \times 10^{-3} \text{ per unit} = (6.0606 \times 10^{-3})(60) = \underline{\underline{0.3636 \text{ Hz}}}$$

(c) Using (11.2.1) with $\Delta P_{ref} = 0$:

$$\Delta P_{m1} = -\left(\frac{1}{0.04}\right)(6.0606 \times 10^{-3}) = -0.1515 \text{ per unit} = \underline{\underline{-15.15 \text{ MW}}}$$

$$\Delta P_{m2} = -\left(\frac{1}{0.025}\right)(6.0606 \times 10^{-3}) = -0.2424 \text{ per unit} = \underline{\underline{-24.24 \text{ MW}}}$$

$$\Delta P_{m3} = -\left(\frac{1}{0.01}\right)(6.0606 \times 10^{-3}) = -0.60606 \text{ per unit} = \underline{\underline{-60.61 \text{ MW}}}$$

11.6 (a) Using (11.2.4) with $\Delta P_{ref} = 0$ and $\Delta P_m = \frac{+75}{100}$ P.U.

$$0.75 = -165\,\Delta f$$

$$\Delta f = -4.5454 \times 10^{-3} \text{ per unit} = -(4.5454 \times 10^{-3})(60) = \underline{\underline{-0.2727 \text{ Hz}}}$$

(b) Using (11.2.1) with $\Delta P_{ref} = 0$:

$$\Delta P_{m1} = -\left(\frac{1}{0.04}\right)(-4.5454 \times 10^{-3}) = 0.1136 \text{ per unit} = \underline{\underline{11.36 \text{ MW}}}$$

$$\Delta P_{m2} = -\left(\frac{1}{0.025}\right)(-4.5454 \times 10^{-3}) = 0.1818 \text{ per unit} = \underline{\underline{18.18 \text{ MW}}}$$

$$\Delta P_{m3} = -\left(\frac{1}{0.01}\right)(-4.5454 \times 10^{-3}) = 0.4545 \text{ per unit} = \underline{\underline{45.45 \text{ MW}}}$$

11.7 Using (11.2.1) with $\Delta P_{ref} = 0$:

$$\Delta P_{m1} = -\left(\frac{1}{0.04}\right)(0.003) = -0.075 \text{ per unit} = \underline{\underline{-7.5 \text{ MW}}}$$

$$\Delta P_{m2} = -\left(\frac{1}{0.025}\right)(0.003) = -0.12 \text{ per unit} = \underline{\underline{-12.0 \text{ MW}}}$$

$$\Delta P_{m3} = -\left(\frac{1}{0.01}\right)(0.003) = -0.30 \text{ per unit} = \underline{\underline{-30.0 \text{ MW}}}$$

11.8

$$\Delta P_{m1} = -\left(\frac{1}{0.04}\right)(-0.005) = 0.125 \text{ per unit} = \underline{\underline{12.5 \text{ MW}}}$$

$$\Delta P_{m2} = -\left(\frac{1}{0.025}\right)(-0.005) = 0.20 \text{ per unit} = \underline{\underline{20.0 \text{ MW}}}$$

$$\Delta P_{m3} = -\left(\frac{1}{0.01}\right)(-0.005) = 0.50 \text{ per unit} = \underline{\underline{50.0 \text{ MW}}}$$

11.9

THE PER-UNIT FREQUENCY CHANGE IS

$$\text{PER-UNIT } \Delta f = \frac{\Delta f}{f_{base}} = \frac{-0.025}{60} = -4.167\times10^{-4}$$

THE CHANGE IN THE TURBINE OUTPUT POWER AS A FUNCTION OF A CHANGE IN THE GENERATOR FREQUENCY IS GIVEN BY

$$\Delta P_m = \Delta P_{ref} - \frac{1}{R}\Delta f$$

$$\therefore \text{ PER-UNIT } \Delta P_m = -\frac{1}{0.05}\left(-4.167\times10^{-4}\right) = 8.33\times10^{-3}$$

THEN THE ACTUAL INCREASE IN OUTPUT POWER IS

$$\Delta P_m = \left(8.33\times10^{-3}\right)(100) = 0.833 \text{ MW}$$

11.10

(a) USING $R_{new} = R_{old}\dfrac{S_{base(new)}}{S_{base(old)}}$

$$R_{1(new)} = 0.04\,\frac{1000}{500} = 0.08 \text{ PU}; \quad R_{2(new)} = 0.05\,\frac{1000}{750} = 0.067 \text{ PU}$$

THE AREA FREQUENCY-RESPONSE CHARACTERISTIC IS GIVEN BY

$$\beta = \sum_{k=1}^{n}\frac{1}{R_k} = \frac{1}{R_1}+\frac{1}{R_2} = \frac{1}{0.08}+\frac{1}{0.067} = 27.5 \text{ PU}$$

(b) THE PER-UNIT INCREASE IN LOAD IS $250/1000 = 0.25$

$$(\Delta P_m)_{TOTAL} = \sum_{k=1}^{n}\Delta P_{mk} = \sum_{k=1}^{n}\Delta P_{ref\,k} - \left(\sum_{k=1}^{n}\frac{1}{R_k}\right)\Delta f = \Delta P_{ref(total)} - \beta\Delta f$$

WITH $\Delta P_{ref(total)} = 0$ FOR STEADY-STATE CONDITIONS,

$$\Delta f = -\frac{1}{\beta}\Delta P_m = -\frac{1}{27.5}(0.25) = -9.091\times10^{-3} \text{ PU}$$

$$\text{OR } \Delta f = -9.091\times10^{-3}\times60 = -0.545 \text{ Hz}.$$

11.11

EXPRESSING THE GOVERNOR SPEED REGULATION OF EACH UNIT TO A COMMON BASE OF 1000 MVA,

$$R_1 = \frac{1000}{600}(0.06) = 0.1 \text{ PU}; \quad R_2 = \frac{1000}{500}(0.04) = 0.08 \text{ PU}$$

PER-UNIT LOAD CHANGE IS $\Delta P_L = 90/1000 = 0.09$ PU

(a)
$$\Delta\omega_{ss} = (-\Delta P_L)\frac{1}{D + \left(\frac{1}{R_1}\right) + \left(\frac{1}{R_2}\right)}$$

WITH $D=0$, THE PER-UNIT STEADY-STATE FREQUENCY DEVIATION IS

$$\Delta\omega_{ss} = \frac{-0.09}{10 + 12.5} = -0.004 \text{ PU}$$

THE STEADY-STATE FREQUENCY DEVIATION IN Hz IS THEN GIVEN BY

$$\Delta f = (-0.004)\,60 = -0.24 \text{ Hz}.$$

AND THE NEW FREQUENCY IS $f = f_0 + \Delta f = 60 - 0.24 = 59.76$ Hz.

THE CHANGE IN GENERATION FOR EACH UNIT IS

$$\Delta P_1 = -\frac{\Delta\omega}{R_1} = -\frac{-0.004}{0.1} = 0.04 \text{ PU} = 40 \text{ MW}$$

$$\Delta P_2 = -\frac{\Delta\omega}{R_2} = -\frac{-0.004}{0.08} = 0.05 \text{ PU} = 50 \text{ MW}$$

THUS UNIT 1 SUPPLIES $500 + 40 = 540$ MW, AND UNIT 2 SUPPLIES $400 + 50 = 450$ MW AT THE NEW OPERATING FREQUENCY OF 59.76 Hz.

(b) FOR $D = 1.5$, THE PER-UNIT STEADY-STATE FREQUENCY DEVIATION IS

$$\Delta\omega_{ss} = \frac{-\Delta P_L}{D + \frac{1}{R_1} + \frac{1}{R_2}} = \frac{-0.09}{1.5 + 10 + 12.5} = -0.00375 \text{ PU}$$

THE STEADY-STATE FREQUENCY DEVIATION IN Hz IS THEN

$$\Delta f = (-0.00375)(60) = -0.225 \text{ Hz}.$$

AND THE NEW FREQUENCY IS $f = f_0 + \Delta f = 60 - 0.225 = 59.775$ Hz.

11.11 CONTD.

THE CHANGE IN GENERATION FOR EACH UNIT IS

$$\Delta P_1 = -\frac{\Delta\omega}{R_1} = -\frac{-0.00375}{0.1} = 0.0375 \text{ PU} = 37.5 \text{ MW}$$

$$\Delta P_2 = -\frac{\Delta\omega}{R_2} = -\frac{-0.00375}{0.08} = 0.0469 \text{ PU} = 46.9 \text{ MW}$$

THUS UNIT 1 SUPPLIES 537.5 MW AND UNIT 2 SUPPLIES 446.9 MW AT THE NEW OPERATING FREQUENCY OF 59.775 HZ.

THE TOTAL CHANGE IN GENERATION IS $37.5 + 46.9 = 84.4$ MW, WHICH IS 5.6 MW LESS THAN THE 90 MW LOAD CHANGE.

THIS IS BECAUSE OF THE CHANGE IN LOAD DUE TO THE FREQUENCY DROP WHICH IS GIVEN BY

$$(\Delta\omega)D = (-0.00375)(1.5) = -0.0056 \text{ PU} = -5.6 \text{ MW}.$$

11.12 Adding (11.2.4) for each area with $\Delta P_{ref} = 0$:

$$\Delta P_{m1} + \Delta P_{m2} = -(\beta_1 + \beta_2)\Delta f$$

$$400 = -(500+800)\Delta f \qquad \Delta f = \frac{-400}{1300} = \underline{\underline{-0.3077 \text{ Hz}}}$$

$$\Delta P_{tie2} = \Delta P_{m2} = -\beta_2 \Delta f = -800(-.3077) = \underline{\underline{246.15 \text{ MW}}}$$

$$\Delta P_{tie1} = -\Delta P_{tie2} = \underline{\underline{-246.15 \text{ MW}}}$$

11.13 In steady state,

$$ACE_2 = \Delta P_{tie2} + B_{f2}\,\Delta f = 0 \qquad \Delta P_{tie2} = \Delta P_{m2}$$

$$\therefore \quad \Delta P_{m2} = \Delta P_{tie2} = -B_{f2}\,\Delta f$$

and $\Delta P_{m1} = -\beta_1 \Delta f$

Also $\Delta P_{m1} + \Delta P_{m2} = 400$ MW

Solving:

$$-(\beta_1 + B_{f2})\Delta f = 400$$

$$\Delta f = \frac{-400}{(500+800)} = \underline{\underline{-0.3077}} \text{ Hz}$$

$$\Delta P_{tie2} = -(800)(-.3077) = \underline{\underline{246.15}} \text{ MW}$$

$$\Delta P_{tie1} = -\Delta P_{tie2} = \underline{\underline{-246.15}} \text{ MW}$$

Note: The results are the same as those in Problem 11.5. That is, LFC is not effective when employed in only one area.

11.14 In Steady State:

$$ACE_1 = \Delta P_{tie1} + B_{f1}\,\Delta f = 0$$

$$ACE_2 = \Delta P_{tie2} + B_{f2}\,\Delta f = 0$$

Adding: $\underbrace{(\Delta P_{tie1} + \Delta P_{tie2})}_{0} + (B_{f1} + B_{f2})\,\Delta f = 0$

$$\Delta f = 0 \qquad \Delta P_{tie1} = 0 \qquad \Delta P_{tie2} = 0$$

In steady-state, area 1 picks up its entire 400. MW load increase.

11.15 In Steady State:

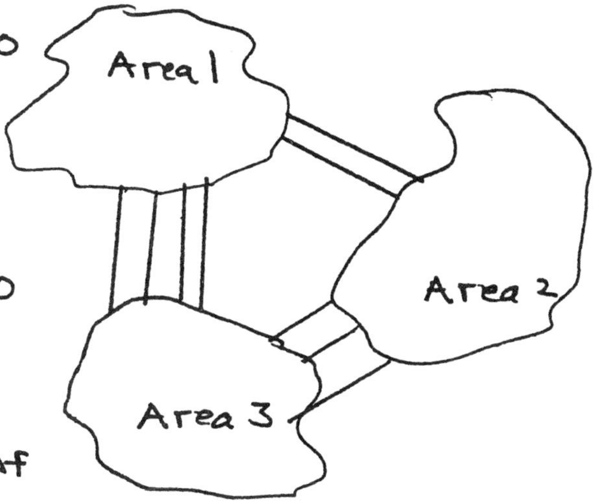

$$ACE_2 = \Delta P_{tie2} + B_{f2}\,\Delta f = 0$$

$$\Delta P_{m1} = -\beta_1\,\Delta f$$

$$\Delta P_{m3} = -\beta_3\,\Delta f$$

and $\Delta P_{m1} + \Delta P_{m2} + \Delta P_{m3} = 400$

solving:

$$\Delta P_{tie2} = \Delta P_{m2} = -B_{f2}\,\Delta f$$

$$-(\beta_1 + B_{f2} + \beta_3)\,\Delta f = 400$$

$$\Delta f = \left(\frac{-400}{500 + 800 + 1500}\right) = \underline{\underline{-0.1429 \text{ Hz}}}$$

11.15 CONTD.

$\Delta P_{tie2} = -(800)(-0.1429) = \underline{\underline{114.29}}$ MW

$\Delta P_{tie3} = -(1500)(-0.1429) = \underline{\underline{214.29}}$ MW

$\Delta P_{tie1} = -(\Delta P_{tie2} + \Delta P_{tie3}) = \underline{\underline{-328.57}}$ MW

When LFC does not operate in areas 1 and 3, area 1 picks up on 71.43 MW of its own 400 MW increase. Areas 2 and 3 export 328.57 MW to area 1. Also, since the system is larger, the steady-state frequency drop of 0.1429 Hz is smaller than in Problem 11.5.

11.16 (a) LFC not employed in any area

$$\Delta P_{m1} + \Delta P_{m2} = -(\beta_1 + \beta_2)\Delta f$$

$$-400 = -(500+800)\Delta f$$

$$\Delta f = \frac{400}{500+800} = \underline{\underline{+0.3077 \text{ Hz}}}$$

$$\Delta P_{tie1} = \Delta P_{m1} = -\beta_1 \Delta f = -(500)(.3077) = \underline{\underline{-153.85 \text{ MW}}}$$

$$\Delta P_{tie2} = -\Delta P_{tie1} = \underline{\underline{+153.85 \text{ MW}}}$$

(b) LFC employed in area 2 alone.

In steady-state

$$ACE_2 = \Delta P_{tie2} + B_{f2}\Delta f = 0$$

$$\therefore \quad \Delta P_{m2} = \Delta P_{tie2} = -B_{f2}\Delta f$$

and $\quad \Delta P_{m1} = -\beta_1 \Delta f$

Also $\quad \Delta P_{m1} + \Delta P_{m2} = -400$

Solving: $\quad -(\beta_1 + B_{f2})\Delta f = -400$

$$\Delta f = \frac{400}{(500+800)} = \underline{\underline{0.3077 \text{ Hz}}}$$

11.16 CONTD.

$\Delta P_{tie1} = -(500)(0.3077) = \underline{\underline{-153.85}}$ MW

$\Delta P_{tie2} = -\Delta P_{tie1} = \underline{\underline{+153.85}}$ MW

(c) LFC employed in both areas 1 and 2.

$ACE_1 = \Delta P_{tie1} + B_{f1}\,\Delta f = 0$

$ACE_2 = \Delta P_{tie2} + B_{f2}\,\Delta f = 0$

Adding: $\underbrace{(\Delta P_{tie1} + \Delta P_{tie2})}_{0} + (B_{f1} + B_{f2})\Delta f = 0$

$\Delta f = 0 \qquad \Delta P_{tie1} = 0 \qquad \Delta P_{tie2} = 0$

Results: (a) without LFC, both areas 1 and 2 respond to the 400 MW decrease in area 2 load. Area 1 drops 153.85 MW and area 2 drops 246.15 MW. The steady-state frequency increases 0.3077 Hz. (b) With LFC employed in only one area, the same results are obtained. Both areas respond to to the load decrease in area 2. (c) With LFC employed in both areas, area 2 generation is reduced by the entire 400 MW load decrease in that area. Area 1 generation remains unchanged. And the steady-state frequency remains unchanged.

11.17

(a) WITHOUT LFC (LOAD FREQUENCY CONTROL), $\Delta P_{ref\,(total)} = 0$

$$\therefore \Delta P_{m\,total} = -(\beta_1 + \beta_2)\Delta f$$

$$\text{or} \quad 60 = -(400 + 300)\Delta f$$

$$\text{or} \quad \Delta f = -\frac{60}{700} = -0.0857 \text{ Hz.}$$

(b) WITH LFC, IN STEADY STATE, $ACE_1 = ACE_2 = 0$

(ACE STANDS FOR AREA CONTROL ERROR.)

OTHERWISE, THE ACE ($= \Delta P_{tie} + B_f \Delta f$) WOULD BE CHANGING THE REFERENCE POWER SETTINGS OF THE GOVERNORS ON LFC. B_f IS KNOWN AS THE FREQUENCY BIAS CONSTANT.

ALSO, THE SUM OF THE NET TIE-LINE FLOWS, $\Delta P_{tie1} + \Delta P_{tie2}$, IS ZERO, NEGLECTING LOSSES.

$$\text{So} \quad ACE_1 + ACE_2 = 0 = (B_1 + B_2)\Delta f$$

$$\text{SINCE } (B_1 + B_2) \neq 0, \quad \Delta f = 0$$

11.18

(a) THE PER-UNIT LOAD CHANGE IN AREA 1 IS

$$\Delta P_{L1} = \frac{187.5}{1000} = 0.1875$$

THE PER-UNIT STEADY-STATE FREQUENCY DEVIATION IS

$$\Delta\omega_{ss} = \frac{-\Delta P_{L1}}{\left(\frac{1}{R_1} + D_1\right) + \left(\frac{1}{R_2} + D_2\right)} = \frac{-0.1875}{(20 + 0.6) + (16 + 0.9)} = -0.005$$

THUS, THE STEADY-STATE FREQUENCY DEVIATION IN Hz IS

$$\Delta f = (-0.005)(60) = -0.3 \text{ Hz}$$

AND THE NEW FREQUENCY IS $f = f_0 + \Delta f = 60 - 0.3 = 59.7$ Hz.

11.18 CONTD.

THE CHANGE IN MECHANICAL POWER IN EACH AREA IS

$$\Delta P_{m1} = -\frac{\Delta\omega}{R_1} = -\frac{-0.005}{0.05} = 0.1 \text{ PU} = 100 \text{ MW}$$

$$\Delta P_{m2} = -\frac{\Delta\omega}{R_2} = -\frac{-0.005}{0.0625} = 0.08 \text{ PU} = 80 \text{ MW}$$

THUS AREA 1 INCREASES THE GENERATION BY 100 MW AND AREA 2 BY 80 MW AT THE NEW OPERATING FREQUENCY OF 59.7 HZ. THE TOTAL CHANGE IN GENERATION IS 180 MW, WHICH IS 7.5 MW LESS THAN THE 187.5 MW LOAD CHANGE BECAUSE OF THE CHANGE IN THE AREA LOADS DUE TO FREQUENCY DROP.

THE CHANGE IN AREA 1 LOAD IS $\Delta\omega . D_1 = (-0.005)(0.6) = -0.003$ PU OR -3.0 MW, AND THE CHANGE IN AREA 2 LOAD IS $\Delta\omega . D_2 = (-0.005)(0.9) = -0.0045$ PU OR -4.5 MW. THUS, THE CHANGE IN THE TOTAL AREA LOAD IS -7.5 MW. THE TIE-LINE POWER FLOW IS

$$\Delta P_{12} = \Delta\omega\left(\frac{1}{R_2} + D_2\right) = -0.005(16.9) = -0.0845 \text{ PU}$$
$$= -84.5 \text{ MW}$$

THAT IS, 84.5 MW FLOWS FROM AREA 2 TO AREA 1. 80 MW COMES FROM THE INCREASED GENERATION IN AREA 2, AND 4.5 MW COMES FROM THE REDUCTION IN AREA 2 LOAD DUE TO FREQUENCY DROP.

(b) WITH THE INCLUSION OF THE ACEs, THE FREQUENCY DEVIATION RETURNS TO ZERO (WITH A SETTLING TIME OF ABOUT 20 SECONDS). ALSO, THE TIE-LINE POWER CHANGE REDUCES TO ZERO, AND THE INCREASE IN AREA 1 LOAD IS MET BY THE INCREASE IN GENERATION ΔP_{m1}.

11·19

$$\frac{dC_1}{dP_1} = \begin{cases} 0.04 P_1 + 2 & 0 < P_1 \le 100 \\ 6 \quad \frac{\$}{\text{MWhr}} & P_1 > 100 \quad \text{MW} \end{cases}$$

$$\frac{dC_2}{dP_2} = 0.06 P_2 \quad \frac{\$}{\text{MWhr}}$$

Using (11.4.8)

$$0.04 P_1 + 2 = 0.06 P_2 = 0.06 (P_T - P_1) \qquad 0 < P_1 \le 100$$

$$6 = 0.06 P_2 = 0.06 (P_T - P_1) \qquad P_1 > 100$$

Solving:

$$P_1 = \begin{cases} 0.6 P_T - 20 & 0 < P_1 \le 100 \\ P_T - 100 & P_1 > 100 \end{cases}$$

The total cost is:

$$C_T = C_1 + C_2 = \begin{cases} 2P_1 + 0.02 P_1^2 + 0.03 P_2^2 & 0 < P_1 \le 100 \\ 6P_1 + 0.03 P_2^2 \quad \frac{\$}{\text{hr}} & P_1 > 100 \end{cases}$$

The incremental cost is:

$$\lambda = \frac{dC_1}{dP_1} = \frac{dC_2}{dP_2} = 0.06 P_2 \quad \frac{\$}{\text{MWhr}}$$

The economic dispatch solution is given in the following table for values of P_T from 200 to 700 MW.

P_T MW	P_1 MW	P_2 MW	λ \$/MWhr	C_T \$/hr
200	100	100	6	700
300	200	100	6	1500
400	300	100	6	2100
500	400	100	6	2700
600	500	100	6	3300
700	600	100	6	3900

Note:
For $200 < P_T < 700$, economic operation is achieved by holding P_2 at 100 MW

11.20 Inspection of the results in problem 11.10 shows that the solution is not changed by the inequality constraints until $P_T > 600$ MW.

At heavy loads when $P_T > 600$ MW, unit 1 operates at its upper limit of 500 MW. Additional load comes from unit 2. Also, the incremental cost is $\lambda = \frac{dc_2}{dP_2} = 0.06 P_2$

P_T	P_1	P_2	$\frac{dc_2}{dP_2}$	C_T
MW	MW	MW	\$/MWhr	\$/hr
200	100	100	6	700
300	200	100	6	1500
400	300	100	6	2100
500	400	100	6	2700
600	500	100	6	3300
650	500	150	9	3675
700	500	200	12	4200

11.21 $P_L = 2\times10^{-4} P_1^2 + 1\times10^{-4} P_2^2$

$$\frac{\partial P_L}{\partial P_1} = 4\times10^{-4} P_1 \qquad \frac{\partial P_L}{\partial P_2} = 2\times10^{-4} P_2$$

Using (11.4.13) and the unit incremental operating costs from Problem 11.10 :

$$\frac{dC_1}{dP_1} L_1 = \frac{6}{1-4\times10^{-4}P_1} = \lambda \qquad \text{for } P_1 > 100$$

$$\frac{dC_2}{dP_2} L_2 = \frac{0.06 P_2}{1-2\times10^{-4}P_2} = \lambda$$

Solving for P_1 and P_2 in terms of λ :

$$P_1 = \frac{\lambda-6}{4\times10^{-4}\lambda} \qquad P_2 = \frac{\lambda}{0.06+2\times10^{-4}\lambda}$$

Also $P_T = P_1 + P_2 - P_L = P_1 + P_2 - (2\times10^{-4}P_1^2 + 1\times10^{-4}P_2^2)$

The solution is shown in the following table for values of λ from 6.25 to 16.19 $\frac{\$}{MWhr}$. At $\lambda = 7.50$, $P_1 = 500$ MW reaches its upper limit. For $\lambda > 7.50$, P_1 is held at 500 MW.

λ $\frac{\$}{MWhr}$	P_1 MW	P_2 MW	P_L MW	P_T MW	C_T \$/hr
6.25	100	102	3	199	712
6.50	192	106	8	290	1489
7.00	357	114	27	444	2532
7.50	500	122	51	571	3447
12.50	500	200	54	646	4200
16.19	500	256	56	700	4966

11.22 (a) No inequality constraints

$$\frac{dC_1}{dP_1} = \begin{cases} 0.04\,P_1 + 2 & 0 < P_1 \le 100 \\ 6 \quad \frac{\$}{\text{MWhr}} & P_1 > 100 \end{cases}$$

$$\frac{dC_2}{dP_2} = 0.08\,P_2$$

Using (11.4.8):

$$0.04\,P_1 + 2 = 0.08\,P_2 = 0.08\,(P_T - P_1) \qquad 0 < P_1 \le 100$$

$$6 = 0.08\,P_2 = 0.08\,(P_T - P_1) \qquad P_1 > 100$$

Solving:

$$P_1 = \begin{cases} 0.6667\,P_T - 16.667 & 0 < P_1 \le 100 \\ P_T - 75 & P_1 > 100 \end{cases}$$

The total cost is:

$$C_T = C_1 + C_2 = \begin{cases} 2\,P_1 + 0.02\,P_1^2 + 0.04\,P_2^2 & 0 < P_1 \le 100 \\ 6\,P_1 + 0.04\,P_2^2 \quad \frac{\$}{\text{hr}} & P_1 > 100 \end{cases}$$

The incremental cost is:

$$\lambda = \frac{dC_1}{dP_1} = \frac{dC_2}{dP_2} = 0.08\,P_2 \quad \frac{\$}{\text{MWhr}}$$

The economic solution is given in the following table for values of P_T from 200 to 700 MW.

P_T	P_1	P_2	λ	C_T
MW	MW	MW	\$/MWh	\$/h
200	125	75	6	975.
300	225	75	6	1575.
400	325	75	6	2175.
500	425	75	6	2775.
600	525	75	6	3375.
700	625	75	6	3975.

For $200 \le P_T \le 700$ economic operation is achieved by holding P_2 at 75. MW

11.22 CONTD.

(b) with the following constraints:

$100. \le P_1 \le 500.$

$50. \le P_2 \le 300$

Inspection of the results in part (a) shows that the solution is not changed by the constraints until $P_T > 575.$ MW

At heavy loads when $P_T > 575.$ MW, unit 1 operates at its upper limit of 500. MW. Additional load is supplied from unit 2. Also, the incremental cost is $\lambda = \frac{dC_2}{dP_2} = .08\,P_2$

P_T	P_1	P_2	$\frac{dC_2}{dP_2}$	C_T
MW	MW	MW	\$/MWh	\$/h
200	125	75	6	975.
300	225	75	6	1575.
400	325	75	6	2175.
500	425	75	6	2775.
575	500	75	6	3225.
600	500	100	8.	3400.
700	500	200	16.	4600.

(c) Including line losses:

$$P_L = 2\times10^{-4}\,P_1^2 + 1\times10^{-4}\,P_2^2$$

$$\frac{\partial P_L}{\partial P_1} = 4\times10^{-4}\,P_1 \qquad \frac{\partial P_L}{\partial P_2} = 2\times10^{-4}\,P_2$$

Using (11.4.13) and the unit incremental operating costs from part (a):

11.22 CONTD. (c) $$\frac{dC_1}{dP_1}L_1 = \frac{6}{1-4\times10^{-4}P_1} = \lambda \quad \text{for } 100 \le P_1 \le 500$$

$$\frac{dC_2}{dP_2}L_2 = \frac{0.08\,P_2}{1-2\times10^{-4}P_2} = \lambda \quad 50 \le P_2 \le 300$$

Solving for P_1 and P_2 in terms of λ:

$$P_1 = \frac{\lambda - 6}{4\times10^{-4}\lambda} \qquad P_2 = \frac{\lambda}{0.08 + 2\times10^{-4}\lambda}$$

Also

$$P_T = P_1 + P_2 - P_L = P_1 + P_2 - (2\times10^{-4}P_1^2 + 1\times10^{-4}P_2^2)$$

$$C_T = 6P_1 + 0.04P_2^2$$

the solution is given in the following table for values of λ from 6.32 to 21.67 \$/MWhr. At $\lambda = 7.5$, $P_1 = 500$ reaches its upper limit. For $\lambda \ge 7.5$, P_1 is held at 500 MW.

λ	P_1	P_2	P_L	P_T	C_T
$/MWhr	MW	MW	MW	MW	$/hr
6.32	127.	78.	3.8	201	1005.
6.50	192.	80.	8.0	264.	1408.
6.75	278.	83.	16.1	345.	1944.
7.00	357.	86.	26.2	417.	2438.
7.50	500.	92.	50.8	541.	3339.
10.0	500.	122	51.5	570.	3595.
16.67	500.	200.	54.	646.	4600.
21.67	500.	257.	57.	700.	5642.

11.22 CONTD.

Comparing with Problems 11.10 – 11.12, the operating cost of unit 2 is higher in Problem 11.13. As such, economic operation is acheived by operating unit 1 at higher levels in Problem 11.13. Also, total costs C_T are higher in Problem 11.13.

11.23 For $N = 2$, (11.4.14) becomes:

$$P_L = \sum_{i=1}^{2} \sum_{j=1}^{2} P_i B_{ij} P_j = \sum_{i=1}^{2} P_i (B_{i1} P_1 + B_{i2} P_2)$$

$$= B_{11} P_1^2 + B_{12} P_1 P_2 + B_{21} P_1 P_2 + B_{22} P_2^2$$

Assuming $B_{12} = B_{21}$,

$$P_L = B_{11} P_1^2 + 2 B_{12} P_1 P_2 + B_{22} P_2^2$$

$$\frac{\partial P_L}{\partial P_1} = 2 (B_{11} P_1 + B_{12} P_2) \qquad \frac{\partial P_L}{\partial P_2} = 2 (B_{12} P_1 + B_{22} P_2)$$

Also, from (11.4.15):

$$i = 1 \qquad \frac{\partial P_L}{\partial P_1} = 2 \sum_{j=1}^{2} B_{1j} P_j = 2 (B_{11} P_1 + B_{12} P_2)$$

$$i = 2 \qquad \frac{\partial P_L}{\partial P_2} = 2 \sum_{j=1}^{2} B_{2j} P_j = 2 (B_{21} P_1 + B_{22} P_2)$$

$$= 2 (B_{12} P_1 + B_{22} P_2)$$

which checks.

11.24

CHOOSING S_{base} AS 100 MVA (3-PHASE),

$\alpha_1 = (S_{3\phi\,base})^2\, 0.01 = 100$; $\alpha_2 = 40$

$\beta_1 = (S_{3\phi\,base})\, 2.00 = 200$; $\beta_2 = 260$

$\gamma_1 = 100$; $\gamma_2 = 80$

IN PER UNIT, $0.25 \le P_{G1} \le 1.5$; $0.3 \le P_{G2} \le 2.0$; $0.55 \le P_L \le 3.5$

$$\lambda_1 = \frac{\partial c_1}{\partial P_{G1}} = 200\,P_{G1} + 200 \ ; \qquad \lambda_2 = \frac{\partial c_2}{\partial P_{G2}} = 80\,P_{G2} + 260$$

CALCULATE λ_1 AND λ_2 FOR MINIMUM GENERATION CONDITIONS (POINT 1, IN FIGURE SHOWN BELOW). SINCE $\lambda_2 > \lambda_1$, IN ORDER TO MAKE λ's EQUAL, LOAD UNIT 1 FIRST UNTIL $\lambda_1 = 284$ WHICH OCCURS AT

$$P_{G1} = \frac{284 - 200}{200} = 0.42 \text{ (POINT 2 IN FIGURE)}$$

NOW, CALCULATE λ_1 AND λ_2 AT THE MAXIMUM GENERATION CONDITIONS: POINT 3 IN FIGURE. NOW THAT $\lambda_1 > \lambda_2$, UNLOAD UNIT 1 FIRST UNTIL λ_1 IS BROUGHT DOWN TO $\lambda_1 = 420$ WHICH OCCURS AT

$$P_{G1} = \frac{420 - 200}{200} = 1.10 \text{ (POINT 4 IN FIGURE)}$$

NOTICE THAT, FOR $0.72 \le P_L \le 3.1$, IT IS POSSIBLE TO MAINTAIN EQUAL λ's. EQUATIONS ARE GIVEN BY

$\lambda_1 = \lambda_2$; $200\,P_{G1} + 200 = 80\,P_{G2} + 260$; AND $P_{G1} + P_{G2} = P_L$

THESE LINEAR RELATIONSHIPS ARE DEPICTED IN THE FIGURE BELOW:

FOR $P_L = 282$ MW $= 2.82$ PU, $P_{G2} = 2.82 - P_{G1}$;

$P_{G1} = 0.4\,P_{G2} + 0.3 = 1.128 - 0.4\,P_{G1} + 0.3$

$1.4\,P_{G1} = 1.428$ OR $P_{G1} = 1.02 = 102$ MW

$P_{G2} = 2.82 - 1.02 = 1.8 = 180$ MW

RESULTS ARE TABULATED IN THE TABLE GIVEN BELOW:

11.24 CONTD.

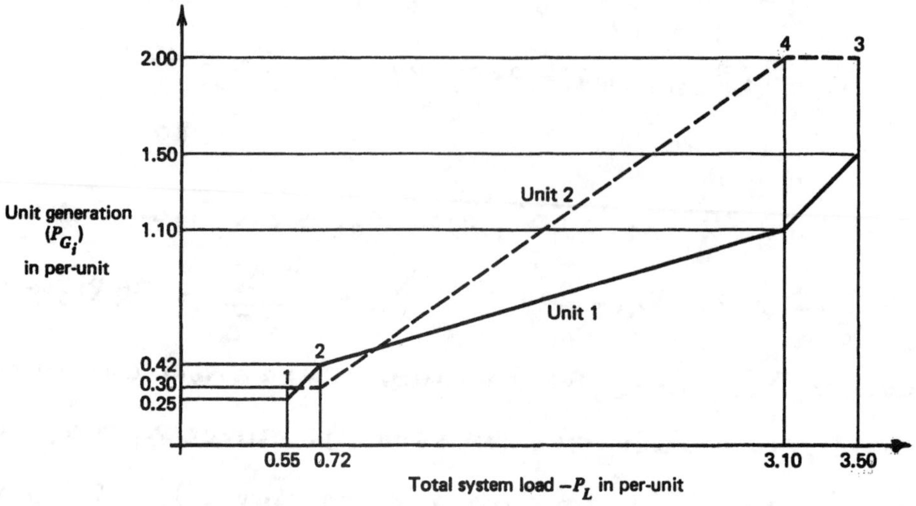

TABLE OF RESULTS

POINT	P_{G1}	P_{G2}	P_L	λ_1	λ_2
1	0.25	0.30	0.55	250	284
2	0.42	0.30	0.72	284	284
3	1.50	2.00	3.50	500	420
4	1.10	2.00	3.10	420	420

11.25

THE LOAD AT EACH BUS WAS INCREASED BY 10%.

(a) IF UNIT 1 PICKS UP THE LOAD,

$\Delta\delta_1 = 0$ (USING BUS 1 AS PHASE REFERENCE)

$\Delta\delta_2 = 6.187 - 6.616 = -0.429°$ OR -0.007487 rad.

$\Delta P_{G1} = 1.3094 - 1.0313 = 0.2781$

$A_{11} = 0$; $A_{21} = \dfrac{-0.007487}{0.278100} = -0.026924$

IF UNIT 2 PICKS UP LOAD,

$\Delta\delta_1 = -7.947 + 6.616 = -1.331°$ OR -0.02323 rad.

$\Delta\delta_2 = 0$ (USING BUS 2 AS PHASE REFERENCE)

$\Delta P_{G2} = 2.1159 - 1.8200 = 0.2959$

$A_{12} = \dfrac{-0.02323}{0.29590} = -0.078507$; $A_{22} = 0$

(b) CALCULATION OF B CONSTANTS:

$$\bar{Y} = \begin{bmatrix} 2.353 - j9.362 & -2.353 + j9.412 \\ -2.353 + j9.412 & 2.353 - j9.362 \end{bmatrix}$$

$g_{11} = g_{22} = 2.353$; $g_{12} = g_{21} = -2.353$

FOR $m = k$, $$\frac{1}{2}\frac{\partial^2 P_{TL}}{\partial\delta_m\,\partial\delta_k} = -\sum_{\substack{i=1\\ i\neq m}}^{2} V_i V_m g_{im}\cos(\delta_i - \delta_m)$$

$$= -(1)(1)\,g_{12}\cos(0 - 6.616°) = 2.337$$

FOR $m \neq k$, $$\frac{1}{2}\frac{\partial P_{TL}}{\partial\delta_m\,\partial\delta_k} = V_m V_k g_{mk}\cos(\delta_m - \delta_k)$$

$$= (1)(1)(-2.337) = -2.337$$

11.25 CONTD.

FINALLY,
$$B_{ij} = \frac{1}{2}\sum_{m=1}^{2}\sum_{k=1}^{2} \frac{\partial^2 P_{TL}}{\partial\delta_m \partial\delta_k} A_{mi} A_{kj}$$
$$= 2.337 \,(A_{1i} A_{1j} - A_{1i} A_{2j} - A_{2i} A_{1j} + A_{2i} A_{2j})$$

$$B_{11} = 2.337\left[(-0.026924)^2\right] = 0.001694$$
$$B_{12} = 2.337\left[-(-0.026924)(-0.078507)\right] = -0.00494$$
$$B_{22} = 2.337\left[+(-0.078507)^2\right] = 0.014406$$

CHECKING,
$$P_{TL} = B_{11} P_{G1}^2 + 2B_{12} P_{G1} P_{G2} + B_{22} P_{G2}^2$$
$$= (0.001694)(1.0313)^2 - 2(0.00494)(1.0313)(1.82) + (0.014406)(1.82)^2$$
$$= 0.031$$

(C) THE PENALTY FACTORS ARE CALCULATED AS

$$PF_1 = \frac{1}{1-(\partial P_{TL}/\partial P_{G1})} = \frac{1}{1 - 0.003388\, P_{G1} + 0.009881\, P_{G2}}$$

$$\left[\text{SAME AS } \left(\frac{1}{1 - 2\sum_{j=1}^{n} B_{ij} P_{Gj}}\right)\right]$$

$$P_{F2} = \frac{1}{1 + 0.009881\, P_{G1} - 0.028811\, P_{G2}}$$

$$\lambda_1 = PF_1(2\alpha_1 P_{G1} + \beta_1) = \frac{200\,(P_{G1}+1)}{1 - 0.003388\, P_{G1} + 0.009881\, P_{G2}}$$

$$\lambda_2 = \frac{80\, P_{G1} + 260}{1 + 0.009881\, P_{G1} - 0.02881\, P_{G2}}$$

$$\left[\text{NOTE: } \lambda_i = \frac{\partial C_i/\partial P_{Gi}}{1-(\partial P_{TL}/\partial P_{G1})} = \frac{2\alpha_i P_{Gi} + \beta_i}{1-(\partial P_{TL}/\partial P_{G1})} = PF_i(2\alpha_i P_{Gi} + \beta_i)\right]$$

USING A PROGRAMMABLE CALCULATOR, SOLVING BY TRIAL AND ERROR, ONE GETS

P_{G1}	P_{G2}	λ_1	λ_2	P_L
1.0313	1.8200	400.4	423.5	2.820
1.1100	1.7400	416.4	415.5	2.823
1.1060	1.7410	415.6	415.6	2.820

Problem 11.26

(To solve the problem change the Min MW field for generator 2 to 0 MW). The minimum value in the plot above occurs when the generation at bus 2 is equal to 180MW. This value corresponds to the value found in example 11.6 for economic dispatch at generator 2 (181MW).

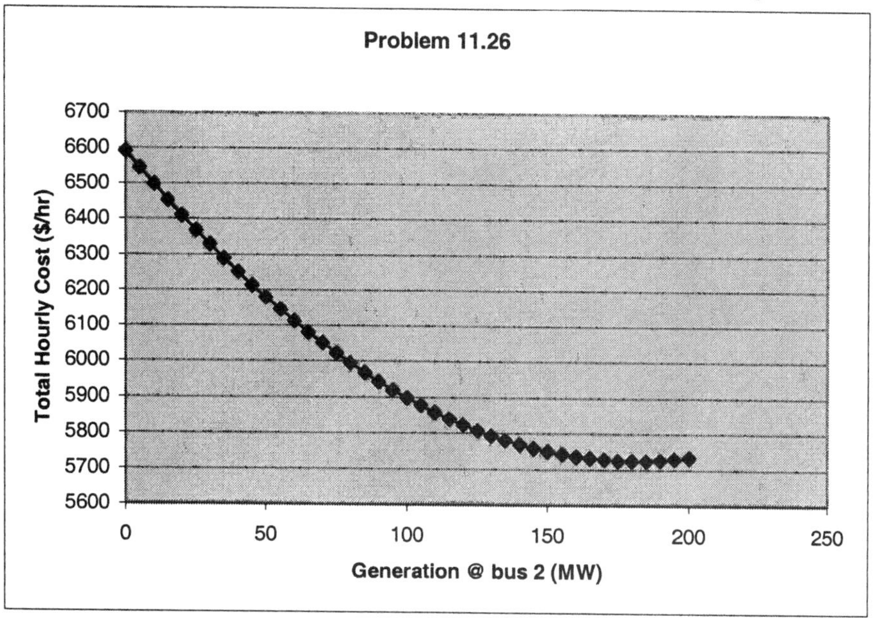

Problem 11.27

To achieve loss sensitivities values that are equal, the generation at bus 2 should be about 159 MW and the generation at bus 4 should be about 215 MW. Minimum losses are 7.79 MW. The operating cost in example 11.8 is lower than that found in this problem indicating that minimizing losses does not usually result in a minimum cost dispatch.

Problem 11.28

To achieve loss sensitivities that are equal, the generation at bus 2 should be about 190 MW and the generation at bus 4 should be about 263 MW. Minimum losses are 11.15 MW.

Problem 11.29

The maximum possible load scalar is 1.69 to avoid overloading a transmission line. At this load level both lines into bus 5 are loaded to 100%. Trying to supply more load will result in at least one of these lines being overloaded. The sharp increase in the marginal cost occurs when the line from bus 2 to bus 5 congests.

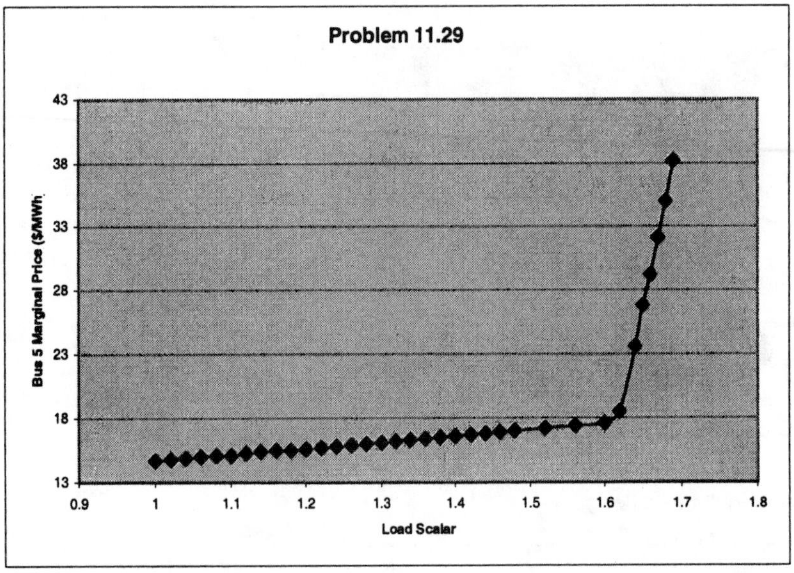

CHAPTER 12

12.1 From the results of Example 12.2 :

$$v(x,t) = \frac{E}{2}\, u_{-1}\left(t - \frac{x}{v}\right) + \frac{E}{2}\, u_{-1}\left(t + \frac{x}{v} - 2\tau\right)$$

$$i(x,t) = \frac{E}{2Z_c}\, u_{-1}\left(t - \frac{x}{v}\right) - \frac{E}{2Z_c}\, u_{-1}\left(t + \frac{x}{v} - 2\tau\right)$$

For $t = \tau/2 = \frac{l}{2v}$:

$$v\left(x,\frac{\tau}{2}\right) = \frac{E}{2} u_{-1}\left(\frac{\frac{l}{2} - x}{v}\right) + \frac{E}{2} u_{-1}\left(\frac{x - \frac{3}{2}l}{v}\right) \qquad i\left(x,\frac{\tau}{2}\right) = \frac{E}{2Z_c} u_{-1}\left(\frac{\frac{l}{2} - x}{v}\right) - \frac{E}{2Z_c} u_{-1}\left(\frac{x - \frac{3}{2}l}{v}\right)$$

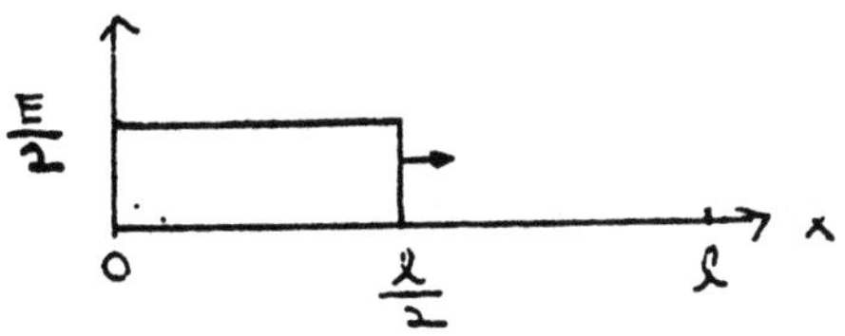

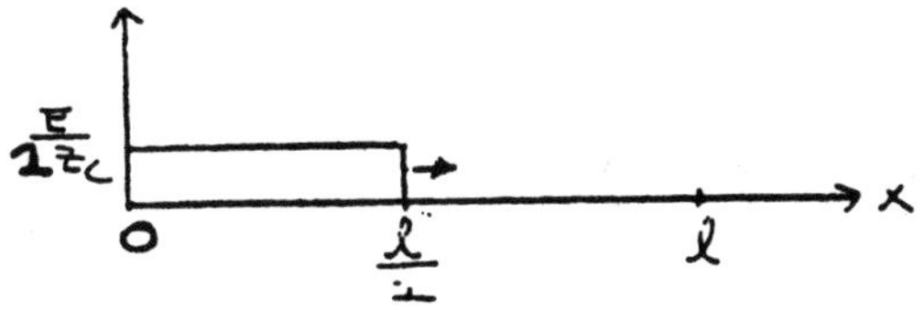

For $t = \tau = \frac{l}{v}$:

$$v(x,\tau) = \frac{E}{2} u_{-1}\left(\frac{l - x}{v}\right) + \frac{E}{2} u_{-1}\left(\frac{x - l}{v}\right) \qquad i(x,\tau) = \frac{E}{2Z_c} u_{-1}\left(\frac{l - x}{v}\right) - \frac{E}{2Z_c} u_{-1}\left(\frac{x - l}{v}\right)$$

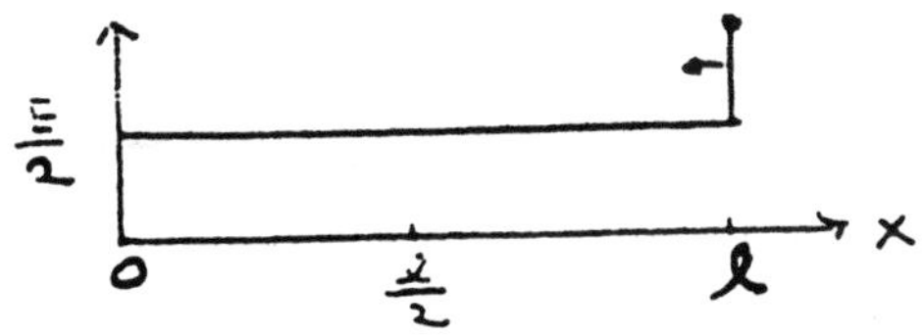

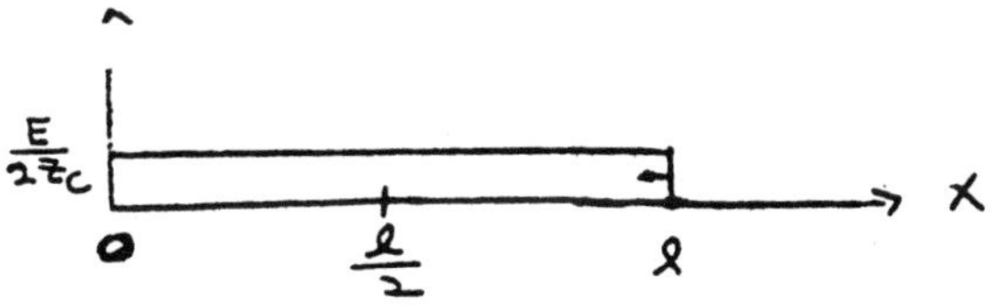

For $t = 2\tau = \frac{2l}{v}$:

$$v(x,2\tau) = \frac{E}{2} u_{-1}\left(\frac{2l - x}{v}\right) + \frac{E}{2} u_{-1}\left(\frac{x}{v}\right) \qquad i(x,2\tau) = \frac{E}{2Z_c} u_{-1}\left(\frac{2l - x}{v}\right) - \frac{E}{2Z_c} u_{-1}\left(\frac{x}{v}\right)$$

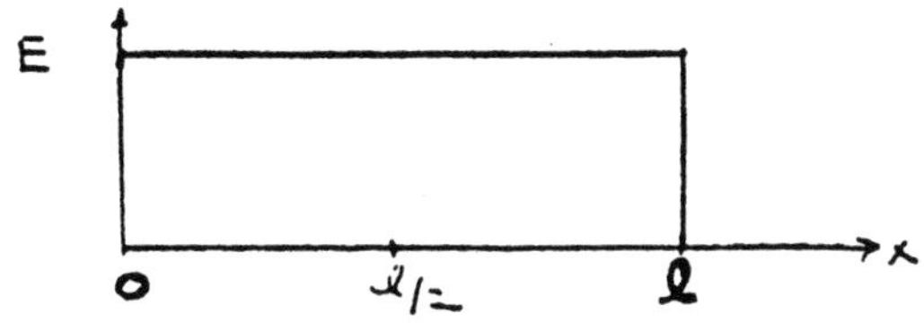

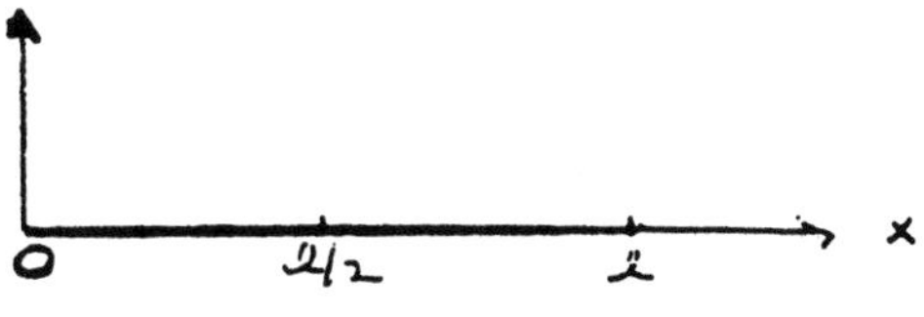

12.2

From Example 12.2 $\Gamma_R = 1$ and $\Gamma_S = 0$

For a ramp voltage source, $E_G(s) = \frac{E}{s^2}$

Then from Eqs. (11.2.10) and (11.2.11),

$$V(x,s) = \left(\frac{E}{s^2}\right)\left(\frac{1}{2}\right)\left[e^{-\frac{sx}{w}} + e^{s\left(\frac{x}{w} - 2\tau\right)}\right]$$

$$I(x,s) = \left(\frac{E}{s^2}\right)\left(\frac{1}{2Z_c}\right)\left[e^{-\frac{sx}{w}} - e^{s\left(\frac{x}{w} - 2\tau\right)}\right]$$

Taking the inverse Laplace Transform:

$$v(x,t) = \frac{E}{2} u_{-2}\left(t - \frac{x}{w}\right) + \frac{E}{2} u_{-2}\left(t + \frac{x}{w} - 2\tau\right)$$

$$i(x,t) = \frac{E}{2Z_c} u_{-2}\left(t - \frac{x}{w}\right) - \frac{E}{2Z_c} u_{-2}\left(t + \frac{x}{w} - 2\tau\right)$$

At the center of the line, where $x = \ell/2$,

$$v\left(\frac{\ell}{2},t\right) = \frac{E}{2} u_{-2}\left(t - \frac{\tau}{2}\right) + \frac{E}{2} u_{-2}\left(t - \frac{3\tau}{2}\right)$$

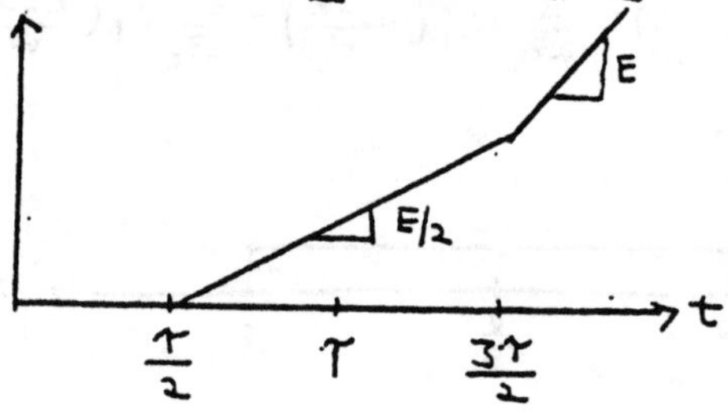

$$i\left(\frac{\ell}{2},t\right) = \frac{E}{2Z_c} u_{-2}\left(t - \frac{\tau}{2}\right) - \frac{E}{2Z_c} u_{-2}\left(t - \frac{3\tau}{2}\right)$$

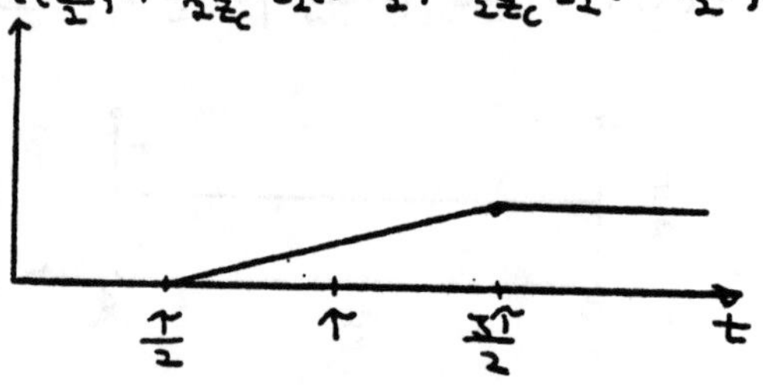

12.3 From Eq (12.2.12) with $Z_R = sL_R$ and $Z_G = Z_c$:

$$\Gamma_R(s) = \frac{\frac{sL_R}{Z_c} - 1}{\frac{sL_R}{Z_c} + 1} = \frac{s - \frac{Z_c}{L_R}}{s + \frac{Z_c}{L_R}} \qquad \Gamma_S(s) = 0$$

Then from Eq (12.2.10) with $E_G(s) = \frac{E}{s}$

$$V(x,s) = \frac{E}{s}\left(\frac{1}{2}\right)\left[e^{-\frac{sx}{v}} + \left(\frac{s - \frac{Z_c}{L_R}}{s + \frac{Z_c}{L_R}}\right) e^{s\left(\frac{x}{v} - 2\tau\right)}\right]$$

Using partial-fraction expansion

$$V(x,s) = \frac{E}{2}\left[\frac{e^{-\frac{sx}{v}}}{s} + \left(\frac{-1}{s} + \frac{2}{s + \frac{Z_c}{L_R}}\right) e^{s\left(\frac{x}{v} - 2\tau\right)}\right]$$

Taking the inverse Laplace transform:

$$v(x,t) = \frac{E}{2} u_{-1}\left(t - \frac{x}{v}\right) + \frac{E}{2}\left[-1 + 2e^{-\frac{1}{L_R/Z_c}\left(t + \frac{x}{v} - 2\tau\right)}\right] u_{-1}\left(t + \frac{x}{v} - 2\tau\right)$$

At the center of the line, where $x = \ell/2$:

$$v\left(\frac{\ell}{2}, t\right) = \frac{E}{2} u_{-1}\left(t - \frac{\tau}{2}\right) + \frac{E}{2}\left[-1 + 2e^{-\left(\frac{t - \frac{3\tau}{2}}{L_R/Z_c}\right)}\right] u_{-1}\left(t - \frac{3\tau}{2}\right)$$

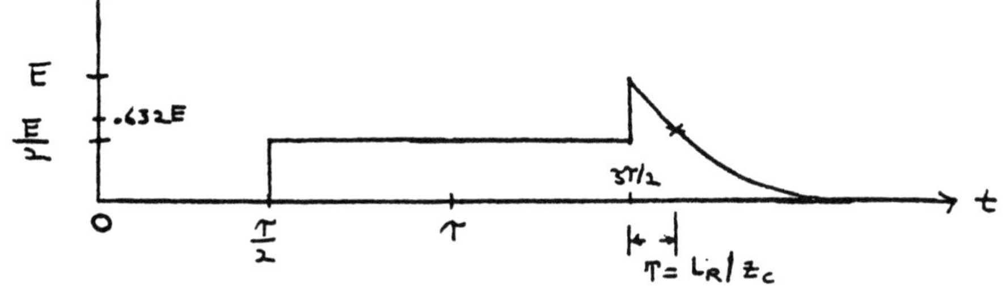

12.4 $\Gamma_R = 0$ $\qquad E_G(s) = \dfrac{E}{s}$

From Eq(12.2.10)

$$V(x,s) = \frac{E}{s}\left[\frac{Z_c/L_G}{s + \frac{Z_c}{L_G}}\right]\left[e^{-\frac{sx}{v}}\right]$$

Using partial fraction expansion:

$$V(x,s) = E\left[\frac{1}{s} - \frac{1}{s + \frac{Z_c}{L_G}}\right]e^{-\frac{sx}{v}}$$

Taking the inverse Laplace transform,

$$v(x,t) = E\left[1 - e^{-\left(\frac{t - x/v}{L_G/Z_c}\right)}\right]u_{-1}\left(t - \frac{x}{v}\right)$$

At the center of the line, where $x = \ell/2$:

$$v\left(\frac{\ell}{2}, t\right) = E\left[1 - e^{\frac{-(t - T/2)}{L_G/Z_c}}\right]u_{-1}(t - T/2)$$

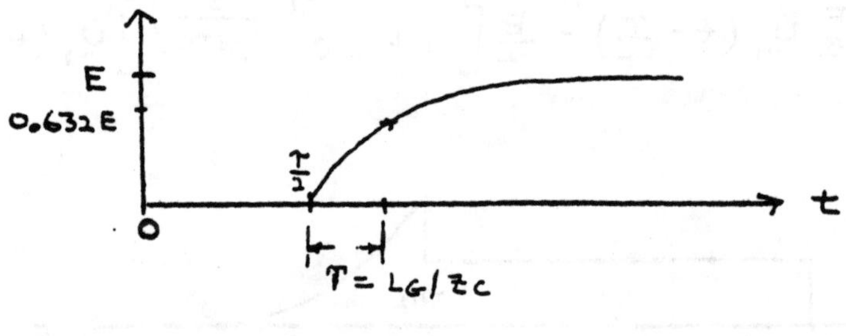

12.5 $\Gamma_R = \dfrac{4-1}{4+1} = 0.6 \qquad \Gamma_S = \dfrac{\frac{1}{3}-1}{\frac{1}{3}+1} = -0.5$

$$E_G(s) = \frac{E}{s}$$

$$V(x,s) = \frac{E}{s}\left[\frac{1}{\frac{1}{3}+1}\right]\frac{\left[e^{-\frac{sx}{v}} + 0.6\,e^{s\left(\frac{x}{v}-2\tau\right)}\right]}{1-(0.6)(-0.5)\,e^{-2s\tau}}$$

$$V(x,s) = \frac{3E}{4s}\left[\frac{e^{-\frac{sx}{v}} + 0.6\,e^{s\left(\frac{x}{v}-2\tau\right)}}{1+0.3\,e^{-2s\tau}}\right]$$

$$V(x,s) = \frac{3E}{4s}\left[e^{-\frac{sx}{v}} + 0.6\,e^{s\left(\frac{x}{v}-2\tau\right)}\right]\left[1-0.3e^{-2s\tau} + (0.3)^2 e^{-4s\tau} \cdots\right]$$

$$V(x,s) = \frac{3E}{4s}\Big[e^{-\frac{sx}{v}} + 0.6\,e^{s\left(\frac{x}{v}-2\tau\right)} - 0.3\,e^{-s\left(\frac{x}{v}+2\tau\right)} - 0.18\,e^{s\left(\frac{x}{v}-4\tau\right)}$$
$$+0.09\,e^{-s\left(\frac{x}{v}+4\tau\right)} + 0.054\,e^{s\left(\frac{x}{v}-6\tau\right)} \cdots\Big]$$

$$v(x,t) = \frac{3E}{4}\Big[u_{-1}\left(t-\frac{x}{v}\right) + 0.6\,u_{-1}\left(t+\frac{x}{v}-2\tau\right) - 0.3\,u_{-1}\left(t-\frac{x}{v}-2\tau\right)$$
$$-0.18\,u_{-1}\left(t+\frac{x}{v}-4\tau\right) + 0.09\,u_{-1}\left(t-\frac{x}{v}-4\tau\right) + 0.054\,u_{-1}\left(t+\frac{x}{v}-6\tau\right) \cdots\Big]$$

At the center of the line, where $x = \frac{\ell}{2}$:

$$v\left(\frac{\ell}{2},t\right) = \frac{3E}{4}\Big[u_{-1}\left(t-\frac{\tau}{2}\right) + 0.6\,u_{-1}\left(t-\frac{3\tau}{2}\right) - 0.3\,u_{-1}\left(t-\frac{5}{2}\tau\right)$$
$$-0.18\,u_{-1}\left(t-\frac{7\tau}{2}\right) + 0.09\,u_{-1}\left(t-\frac{9\tau}{2}\right) + 0.054\,u_{-1}\left(t-\frac{11\tau}{2}\right)\cdots\Big]$$

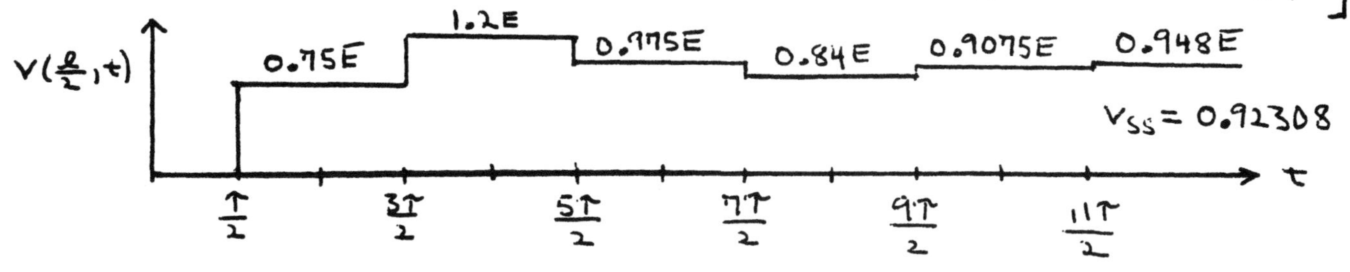

12.6 (a) $Z_c = \sqrt{\frac{L}{C}} = \sqrt{\frac{\frac{1}{3}\times 10^{-6}}{\frac{1}{3}\times 10^{-10}}} = 100.\ \Omega$

$$v = \frac{1}{\sqrt{LC}} = \frac{1}{\sqrt{(\frac{1}{3}\times 10^{-6})(\frac{1}{3}\times 10^{-10})}} = 3.0\times 10^{8}\ \text{m/s}$$

$$\tau = \frac{l}{v} = \frac{30\times 10^{3}}{3\times 10^{8}} = 1\times 10^{-4}\ \text{s} = 0.1\ \text{ms}$$

(b) $\Gamma_S = \dfrac{\frac{Z_G}{Z_c} - 1}{\frac{Z_G}{Z_c} + 1} = 0 \qquad E_G(s) = \dfrac{100}{s}$

$$Z_R(s) = \frac{R(sL)}{sL+R} = \frac{Rs}{s+\frac{R}{L}} = \frac{100\ s}{s+50{,}000.}$$

$$\Gamma_R(s) = \frac{\frac{Z_R(s)}{Z_c} - 1}{\frac{Z_R(s)}{Z_c} + 1} = \frac{\frac{s}{s+50{,}000.} - 1}{\frac{s}{s+50{,}000.} + 1} = \frac{-50{,}000.}{2s+50{,}000.}$$

$$\Gamma_R(s) = \frac{-25{,}000.}{s+25{,}000.} \quad \text{per unit}$$

(c) Using (12.2.11) with $x = l$ (receiving end)

$$I_R(s) = I(l,s) = \left[\frac{100/s}{200}\right]\left[e^{-s\tau} + \frac{25000}{s+25000}e^{-s\tau}\right]$$

$$I_R(s) = \frac{1}{2}\left[\frac{1}{s} + \frac{25000.}{s(s+25000)}\right]e^{-s\tau} = \frac{1}{2}\left[\frac{1}{s} + \frac{1}{s} + \frac{-1}{s+25000}\right]e^{-s\tau}$$

$$I_R(s) = \frac{1}{2}\left[\frac{2}{s} + \frac{-1}{s+25000}\right]e^{-s\tau}$$

$$i_R(t) = \frac{1}{2}\left[2 - e^{\frac{-(t-\tau)}{0.04\times 10^{-3}}}\right]u_{-1}(t-\tau) \quad \text{A}$$

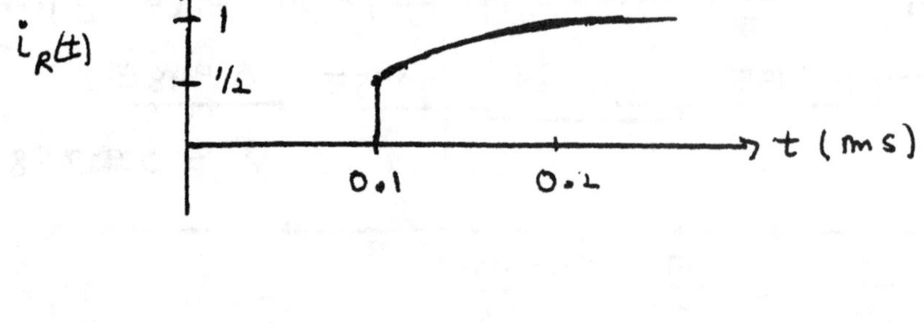

12.7 (a) $Z_c = \sqrt{\frac{L}{C}} = \sqrt{\frac{2\times10^{-6}}{1.25\times10^{-11}}} = 400.\ \Omega$

$$w = \frac{1}{\sqrt{LC}} = \frac{1}{\sqrt{(2\times10^{-6})(1.25\times10^{-11})}} = 2.0\times10^{8}\ \frac{m}{s}$$

$$\tau = \frac{l}{w} = \frac{100.\times10^{3}}{2\times10^{8}} = 5\times10^{-4}\ s = 0.5\ ms$$

(b) $\Gamma_S = \dfrac{\frac{Z_G}{Z_c} - 1}{\frac{Z_G}{Z_c} + 1} = 0 \qquad E_G(s) = \dfrac{100}{s}$

$$Z_R(s) = sL_R + \frac{1}{sC_R} \qquad L_R = 100.\times10^{-3}\ H \qquad C_R = 1\times10^{-6}\ F$$

$$\Gamma_R(s) = \frac{\frac{Z_R(s)}{Z_c} - 1}{\frac{Z_R(s)}{Z_c} + 1} = \frac{s\frac{L_R}{Z_c} + \frac{1}{sC_RZ_c} - 1}{s\frac{L_R}{Z_c} + \frac{1}{sC_RZ_c} + 1}$$

$$\Gamma_R(s) = \frac{s^2 - \frac{Z_c}{L_R}s + \frac{1}{L_RC_R}}{s^2 + \frac{Z_c}{L_R}s + \frac{1}{L_RC_R}} = \frac{s^2 - 4\times10^{3}s + 1\times10^{7}}{s^2 + 4\times10^{3}s + 1\times10^{7}}$$

(c) Using (12.2.10) with $x = l$ (receiving end)

$$V_R(s) = \frac{100}{s}\left(\frac{400}{400+400}\right)\left[e^{-s\tau} + \left(\frac{s^2 - 4\times10^{3}s + 1\times10^{7}}{s^2 + 4\times10^{3}s + 1\times10^{7}}\right)e^{-s\tau}\right]$$

$$V_R(s) = 50\left[\frac{1}{s} + \frac{(s-2000+j2449.5)(s-2000-j2449.5)}{s(s+2000+j2449.5)(s+2000-j2449.5)}\right]e^{-s\tau}$$

12.7 CONTD.

$$V_R(s) = 50\left[\frac{1}{s} + \frac{1}{s} + \frac{-j1.633}{s+2000+j2449.5} + \frac{+j1.633}{s+2000-j2449.5}\right]e^{-s\tau}$$

$$V_R(s) = 50\left[\frac{2}{s} + \frac{-3.266(2449.5)}{(s+2000)^2+(2449.5)^2}\right]e^{-s\tau}$$

$$v_R(t) = 50\left\{2 - 3.266\,e^{\frac{-(t-\tau)}{0.5\times10^{-3}}}\sin[(2449.5)(t-\tau)]\right\}U_{-1}(t-\tau)$$ V

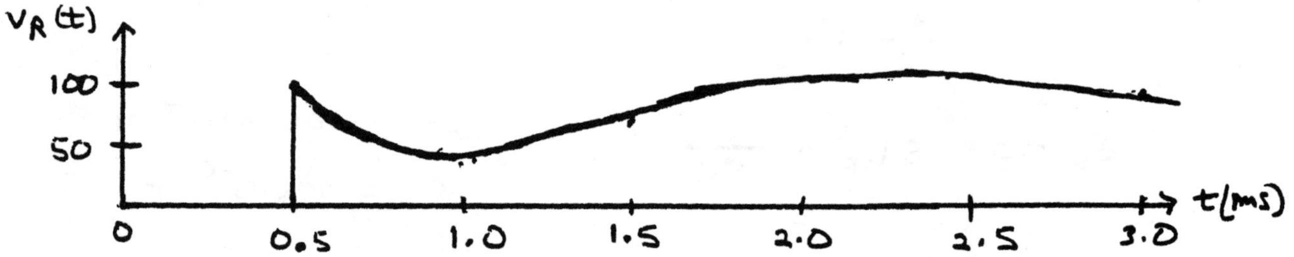

12.8 (a) $Z_C = \sqrt{\frac{L}{C}} = \sqrt{\frac{0.999\times10^{-6}}{1.112\times10^{-11}}} = \underline{\underline{299.73}}\ \Omega$

$$\omega = \frac{1}{\sqrt{LC}} = \frac{1}{\sqrt{(0.999\times10^{-6})(1.112\times10^{-11})}} = \underline{\underline{3.0\times10^{8}}}\ \frac{m}{s}$$

$$\tau = \frac{\ell}{\omega} = \frac{60.\times10^3}{3.0\times10^8} = 1.9998\times10^{-4}\,s = \underline{\underline{0.2}}\ ms$$

(b) $\Gamma_S = \dfrac{\frac{Z_G}{Z_C}-1}{\frac{Z_G}{Z_C}+1} = 0 \qquad E_G(s) = \dfrac{E}{s^2}$

$$Z_R = \frac{R_R\left(\frac{1}{sC_R}\right)}{R_R+\frac{1}{sC_R}} = \frac{(1/C_R)}{s+\frac{1}{R_RC_R}}$$

$R_R = 150.\ \Omega$
$C_R = 1\times10^{-6}$ F

12.8 CONTD.

$$\Gamma_R = \frac{\frac{Z_R}{Z_C} - 1}{\frac{Z_R}{Z_C} + 1} = \frac{\dfrac{\left(\frac{1}{Z_C C_R}\right)}{s + \frac{1}{R_R C_R}} - 1}{\dfrac{\left(\frac{1}{Z_C C_R}\right)}{s + 1/R_R C_R} + 1}$$

$$\Gamma_R = \frac{-s - \left(\frac{1}{R_R C_R} - \frac{1}{Z_C C_R}\right)}{s + \left(\frac{1}{R_R C_R} + \frac{1}{Z_C C_R}\right)} = \frac{-s - 3.330 \times 10^3}{s + 1.0003 \times 10^4} \text{ per unit}$$

(c) Using (12.2.10) with $x = 0$ (sending end)

$$v(0,s) = V_S(s) = \frac{E}{s^2}\left(\frac{1}{2}\right)\left[1 + \left(\frac{-s - 3.33 \times 10^3}{s + 1.0003 \times 10^4}\right) e^{-2s\tau}\right]$$

$$V_S(s) = \frac{E}{2}\left[\frac{1}{s^2} + \frac{-s - 3.33 \times 10^3}{s^2 (s + 1.0003 \times 10^4)} e^{-2s\tau}\right]$$

$$V_S(s) = \frac{E}{2}\left[\frac{1}{s^2} + \left(\frac{-0.333}{s^2} + \frac{-6.67 \times 10^{-5}}{s} + \frac{6.67 \times 10^{-5}}{s + 1.0003 \times 10^4}\right) e^{-2s\tau}\right]$$

(d)
$$V_S(t) = \frac{E}{2}\left\{t\, u_{-1}(t) - \left[0.333(t - 2\tau) + 6.69 \times 10^{-5} - 6.67 \times 10^{-5} e^{\frac{-(t-2\tau)}{0.1 \times 10^{-3}}}\right] u_{-1}(t - 2\tau)\right\}$$

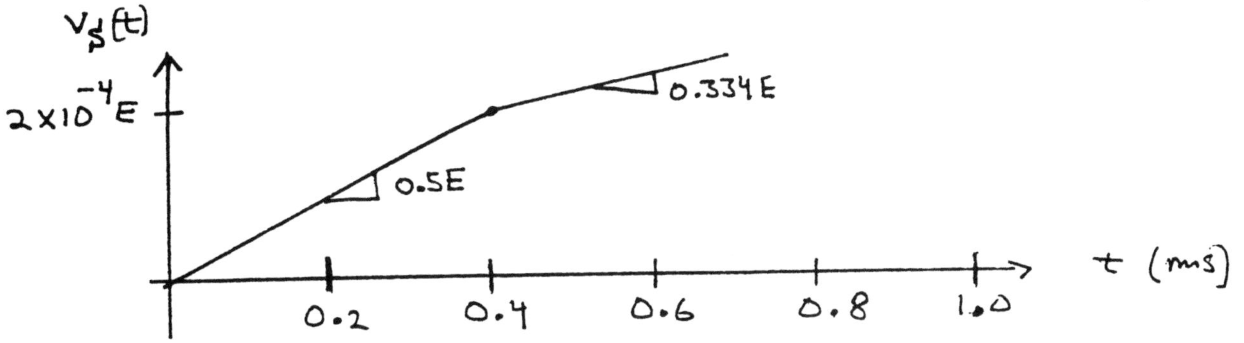

12.9

VOLTAGE

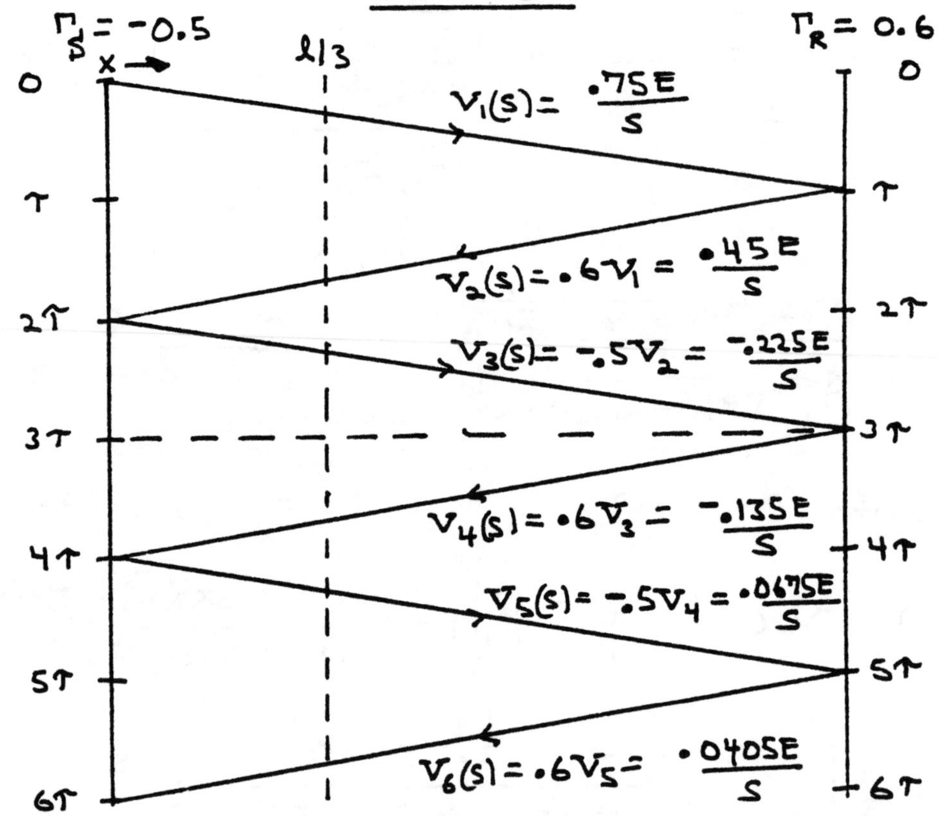

$\Gamma_S = -0.5$
$\Gamma_R = 0.6$
x →
ℓ/3
0
τ
2τ
3τ
4τ
5τ
6τ
$V_1(s) = \frac{.75E}{s}$
$V_2(s) = .6V_1 = \frac{.45E}{s}$
$V_3(s) = -.5V_2 = \frac{-.225E}{s}$
$V_4(s) = .6V_3 = \frac{-.135E}{s}$
$V_5(s) = -.5V_4 = \frac{.0675E}{s}$
$V_6(s) = .6V_5 = \frac{.0405E}{s}$

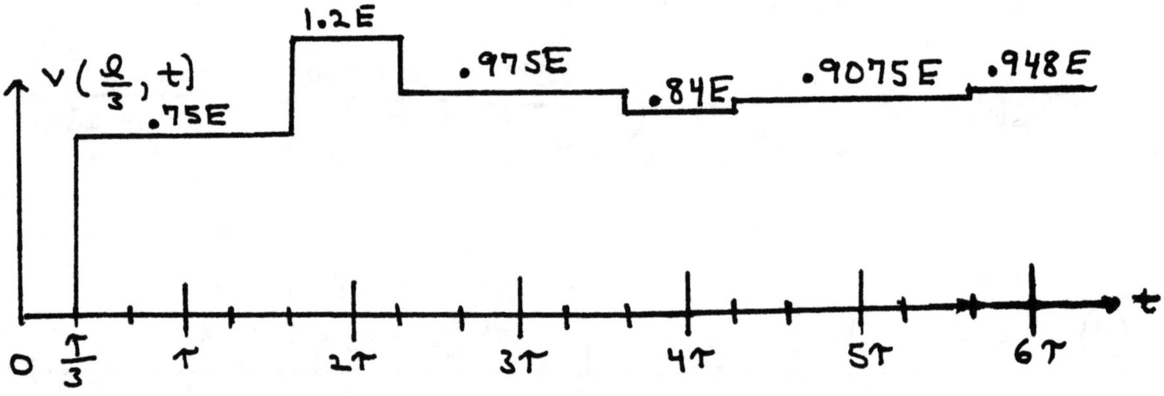

$v(\frac{\ell}{3}, t)$
.75E
1.2E
.975E
.84E
.9075E
.948E
0
$\frac{\tau}{3}$
τ
2τ
3τ
4τ
5τ
6τ
t

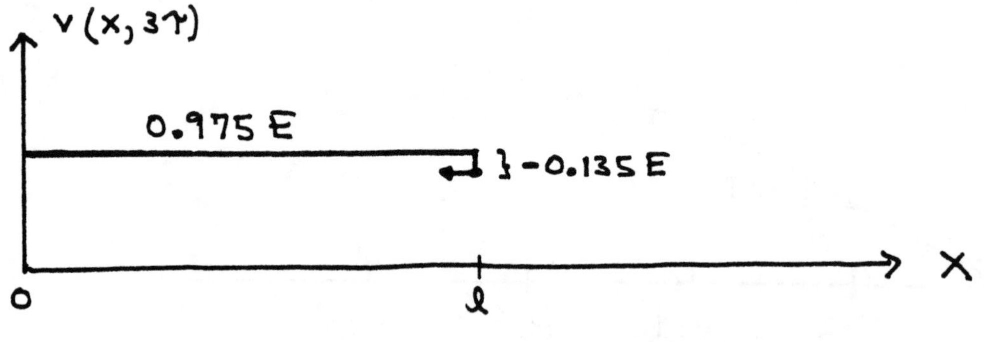

v(x, 3τ)
0.975 E
} -0.135 E
0
ℓ
x

VOLTAGE

12.10

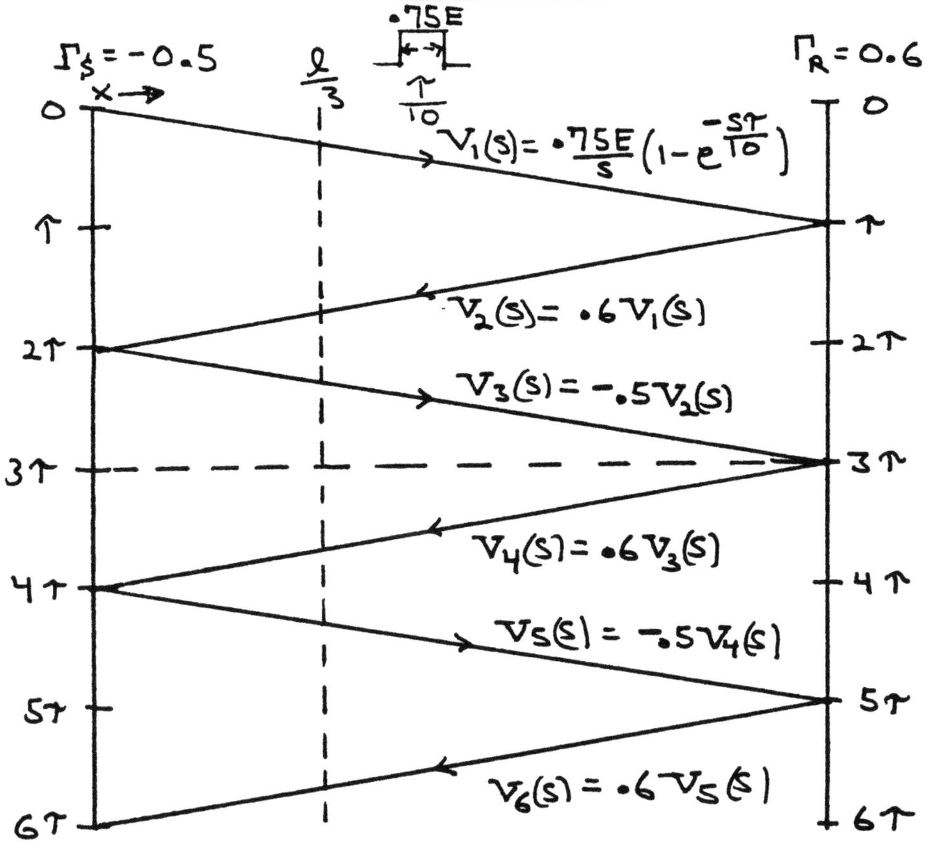

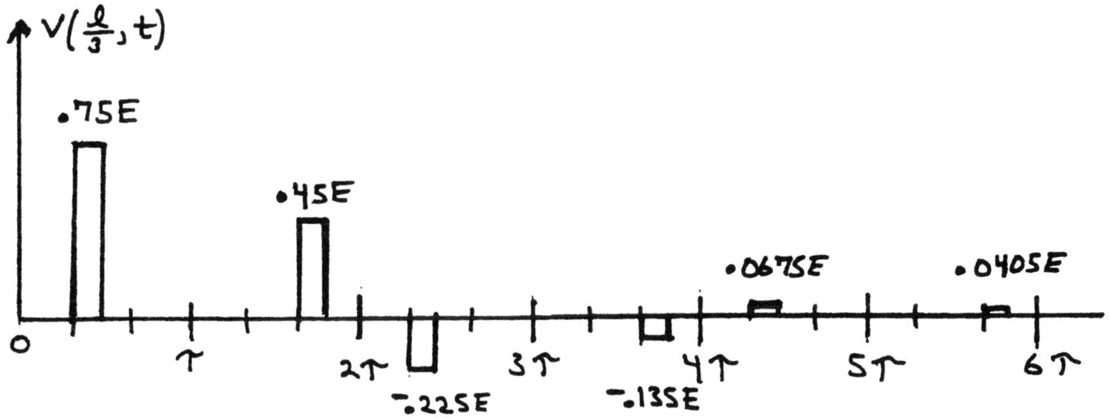

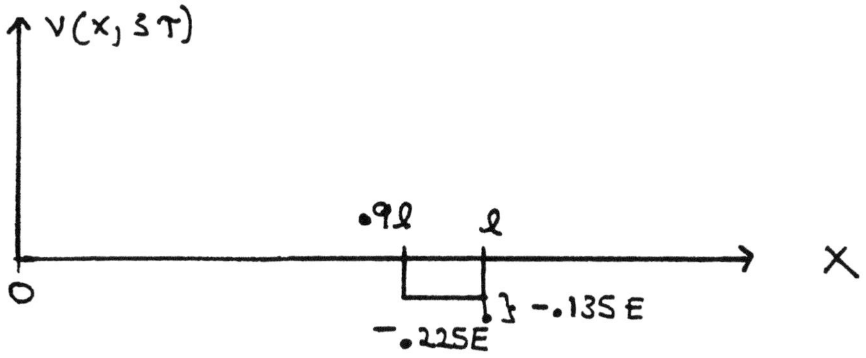

VOLTAGE

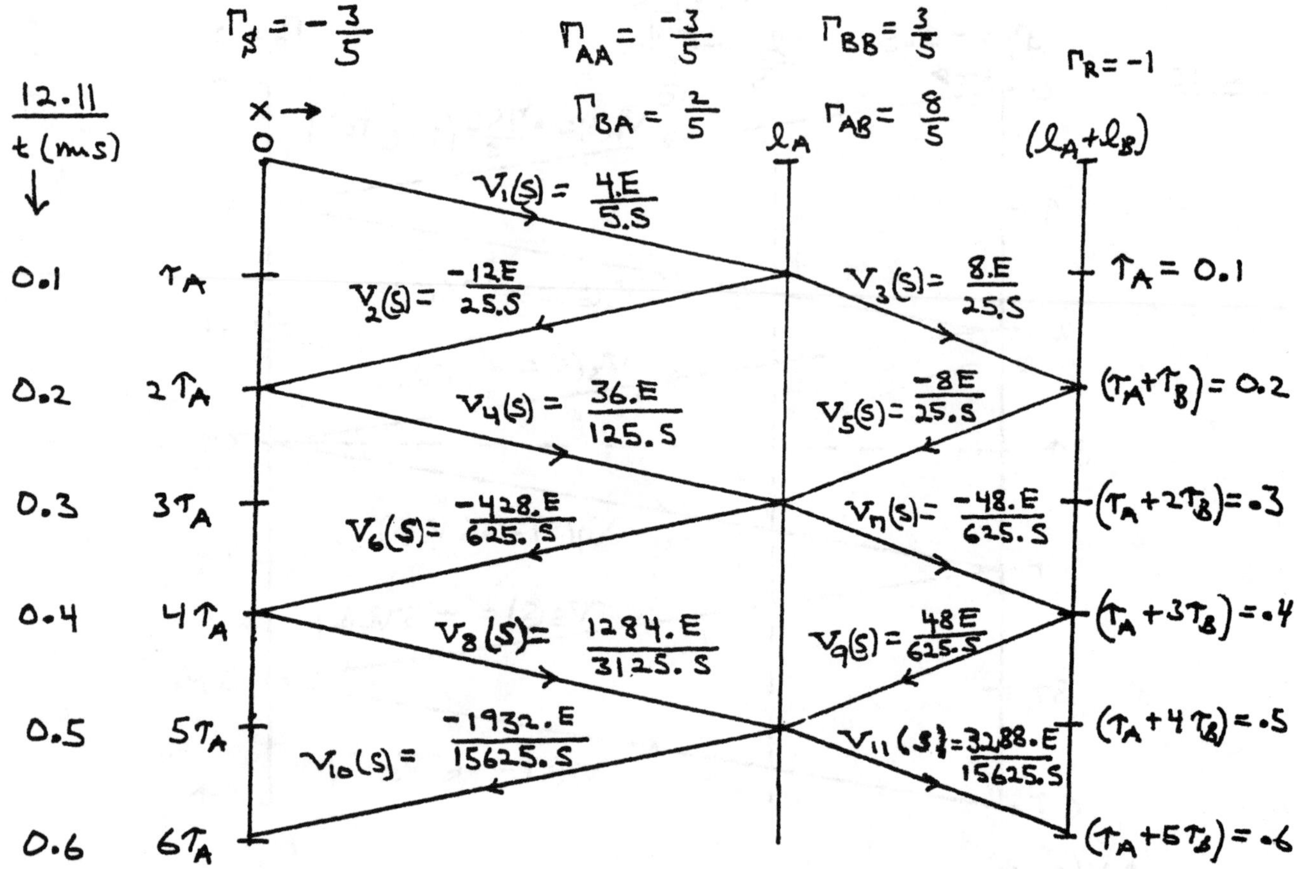

12.11
t (ms)
x →
0
ℓA
(ℓA+ℓB)
Γs = −3/5
ΓAA = −3/5
ΓBA = 2/5
ΓBB = 3/5
ΓAB = 8/5
ΓR = −1
0.1 τA
0.2 2τA
0.3 3τA
0.4 4τA
0.5 5τA
0.6 6τA
V1(s) = 4.E/5.s
V2(s) = −12E/25.s
V3(s) = 8.E/25.s
V4(s) = 36.E/125.s
V5(s) = −8E/25.s
V6(s) = −428.E/625.s
V7(s) = −48.E/625.s
V8(s) = 1284.E/3125.s
V9(s) = 48E/625.s
V10(s) = −1932.E/15625.s
V11(s) = 3288.E/15625.s
τA = 0.1
(τA+τB) = 0.2
(τA+2τB) = .3
(τA+3τB) = .4
(τA+4τB) = .5
(τA+5τB) = .6

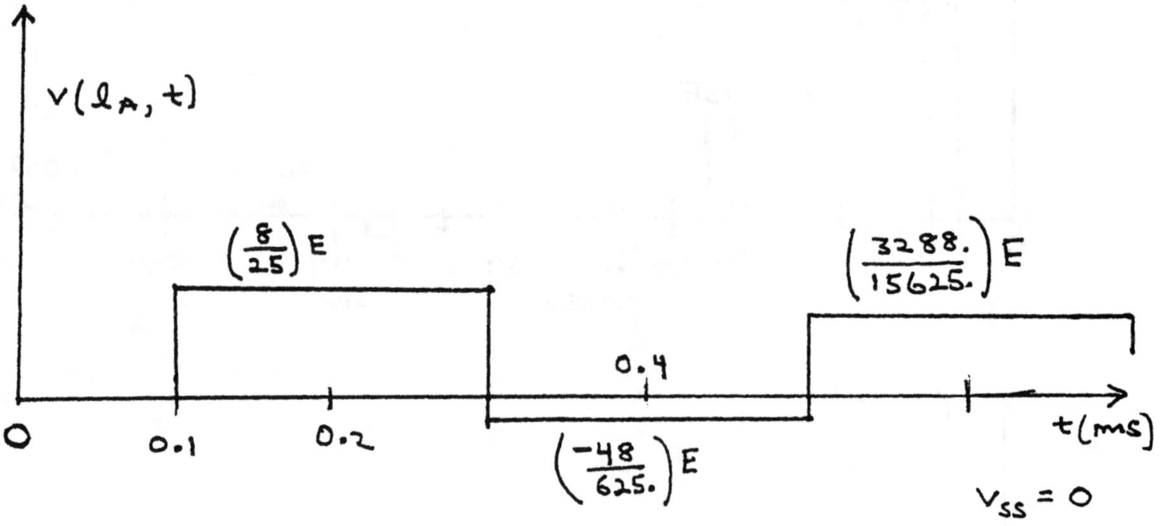

v(ℓA, t)
(8/25) E
(3288./15625.) E
(−48/625.) E
0
0.1
0.2
0.4
t(ms)
Vss = 0

12.12

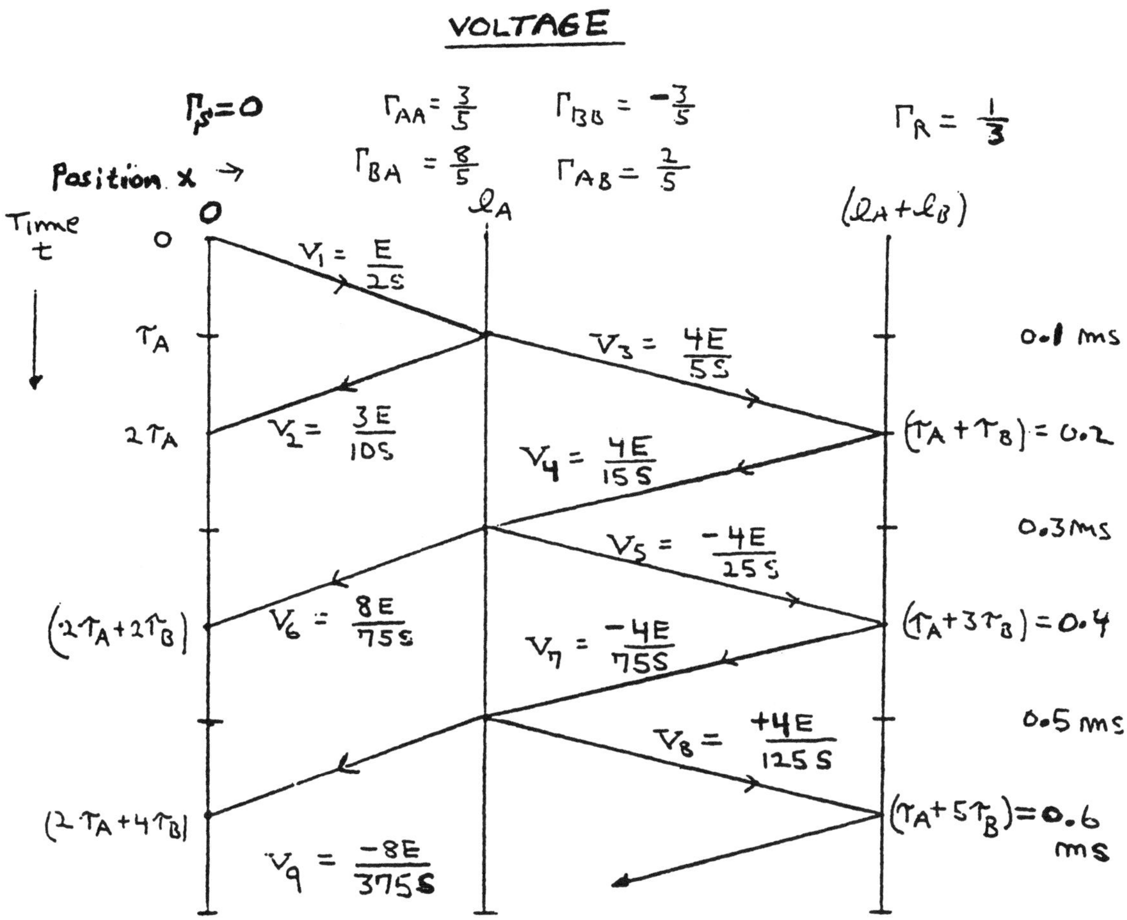

VOLTAGE
$\Gamma_S = 0$
$\Gamma_{AA} = \frac{3}{5}$
$\Gamma_{BB} = -\frac{3}{5}$
$\Gamma_R = \frac{1}{3}$
$\Gamma_{BA} = \frac{8}{5}$
$\Gamma_{AB} = \frac{2}{5}$
Position x →
Time t
0
ℓ_A
$(\ell_A + \ell_B)$
0
τ_A
$2\tau_A$
$(2\tau_A + 2\tau_B)$
$(2\tau_A + 4\tau_B)$
$V_1 = \frac{E}{2S}$
$V_2 = \frac{3E}{10S}$
$V_3 = \frac{4E}{5S}$
$V_4 = \frac{4E}{15S}$
$V_5 = \frac{-4E}{25S}$
$V_6 = \frac{8E}{75S}$
$V_7 = \frac{-4E}{75S}$
$V_8 = \frac{+4E}{125S}$
$V_9 = \frac{-8E}{375S}$
0.1 ms
$(\tau_A + \tau_B) = 0.2$
0.3 ms
$(\tau_A + 3\tau_B) = 0.4$
0.5 ms
$(\tau_A + 5\tau_B) = 0.6$ ms

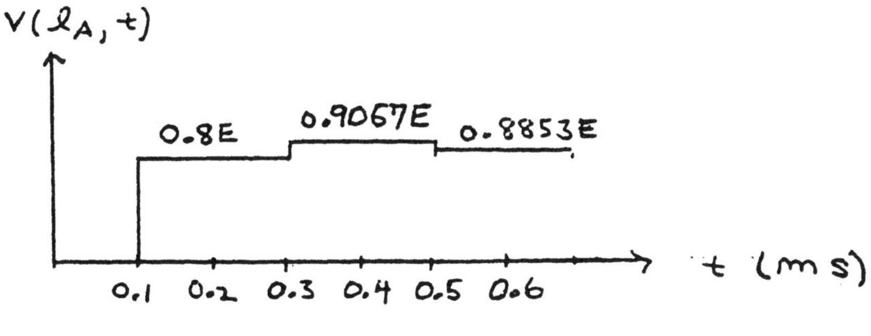

$V(\ell_A, t)$
0.8E
0.9067E
0.8853E
0.1
0.2
0.3
0.4
0.5
0.6
t (ms)

12.13

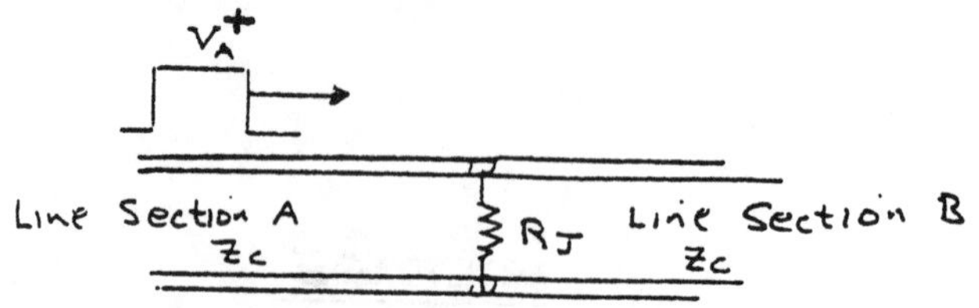

For a voltage wave V_A^+ arriving at the junction:

KVL: $V_A^+ + V_A^- = V_B^+$ (1)

KCL: $I_A^+ + I_A^- = I_B^+ + \dfrac{V_B^+}{R_J}$

$$\frac{V_A^+}{Z_c} - \frac{V_A^-}{Z} = \frac{V_B^+}{Z_c} + \frac{V_B^+}{R_J} = V_B^+\left(\frac{1}{Z_c} + \frac{1}{R_J}\right) = \frac{V_B^+}{Z_{eq}} \qquad (2)$$

where $Z_{eq} = \dfrac{R_J Z_c}{R_J + Z_c}$

Solving (1) and (2):

$$V_A^- = \left(\frac{\frac{Z_{eq}}{Z_c} - 1}{\frac{Z_{eq}}{Z_c} + 1}\right) V_A^+ = \Gamma_{AA} V_A^+ \qquad V_B^+ = \left(\frac{2\left(\frac{Z_{eq}}{Z_c}\right)}{\frac{Z_{eq}}{Z_c} + 1}\right) V_A^+ = \Gamma_{BA} V_A^+$$

Since Line sections A and B have the same characteristic impedance Z_c, $\Gamma_{BB} = \Gamma_{AA}$ and $\Gamma_{AB} = \Gamma_{BA}$.

$\tau = \dfrac{\ell}{v} = \dfrac{100 \times 10^3}{3 \times 10^8} = \dfrac{1}{3}$ ms VOLTAGE $Z_{eq} = 200\,\Omega$

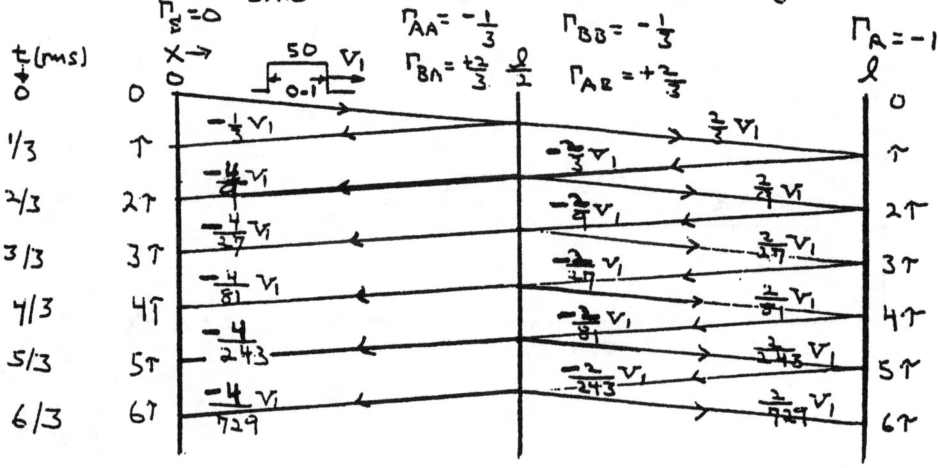

12.13 CONTD.

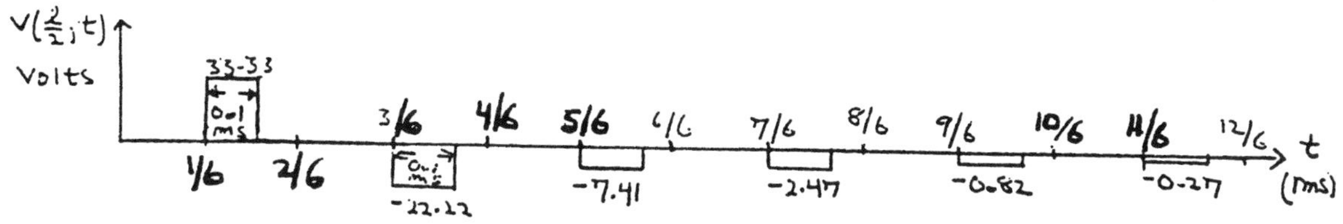

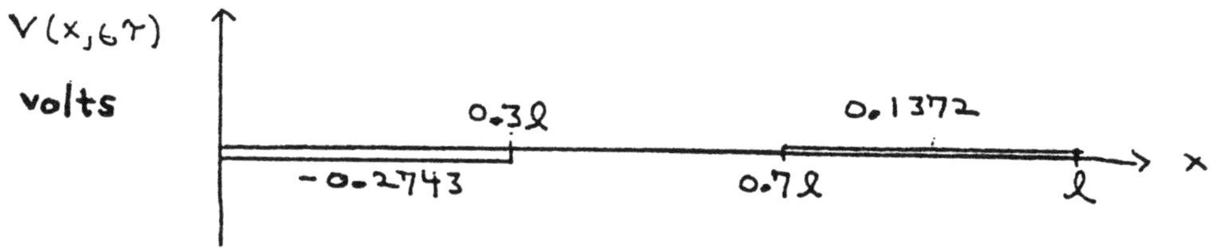

12.14

For a voltage wave V_A^+ arriving at the junction from line A,

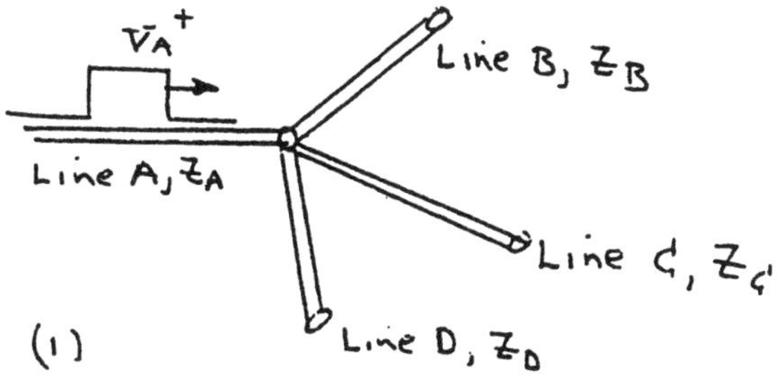

KVL $\quad V_A^+ + V_A^- = V_B^+ \qquad (1)$

$$V_B^+ = V_C^+ \qquad (2)$$

$$V_B^+ = V_D^+ \qquad (3)$$

KCL $\quad I_A^+ + I_A^- = I_B^+ + I_C^+ + I_D^+$

$$\frac{V_A^+}{Z_A} - \frac{V_A^-}{Z_A} = \frac{V_B^+}{Z_B} + \frac{V_C^+}{Z_C} + \frac{V_D^+}{Z_D} \qquad (4)$$

Using Eqs (2) and (3) in Eq (4):

$$\frac{V_A^+}{Z_A} - \frac{V_A^-}{Z_A} = V_B^+\left(\frac{1}{Z_B} + \frac{1}{Z_C} + \frac{1}{Z_D}\right) = \frac{V_B^+}{Z_{eq}} \qquad (5)$$

where $Z_{eq} = Z_B \| Z_C \| Z_D = \dfrac{1}{\frac{1}{Z_B} + \frac{1}{Z_C} + \frac{1}{Z_D}}$

solving Eqs (1) and (5):

$$V_A^- = \left[\frac{\frac{Z_{eq}}{Z_A} - 1}{(Z_{eq}/Z_A) + 1}\right] V_A^+ = \Gamma_{AA} V_A^+ \qquad V_B^+ = \left[\frac{2(Z_{eq}/Z_A)}{(Z_{eq}/Z_A) + 1}\right] V_A^+ = \Gamma_{BA} V_A^+$$

Also $\quad V_C^+ = \Gamma_{CA} V_A^+ \qquad V_D^+ = \Gamma_{DA} V_A^+ \qquad \Gamma_{CA} = \Gamma_{DA} = \Gamma_{BA}$

12.15

$$\Gamma_S(s) = \frac{\frac{sL_G}{Z_C} - 1}{\frac{sL_G}{Z_C} + 1} = \frac{s - Z_C/L_G}{s + Z_C/L_G} \qquad \Gamma_R = \frac{\frac{1}{4} - 1}{\frac{1}{4} + 1} = \frac{-3}{5}$$

$$V_1(s) = \frac{E}{s}\left(\frac{Z_C}{sL_G + Z_C}\right) = E\left(\frac{1}{s} - \frac{1}{s + \frac{Z_C}{L_G}}\right)$$

VOLTAGE

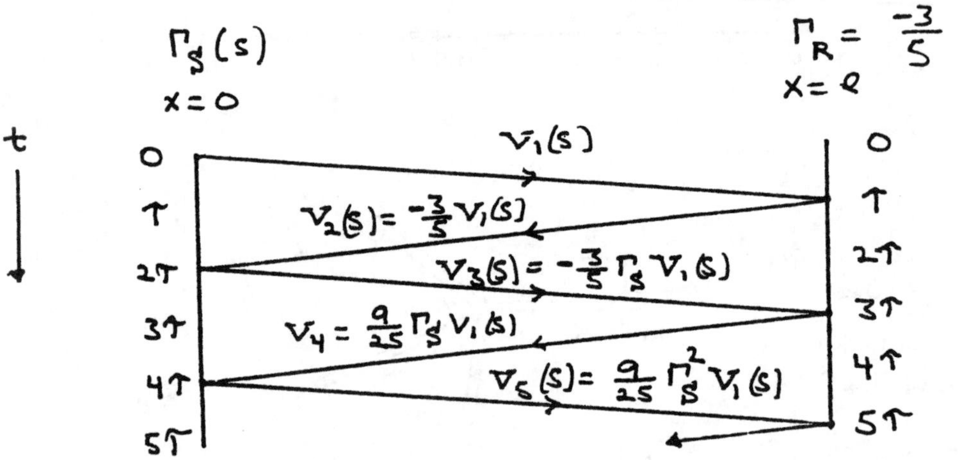

For $0 \le t \le 5\tau$:

$$v(l,s) = \left(1 - \frac{3}{5}\right)V_1(s)e^{-s\tau} + \left(-\frac{3}{5} + \frac{9}{25}\right)\Gamma_S(s)V_1(s)e^{-s(3\tau)}$$

$$v(l,s) = \frac{2E}{5}\left(\frac{1}{s} - \frac{1}{s + \frac{Z_C}{L_G}}\right)e^{-s\tau} - \frac{6E}{25}\left(\frac{1}{s}\right)\left(\frac{s - Z_C/L_G}{s + Z_C/L_G}\right)\left(\frac{Z_C/L_G}{s + Z_C/L_G}\right)e^{-s(3\tau)}$$

$$v(l,s) = \frac{2E}{5}\left(\frac{1}{s} - \frac{1}{s + \frac{Z_C}{L_G}}\right)e^{-s\tau} + \frac{6E}{25}\left[\frac{1}{s} - \frac{1}{s + \frac{Z_C}{L_G}} - \frac{2\,Z_C/L_G}{\left(s + \frac{Z_C}{L_G}\right)^2}\right]e^{-s(3\tau)}$$

Taking the inverse Laplace transform:

$$v(l,t) = \frac{2E}{5}\left[1 - e^{\frac{-(t-\tau)}{L_G/Z_C}}\right]u_{-1}(t-\tau) + \frac{6E}{25}\left[1 - e^{\frac{-(t-3\tau)}{L_G/Z_C}} - \frac{2(t-3\tau)}{L_G/Z_C}e^{\frac{-(t-3\tau)}{L_G/Z_C}}\right]u_{-1}(t-3\tau)$$

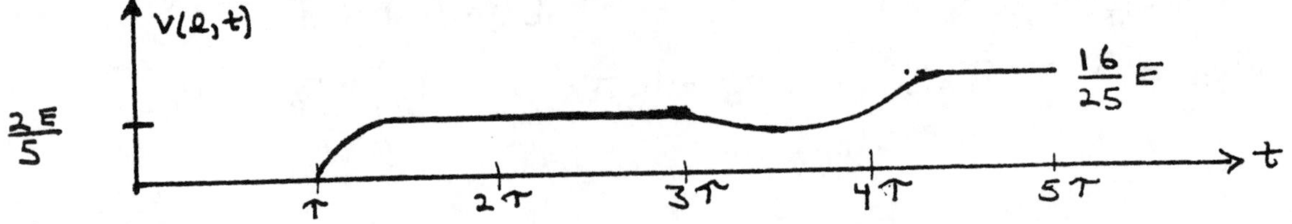

12.16

(a)

$v_S(t) = E\,u_{-1}(t)$

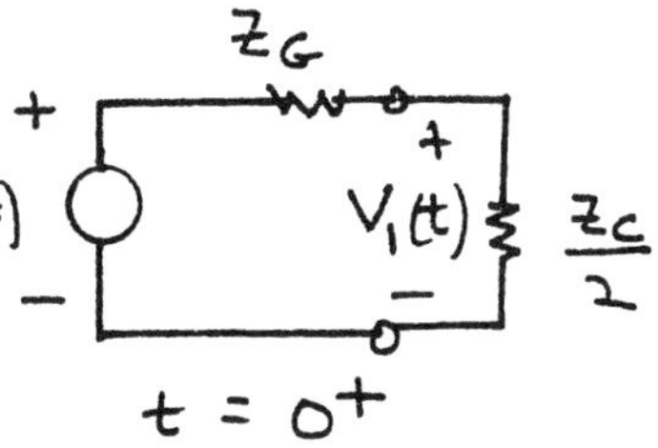

$Z_G = 100.\ \Omega$

$Z_c = 400.\ \Omega$

$E = 100.\ \text{kV}$

$$V_1(t) = E\,u_{-1}(t)\left[\frac{Z_c/2}{\frac{Z_c}{2} + Z_G}\right] = 100\left(\frac{200}{200+100}\right)u_{-1}(t)$$

$$V_1(t) = 66.67\ u_{-1}(t)\ \text{kV}$$

(b)

$$\Gamma_S = \frac{\frac{Z_G}{(Z_c/2)} - 1}{\frac{Z_G}{(Z_c/2)} + 1} = \frac{\frac{100}{200} - 1}{\frac{100}{200} + 1} = -\frac{1}{3} \qquad \Gamma_R = -1$$

(c)

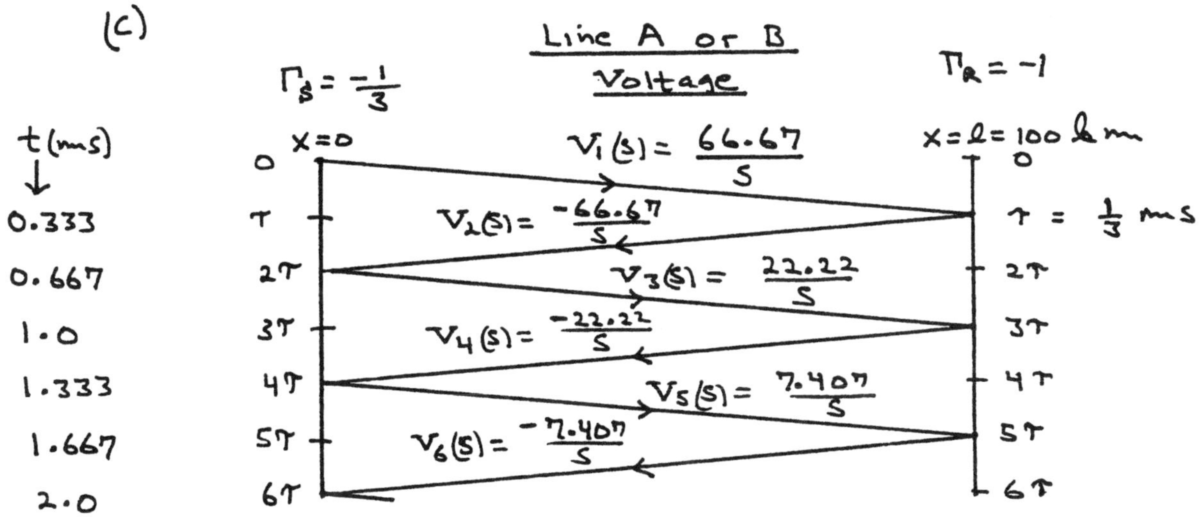

(d)

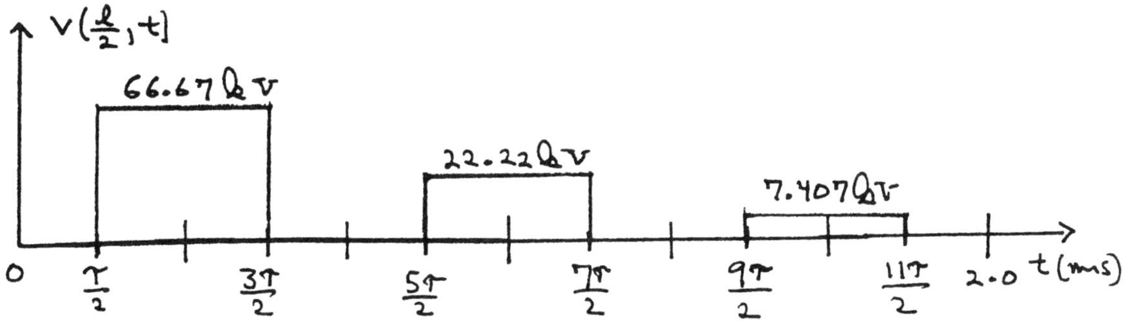

12.17

(a)

$$\Gamma_S = \frac{\frac{400}{200} - 1}{\frac{400}{200} + 1} = \frac{1}{3} \qquad \Gamma_R = \frac{\frac{100}{300} - 1}{\frac{100}{300} + 1} = -\frac{1}{2}$$

$$\Gamma_{AA} = \frac{\frac{300}{200} - 1}{\frac{300}{200} + 1} = \frac{1}{5} \qquad \Gamma_{BA} = \frac{2\left(\frac{300}{200}\right)}{\frac{300}{200} + 1} = \frac{6}{5}$$

$$\Gamma_{BB} = \frac{\frac{200}{300} - 1}{\frac{200}{300} + 1} = -\frac{1}{5} \qquad \Gamma_{AB} = \frac{2\left(\frac{200}{300}\right)}{\frac{200}{300} + 1} = \frac{4}{5}$$

(b)

VOLTAGE

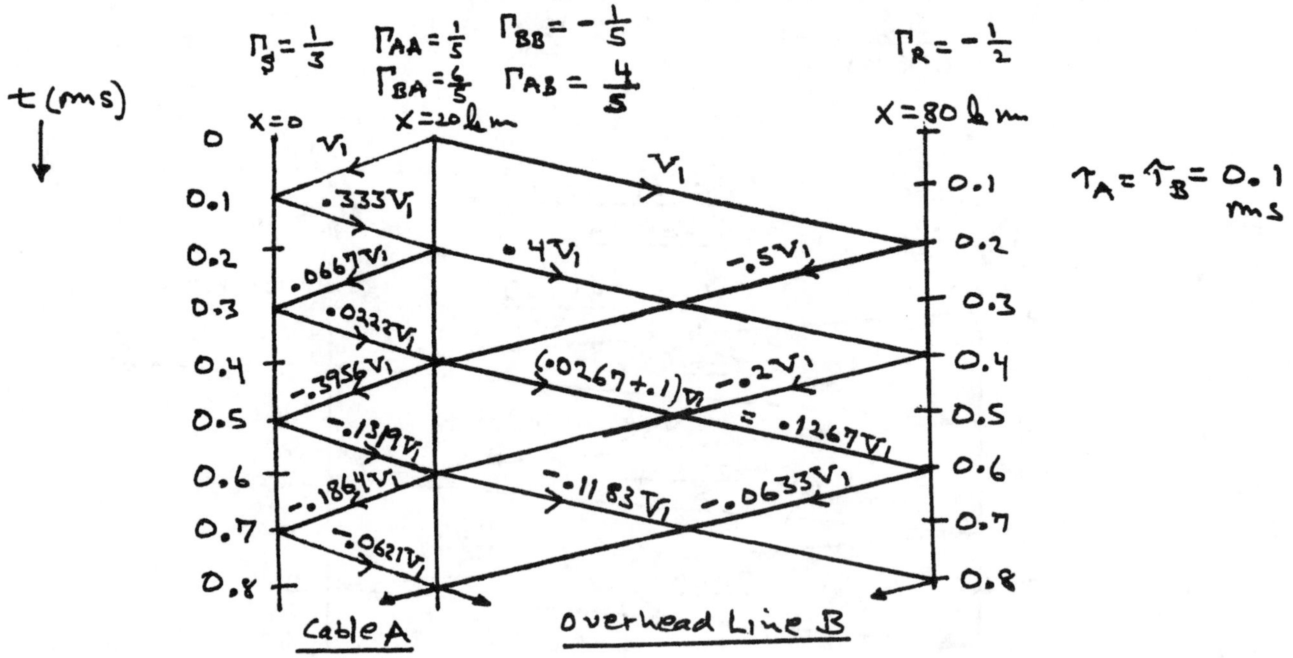

At $t=0$, the 10 kA pulsed current source at the junction encounters $200 \| 300 = 120.\ \Omega$. Therefore the first voltage waves, which travel on both the cable and overhead line, are pulses of width 50 μs and magnitude $10\text{ kA} \times 120\ \Omega = 1200.\text{ kV}$.

$$V_1(s) = \frac{E}{s}\left(1 - e^{-\tau s}\right) \qquad E = 1200.\text{ kV} \qquad \tau = 50.\ \mu s$$

12.17 CONTD.

(c)

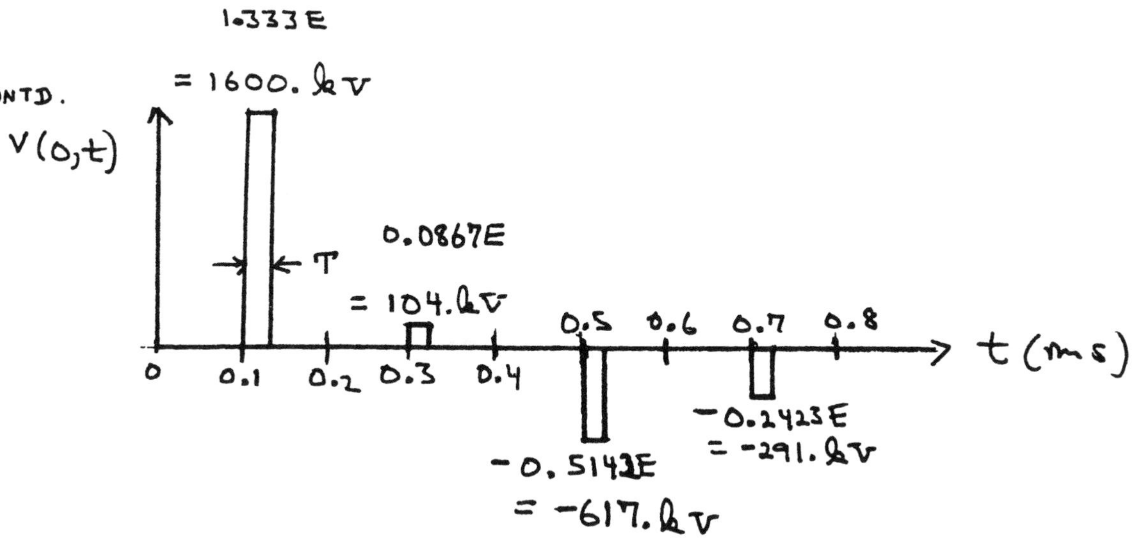

1.333E
= 1600. kV
V(0,t)
T
0.0867E
= 104. kV
0
0.1
0.2
0.3
0.4
0.5
0.6
0.7
0.8
t (ms)
-0.5142E
= -617. kV
-0.2423E
= -291. kV

12.18

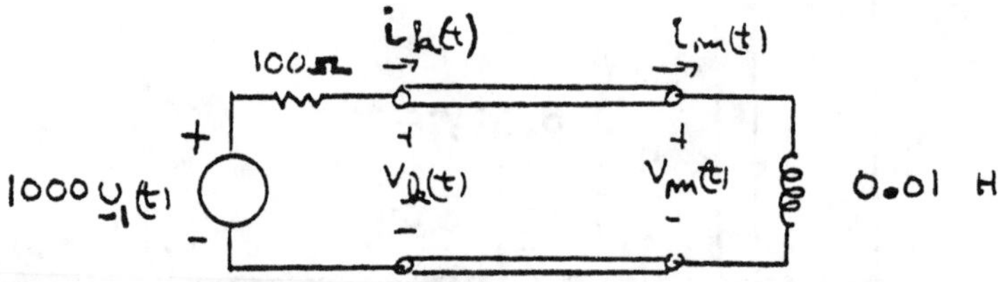

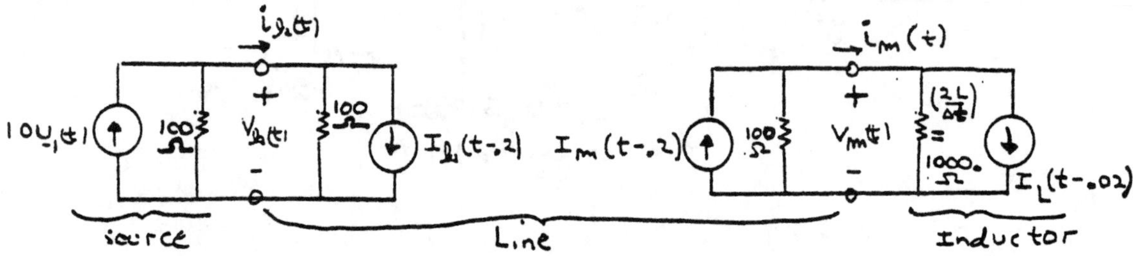

Nodal Equations:

$$0.02 \, V_{\ell}(t) = 10 - I_{\ell}(t - 0.2)$$

$$0.011 \, V_m(t) = I_m(t - 0.2) - I_L(t - 0.02)$$

Solving:

$$V_{\ell}(t) = 50.0 \left[10 - I_{\ell}(t - 0.2) \right] \qquad (a)$$

$$V_m(t) = 90.909 \left[I_m(t - 0.2) - I_L(t - 0.02) \right] \qquad (b)$$

$$\underset{\tau}{\curvearrowright} \qquad \underset{\Delta t}{\curvearrowright}$$

Dependent current sources:

Eq (12.4.10) $\qquad I_{\ell}(t) = I_m(t - 0.2) - \frac{2}{100} V_m(t) \qquad (c)$

Eq (12.4.9) $\qquad I_m(t) = I_{\ell}(t - 0.2) + \frac{2}{100} V_{\ell}(t) \qquad (d)$

Eq (12.4.14) $\qquad I_L(t) = I_L(t - 0.02) + \frac{V_m(t)}{500.} \qquad (e)$

Equations (a)-(e) can now be solved iteratively
by digital computer for time $t = 0, 0.02, 0.04 \dots$ ms
Note that $I_{\ell}()$ and $I_m()$ on the right hand
side of Eqs (a)-(e) are zero during the first 10
iterations while their arguments () are negative.

<u>12.19</u>

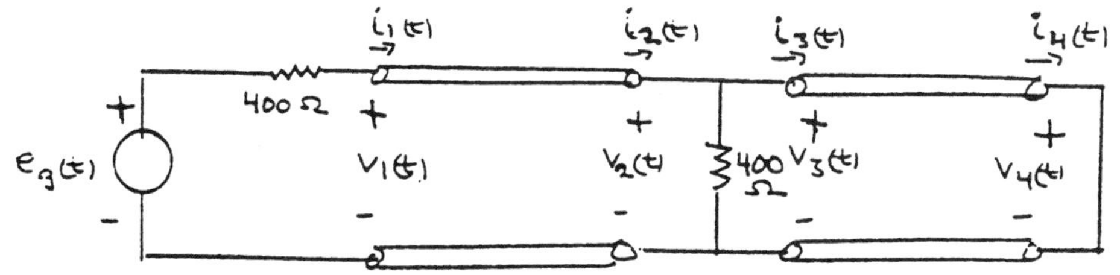

$e_g(t) = 100[u_{-1}(t) - u_{-1}(t-0.1)]$

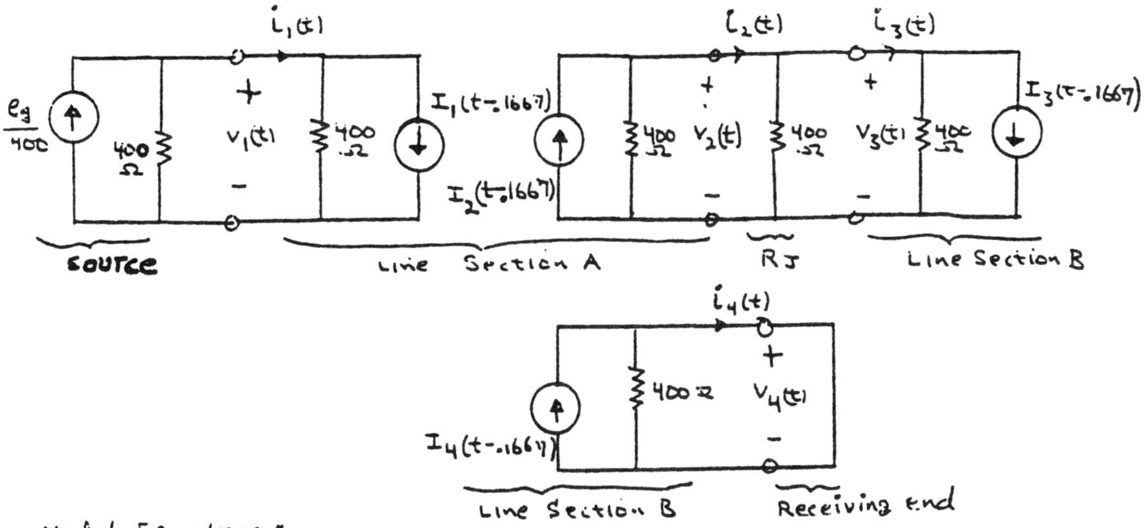

Nodal Equations:

$$v_1(t) = 200\left[\tfrac{1}{4} - \tfrac{1}{4}u_{-1}(t-0.1) - I_1(t-.1667)\right] \quad \text{(a)}$$

$$v_2(t) = 133.33\left[I_2(t-.1667) - I_3(t-.1667)\right] \quad \text{(b)}$$

$$v_3(t) = v_2(t) \quad \text{(c)}$$

$$v_4(t) = 0 \quad \text{(d)}$$

Dependent Current Sources:

Eq (12.4.10) $\quad I_1(t) = I_2(t-.1667) - \left(\frac{2}{400}\right)v_2(t) \quad$ (e)

Eq (12.4.9) $\quad I_2(t) = I_1(t-.1667) + \left(\frac{2}{400}\right)v_1(t) \quad$ (f)

Eq (12.4.10) $\quad I_3(t) = I_4(t-.1667) - \left(\frac{2}{400}\right)v_4(t) \quad$ (g)

Eq (12.4.9) $\quad I_4(t) = I_3(t-.1667) + \left(\frac{2}{400}\right)v_3(t) \quad$ (h)

Equations (a) - (h) can be solved iteratively for $t = 0, \Delta t, 2\Delta t \ldots$ where $\Delta t = 0.03333$ ms. $I_1(\ )$, $I_2(\ )$, $I_3(\ )$ and $I_4(\ )$ on the right hand side of Eqs (a)-(h) are zero for the first 5 iterations.

12.20

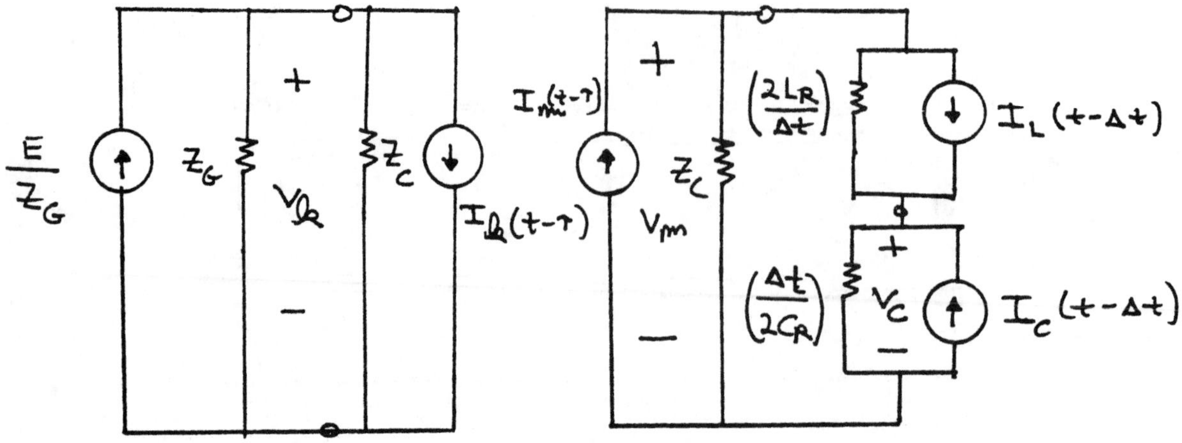

$E = 100.\,kV$ $\quad Z_G = Z_c = 400.\,\Omega$ $\quad \tau = 500.\,\mu s$

$\Delta t = 100.\,\mu s$ $\quad (2L_R/\Delta t) = 2000.\,\Omega$ $\quad \left(\frac{\Delta t}{2C_R}\right) = 50.\,\Omega$

Nodal equations:

$$\begin{bmatrix} \left(\frac{1}{400}+\frac{1}{400}\right) & 0 & 0 \\ 0 & \left(\frac{1}{400}+\frac{1}{2000}\right) & \frac{-1}{2000} \\ 0 & \frac{-1}{2000} & \left(\frac{1}{50}+\frac{1}{2000}\right) \end{bmatrix} \begin{bmatrix} V_k(t) \\ V_m(t) \\ V_c(t) \end{bmatrix} = \begin{bmatrix} \frac{1}{4} - I_k(t-500) \\ I_m(t-500) - I_L(t-100) \\ I_L(t-100) + I_c(t-100) \end{bmatrix}$$

Solving:

$$V_k(t) = 200\left[\frac{1}{4} - I_k(t-500)\right]$$

$$\begin{bmatrix} V_m(t) \\ V_c(t) \end{bmatrix} = \begin{bmatrix} 334.7 & 8.136 \\ 8.136 & 48.98 \end{bmatrix} \begin{bmatrix} I_m(t-500) - I_L(t-100) \\ I_L(t-100) + I_c(t-100) \end{bmatrix}$$

12.20 CONTD.

current sources:

(12.4.9) $I_m(t) = I_k(t-500) + \left(\frac{2}{400}\right) V_k(t)$

(12.4.10) $I_k(t) = I_m(t-500) - \left(\frac{2}{400}\right) V_m(t)$

(12.4.14) $I_L(t) = I_L(t-100) + \frac{1}{1000}\left[V_m(t) - V_C(t)\right]$

(12.4.18) $I_C(t) = -I_C(t-100) + \left(\frac{1}{2.5}\right) V_C(t)$

t	V_k	V_m	V_C	I_m	I_k	I_L	I_C
μs	kV	kV	kV	kA	kA	kA	kA
0	50.	0	0	.25	0	0	0
100	50.	0	0	.25	0	0	0
200	50.	0	0	.25	0	0	0
300	50.	0	0	.25	0	0	0
400	50.	0	0	.25	0	0	0
500	50.	83.68	2.034	.25	.2398	.0816	.0814
600	50.	57.69		.25			

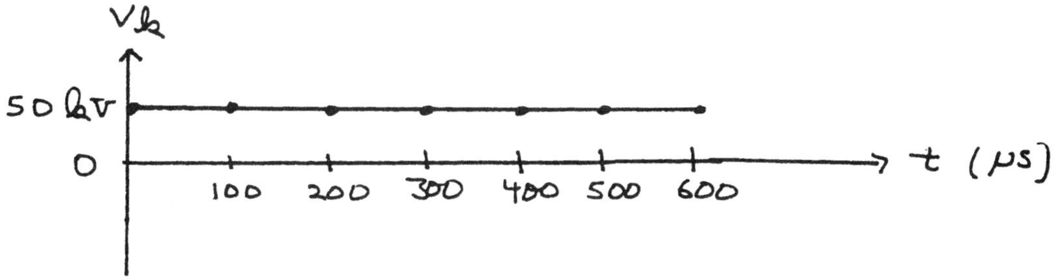

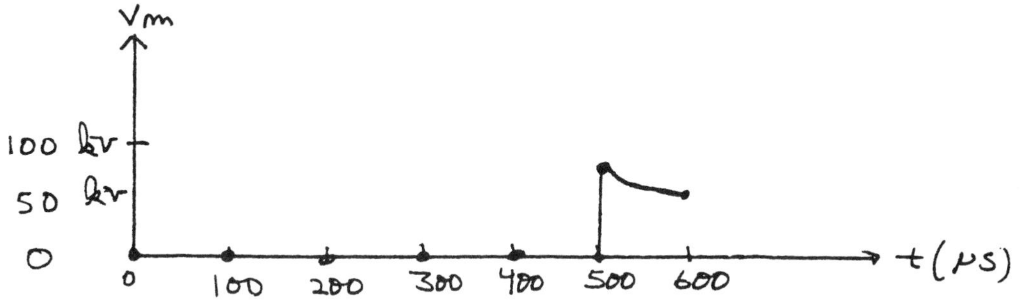

12.21

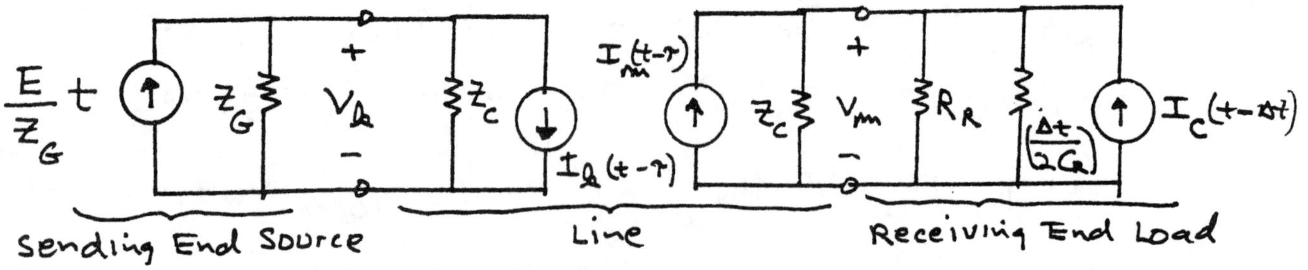

$E = 100.\ kV \qquad Z_G = Z_c = 299.73\ \Omega \qquad R_R = 150\ \Omega$

$\Delta t = 50.\ \mu s \qquad \tau = 200.\ \mu s \qquad (\Delta t/2C_R) = 25.\ \Omega$

Writing nodal equations:

$$\begin{bmatrix} \left(\frac{1}{299.73} + \frac{1}{299.73}\right) & 0 \\ 0 & \left(\frac{1}{299.73} + \frac{1}{150.} + \frac{1}{25.}\right) \end{bmatrix} \begin{bmatrix} V_k(t) \\ V_m(t) \end{bmatrix} = \begin{bmatrix} \frac{t}{2.9973} - I_k(t-200) \\ I_m(t-200) + I_c(t-50) \end{bmatrix}$$

solving:

$$V_k(t) = 50.t - 149.865\ I_k(t-200)$$

$$V_m(t) = 19.999\left[I_m(t-200) + I_c(t-50)\right]$$

current sources:

(12.4.9) $\qquad I_m(t) = I_k(t-200) + \left(\frac{2}{299.73}\right) V_k(t)$

(12.4.10) $\qquad I_k(t) = I_m(t-200) - \left(\frac{2}{299.73}\right) V_m(t)$

(12.4.18) $\qquad I_c(t) = -I_c(t-50) + \left(\frac{1}{12.5}\right) V_m(t)$

t	V_k	V_m	I_m	I_k	I_c
μs	kV	kV	kA	kA	kA
0	0	0	0	0	0
50	.0025	0	1.66×10^{-5}	0	0
100	.0050	0	3.33×10^{-5}	0	0
150	.0075	0	5.0×10^{-5}	0	0
200	.0100	0	6.67×10^{-5}	0	0
250	.0125	3.32×10^{-4}	8.34×10^{-5}	1.43×10^{-5}	2.66×10^{-5}
300	.0150	1.20×10^{-3}	10.0×10^{-5}	2.53×10^{-5}	6.94×10^{-5}

12.22

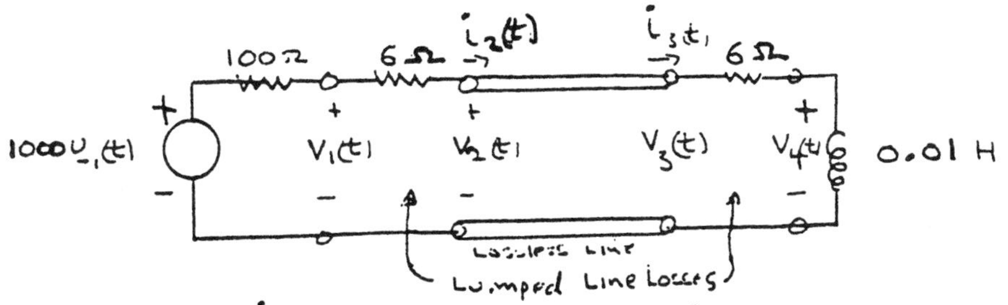

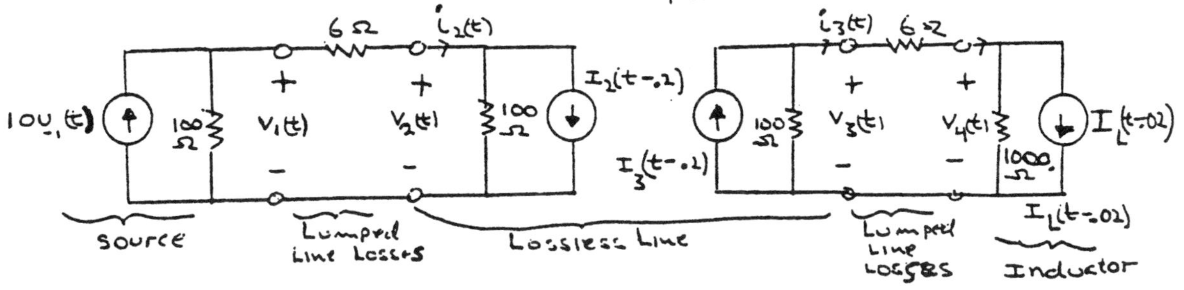

Nodal Equations:

$$\begin{bmatrix} V_1(t) \\ V_2(t) \end{bmatrix} = \begin{bmatrix} 0.1767 & -0.1667 \\ -0.1667 & 0.1767 \end{bmatrix}^{-1} \begin{bmatrix} 10 \\ -I_2(t-0.2) \end{bmatrix} \quad \begin{matrix} (a) \\ (b) \end{matrix}$$

$$\begin{bmatrix} V_3(t) \\ V_4(t) \end{bmatrix} = \begin{bmatrix} 0.1767 & -0.1667 \\ -0.1667 & 0.1677 \end{bmatrix}^{-1} \begin{bmatrix} I_3(t-0.2) \\ -I_L(t-0.02) \end{bmatrix} \quad \begin{matrix} (c) \\ (d) \end{matrix}$$

Dependent Current sources:

Eq (12.4.10) $I_2(t) = I_3(t-0.2) - \left(\frac{2}{100}\right)V_3(t)$ (e)

Eq (12.4.9) $I_3(t) = I_2(t-0.2) + \left(\frac{2}{100}\right)V_2(t)$ (f)

Eq (12.4.14) $I_L(t) = I_L(t-0.02) + \dfrac{V_4(t)}{500}$ (g)

Equations (a) - (g) can be solved iteratively for $t = 0, \Delta t, 2\Delta t \ldots$ where $\Delta t = 0.02$ ms. $I_2(\ )$ and $I_3(\ )$ on the right hand side of Eqs (a) - (g) are zero for the first 10 iterations.

12.23 (a) The maximum 60-Hz voltage operating voltage under normal operating conditions is $1.08(115/\sqrt{3}) = 71.7$ kV. From Table 12.2, select a station-class surge arrester with 84-kV MCOV. This is the station-class arrester with the lowest MCOV that exceeds 71.7kV, providing the greatest protective margin and economy. (Note: where additional economy is required, an intermediate-class surge arrester with an 84-kV MCOV may be selected.)

(b) From Table 12.2 for the selected station-class arrester, the maximum discharge voltage (also called Front-of-Wave Protective Level) for a 10-kA impulse current cresting in 0.5μs ranges from 2.19 to 2.39 in per unit of MCOV, or 184 to 201 kV, depending on arrester manufacturer. Therefore, the protective margin varies from (450-201) = 249 kV to (450-184) = 266 kV.

Note. From Table 3 of the Case Study for Chapter 12, select a VariSTAR Type AZE station-class surge arrester, manufactured by Cooper Power Systems, rated at 108 kV with an 84-kV MCOV. From Table 3 for the selected arrester, the Front-of-Wave Protective Level is 313 kV, and the protective margin is therefore (450-313) = 137 kV or 137/84 = 1.63 per unit of MCOV.

12.24 The maximum 60-Hz line-to-neutral voltage under normal operating conditions on the HV side of the transformer is $1.1(345/\sqrt{3}) = 219.1$ kV. From Table 3 of the Case Study for Chapter 12, select a VariSTAR Type AZE station-class surge arrester, manufactured by Cooper Power Systems, with a 276-kV rating and a 220-kV MCOV. This is the Type AZE station-class arrester with the lowest MCOV that exceeds 219.1 kV, providing the greatest protective margin and economy. For this arrester, the maximum discharge voltage (also called Front-of-Wave Protective Level) for a 10-kA impulse current cresting in 0.5μs is 720 kV. The protective margin is (1300 - 720) = 580 kV = 580/220 = 2.64 per unit of MCOV.

CHAPTER 13

13.1 (a) $\omega_{syn} = 2\pi 60 = \underline{\underline{377.}}$ rad/s

$$\omega_{msyn} = \frac{2}{P}\omega_{syn} = \frac{2}{4}(377) = \underline{\underline{188.5}} \text{ rad/s}$$

(b) $KE = H\,S_{rated} = (5)(400\times10^6) = \underline{\underline{2.0\times10^9}}$ joules

(c) Using (13.1.16) $\frac{2H}{\omega_{syn}}\omega_{pu}(t)\,\alpha(t) = P_{a\,pu}(t)$

$$\alpha = \frac{P_{a\,pu}\,\omega_{syn}}{2H\,\omega_{pu}} = \frac{\left(\frac{400}{400}\right)(2\pi 60)}{(2)(5)(1)} = \underline{\underline{37.70}} \text{ rad/s}^2$$

$$\alpha_m = \frac{2}{P}\alpha = \left(\frac{2}{4}\right)(37.70) = \underline{\underline{18.85}} \text{ rad/s}^2$$

13.2 using (13.1.7)

$$J = \frac{2H\,S_{rated}}{\omega_{msyn}^2} = \frac{(2)(5)(400\times10^6)}{(188.5)^2} = \underline{\underline{1.1258\times10^5}} \text{ kg m}^2$$

13.3 (a) The kinetic energy in ft-lb is:

$$KE = \frac{1}{2}\left(\frac{WR^2}{32.2}\right)\omega_m^2 \quad \text{ft-lb}$$

(b)

Using $\omega_m = \left(\frac{2\pi}{60}\right)(\text{rpm})$

$$KE = \frac{1}{2}\left(\frac{WR^2}{32.2}\right)\left[\frac{2\pi}{60}(\text{rpm})\right]^2 \text{ ft-lb} \times \frac{1.356 \text{ joules}}{\text{ft-lb}}$$

$$KE = 2.31\times10^{-4}\,(WR^2)(\text{rpm})^2 \quad \text{joules}$$

Then from (13.1.7):

$$H = \frac{(2.31\times10^{-4})(WR^2)(\text{rpm})^2}{S_{rated}} \quad \text{per unit-seconds}$$

(c) $$H = \frac{(2.31\times10^{-4})(4\times10^6)(3600)^2}{800\times10^6} = \underline{\underline{14.97}} \text{ per unit-seconds}$$

13.4 Per unit swing equation:

$$2H \frac{\omega_{pu}(t)}{\omega_{syn}} \frac{d^2\delta(t)}{dt^2} = P_{mpu}(t) - P_{epu}(t) = P_{apu}(t)$$

Assuming $\omega_{pu}(t) \approx 1$: $\frac{2H}{\omega_{syn}} \frac{d^2\delta(t)}{dt^2} = P_{apu}(t)$

$$\frac{2(5)}{2\pi 60} \frac{d^2\delta(t)}{dt^2} = 0.7 - (0.30)(.70) = 0.49$$

Initial conditions:

$\delta(0) = 12^\circ = 0.2094$ rad ; $\frac{d\delta(0)}{dt} = 0$

Integrating twice and using the above initial conditions:

$$\frac{d\delta(t)}{dt} = 18.473t + 0$$

$$\delta(t) = 9.2363\, t^2 + 0.2094$$

at $t = 5$ cycles $= 0.08333$ seconds,

$$\delta(5\text{cycles}) = 9.2363(.08333)^2 + 0.2094$$

$$\delta(5\text{ cycles}) = 0.2735 \text{ radians} = \underline{\underline{15.7^\circ}}$$

13.5

$$\frac{2(5)}{2\pi 60} \frac{d^2\delta(t)}{dt^2} = 0.70 \qquad \delta(0) = 0.2094 \text{ rad}$$

$$\frac{d\delta(0)}{dt} = 0$$

$$\frac{d\delta(t)}{dt} = 26.389t + 0$$

$$\delta(t) = 13.195t^2 + 0.2094$$

$$\delta(5\text{ cycles}) = 13.195(0.08333)^2 + 0.2094$$

$$\delta(5\text{ cycles}) = 0.3010 \text{ radians} = \underline{\underline{17.2^\circ}}$$

Since the accelerating power is larger in this problem, the power angle 5 cycles after the fault is larger than in problem 13.4.

13.6 Converting H_3 from its 400 MVA rating to the 100 MVA system base:

$$H_{3\,new} = (3.5)\left(\frac{400}{100}\right) = 14 \quad \text{pu-s}$$

$$\frac{2(H_{1new} + H_{2new} + H_{3new})}{\omega_{syn}} \omega_{pu}(t) \frac{d^2\delta(t)}{dt^2} = P_{mpu}(t) - P_{epu}(t)$$

$$= P_{apu}(t)$$

$$\frac{2(10 + 7.5 + 14)}{2\pi 60} \omega_{pu}(t) \frac{d^2\delta(t)}{dt^2} = P_{apu}(t)$$

$$\frac{63}{2\pi 60} \omega_{pu}(t) \frac{d^2\delta(t)}{dt^2} = P_{apu}(t)$$

13.7

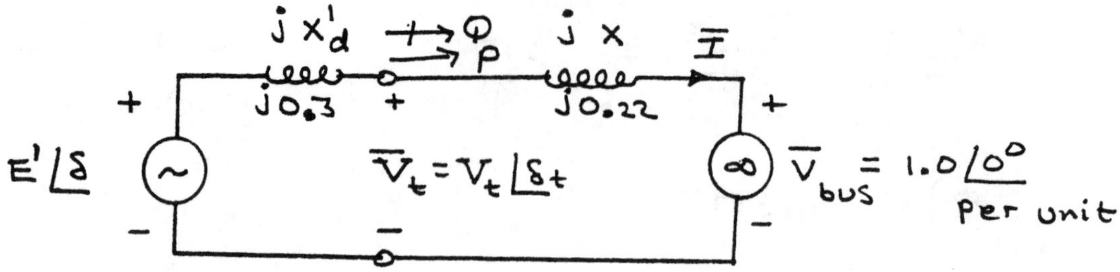

(a) $P = \frac{V_t V_{bus}}{X} \sin \delta_t$ $\quad \sin \delta_t = \frac{(0.9)(0.22)}{(1.08)(1.0)}$

$\delta_t = \sin^{-1}(0.1833) = 10.56°$

$\bar{I} = \frac{\bar{V}_t - \bar{V}_{bus}}{jx} = \frac{1.08\angle 10.56° - 1.0\angle 0°}{j0.22}$

$\bar{I} = \frac{0.06169 + j0.198}{j0.22} = 0.9427\angle -17.31°$

$\bar{S} = \bar{V}_t \bar{I}^* = (1.08\angle 10.56°)(.9427\angle 17.31°) = 1.018\angle 27.87°$

$\bar{S} = 0.9 + j0.4759 \qquad Q = I_m \bar{S} = \underline{\underline{0.4759}}$ per unit

(b) $\bar{E}' = \bar{V}_{bus} + j(x'_d + x)\bar{I} = 1.0\angle 0° + j(0.3+0.22).9427\angle -17.31°$

$\bar{E}' = 1.0\angle 0° + 0.4902\angle 72.69° = 1.146 + j0.4680$

$\bar{E}' = \underline{\underline{1.238\angle 22.21°}}$ per unit

(c) $P = \frac{E' V_{bus}}{(x'_d + x)} \sin \delta = \frac{(1.238)(1.0)}{(0.3+0.22)} \sin \delta$

$\underline{\underline{P = 2.381 \sin \delta}}$ per unit

13.8 Circuit during the fault at bus 3:

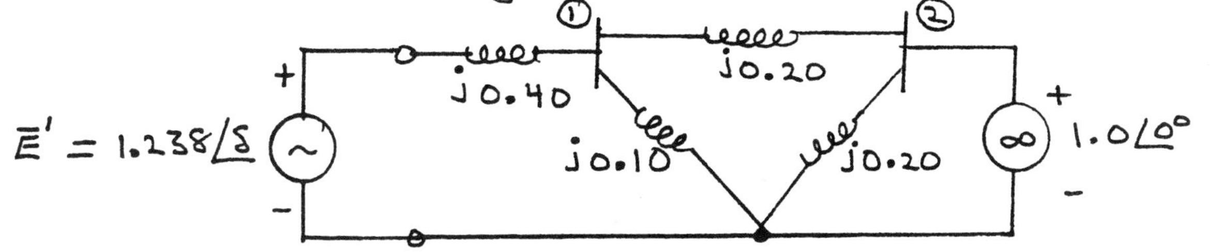

where $\bar{E}' = 1.238\angle\delta$ is determined in Problem 13.7. The Thevenin equivalent, as viewed from the generator internal voltage source, shown here, is the same as in Figure 13.9.

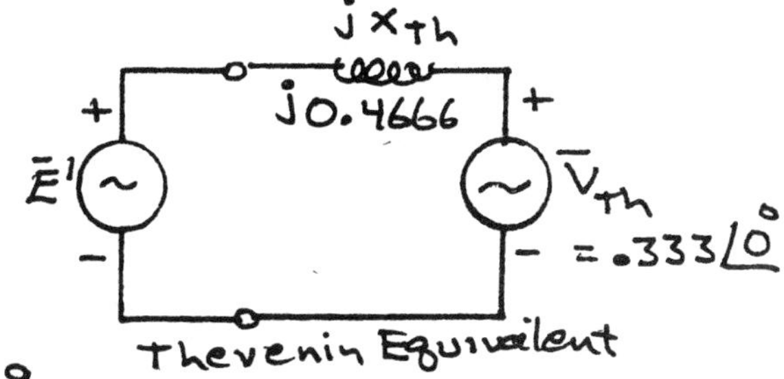

$$P = \frac{E' V_{Th}}{X_{Th}} \sin\delta = \frac{(1.238)(0.333)}{0.4666} \sin\delta = \underline{\underline{0.8843 \sin\delta}}$$

per unit

13.9

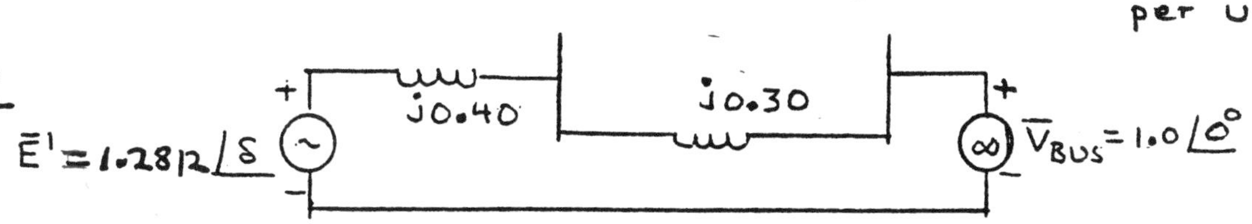

$$P = \frac{E' V_{BUS}}{X_{eq}} \sin\delta = \frac{(1.2812)(1.0)}{0.70} \sin\delta = 1.8303 \sin\delta$$

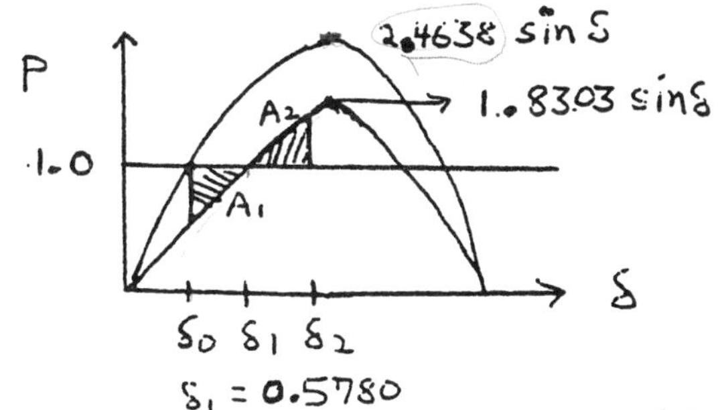

$$\delta_0 = \sin^{-1}\left(\frac{1}{2.4638}\right) = 0.4179 \text{ rad}$$

$$\delta_1 = \sin^{-1}\left(\frac{1}{1.8303}\right) = 0.5780 \text{ rad}$$

$$A_1 = \int_{\delta_0 = 0.4179}^{\delta_1 = 0.5780} (1.0 - 1.8303 \sin\delta)\, d\delta = \int_{\delta_1 = 0.5780}^{\delta_2} (1.8303 \sin\delta - 1)\, d\delta = A_2$$

$$(0.5780 - 0.4179) + 1.8303(\cos 0.5780 - \cos 0.4179) = 1.8303(\cos .5780 - \cos\delta_2) - (\delta_2 - 0.5780)$$

$$1.8303 \cos\delta_2 + \delta_2 = \mathbf{2.0907}$$

Solving iteratively (Newton Raphson) $\delta_2 = \underline{\underline{0.7439}}$ rad $= \underline{\underline{42.62°}}$

13.10

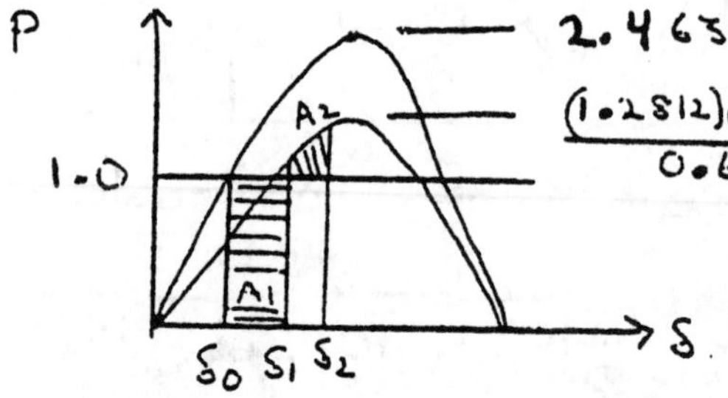

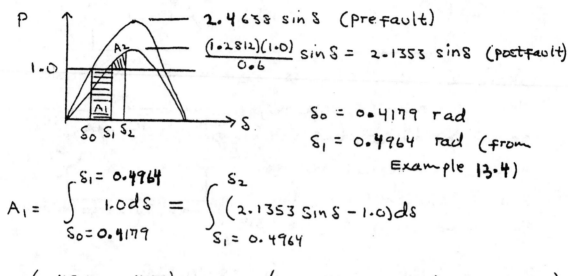

$2.4633 \sin\delta$ (prefault)

$\frac{(1.2812)(1.0)}{0.6} \sin\delta = 2.1353 \sin\delta$ (postfault)

$\delta_0 = 0.4179$ rad

$\delta_1 = 0.4964$ rad (from Example 13.4)

$$A_1 = \int_{\delta_0 = 0.4179}^{\delta_1 = 0.4964} 1.0 \, d\delta = \int_{\delta_1 = 0.4964}^{\delta_2} (2.1353 \sin\delta - 1.0) d\delta$$

$$(0.4964 - 0.4179) = 2.1353(\cos 0.4964 - \cos \delta_2) - (\delta_2 - 0.4964)$$

$$2.1353 \cos\delta_2 + \delta_2 = 2.2955$$

Solving iteratively using Newton Raphson with $\delta_2(0) = 0.60$ rad

$$\delta_2(i+1) = \delta_2(i) + [-2.1353 \sin\delta_2(i) + 1]^{-1} [2.2955 - 2.1353 \cos\delta_2(i) - \delta_2(i)]$$

i	0	1	2	3	4
δ_2	0.60	0.925	0.804	0.785	0.7850

$\delta_2 = 0.7850$ rad $= 44.98°$

13.11

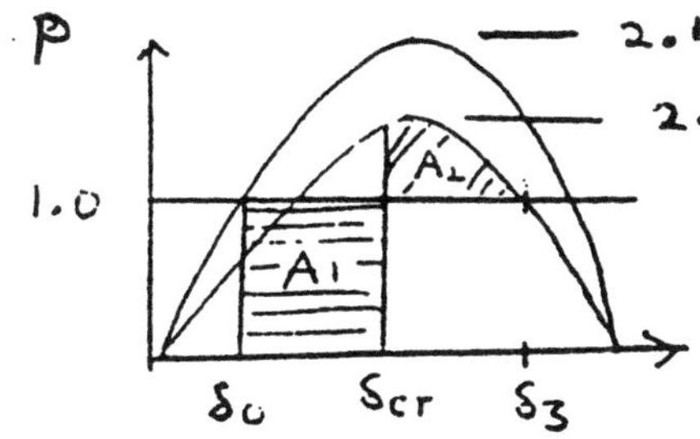

$\delta_0 = 0.4179$ rad

$\delta_3 = \pi - \sin^{-1}\left(\frac{1}{2.1353}\right) = 2.6542$ rad

$$A_1 = \int_{\delta_0 = 0.4179}^{\delta_{cr}} 1.0\, d\delta = \int_{\delta_{cr}}^{\delta_3 = 2.6542} (2.1353 \sin\delta - 1.0)\, d\delta = A_2$$

$$\delta_{cr} - 0.4179 = 2.1353(\cos\delta_{cr} - \cos 2.6542) - (2.6542 - \delta_{cr})$$

$$2.1353 \cos\delta_{cr} = 0.3496$$

$$\delta_{cr} = \cos^{-1}(0.1637) = \underline{\underline{1.406 \text{ rad}}} = \underline{\underline{80.58^\circ}}$$

13.12

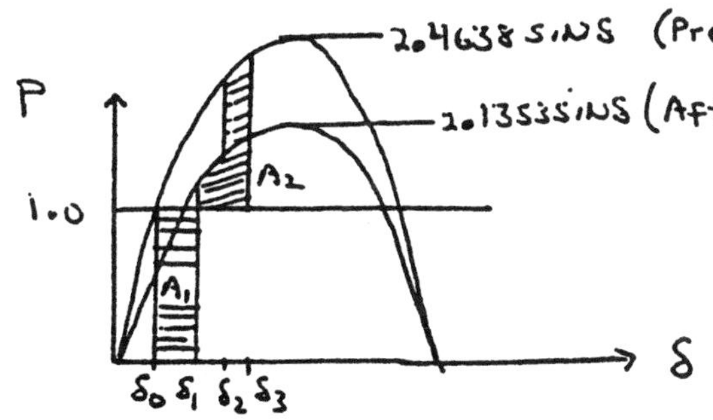

STARTING AT $\delta_0 = 0.4179$ rad, CLEARING AT $\delta_1 = 0.4964$ rad, RECLOSING AT $\delta_2 = 35^\circ$ $= .6109$ rad

$$A_1 = (\delta_1 - \delta_0) = A_2 = \int_{\delta_1 = .4964}^{\delta_2 = .6109} (2.1353 \sin\delta - 1)\, d\delta + \int_{\delta_2 = .6109}^{\delta_3} (2.4638 \sin\delta - 1)\, d\delta$$

$$.0785 = 2.1353(\cos .4964 - \cos .6109) - .1145 + 2.4638(\cos .6109 - \cos\delta_3) - (\delta_3 - .6109)$$

$$2.4638 \cos\delta_3 + \delta_3 = 2.5646$$

Solving iteratively, $\delta_3 = 0.732$ rad $= \underline{\underline{41.9^\circ}}$

13.13 Circuit when breaker B12 opens:

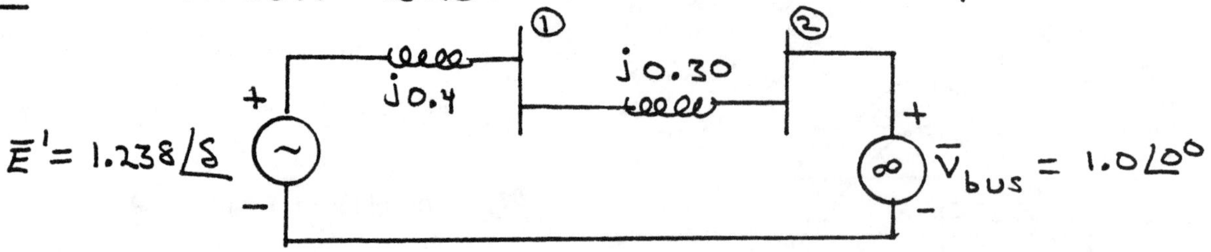

$$P = \frac{E' V_{bus}}{X_{eq}} \sin\delta = \frac{(1.238)(1.0)}{0.70} \sin\delta = 1.769 \sin\delta$$

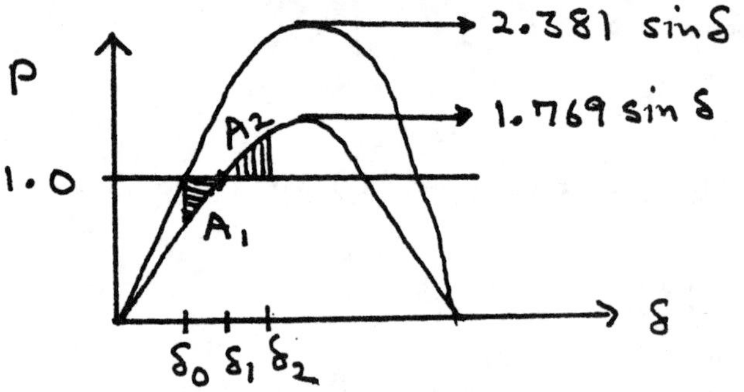

$$\delta_0 = \sin^{-1}\left(\frac{1}{2.381}\right) = 0.4334 \text{ rad}$$

$$\delta_1 = \sin^{-1}\left(\frac{1}{1.769}\right) = 0.6008 \text{ rad}$$

$$A_1 = \int_{\delta_0 = 0.4334}^{\delta_1 = 0.6008} (1.0 - 1.769 \sin\delta)\, d\delta = \int_{\delta_1 = 0.6008}^{\delta_2} (1.769 \sin\delta - 1)\, d\delta = A_2$$

$$(0.6008 - 0.4334) + 1.769(\cos 0.6008 - \cos 0.4334)$$
$$= 1.769(\cos .6008 - \cos\delta_2) - (\delta_2 - .6008)$$

$$1.769 \cos\delta_2 + \delta_2 = 2.039$$

Solving iteratively (Newton Raphson) =

$\delta_2 =$ <u>0.7742</u> rad = <u>44.36°</u>

13.14

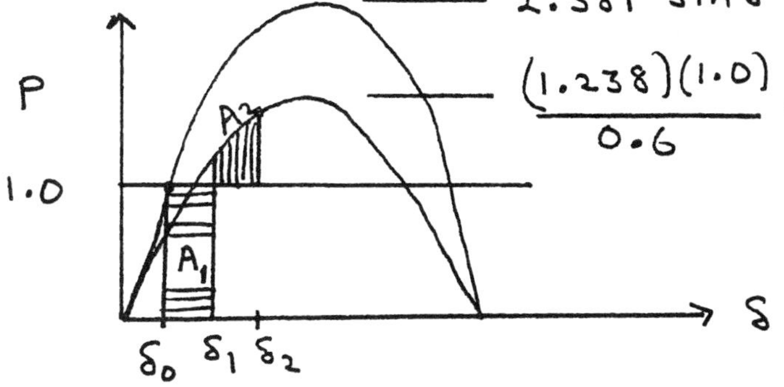

2.381 sin δ (prefault)

$\frac{(1.238)(1.0)}{0.6}$ sin δ = 2.063 sin δ (postfault)

$δ_0 = 0.4334$ rad

From Example 13.4 :

$$δ_1 = \frac{2\pi 60}{12}(0.05)^2 + δ_0$$

$$δ_1 = 0.07854 + 0.4334 = 0.5119 \text{ rad}$$

$$A_1 = \int_{δ_0=0.4334}^{δ_1=0.5119} 1.0 \, dδ = \int_{δ_1=.5119}^{δ_2} (2.063 \sin δ - 1) \, dδ$$

$$\left(0.5119 - 0.4334\right) = 2.063\left(\cos .5119 - \cos δ_2\right) - \left(δ_2 - .5119\right)$$

$$2.063 \cos δ_2 + δ_2 = 2.232$$

solving iteratively using Newton-Raphson with $δ_2(0) = 0.60$ radians

$$δ_2(i+1) = δ_2(i) + \left[-2.063 \sin δ_2(i) + 1\right]^{-1}\left[2.232 - 2.063 \cos δ_2(i) - δ_2(i)\right]$$

i	0	1	2	3	4	5
$δ_2$	0.60	1.029	0.848	0.813	0.811	0.8109

$$δ_2 = 0.8109 \text{ rad} = 46.46°$$

13.15

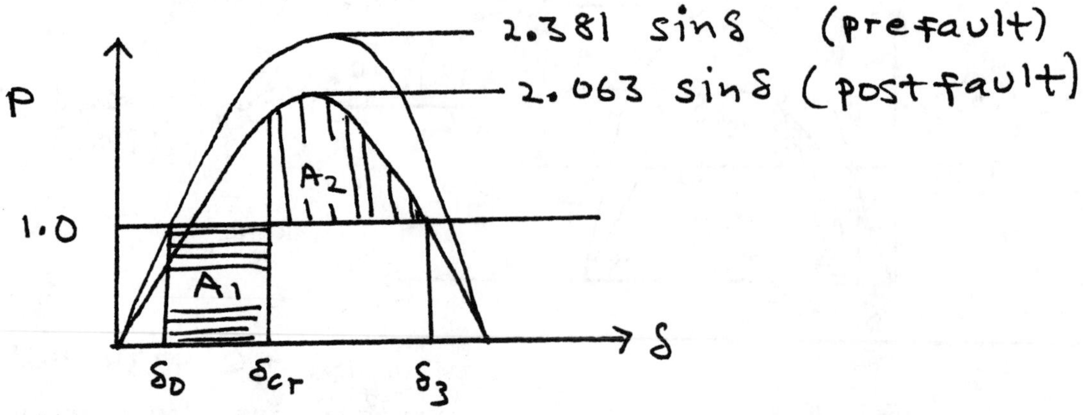

$\delta_0 = 0.4334$ rad

$\delta_3 = \pi - \sin^{-1}\left(\frac{1}{2.063}\right) = \pi - 0.5061 = 2.636$ rad

$$A_1 = \int_{\delta_0 = 0.4334}^{\delta_{cr}} 1.0\, d\delta = \int_{\delta_{cr}}^{\delta_3 = 2.636} (2.063 \sin\delta - 1)\, d\delta = A_2$$

$$(\delta_{cr} - 0.4334) = 2.063(\cos\delta_{cr} - \cos 2.636) - (2.636 - \delta_{cr})$$

$$2.063 \cos\delta_{cr} = 0.3977$$

$$\delta_{cr} = \cos^{-1}(0.1928) = \underline{\underline{1.377 \text{ rad}}} = \underline{\underline{78.88^\circ}}$$

13.16

OUTPUT

TIME s	DELTA rad	OMEGA rad/s
0.000	0.4179	377.0
0.020	0.4211	377.3
0.040	0.4307	377.6
0.060	0.4461	377.9
0.080	0.4669	378.1
0.100	0.4920	378.3
0.120	0.5206	378.5
0.140	0.5514	378.6
0.160	0.5832	378.6
0.180	0.6148	378.5
0.200	0.6451	378.4
0.220	0.6728	378.3
0.240	0.6970	378.1
0.260	0.7168	377.9
0.280	0.7316	377.6
0.300	0.7407	377.3
0.320	0.7440	377.0
0.340	0.7412	376.7
0.360	0.7325	376.4
0.380	0.7182	376.1
0.400	0.6987	375.9
0.420	0.6748	375.7
0.440	0.6472	375.5
0.460	0.6170	375.4
0.480	0.5853	375.4
0.500	0.5534	375.4
0.520	0.5224	375.5
0.540	0.4936	375.6
0.560	0.4681	375.8
0.580	0.4471	376.1
0.600	0.4313	376.3
0.620	0.4214	376.7
0.640	0.4178	377.0
0.660	0.4207	377.3
0.680	0.4299	377.6
0.700	0.4451	377.9
0.720	0.4656	378.1
0.740	0.4906	378.3
0.760	0.5190	378.5
0.780	0.5498	378.6
0.800	0.5816	378.6

PROGRAM LISTING

```
10   REM  PROBLEM 13.9
20   REM SOLUTION TO SWING EQUATION
30   REM THE STEP SIZE IS DELT
40   DELT=.01
50   J=1
60   PMAX = 1.8303
70   PI=3.1415927#
80   T=0
90   X1=.4179
100 X2=2*PI*60
110 LPRINT "    TIME      DELTA    OMEGA"
120 LPRINT "      s        rad     rad/s  "
130 LPRINT USING "#####.###" ;T;
140 LPRINT USING "#####.####" ;X1;
150 LPRINT USING "#####.#" ;X2
160 FOR K=1 TO 86
170 REM LINE 180 IS EQ(13.4.7)
180 X3=X2-(2*PI*60)
190 REM LINES 200 AND 210 ARE EQ(13.4.8)
200 X4=1- PMAX*SIN(X1)
210 X5=X4*(2*PI*60)*(2*PI*60)/(6*X2)
220 REM LINE 230 IS EQ(13.4.9)
230 X6=X1 +X3*DELT
240 REM LINE 250 IS EQ(13.4.10)
250 X7=X2+X5*DELT
260 REM LINE 270 IS EQ(13.4.11)
270 X8=X7-2*PI*60
280 REM LINES 290 AND 300 ARE EQ(13.4.12)
290 X9=1- PMAX*SIN(X6)
300 X10=X9*(2*PI*60)*(2*PI*60)/(6*X7)
310 REM LINE 320 IS EQ(13.4.13)
320 X1=X1+(X3+X8)*(DELT/2)
330 REM LINE 340 IS EQ(13.4.14)
340 X2=X2+(X5+X10)*(DELT/2)
350 T=K*DELT
360 Z=K/2
370 M=INT(Z)
380 IF M=Z THEN  LPRINT USING "#####.###";T;
390 IF M=Z THEN  LPRINT USING "#####.####";X1;
400 IF M=Z THEN  LPRINT USING "#####.#";X2
410 NEXT K
420 END
```

From the above output, the maximum angle is 0.7440 radians = 42.63°, compared to 42.62° in Problem 13.9. Note that in the above computer program, the approximation $\omega_{pu}(t) = 1.0$ in the swing equation is <u>not</u> made.

13.17

OUTPUT

TIME s	DELTA rad	OMEGA rad/s
0.000	0.4179	377.0
0.020	0.4210	377.3
0.040	0.4302	377.6
0.060	0.4450	377.9
0.080	0.4650	378.1
0.100	0.4892	378.3
0.120	0.5166	378.4
0.140	0.5462	378.5
0.160	0.5768	378.5
0.180	0.6071	378.5
0.200	0.6362	378.4
0.220	0.6627	378.2
0.240	0.6859	378.0
0.260	0.7048	377.8
0.280	0.7189	377.6
0.300	0.7275	377.3
0.320	0.7304	377.0
0.340	0.7275	376.7
0.360	0.7189	376.4
0.380	0.7049	376.2
0.400	0.6859	375.9
0.420	0.6627	375.7
0.440	0.6360	375.6
0.460	0.6069	375.5
0.480	0.5764	375.5
0.500	0.5458	375.5
0.520	0.5161	375.6
0.540	0.4887	375.7
0.560	0.4645	375.9
0.580	0.4446	376.1
0.600	0.4299	376.4
0.620	0.4208	376.7
0.640	0.4179	377.0
0.660	0.4211	377.3
0.680	0.4305	377.6
0.700	0.4455	377.9
0.720	0.4655	378.1
0.740	0.4898	378.3
0.760	0.5173	378.4
0.780	0.5469	378.5
0.800	0.5775	378.5

PROGRAM LISTING

```
10  REM PROBLEM 13.17
20  REM SOLUTION TO SWING EQUATION
30  REM THE STEP SIZE IS DELT
40  DELT=.01
50  J=1
60  PMAX = 1.8303
70  PI=3.1415927#
80  T=0
90  X1=.4179
100 X2=2*PI*60
110 LPRINT "    TIME      DELTA     OMEGA"
120 LPRINT "     s         rad      rad/s   "
130 LPRINT USING "#####.###" ;T;
140 LPRINT USING "#####.####" ;X1;
150 LPRINT USING "#####.#" ;X2
160 FOR K=1 TO 86
170 REM LINE 180 IS EQ(13.4.7)
180 X3=X2-(2*PI*60)
190 REM LINES 200 AND 210 ARE EQ(13.4.8)
200 X4=1- PMAX*SIN(X1)-.01*X2/(2*PI*60)
210 X5=X4*(2*PI*60)*(2*PI*60)/(6*X2)
220 REM LINE 230 IS EQ(13.4.9)
230 X6=X1 +X3*DELT
240 REM LINE 250 IS EQ(13.4.10)
250 X7=X2+X5*DELT
260 REM LINE 270 IS EQ(13.4.11)
270 X8=X7-2*PI*60
280 REM LINES 290 AND 300 ARE EQ(12.4.12)
290 X9=1- PMAX*SIN(X6)-.01*X2/(2*PI*60)
300 X10=X9*(2*PI*60)*(2*PI*60)/(6*X7)
310 REM LINE 320 IS EQ(13.4.13)
320 X1=X1+(X3+X8)*(DELT/2)
330 REM LINE 340 IS EQ(13.4.14)
340 X2=X2+(X5+X10)*(DELT/2)
350 T=K*DELT
360 Z=K/2
370 M=INT(Z)
380 IF M=Z THEN  LPRINT USING "#####.###";T;
390 IF M=Z THEN  LPRINT USING "#####.####";X1;
400 IF M=Z THEN  LPRINT USING "#####.#";X2
410 NEXT K
420 END
```

Damping torque included here (lines 200 and 290)

From the above output, the maximum angle is 0.7304 rad = 41.85° with damping, compared to 42.62° in Problem 13.16 without damping.

Damping torques improve stability.

This case is more stable (smaller swing).

13.18

OUTPUT

CASE 1 — STABLE

TIME s	DELTA rad	OMEGA rad/s
0.000	0.4179	377.0
0.020	0.4305	378.2
0.040	0.4681	379.5
0.060	0.5306	380.7
0.080	0.6181	382.0
0.100	0.7304	383.2
0.120	0.8673	384.5
0.140	1.0290	385.7
0.160	1.2152	386.9
FAULT CLEARED		
0.180	1.4195	386.9
0.200	1.6031	385.5
0.220	1.7590	384.1
0.240	1.8878	382.8
0.260	1.9912	381.6
0.280	2.0710	380.4
0.300	2.1291	379.4
0.320	2.1670	378.4
0.340	2.1856	377.5
0.360	2.1856	376.5
0.380	2.1668	375.6
0.400	2.1287	374.6
0.420	2.0701	373.5
0.440	1.9893	372.4
0.460	1.8843	371.1
0.480	1.7530	369.7
0.500	1.5937	368.3
0.520	1.4052	366.9
0.540	1.1883	365.5
0.560	0.9461	364.4
0.580	0.6851	363.6
0.600	0.4151	363.5
0.620	0.1488	364.0
0.640	-0.0998	365.3
0.660	-0.3169	367.1
0.680	-0.4911	369.5
0.700	-0.6139	372.2
0.720	-0.6800	375.2
0.740	-0.6869	378.1
0.760	-0.6348	381.0
0.780	-0.5264	383.7
0.800	-0.3668	386.1
0.820	-0.1639	388.0
0.840	0.0719	389.4
0.860	0.3284	390.1

CASE 2 — UNSTABLE

TIME s	DELTA rad	OMEGA rad/s
0.000	0.4179	377.0
0.020	0.4305	378.2
0.040	0.4681	379.5
0.060	0.5306	380.7
0.080	0.6181	382.0
0.100	0.7304	383.2
0.120	0.8673	384.5
0.140	1.0290	385.7
0.160	1.2152	386.9
0.180	1.4258	388.1
FAULT CLEARED		
0.200	1.6350	386.8
0.220	1.8166	385.4
0.240	1.9720	384.1
0.260	2.1036	383.0
0.280	2.2145	382.1
0.300	2.3078	381.3
0.320	2.3868	380.6
0.340	2.4542	380.1
0.360	2.5128	379.7
0.380	2.5650	379.5
0.400	2.6131	379.3
0.420	2.6593	379.3
0.440	2.7058	379.4
0.460	2.7547	379.5
0.480	2.8085	379.9
0.500	2.8699	380.3
0.520	2.9418	380.9
0.540	3.0281	381.7
0.560	3.1333	382.8
0.580	3.2628	384.2
0.600	3.4232	385.9
0.620	3.6228	388.1
0.640	3.8709	390.8
0.660	4.1775	394.0
0.680	4.5521	397.5
0.700	5.0002	401.2
0.720	5.5195	404.5
0.740	6.0963	406.8
0.760	6.7054	407.7
0.780	7.3180	407.3
0.800	7.9121	406.1
0.820	8.4809	404.9
0.840	9.0333	404.6
0.860	9.5905	405.5

PROGRAM LISTING

```
10   REM  PROBLEM 13.18
20   REM SOLUTION TO SWING EQUATION
30   REM THE STEP SIZE IS DELT
40   REM THE CLEARING ANGLE IS DLTCLR
50   DELT=.01
60   DLTCLR = 1.22
70   J=1
80   PMAX = 0
90   PI=3.1415927#
100 T=0
110 X1=.4179
120 X2=2*PI*60
130 LPRINT  "    TIME      DELTA    OMEGA"
140 LPRINT  "      s        rad      rad/s   "
150 LPRINT USING "#####.###" ;T;
160 LPRINT USING "#####.####" ;X1;
170 LPRINT USING "#####.#" ;X2
180 FOR K=1 TO 86
190 REM LINE 200 IS EQ(13.4.7)
200 X3=X2-(2*PI*60)
210 IF J=2  THEN GOTO  260
220 IF X1> DLTCLR OR X1=DLTCLR  THEN PMAX=2.1353
230 IF X1> DLTCLR OR X1=DLTCLR  THEN LPRINT "         F
240 IF X1> DLTCLR OR X1=DLTCLR THEN J=2
250 REM LINES 260 AND 270 ARE EQ(13.4.8)
260 X4=1- PMAX*SIN(X1)
270 X5=X4*(2*PI*60)*(2*PI*60)/(6*X2)
280 REM LINE 290 IS EQ(13.4.9)
290 X6=X1 +X3*DELT
300 REM LINE 180 IS EQ(13.4.10)
310 X7=X2+X5*DELT
320 REM LINE 330 IS EQ(13.4.11)
330 X8=X7-2*PI*60
340 REM LINES 350 AND 360 ARE EQ(13.4.12)
350 X9=1- PMAX*SIN(X6)
360 X10=X9*(2*PI*60)*(2*PI*60)/(6*X7)
370 REM LINE 220 IS EQ(13.4.13)
380 X1=X1+(X3+X8)*(DELT/2)
390 REM LINE 400 IS EQ(13.4.14)
400 X2=X2+(X5+X10)*(DELT/2)
410 T=K*DELT
420 Z=K/2
430 M=INT(Z)
440 IF M=Z THEN  LPRINT USING "#####.###";T;
450 IF M=Z THEN  LPRINT USING "#####.####";X1;
460 IF M=Z THEN  LPRINT USING "#####.#";X2
470 NEXT K
480 END
```

As shown above, the system is stable if the fault is cleared at $t = 0.160$ seconds when $\delta = 1.2152$ radians, but unstable if the fault is cleared at $t = 0.180$ seconds when $\delta = 1.4258$ radians. Thus the critical clearing angle $\delta_{cr} = 1.406$ radians $= 80.58°$ as calculated in Problem 13.11 is verified

13.19 The initial conditions at t= 0 are $\delta_0 = 0.4179$ rad and $\omega_0 = 2\ \pi 60$ rad/s.

During the three-phase-to-ground fault at point F:

$0 \le t < 0.05s \quad Pe = 0.$

After the fault clears:

$0.05 \le t < 0.40s \quad Pe = (1.2812)(1.0/0.6) \sin\delta = 2.1353 \sin\delta$

After reclosure:

$0.40 \le t \qquad Pe = (1.2812)(1.0/0.520) \sin = 2.4638 \sin\delta$

Using the above equations, the BASIC program listing given in TABLE 13.1 is revised as follows:

BASIC PROGRAM LISTING - PROBLEM 13.19

```
10    REM PROBLEM 13.19
20    REM THE TIME IN SECONDS IS T
30    REM THE STEP SIZE IN SECONDS IS DELTA
35    REM THE POWER ANGLE IN RADIANS IS X1
40    REM THE ELECTRICAL FREQUENCY IN RAD/S IS X2
50    DELTA = 0.01
70    J=1
80    PMAX=0
90    PI=3.1415927#
100   T=0
110   X1=0.4179
120   X2=2*PI*60
130   LPRINT "TIME DELTA OMEGA"
140   LPRINT "s rad  rad/s"
150   LPRINT USING "####.###";T;X1;X2
160   FOR K=1 TO 200
170   REM LINE 180 IS EQ(13.4.7)
180   X3=X2 - (2*PI*60)
185   IF J=3 THEN GOTO 240
190   IF J=2 THEN GOTO 220
200   IF T=0.05 OR T>0.05  THEN PMAX=2.1353
205   IF T=0.05 OR T>0.05  THEN LPRINT "FAULT CLEARED"
210   IF T=0.05 OR T>0.05  THEN J=2
220   IF T=0.40 OR T>0.40  THEN PMAX=2.4638
225   IF T=0.40 OR T>0.40  THEN LPRINT "RECLOSURE"
230   IF T=0.40 OR T>0.40  THEN J=3
```

13.19 CONTD.

```
260    REM LINE 270 IS EQ(13.4.9)
270    X6=X1 + X3*DELTA
280    REM LINE 290 IS EQ(13.4.10)
290    X7=X2 + X5*DELTA
300    REM LINE 310 IS EQ(13.4.11)
310    X8=X7 - 2*PI*60
320    REM LINES 330 AND 340 ARE EQ(13.4.12)
330    X9=1.0 - PMAX*SIN(X6)
340    X10 =X9*(2*PI*60)*(2*PI*60)/(6*X7)
350    REM LINE 360 IS EQ(13.4.13)
360    X1=X1 + (X3 +X8)*(DELTA/2)
370    REM LINE 380 IS EQ(13.4.14)
380    X2=X2 + (X5 +X10)*(DELTA/2)
390    T=K*DELTA
400    LPRINT USING "####.###";T;X1;X2
410    NEXT K
420    END
```

The above BASIC program can be run to determine the maximum power angle $\delta_{MAX} = X1_{MAX}$.

13.20

(a) By inspection:

$$\bar{Y}_{bus} = j\begin{bmatrix} -30.000 & 20.000 & 10.000 & 0.000 & 0.000 & 0.000 \\ 20.000 & -30.000 & 0.000 & 10.000 & 0.000 & 0.000 \\ 10.000 & 0.000 & -50.000 & 0.000 & 40.000 & 0.000 \\ 0.000 & 10.000 & 0.000 & -50.000 & 40.000 & 0.000 \\ 0.000 & 0.000 & 40.000 & 40.000 & -100.000 & 20.000 \\ 0.000 & 0.000 & 0.000 & 0.000 & 20.000 & -20.000 \end{bmatrix}$$

(b)

$$\bar{Y}_{22} = \begin{bmatrix} \frac{1}{jX'_{d1}} & 0 & 0 \\ 0 & \frac{1}{jX'_{d2}} & 0 \\ 0 & 0 & \frac{1}{jX'_{d3}} \end{bmatrix} = \begin{bmatrix} -j5.0 & 0 & 0 \\ 0 & -j10 & 0 \\ 0 & 0 & -j10 \end{bmatrix} \text{ per unit}$$

$$\bar{Y}_{12} = \begin{bmatrix} \frac{-1}{jX'_{d1}} & 0 & 0 \\ 0 & \frac{-1}{jX'_{d2}} & 0 \\ 0 & 0 & 0 \\ 0 & 0 & 0 \\ 0 & 0 & 0 \\ 0 & 0 & \frac{-1}{jX'_{d3}} \end{bmatrix} = \begin{bmatrix} j5.0 & 0 & 0 \\ 0 & j10. & 0 \\ 0 & 0 & 0 \\ 0 & 0 & 0 \\ 0 & 0 & 0 \\ 0 & 0 & j10. \end{bmatrix} \text{ per unit}$$

13.21 (a) By inspection of Figure 13.13, with line 1-2 open:

$$
Y_{BUS} = j \begin{bmatrix} -10 & 0 & 10 & 0 & 0 & 0 \\ 0 & -10 & 0 & 10 & 0 & 0 \\ 10 & 0 & -50 & 0 & 40. & 0 \\ 0 & 10 & 0 & -50 & 40 & 0 \\ 0 & 0 & 40 & 40 & -100 & 20 \\ 0 & 0 & 0 & 0 & 20 & -20 \end{bmatrix} \text{ per unit}
$$

The load admittances at buses 3, 4 and 5 are:

$$Y_{Load3} = \frac{P_{L3} - j\,Q_{L3}}{(V_3)^2} = \frac{3.0 - j2.0}{(1.0)^2} = 3.0 - j2.0 \text{ per unit}$$

$$Y_{Load4} = \frac{P_{L4} - j\,Q_{L4}}{(V_4)^2} = \frac{2.0 - j0.9}{(1.0)^2} = 2.0 - j0.9 \text{ per unit}$$

$$Y_{Load5} = \frac{P_{L5} - j\,Q_{L5}}{(V_5)^2} = \frac{1.0 - j0.3}{(1.0)^2} = 1.0 - j0.3 \text{ per unit}$$

The inverted generator impedances are:

For machine 1 connected to bus1: $1/(jX'_{d1}) = 1/(j0.20) = -j5.0$ per unit

For machine 2 connected to bus2: $1/(jX'_{d2}) = 1/(j0.10) = -j10.0$ per unit

For machine 3 connected to bus6: $1/(jX'_{d3}) = 1/(j0.10) = -j10.0$ per unit

To obtain $\boldsymbol{Y}_{11}$, add $1/(jX'_{d1})$ to the first diagonal element of $\boldsymbol{Y}_{BUS}$, add $1/(jX'_{d2})$ to the second diagonal element, add Y_{Load3} to the third diagonal element, add Y_{Load4} to the fourth diagonal element, add Y_{Load5} to the fifth diagonal element, and add $1/(jX'_{d3})$ to the sixth diagonal element. The 6x6 matrix $\boldsymbol{Y}_{11}$ is then:

13.21 CONTD.

$$Y_{11} = \begin{bmatrix} -j15 & 0 & j10 & 0 & 0 & 0 \\ 0 & -j20 & 0 & j10 & 0 & 0 \\ j10 & 0 & (3-j52) & 0 & j40. & 0 \\ 0 & j10 & 0 & (2-j59) & j40 & 0 \\ 0 & 0 & j40 & j40 & (1-j103) & j20 \\ 0 & 0 & 0 & 0 & j20 & -j30 \end{bmatrix} \text{ per unit}$$

From (13.5.6), the 3x3 matrix Y_{22} is

$$Y_{22} = \begin{bmatrix} 1/(jX'_{d1}) & 0 & 0 \\ 0 & 1/(jX'_{d2}) & 0 \\ 0 & 0 & 1/(jX'_{d3}) \end{bmatrix} = \begin{bmatrix} -j5.0 & 0 & 0 \\ 0 & -j10 & 0 \\ 0 & 0 & -j10 \end{bmatrix} \text{ per unit}$$

From (13.5.7), the 6x3 matrix Y_{12} is:

$$Y_{12} = \begin{bmatrix} j5 & 0 & 0 \\ 0 & j10 & 0 \\ 0 & 0 & 0 \\ 0 & 0 & 0 \\ 0 & 0 & 0 \\ 0 & 0 & j10 \end{bmatrix} \text{ per unit}$$

Note: Y_{22} and Y_{12} are the same as in problem 13.20.

(b) For the case when the load $P_{L4} + jQ_{L4}$ is removed, Y_{BUS} is the same as in Problem 13.20. To obtain Y_{11}, add $1/(jX'_{d1})$ to the first diagonal element of Y_{BUS}, add $1/(jX'_{d2})$ to the second diagonal element, add Y_{Load3} to the third diagonal element, add Y_{Load5} to the fifth diagonal element, and add $1/(jX'_{d3})$ to the sixth diagonal element. The 6x6 matrix Y_{11} is then:

13.21 CONTD.

$$Y_{11} = \begin{bmatrix} -j35 & j20 & j10 & 0 & 0 & 0 \\ j20 & -j30 & 0 & j10 & 0 & 0 \\ j10 & 0 & (3-j52) & 0 & j40. & 0 \\ 0 & j10 & 0 & j50 & j40 & 0 \\ 0 & 0 & j40 & j40 & (1-j103) & j20 \\ 0 & 0 & 0 & 0 & j20 & -j30 \end{bmatrix} \text{ per unit}$$

Y_{22} and Y_{12} are the same as in problems 13.20 and 13.21(a).

13.22

Assuming a 100 MVA base and a base voltage of 138 kV, the flows/voltages are

```
BUS        1 One        138.0     MW      Mvar       MVA    1.0000    0.00
 GENERATOR 1               -100.00   -12.13R   100.7
 TO        2 Two          1  -60.00    -7.28     60.4
 TO        3 Three        1  -40.00    -4.85     40.3

BUS        2 Two        138.0     MW      Mvar       MVA    1.0216    6.75
 TO        1 One          1   60.00    14.59     61.7
 TO        3 Three        1   40.00     9.72     41.2
 TO        4 Four         1 -100.00   -24.31    102.9

BUS        3 Three      138.0     MW      Mvar       MVA    1.0129    4.53
 TO        1 One          1   40.00     8.10     40.8
 TO        2 Two          1  -40.00    -8.10     40.8

BUS        4 Four       138.0     MW      Mvar       MVA    1.0500   12.09
 GENERATOR 1                100.00    34.46R   105.8
 TO        2 Two          1  100.00    34.46    105.8
```